No

TEXTILE CHEMISTRY

THE CHEMISTRY OF FIBRES

TEXTILE CHEMISTRY

VOLUME I

THE CHEMISTRY OF FIBRES

★

VOLUME II

THE CHEMISTRY OF SCOURING,
BLEACHING AND SURFACE-ACTIVE AGENTS

★

VOLUME III

THE CHEMISTRY OF DYEING
AND FINISHING AGENTS

ELSEVIER PUBLISHING COMPANY
AMSTERDAM / LONDON / NEW YORK

TEXTILE CHEMISTRY

by

R. H. PETERS

Professor of Textile Chemistry,
Manchester College of Science and Technology,
University of Manchester (England)

VOLUME I

THE CHEMISTRY OF FIBRES

ELSEVIER PUBLISHING COMPANY
AMSTERDAM / LONDON / NEW YORK
1963

SOLE DISTRIBUTORS FOR THE UNITED STATES AND CANADA
AMERICAN ELSEVIER PUBLISHING COMPANY, INC.
52 VANDERBILT AVENUE, NEW YORK 17, N.Y.

LIBRARY OF CONGRESS CATALOG CARD NUMBER 62-16536

WITH 164 ILLUSTRATIONS AND 42 TABLES

PREFACE

Although textile materials by their very utility may be described as commonplace, they are of such extraordinary importance to civilisation that the production of fibres and manufacture of garments is 'big business'. The attention of some of the world's best chemists, physicists and technologists has resulted in the attainment of the present position where a bewildering variety of fabrics in increasingly wide ranges of colours is available. Further, the goal set by the desire to make truly synthetic fibres has given great impetus to the study of polymer science, a fact which tends to be overlooked.

It is true to say that in recent years a revolution has taken place in the field of fibres. Before World War II only the natural products (silk, wool and cotton) together with one or two fibres made from natural products (viscose and acetate) were available; by contrast in the post-war period an extensive range of synthetic fibres derived from widely different chemical types has been developed.

The kinds of treatments which textiles undergo have also changed. A large proportion of the cotton we use, for example, is treated with resins; our dyes are from numerous and diverse chemical systems, some of which may undergo chemical combination with the fibres. Speeds of production have markedly increased by the expansion and development of continuous processing.

All this goes to emphasise the fact that what might have been truly described as an art 50 years ago has now changed to such an extent that a considerable knowledge of chemistry and physics is required in order to appreciate the nature of the different fibrous polymers in use as well as the resins and dyes which are applied to them.

Textile chemistry encompasses these points so that it must be realised that, before a real understanding can be achieved, the worker in this field must have considerable scientific knowledge of a very sophisticated kind. The textile chemist may be faced with problems of both a chemical and a physical nature. It is regrettable that the intrinsic interest and fascination of such a study is not more widely appreciated.

In this book, an attempt has been made to illustrate the scientific content of the field. No attention has been given to the technological side. The book does not purport to be an up-to-date treatise, but rather it is intended to be suitable for the introduction of a student with some knowledge of chemistry and physics to an area of study which is fascinating and in which developments are taking place at an astonishingly rapid pace.

The first volume deals exclusively with polymer science since this is the basis of the materials with which a textile man must work. In subsequent volumes it is hoped to cover other aspects such as bleaching, dyeing and finishing.

I would like to recognise the patience which my wife has displayed as well as the assistance which she has given in reading the proofs of this book. My thanks also go to the members of the staff of the Textile Chemistry Department who have assisted in compiling this work.

Manchester, October 1962   R.H.P.

CONTENTS

CHAPTER 1

INTRODUCTION

The term textile chemistry needs some explanation. As with most branches of applied chemistry, the subject matter impinges on many aspects of pure science. For the present purpose textile chemistry is taken to be the chemistry of textile fibres and of substances applied to textiles together with physico-chemical aspects of their application. No attempt is made in this book to discuss the technological application of such substances as dyes, detergents etc. to textiles. Even with this restriction the subject is an extremely wide one. This volume is concerned with the origin, production and chemistry of fibres.

1. Textile Materials

There are in general two methods for constructing a fabric, namely weaving or knitting. The yarns used may be produced from fibres of relatively short length (staple fibre) or from continuous filaments; the properties of the yarn are dependent on whether it is constructed from staple fibre or from continuous filaments. The "man made" fibres are normally manufactured in the form of continuous filaments, many of which may be twisted together to give pliability and flexibility to the yarn. A yarn made from continuous filaments may contain between 15–100 separate filaments each of which will be very fine. For some purposes single continuous filaments may be used; nylon stockings may be knitted from relatively fine monofilaments whereas the coarser ones may be used as bristles for brushes, fishing lines, tyre cords etc. Alternatively the continuous filaments are cut to lengths comparable to those of the staple fibres, *e.g.* cotton and wool and are spun into yarn in the usual manner. The properties of the final fabric are dependent on many factors. Whether the yarn is woven or knitted, the degree to which the yarn is twisted, whether the fibre is coarse or fine are some of the factors affecting the handle and use to which the fabric may be put.

However, fibres as distinct from yarns or fabrics, have one feature common, that is, the length is enormously greater than the diameter. Variations do occur as regards this property. The range of possible dimensions of some of the natural fibres is given in Table 1.

In practical working with yarns and fibres, dimensions put in terms of length and diameter are not convenient. The simplest characterisation of

TABLE 1
TYPICAL DIMENSIONS OF NATURAL FIBRES[1]

Fibre	Length in cm	Diameter in mm
Wool (Merinos)	5.5−7.5	0.018−0.027
Silk (Canton)	—	0.005−0.018
Flax	20−140	0.04 −0.62
Jute	150−360	0.03 −0.14
Ramie	10−180	0.06 −9.04
Hemp	100−300	—
Hemp, sisal	75−120	0.10 −0.46
Cotton	1.5−5.6	0.012−0.025

the fineness of a filament or yarn is given by the denier. This is the weight in grams of a fixed length of yarn (9000 metres). In the case of a monofil of circular cross section, the diameter can readily be calculated from a knowledge of the denier and the density. Another method of defining the

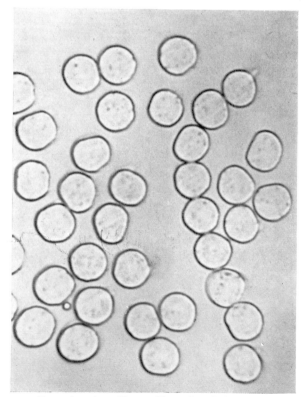

Fig. 1. Cross section of nylon fibres. (Reproduced by permission of BCIRA)

fineness of yarns is by the count. This is the number of hanks of a certain length which weigh a fixed amount; for cotton the length of yarn to make the hanks is 840 yds, for worsted 560, and the weight 1 lb.

In addition to this wide range of dimensions, fibres vary considerably in the shapes of their cross sections. Some of the man-made fibres have almost circular cross sections (nylon is shown in Fig. 1) others are serrated (viscose is shown in Fig. 2) whereas some have dumb-bell shapes (*e.g.* Orlon, Fig. 3). The natural fibres perhaps show the more interesting morphological features. Wool is covered with overlapping scales and has a somewhat irregular but almost circular cross section, cotton has a section more like an ellipse whilst that of silk is triangular (Fig. 4). The shape of the cross section will have its effect on properties of the final fabric. Fibres whose sections are narrow give fabrics which are harsh to the feel but have as compensation a high lustre and covering power.

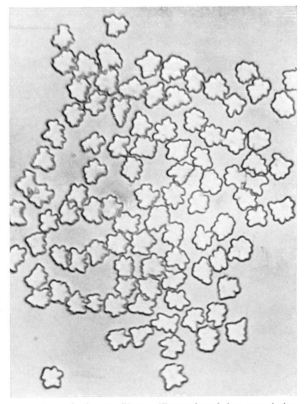

Fig. 2. Cross section of viscose fibres. (Reproduced by permission of BCIRA)

References p. 13

Fibres with triangular cross sections give fabrics which are more silk-like in handle; those with circular cross sections give fabrics with less covering power but with a pleasant handle.

The chemistry of the fibres is as diverse as the physical aspects mentioned above. The fibres such as cotton, jute, flax, etc. are composed in the main of the carbohydrate cellulose and hence contain carbon, hydrogen and oxygen. Others contain carbon, hydrogen, oxygen, nitrogen and in some

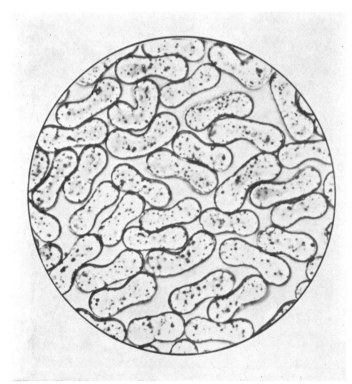

Fig. 3. Cross section of Orlon fibres. (Reproduced by permission of DuPont)

cases sulphur. Fibres of this kind are the proteins – silk and wool. Others may contain carbon, hydrogen and chlorine as in Vinyon or may even be made from inorganic materials such as asbestos. Nevertheless, they all come into the class of chemical materials known as Polymers.

"Man-made" fibres were introduced about eighty years ago. In the early days they were known as artificial silk since they were produced as a replacement for natural silk. This term has gone out of use for the most part and is, in fact, an anachronism since modern fibres are products in their own right, each having its own specific properties. A word which is in common usage is "rayon"; nowadays this term is confined to those fibres (viscose, acetate, etc.) which have cellulose or its derivatives as their raw material. The term synthetic fibre can be applied to those materials which are truly made from simple chemicals, *e.g.* nylon. To cover these two groups of fibres the word "man-made" may be used.

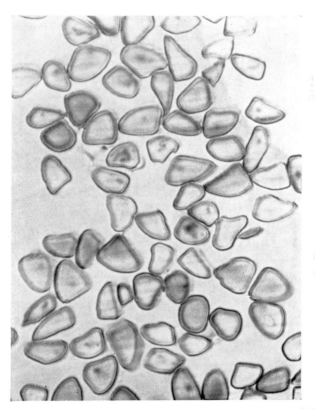

Fig. 4. Cross section of silk fibres. (Reproduced by permission of BCIRA)

The first man-made fibres were, according to this definition, rayons made by dissolution of a natural fibrous material such as cotton, or a derivative prepared from cotton, and extrusion of the solution through small orifices into a suitable aqueous bath when a fibre was produced by coagulation or into air when the solvent evaporated to give filaments. This process produced a continuous filament and, although often referred to as spinning, a better term is probably extrusion in order to avoid confusion with the spinning process employed to transform fibres into yarn. This regeneration of one fibrous material from another is dependent on having a suitable solvent available. The first rayons were made from cellulose nitrate (nitrocellulose) obtained by reacting cotton, wood etc. with a mixture of nitric and sulphuric acids. Nitrocellulose was first made by Braconnet (1832) and later Schonbein and was shown to be soluble in mixtures of alcohol and ether containing caoutchouc by Audermans (1855) who produced threads of regenerated nitrocellulose by withdrawing a steel needle which had been immersed in the solution. Later, Swan (1883) extruded a solution of cellulose nitrate in glacial acetic acid through holes and produced filaments which, because of the dangerously inflammable nature of nitrocellulose, were denitrated and re-converted into cellulose before use. Swan's filaments were used to produce carbon filaments in electric lamps.

It was left to Chardonet (1885) to exploit commercially the production of rayon by this kind of technique. Many processes were patented at that time and one possible method of production was to dissolve nitrocellulose in alcohol/ether and extrude the solution into air when the fibre formed as the solvent evaporated. The fibres were then de-nitrated by treatment with alkali. Rayons made by this process have been superseded.

The modern man-made fibre industry really began with the work of Cross and Bevan (1892) who showed that cellulose could be dissolved in dilute alkali after treatment with caustic soda and carbon disulphide and the cellulose re-precipitated by extrusion into solutions of dilute acids. However, this apparently simple process did not get under way until about 1910 as many technological difficulties had to be resolved. This procedure is known as the viscose process; the quantity of rayon made in this way has expanded enormously since those days, making "viscose rayon" the most important of the man-made fibres.

Other ways have been used to produce regenerated fibres. Cellulose may be dissolved in cuprammonium hydroxide and the solution extruded or derivatives of cellulose other than the nitrates (notably the acetates) may be transformed into rayons. Proteins such as casein from milk or zein from maize have been made into fibres in the last three decades. The advent of the truly synthetic fibres made from simple chemical starting materials did not come about until the 1930's and arose largely as a result of the work of Carothers[2] at the DuPont Company in the U.S.A. His remarkable work opened up an entirely new field, namely the formation of fibrous polymers from simple chemicals obtained from coal or the petroleum industries and led to the preparation of nylon in 1935. Since the announcement of the latter, many other synthetic fibres have been produced *e.g.* Terylene, Orlon, Courtelle etc.

2. Polymers

The word polymer essentially means many-membered and is a term applied to substances built up from simple compounds which are joined together by means of covalent linkages. The possibility of existence of polymers may be regarded as a direct consequence of simple ideas of valency since, if an atom or group has two valencies, it may join with others to form a chain. Perhaps the simplest such group would be methylene which can, formally at least, form long paraffin chains

$$-CH_2-CH_2-CH_2-CH_2-$$

This simple conception of groups or atoms joined together in linear chains by means of covalent links was not accepted generally by chemists until as late as 1930.

The earlier chemists regarded polymeric materials such as glue, gums, cellulose, rubber etc. as composed of relatively small units combined together by partial valencies. Applications of physico-chemical techniques (elevation of the boiling point, depression of the freezing point, diffusion etc.) showed clearly that many products classified as colloids by Graham[3] were large molecules. Molecular weights of 30,000 and 17,500 for amylodextrin[4,5], 10,000 for cellulose nitrate and 6,000–12,000 for rubber[6] were obtained. Another example is rubber whose molecule was written as $(C_5H_8)_n$ or $(C_{10}H_{16})_n$ being regarded as made up of C_5H_8 or $C_{10}H_{16}$ units. Other chemists postulated aggregates of molecules which had a cyclic structure. For rubber the formula (I) has been suggested[7]

$$\left[\begin{array}{c} CH_3 \\ | \\ CH_2-CH=C-CH_2 \\ | \quad\quad\quad | \\ CH_2-CH=C-CH_2 \\ | \\ CH_3 \end{array}\right]_n$$

(I)

A cyclic unit has the advantage of explaining the apparent absence of groups at the end of the chain molecule which would be capable of reacting chemically but which chemists found difficult to detect.

Work on synthetic polymers dates back to the middle of the nineteenth century. For example Simon[8] in 1839 polymerised styrene and in 1879 Bouchardat[9] polymerised isoprene. Workers with these products (e.g. Stobbe and Posnjak in 1910)[10] imagined polystyrene to be a colloidal material and attempted to fit a cyclic formula. Polymers produced by reactions of carboxyanhydrides (II) of α-amino acids were considered to be aggregates of cyclic formulae[11] (III), the reaction being written as

$$(II) \qquad\qquad\qquad\qquad (III)$$

With polymers made from ε-aminocaproic acid, $NH_2(CH_2)_5COOH$ the formula was given as

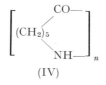

$$(IV)$$

This kind of formula was rather misleading. It seems extraordinary, in the light of present day knowledge of polymers, that chemists should have avoided the simple hypothesis of long chain molecules. This confusion arose partly from the idea that these products were colloidal in character and hence, at that time, were considered to be made up of aggregates of simpler molecules. Workers were also discouraged by the fact that polymeric materials were not well defined or crystallisable.

Staudinger in 1920[12] proposed the normal covalent kind of formulae for polymers. He wrote polystyrene for example as

$$\begin{array}{ccc} -CH_2-CH-CH_2-CH- \\ | \qquad\quad | \\ C_6H_5 \qquad C_6H_5 \end{array}$$

Molecules of this kind with long chains might be expected to exhibit colloidal properties because of their very size[13]. The existence of the giant or macromolecular structure of polymers was unequivocably demonstrated by the work of Carothers[2] in a brillant series of investigations in which he showed that covalent molecules of high molecular weight could be built up when simple compounds underwent well known chemical reactions. This work was a turning point and the decades 1930–40–50 have produced polymeric materials in ever increasing variety and quantity.

On the basis of this simple idea, it is easy to see how many polymers may be prepared. An amino acid can be condensed with itself to give a polyamide

$$NH_2(CH_2)_5COOH + NH_2(CH_2)_5COOH \rightarrow NH_2(CH_2)_5CONH(CH_2)_5COOH + H_2O$$

$NH_2(CH_2)_5CONH(CH_2)_5COOH + NH_2(CH_2)_5COOH \rightarrow$
$$\rightarrow NH_2(CH_2)_5CONH(CH_2)_5CONH(CH_2)_5COOH + H_2O \text{ etc. } \rightarrow$$
$$\rightarrow NH_2(CH_2)_5[CONH(CH_2)_5]_{n-1}COOH$$

(V)

or polyesters may be prepared from hydroxy acids

$HO(CH_2)_6COOH + HO(CH_2)_6COOH \rightarrow HO(CH_2)_6COO(CH_2)_6COOH + H_2O$

$HO(CH_2)_6COO(CH_2)_6COOH + HO(CH_2)_6COOH \rightarrow$
$$\rightarrow HO(CH_2)_6COO(CH_2)_6COO(CH_2)_6COOH + H_2O \text{ etc. } \rightarrow$$
$$\rightarrow HO(CH_2)_6[COO(CH_2)_6]_{n-1}COOH$$

(VI)

Alternatively, a free radical written as $\dot{M}$ may react with a vinyl compound to produce an activated vinyl group *e.g.*

$$\dot{M} + CH_2{=}CHR \rightarrow MCH_2{-}\dot{C}H + CH_2{=}CH \rightarrow MCH_2CH{-}CH_2{-}\dot{C}H \rightarrow \text{etc.}$$
$$\begin{array}{cccc} & | & | & | & | \\ & R & R & R & R \end{array}$$

(VII)

This new radical (VII) can then react with a further vinyl group and so on. A chain reaction is set up and a compound of the form (VIII) is produced

$$M{-}CH_2{-}CH{-}CH_2{-}CH{-}CH_2{-}CH{-}M \quad \text{or} \quad M\left[CH_2{-}CH\right]_{n-2} M$$
$$\begin{array}{ccc} | & | & | \\ R & R & R \end{array} \qquad \qquad \begin{array}{c} | \\ R \end{array}$$

(VIII)

The chain growth is stopped when two radical ends meet and combine.

3. Classification of Polymers

The formulae (V), (VI) and (VIII) have been purposely written in a manner which indicates that the molecule can be regarded as constructed from groups or structural units. In the polymer (VIII) the structural unit is $CH_2{-}CH$, in the polyamide (V), $CONH(CH_2)_5$ and so on. Each of these
$\quad\quad\quad |$
$\quad\quad\quad R$
units has valencies of 2 and hence when joined together, they lead to a polymer whose molecules are linear in shape. The group at the ends of the molecule will have a valency of 1 and therefore will be different in character from the structural unit. The properties of the polymer molecule will depend not only on the chemical character of the structural units but also on its size which, for linear polymers, is given by the length. This latter dimension may simply be measured in terms of the degree of

References p. 13

polymerisation. This is defined as the total number of units in the chain. For a polymer of formula $MX_{n-2}M_1$, n would be the degree of polymerisation or simply the D.P. The end groups M and M_1 may appear to be a complication, but this is not so in practice since polymer molecules have values of the D.P. running into hundreds and their inclusion makes little difference to the actual value of n.

Characterisation of polymers in which the units involved have valencies greater than 2 is somewhat more difficult. In a simple case of carbon atoms it is possible to build up a macromolecular network in three dimensions. Each carbon atom may be joined to four others to give the three-dimensional structure of a diamond. Three-dimensional networks may be synthesised from units whose valencies are greater than 2. Thus the condensation of glycerol, G, and succinic acid, S, will give a complicated polymer (IX)

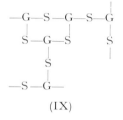

(IX)

where rings may be formed of different sizes. Although a polymer with structural units greater than 2 can lead to a 2-dimensional network, as in graphite, in general a 3-dimensional network will result. The specification of such a network is difficult but such substances are of considerable practical importance, *e.g.* resins formed from urea and formaldehyde to give non-crease finishes to textile fabrics or alkyd resins used in the paint and varnish trade. The structural units which have a valency of two, for example, are derived from monomers which are difunctional, functionality being described by the number of groups with which the monomer will join. Thus an ethylenic compound such as vinyl chloride (X) will join with two, divinylbenzene (XI) with four and is therefore tetrafunctional whereas triallyl-cyanurate (XII) is hexafunctional. Similarly ethylene glycol and adipic acid are difunctional, glycerol is trifunctional and so on

$CH_2=CHCl$

(X)   (XI)

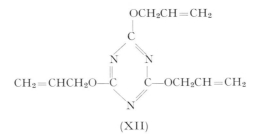

(XII)

Three dimensional structures are not discussed in this volume since textile materials are made from linear polymers. The requirement of linearity of polymer molecules which form fibres suggests that just as a yarn is formed from fibres by twisting so an analogous situation exists on a molecular scale with the linear units which go to make up a fibre. Mica and graphite which have planar molecules form flat plates. This analogy, although it must not be pressed too far, does suggest some qualitative correspondence between macro and molecular shape.

Carothers showed that polymers could be classified according to the chemistry of their preparation. He identified two broad categories, *viz.* polymers made, via (a) an addition reaction and (b) a condensation reaction.

(a) Addition polymers

These are formed from monomers without the elimination of any molecules. One obvious example is that described earlier where a radical reacts with an ethylenic compound to set up a chain reaction.

There are many examples of monomers containing double bonds which are capable of reacting in this manner. Some are listed below.

Monomer	*Formula*
Ethylene	$CH_2=CH_2$
Acrylonitrile	$CH_2=CHCN$
Vinyl acetate	$CH_2=CHOOCCH_3$
Styrene	$CH_2=CHPh$
Methyl methacrylate	$CH_2=C-COOMe$
	$\quad\quad\quad\;\; \overset{\displaystyle |}{CH_3}$

Polymers formed by addition processes have the same number of atoms in the structural unit as the monomer from which the polymer was made.

(b) Condensation polymers

These are, in general, prepared by condensation reactions and hence a simple molecule is eliminated. Thus the formation of polyamides from amino acids or polyesters from hydroxy acids proceeds with elimination of water. These polymers have structural units which contain a smaller number of atoms than the monomeric starting materials.

This simple distinction made between addition and condensation reactions is justified by the large chemical differences between the two kinds of polymers. Addition polymers have in general a chain composed of the same atoms. Thus the polymers produced from the ethylenic compounds mentioned above have a backbone composed entirely of carbon atoms and any polar groups, which are present, form side chains or end groups. By contrast, condensation polymers have polar groups as part of the backbone of the polymer and the presence of these has effects on the properties of the resulting polymer which are not found in the addition polymers.

The difference between the mechanisms of preparation of the two kinds of polymer is considerable. Addition polymerisation is essentially a chain reaction in which monomer units are being added to the growing polymer. In the examples of condensation polymerisation quoted above the reaction mechanism is "step-wise"; if two units of monomer condense to form a dimer, the next stage in the reaction may be for the dimer to condense with a third unit of monomer or to condense with other dimers. In other words any molecule, no matter what its size, is capable of reacting with any other.

Nevertheless these definitions do not give the complete picture. Some polymers have the characteristics of condensation polymers but it may be possible to synthesise them without elimination of molecules. Products made from compounds like lactams which polymerise without the elimination of water give a typical condensation polymer (XIII)

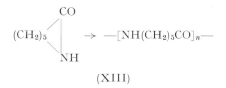

$$(CH_2)_5 \begin{matrix} CO \\ \\ NH \end{matrix} \rightarrow -[NH(CH_2)_5CO]_n-$$

(XIII)

Reactions such as that of a diisocyanate with a dihydric alcohol give a linear polymer (XIV) which has polar groups interspersed along the chain, *e.g.*

nHOR$_1$OH + nOCNR$_2$NCO →

→ HO[R$_1$OCONHR$_2$NHCOO]$_{n-1}$—R$_1$OCONHR$_2$NCO

(XIV)

The definition must be expanded to include compounds such as these as follows: a polymerisation process which proceeds by a reaction between pairs of functional groups with the formation of a type of inter-unit functional groups not present in the monomer(s) will be regarded as a condensation polymerisation. If the net process involves merely the scission of a bond in the monomer and the re-formation of similar connections with other monomers and if no by-product is evolved, it will be referred to as an addition polymerisation. However, this definition of condensation polymers does not include substances such as cellulose which cannot be synthesised in the laboratory; such materials may be degraded chemically (usually by hydrolysis) to yield monomeric products differing in composition from the structural units. If this addendum be added to the definition cellulose may be classified as a condensation polymer since it can by hydrolysed to yield a monomer glucose.

The distinction between condensation and addition polymerisations is a very valuable one. It must be admitted however, that it is not perfect and instances do exist where the picture breaks down. The classical example is that given by the work of Carothers who prepared a polymethylene by Wurtz's reaction of the alkyl bromide with sodium or magnesium *i.e.*

$$n\mathrm{Br(CH_2)_{10}Br} + n\mathrm{Na} \rightarrow [\!-\!(\mathrm{CH_2})_{10}\!-\!]_n + n\mathrm{NaBr}$$

The polymer is the straight chain hydrocarbon and should at first sight be an addition polymer. However, the reaction here has all the characteristics of condensation polymerisation (*i.e.* it is stepwise). This is an example of one of the few polymers which do not readily fall into the definitions above but which are sufficiently few not to detract from the utility of the definition.

REFERENCES

[1] *Handbook of Textile Fibres*, ed. M. HARRIS, Research Labs., Washington D.C.
[2] Collected Works of W. H. CAROTHERS on High Polymeric Substances, *High Polymers*, Vol. I., Interscience, New York, 1940.
[3] T. GRAHAM, *Phil. Trans. Roy. Soc. London*, 151 (1861) 183.
[4] H. T. BROWN and G. M. MORRIS, *J. Chem. Soc.*, 53 (1888) 610.
[5] C. LINTNER and G. DULL, *Ber.*, 26 (1893) 2533.
[6] J. H. GLADSTONE and W. HIBBERT, *J. Chem. Soc.*, 53 (1888) 688; *Phil. Mag.*, [5] 28 (1889) 38.
[7] C. HARRIES, *Ber.*, 37 (1904) 2708; *Ber.*, 38 (1905) 1195, 3985.
[8] E. SIMON, *Ann.*, 31 (1839) 265.
[9] M. G. BOUCHARDAT, *Compt. Rend.*, 89 (1879) 1117.
[10] H. STOBBE and G. POSNJAK, *Ann.*, 371 (1910) 259.
[11] H. LEUCHS, *Ber.*, 39 (1906) 857; H. LEUCHS and W. MANASSE, *Ber.*, 40 (1907) 3235; H. LEUCHS and W. GEIGER, *Ber.*, 41 (1908) 1721.
[12] H. STAUDINGER, *Ber.*, 53 (1920) 1073.
[13] H. STAUDINGER, *Ber.*, 59 (1926) 3019; H. STAUDINGER, K. FREY and W. STARK, *Ber.*, 66 (1927) 1782.

CHAPTER 2

CONDENSATION POLYMERS

1. Formation

Almost any condensation reaction can be used to prepare polymers provided that the reaction is carried out with starting materials or monomers carrying at least two functional groups. The polymers may be classified according to the chemical grouping joining the monomer units (*e.g.* polyamides, polyesters, polyanhydrides etc.). If fibre forming materials are to be studied, attention may be confined to the linear polymers which arise from the reactions of bifunctional monomers. Condensation polymers were made by Fischer[1] from x-amino acids to give polypeptides and from p-hydroxybenzoic acid to give polyesters[2]. Polyesters were also made by Bischoff[3] from dihydric phenols and dicarboxylic acids. Staudinger[4] prepared high polymers, synthesising polyoxymethylenes from formaldehyde.

Carothers' pioneering investigations[5] into the nature of polymeric substances were concerned to a large extent with condensation reactions. Essentially his work in this field was to examine the products which arose from reactions of bifunctional molecules. He studied simple organic reactions in which molecules were condensed to give esters, anhydrides, amides, etc. In one paper[6] a series of esters was prepared from glycols of formulae $HO(CH_2)_xOH$ and acids of formulae $HOOC(CH_2)_yCOOH$. x was 2, 3, 6 or 10 and y was 1, 2, 4, 8. The products were prepared simply by heating the glycol with the acid when, at a temperature around 160°C, reaction set in and water distilled off. The residue of ester in the flask was crystallised from solvents such as ethyl acetate, acetone and glacial acetic acid. Some of the esters were crystalline, others came down in the form of dusty powders. All became, when molten, quite viscous and those which did not form crystals on cooling became tough and glassy. The esters had molecular weights in the range 2300–5000 and behaved similarly as far as their physical properties were concerned. In addition, the molecular weights of the products bore no relation to those of the starting materials since the molecular weight of the ester did not increase with the number of carbon atoms in the glycol and acid. In an esterification of this kind it is possible to produce, at least on the grounds of structural formulae, linear polymers such as (III) or cyclic esters (I).

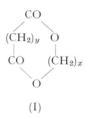

(I)

Carothers concluded that the products did not have cyclic formulae but were linear in structure. The analysis of the products for carbon and hydrogen gave results which were in agreement with a linear formula.

Other ranges of esters were made e.g. carbonates[7] using glycols ranging from trimethylene to decamethylene and oxalates[8] of ethylene, propylene, hexa- and decamethylene glycols. The esters were prepared by alcoholysis i.e. by heating the glycol with ethyl carbonate (II) or oxalate, when ethyl alcohol was eliminated. The reaction with the carbonates is,

These esters showed all the signs of being linear polymers except the lower members which gave cyclic monomers with 5 or 6 atoms in the ring. Some products, e.g., ethylene oxalate (IV) and trimethylene carbonate (V)

were obtained in two forms which could be transformed one to the other. This was obtained by the following kind of experiment. Trimethylene glycol was heated with ethyl carbonate. Ethyl alcohol produced by alcohol interchange was driven off; the residue was distilled in vacuum when some pure monomeric trimethylene carbonate (V) distilled over (a liquid with b.p. of 160–165°C at 6 mm Hg which crystallises in colourless needles of m.p. 47–48°C). A viscous residue was left in the flask after distillation; this cooled to a sticky colourless resinous polymer of m.p. 235°C which depolymerises on re-heating in vacuum yielding further amounts of the trimethylene carbonate. A trace of potassium carbonate added to the monomeric form and the whole heated gave a viscous liquid which cooled to a clear glass.

Cyclisation

Polymer/monomer interconversion has been shown in other systems such as the lactones of δ-hydroxyvaleric acid (VI)[9].

(VI)

Carothers could not polymerise the five-membered ethylene carbonate (VII) and it seems that 5-membered rings are in general too stable to be transformed into polymers. On the other hand, tetramethylene carbonate would, if it depolymerised, give a monomer with a seven-membered ring structure. Carothers could not achieve this; the nearest he could get was a small yield of dimer (VIII).

(VII)   (VIII)   (IX)

Amides show some analogous features; ε-aminocaproic acid gives on heating a lactam (IX) (20–30%)[10,12] and an undistillable product (80–70%). The lactam has a seven-membered ring. Other acids such as γ-aminobutyric and δ-aminovaleric readily form 5- and 6-membered lactams. The next highest member from caproic is ζ-aminoheptoic acid which, on heating, gives an undistillable product different in properties from its known lactam[11] (an eight-membered ring).

The ability of bifunctional compounds such as anhydrides, lactones and lactams to form cyclic rings has been discussed by Carothers. It is clear that the five-membered ring systems stand out as being very stable. The six-membered ones can be converted into linear polymers and by suitable treatment back to the monomeric form.

Hence, polyfunctionality alone is not adequate to ensure that reaction will lead to a polymer. Monomeric forms may be produced *e.g.* ε-aminocaproic acid leads to a certain yield of the lactam (IX), an α-hydroxy acid (X) yields both a linear polymer (XII) and a dimeric cyclic ester (XI).

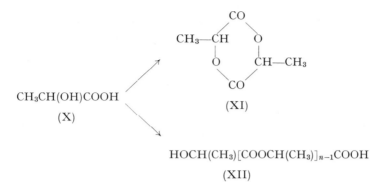

$$HOCH(CH_3)[COOCH(CH_3)]_{n-1}COOH$$

(XII)

The most important factor which determines the course of reaction is the size of the ring which may be obtained if the bifunctional molecule reacts intramolecularly. As Carothers and Spanagel[13] have shown, a five-membered ring may be produced to the exclusion of the linear polymer e.g. ethylene carbonate but if the cyclic product has a ring of six or seven members, both ring and polymeric products are possible. Ring compounds of a larger size are obtained only under special experimental conditions of high dilution[14] or, as in the experiments of Carothers et al., by heating the polymeric form of the ester in a vacuum to a temperature around 270°C and with a catalyst (e.g. $FeCl_2 \cdot 4H_2O$, $MgCl_2 \cdot 6H_2O$)[13]. The polymer depolymerises yielding a cyclic product of large ring size.

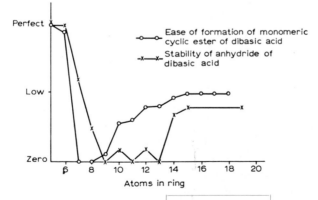

Fig. 5. Ease of formation of cyclic esters $O(CH_2)_2OCO(CH_2)_{n-6}CO$ and the stability of cyclic anhydrides $CO(CH_2)_{n-3}COO$ versus ring size[13]. (Courtesy American Chemical Society)

In Fig. 5 is reproduced the diagram given by Carothers and Spanagel where the ease of formation of cyclic esters from ethylene glycols and dibasic acids together with the stability of the anhydrides of the acids is plotted against the number of carbon atoms in the ring. Data of a similar kind has been obtained quantitatively by measuring the unimolecular rate constants for the formation of cyclic lactones from ω-hydroxy acids and comparing these with the bimolecular constant of the reaction to form polymer[15]. The broad picture is the same for the three systems. Stable 5- and 6-membered ring systems are possible. As the ring size increases there is a rapid decrease in stability but this slowly improves for systems containing a larger number of members.

The ease of formation of five-membered rings arises from the ability to form rings which are strain free; for larger ring sizes the cyclic molecule must take up a non-planar configuration in order to relieve the strain which may be imposed on the valency angles. However, simply arranging the atoms out of the plane of the molecule to relieve strain may not be entirely successful since steric interference can arise from substituents. The minimum in the curve was attributed by Carothers[16,17] to two factors (a) the probability that the ends of the molecule will react to form a cyclic compound and (b) the crowding which occurs between the hydrogen substituents. The molecule must, before reaction can occur, coil itself into a specific configuration which is an event statistically unfavourable whereas numerous configurations are possible when one molecule is to react with another molecule *i.e.* intermolecularly. In 8–12-membered rings, a scale model will show that crowding of the hydrogen atoms will occur. For larger sizes, the number of configurations which the ring can assume increases and this crowding may be avoided; the stability of the rings therefore increases. In the reaction of a bifunctional compound however, the probability that the chain will take up a configuration which will allow the ends of the molecule to react is low and such ring configurations will only be few in number compared with all possible ones. It has been calculated by Kähn and others[18] that the probability that the two ends of a long chain will occupy positions adjacent to one another and hence be in a position to react intramolecularly, varies roughly as (chain length)$^{-\frac{3}{2}}$. Thus intramolecular reactions become less probable as the number of atoms in the molecule increases.

The above explanation unfortunately does not explain why five-membered ring systems are formed to the exclusion of polymer (*e.g.* succinic acid gives a cyclic anhydride and ethylene carbonate is available only in cyclic form). The cyclic monomers are also readily formed and are relatively stable to reactions such as hydrolysis.

Table 2 taken from Flory's review[19] gives the products obtained from

TABLE 2

THE ABILITY OF COMPOUNDS TO FORM RING SYSTEMS OF LINEAR POLYMERS

Type	Structural unit	Products of bifunctional condensation	
		six-membered	seven-membered
ω-Hydroxy acid	$-O(CH_2)_nCO-$	Both ring and polymer spontaneously interconvertible[20].	Chiefly ring; interconvertible[21].
α-Hydroxy acid self ester	$-OCHCOOCHCO-$ $\;\;\;\;\;\mid\;\;\;\;\;\;\;\;\mid$ $\;\;\;\;CH_3\;\;\;\;CH_3$	Linear polymer probably the primary product. Interconversion easy[20,22].	—
Alkylene carbonate	$-(CH_2)_nOCOO-$	Both ring and polymer easily convertible[7,20].	Linear polymer only[7].
Dibasic anhydride	$-(CH_2)_nCOOCO-$	Ring only.	Linear polymer convertible to ring[23].
Alkylene formal	$-(CH_2)_nOCH_2O-$	Ring only[24].	Both ring and polymer[24].
ω-Amino acid self amide	$-NH(CH_2)_nCO-$	Ring only.	Both ring and polymer interconvertible[12].

various bifunctional molecules which could produce six- and seven-membered ring systems.

In polymer preparation the ability of monomers to form cyclic systems is a disadvantage and such monomers are to be avoided. This is simply done by using monomers with a larger number of atoms. The cyclic compounds with six or seven members however will quite readily transform to the polymer. Thus δ-valerolactone (XIII) which is formed from the corresponding hydroxy acid will give a linear polymer (XIV)

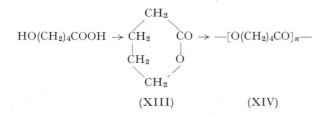

$$HO(CH_2)_4COOH \rightarrow \quad \text{(XIII)} \quad \rightarrow \quad -[O(CH_2)_4CO]_n-$$

(XIII)   (XIV)

The seven-membered ring ε-caprolactam (IX) will readily give a polyamide. The mechanism by which the ring opening occurs may be elucidated to some extent from the fact that the reaction is induced catalytically or by the presence of small amounts of substances which will produce end groups *e.g.* water reacts to give the acid (XV) which can then react with the cyclic compound to give the amide (XVI); addition of further molecules of caprolactam forms the polyamide (XVII)

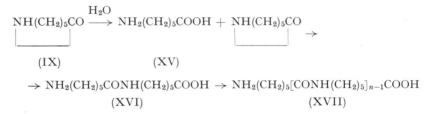

This mechanism is an addition one. However the product is clearly a condensation polymer and must be classified as such. The reaction at first sight is similar to that of a vinyl polymerisation to be discussed in the next chapter in so far as the monomer units are being added on to a growing chain. However, there are differences between this and the characteristic chain reaction of the vinyl polymerisations. The initial step – the opening of the ring – is similar to the succeeding ones. During the polymerisation, polymer and monomer are present together but since there is no termination reaction, the molecular weight goes on increasing; in addition reactions with vinyl derivatives the termination reaction is important in determining the molecular weight.

2. Fibre-forming Polymers

The products discussed above are polymer substances of relatively low molecular weight. Carothers, however, took his investigations further and produced by prolonged heating of the esters products of high molecular weights (*ca.* 12,000). He called these "superpolyesters". These products were harder and tougher than the esters of lower molecular weight and are very sparingly soluble, if at all, in the common organic solvents. In another paper[26], he showed that polyesters and other condensation polymers of high molecular weight could be made into fibres. His work laid the basis for the commercial exploitation of nylon.

It has been mentioned that almost any condensation reaction is capable of yielding a polymer. In Table 3 are given some of the types of polymers formed via condensation reactions. Although many polymers which have sufficiently high molecular weights and potential fibre forming properties are available, only relatively few are utilised commercially. This is not surprising because many fibrous polymers will not possess all the properties necessary (dyeability, resistance to light and chemicals etc.) and the capital expenditure required in development from the laboratory to the launching in a commercial market is extremely high.

TABLE 3

TYPES OF SYNTHETIC CONDENSATION POLYMERS

Type	Linking group	Examples	Characteristics
Polyester	$-\overset{\displaystyle O}{\underset{\displaystyle \parallel}{C}}-O-$	$HO(CH_2)_9COOH \rightarrow -[(CH_2)_9COO]_n-$	Hard, crystalline, fibre-forming, can be cold-drawn, m.p. 76°C.
		$HO(CH_2)_{10}OH + HOOC(CH_2)_4COOH \rightarrow$ $\rightarrow -[(CH_2)_{10}OOC(CH_2)_4COO]_n-$	Hard, crystalline, fibre-forming, can be cold-drawn, m.p. 80°C.
		$HO(CH_2)_2OH + HOOC\!\!-\!\!\bigcirc\!\!-\!\!COOH \rightarrow$ $\rightarrow -[(CH_2)_2OOC\!\!-\!\!\bigcirc\!\!-\!\!COO]_n-$	Hard, crystalline, fibre-forming, can be drawn, m.p. 264°C.
Polyanhydride	$-\overset{\displaystyle O}{\underset{\displaystyle \parallel}{C}}-O-\overset{\displaystyle O}{\underset{\displaystyle \parallel}{C}}-$	$HOOC(CH_2)_8COOH + (CH_3CO)_2O \rightarrow$ $\rightarrow -[CO(CH_2)_8COO]_n- + CH_3COOH$	Crystalline, fibre-forming, can be cold-drawn, sensitive to water, m.p. 83°C.
Poly-oxymethylene	$-O-$	$HCHO \rightarrow -[CH_2O]_n-$	Crystalline.
Polyether		$\overset{\displaystyle CH_2}{\underset{\displaystyle CH_2}{\diagdown}} O \rightarrow -[CH_2CH_2O]_n-$	Crystalline waxes, m.p. 38–60°C at. mol. wt. above 1000.
Polysulphide	$-S-$	$ClCH_2CH_2Cl + Na_2S \rightarrow -[CH_2CH_2SCH_2CH_2S]_n-$	Crystalline.
	$-\overset{\displaystyle S}{\underset{\displaystyle \parallel}{S}}-\overset{\displaystyle S}{\underset{\displaystyle \parallel}{S}}-$	$ClCH_2CH_2Cl + Na_2S_4 \rightarrow -[CH_2CH_2\underset{\parallel}{\overset{S}{S}}\ S\underset{\parallel}{\overset{S}{C}}H_2CH_2\underset{\parallel}{\overset{S}{S}}\ S]_n-$	Rubber-like; crystallises on stretching.

TABLE 3 (continued)

Type	Linking group	Examples	Characteristics
Polyacetal	$—O—\overset{R}{\underset{H}{C}}—O—$	$HO(CH_2)_{10}OH + CH_2(OBu)_2 \rightarrow —[(CH_2)_{10}OCH_2O]_n—$	Fibre-forming, crystalline.
Polyamide	$—\overset{O}{\overset{\|}{C}}NH—$	$NH_2(CH_2)_5COOH \rightarrow —[(CH_2)_5CONH]_n—$	Crystalline, fibre-forming, can be readily cold-drawn, m.p. 215°C.
		$NH_2(CH_2)_6NH_2 + HOOC(CH_2)_4COOH \rightarrow$ $\rightarrow —[(CH_2)_6NHCO(CH_2)_4CONH]_n—$	Crystalline, fibre-forming, can be readily cold-drawn, m.p. 265°C.
Polyurethan	$—O\overset{O}{\overset{\|}{C}}NH—$	$HO(CH_2)_4OH + OCN(CH_2)_6NCO \rightarrow$ $\rightarrow —\left[(CH_2)_4O\overset{O}{\overset{\|}{C}}NH(CH_2)_6NH\overset{O}{\overset{\|}{C}}O\right]_n—$	Crystalline, fibre-forming, can be cold-drawn, m.p. 184°C.
Polyurea	$—NH\overset{O}{\overset{\|}{C}}NH—$	$NH_2(CH_2)_{10}NH_2 + OCN(CH_2)_{10}NCO \rightarrow$ $\rightarrow —[(CH_2)_{10}NHCONH(CH_2)_{10}NHCONH]_n—$	Crystalline, fibre-forming, can be cold-drawn, m.p. 210°C.
Polytriazole	(triazole ring structure)	$NH_2NH\overset{O}{\overset{\|}{C}}(CH_2)_8\overset{O}{\overset{\|}{C}}NHNH_2 + NH_2\overset{O}{\overset{\|}{C}}(CH_2)_8\overset{O}{\overset{\|}{C}}NH_2 \rightarrow$ (polytriazole ring structure)	Crystalline, fibre-forming, can be cold-drawn, m.p. 240–260°C.

For use as a fibre, the polymer must have among other attributes a suitable molecular weight. The results in Table 4 obtained from the work of Carothers and Van Natta[27] for a series of polymers made from ω-hydroxydecanoic acid $(HO(CH_2)_{10}COOH)$ show that as the molecular

TABLE 4

MOLECULAR WEIGHT AND FIBRE FORMATION: POLYESTERS FROM
ω-HYDROXYDECANOIC ACID

Number average mol. wt.	Calc. average length of chains (Å)	m.p. (°C)	Spinnability	Drawability	Fibre strength (kg/mm²)
780	60	66–67	Absent	—	—
4170	313	74–76	Absent	—	—
5670	440	73–75	Short filaments	Absent	—
7330	570	74–75	Long filaments	Absent	Very weak
9330	730	75–76	Long filaments	Present	Very weak
16,900	1320	77–78	Good	Good	13.1
20,700	1610	77–78	Difficult	Good	12.3
25,200	1970	75–80	Spins above 210°	Present	7.0

weight increases the melting point rises to a limiting value. At the same time, the ability to form fibres increases but once a certain molecular weight is reached, further increase is of little advantage as more difficulties are experienced in melting and in the subsequent spinning or extrusion of the polymer. Other workers[28] have fractionated polymers and studied the ability of the different fractions to form fibres. With polyhexamethylene fumaramide (XVIII) good fibrous properties were evident at a molecular weight of 12,000, whereas the closely related polyhexamethylene succinamide (XIX) required a molecular weight of greater than 25,000.

$$NH_2(CH_2)_6NHCOCH=CH[CONH(CH_2)_6NHCOCH=CH]_{n-1}COOH$$

(XVIII)

$$NH_2(CH_2)_6NHCO(CH_2)_2[CONH(CH_2)_6NHCO(CH_2)_2]_{n-1}COOH$$

(XIX)

In general, however, there seems to be little advantage in increasing the molecular weight above a certain value. This value will be characteristic of each polymer but seems to be in the range 10,000–50,000.

3. Preparation

Condensation polymers which are important commercially are tough solids which are not soluble to any extent in conventional solvents (benzene, alcohols etc.) but may be dissolved in polar liquids of high solvating power (*e.g.* phenols, dimethylformamide). The polymerisation reactions can be carried out by interaction of the intermediates when molten or in solution, but the reaction must give a product of high molecular weight and hence must be carried a long way towards completion. The most economical method of production is in the melt as isolation of the product is not necessary. This method requires that the intermediates are stable at the temperatures used (200–250°C) and that local overheating of the reaction mixture must be avoided to prevent side reactions. Oxidation of the melt at this high temperature may occur leading to the discolouration of the product but can be avoided by carrying out the reaction under an atmosphere of nitrogen. Agitation of the melt may be achieved either by mechanical means or by the water which boils off during many of the condensations. At the end of the reaction, the melted polymer may be obtained in the laboratory as a solid plug on cooling the reaction mixture or commercially it may be extruded as a ribbon which is cut into "chips" of irregular shape but average size about $\frac{1}{4}''$ across. Alternatively the ribbon may be put through a cube cutter when the polymer is cut into particles of a regular shape.

In this chapter the preparation of three important polycondensates will be considered, polyamides, polyesters and polyurethans. Some routes to the production are given but for fuller details the reader is referred to other sources[29].

(a) Polyesters

Although the work of Carothers and co-workers demonstrated that polyesters of a suitable molecular weight could be transformed into fibres, those actually made suffered from having low melting points and susceptibility to hydrolytic attack. It was left to the work of Dickson and Whinfield[30] to show that polyesters of adequately high melting points could be produced in a highly polymerised form from aromatic dicarboxylic acids. Since Whinfield's work many polyesters of this kind have been synthesised[31]. It has been demonstrated that a fibre forming polymer may be obtained from α,ω-dihydric glycols condensed with aromatic dicarboxylic acids provided that the carboxylic acid groups are symmetrically placed.

Polyesters may be prepared in many ways.

(1) Reaction of the diacetate of the glycol (XX) with the acid or its ester

$$\underset{(\text{XX})}{R\begin{cases} OCOCH_3 \\ OCOCH_3 \end{cases}} + \quad R_1\begin{cases} COOH \\ COOH \end{cases} \rightarrow CH_3COORO[COR_1COORO]_{n-1}COR_1COOH + \\ + CH_3COOH$$

(2) Glycol with the acid chloride

$$R \overset{OH}{\underset{OH}{<}} + R_1 \overset{COCl}{\underset{COCl}{<}} \rightarrow HORO[COR_1COORO]_{n-1}COR_1COCl + HCl$$

This reaction is more rapid than direct esterification and has been suggested in patents to be suitable for forming polyesters from aliphatic glycols with more than four carbon atoms but care must be taken since, in some systems studied, side reactions may occur *e.g.* replacement of the glycol hydroxyl groups by chlorine.

(3) Alcoholysis or ester interchange

$$R \overset{OH}{\underset{OH}{<}} + R_1 \overset{COOC_2H_5}{\underset{COOC_2H_5}{<}} \rightarrow HORO[COR_1COORO]_{n-1}COR_1COOC_2H_5 + \\ + C_2H_5OH$$

(4) Direct esterification

$$R \overset{OH}{\underset{OH}{<}} + R_1 \overset{COOH}{\underset{COOH}{<}} \rightarrow HORO[COR_1COORO]_{n-1}COR_1COOH + H_2O$$

In the case of the difficult esterification of phenols *e.g.* hydroquinone the reaction may be brought about through the use of acetic anhydride. Alcohols and carboxylic acids will react easily in the presence of trifluoroacetic anhydride[32] and this reagent has been suggested for the preparation of the polyester of *p*-hydroxybenzoic acid.

(5) Reaction of ethylene chlorohydrin and sodium terephthalate when di(β-hydroxyethyl) terephthalate (XXI) is formed.

$$2CH_2OHCH_2Cl + NaOOC\overset{}{\underset{}{\bigcirc}}COONa \rightarrow$$

$$\rightarrow CH_2OHCH_2OCO\overset{}{\underset{}{\bigcirc}}COOCH_2CH_2OH + 2NaCl$$

(XXI)

The polymer is prepared by heating this product, ethylene glycol being eliminated by interchange.

The molecular weight of the polymer will be dependent on the conditions of reaction in particular removal of the by-product, water, alcohol etc. The only commericially important polymer in the polyester field is polyethylene terephthalate, marketed under the trade name "Terylene" in the U.K. by I.C.I., and "Dacron" in the U.S.A. by DuPont. Discovered by Whinfield and Dickson in 1941, development was delayed by the advent of World War II. The manufacturing route is by reaction of dimethyl terephthalate with an excess of ethylene glycol. The preparation of the intermediates is as follows:

(1) *Ethylene glycol*[33]. The most important source comes from ethylene chlorohydrin. The chlorine atom may be exchanged for hydroxyl by heating with a mild alkali (lime or sodium carbonate). Alternatively ethylene may be catalytically oxidised to ethylene oxide which is then hydrolysed to the glycol

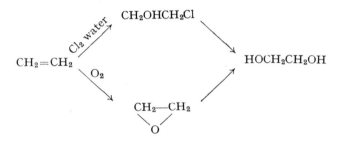

(2) *Terephthalic acid*. Oxidation of *p*-alkylbenzenes is the simplest route. *p*-Xylenes are found in certain fractions obtained in petroleum cracking usually in association with the *ortho* and *meta* isomers. *o*-Xylene may be removed by distillation; since the *meta* boils within a degree of the *para* isomer, recourse must be made to other means of separation such as freezing. Removal of these isomers is essential; their presence will lead to polyesters whose chains alter direction at the points where the isomers of terephthalic acid occur. *p*-Cymene (XXII) may be obtained from the oxidation of turpentine with iodine or strong sulphuric acid; both *p*-xylene and *p*-cymene may be oxidised to *p*-toluic acid (XXIII) and thence to terephthalic acid:

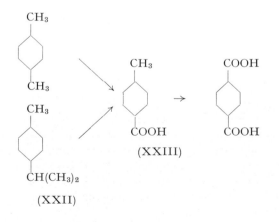

Suitable oxidising agents are air and nitric acid and the process may be
done in the two stages indicated above.

Terephthalic acid is high melting and not very soluble. However, the
dimethyl ester, formed from the acid and methanol in the presence of
sulphuric acid is easier to use and may be obtained pure by distillation
under a vacuum or by crystallisation from a solvent. It is a white crystalline substance of m.p. 140.8°C.

Polymerisation. Dimethyl terephthalate is reacted at a temperature
around 195°C with more than two moles of ethylene glycol using a substance such as litharge, zinc borate or magnesium methoxide[34] as a
catalyst. Methanol is evolved during the reaction and distils off. Heating
is continued until the interchange is complete but, to obtain the high
molecular weight required, the temperature is raised to about 280°C and
at the same time the pressure is reduced to 1 mm Hg. In this stage the
excess glycol is removed.

Whinfield[35] has described direct esterification of the acid by the glycol.
The most satisfactory manner to do this, and avoid loss of glycol along
with the evolved water, is first to form an ester of low molecular weight by
allowing the reaction to proceed so that molecules containing 1, 2 or 3
ester groups are formed; the product is heated above the boiling point of
the glycol which is then driven off. The removal of the glycol is facilitated
by reducing the pressure.

Quantitative yields of the linear polymers are not always obtained.
With polyethylene terephthalate a small amount of cyclic oligomers
(XXIV) is formed[36].

$$O\text{---}(CH_2)_2O\text{---}CO\text{---}C_6H_4CO$$
$$[\overset{|}{C}OC_6H_4\text{---}COO(CH_2)_2\text{---}\overset{|}{O}]_n$$
$$\text{(XXIV)} \qquad\qquad n = 2,3,4$$

The ring sizes of such compounds are large. Other systems may give
larger quantities of these oligomers and in the preparation of polyethylene
isophthalate as much as 10–15% may be present[37].

Other polyesters. In view of the attractive properties of polyethylene
terephthalate, extensive search for other polyesters has been made.
Polyesters made from polyhydroquinone adipate[38], polytetramethylene
terephthalate[39], halogenated terephthalic acids have been described. The
aromatic materials give spinnable fibres whereas the aliphatic polyesters
suffer from low softening points.

(b) Polyamides

In contrast to polyesters there are several polyamides which have been developed as commercial fibres. The generic word for these products is nylon
but commercial names include "Enkalon" (Dutch) "Grilon" (Swiss) etc.

It is possible to characterise both polyesters and polyamides according to the number of carbon atoms in the structural units in the molecule. If the nylon is made from an amino acid, there will only be one number required *e.g.* the polyamide from caprolactam (IX) is classified as nylon 6. Products made from the condensation of a diamine and a dicarboxylic acid are classified according to the number of carbon atoms in the amine and acid respectively. Thus the polyamide from hexamethylenediamine $NH_2(CH_2)_6NH_2$ and sebacic acid $HOOC(CH_2)_8COOH$ is nylon 610 (nylon six ten).

The first fibre forming polyamide was prepared by Carothers from ω-aminononanoic acid, $NH_2(CH_2)_9COOH$ in 1935. The properties of this product were such as to intensify research in this field leading to the development of nylon 66[40].

There are many organic reactions capable of giving polymers containing amide groups.

(1) Condensation of an amino acid or its ester

$$NH_2RCOOH \rightarrow NH_2R[CONHR]_{n-1}COOH + H_2O$$

The fibre "Rilsan" is made in this way from 11-aminoundecanoic acid, $NH_2(CH_2)_{10}COOH$. The formation of the linear polymer will not occur with all amino acids. If the functional groups are separated by less than 5 atoms *i.e.* x in the formula $NH_2(CH_2)_xCOOH$ is less than five then 5-and 6-membered ring compounds are formed in preference. If x in the above formula is 1, condensation produces diketopiperazine (XXV)

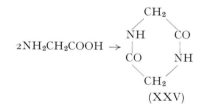

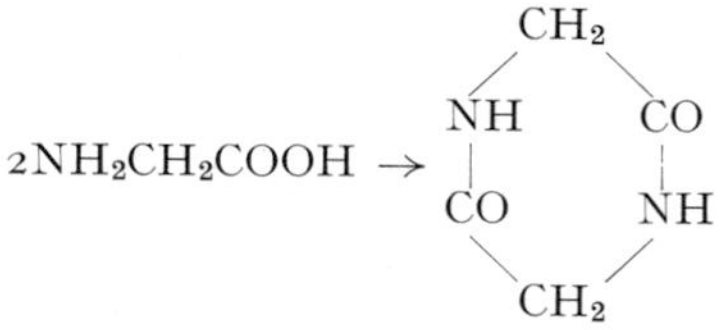

$$2NH_2CH_2COOH \rightarrow$$

(XXV)

When x is 2, the acid on heating splits off ammonia

$$NH_2(CH_2)_2COOH \rightarrow CH_2{=}CHCOOH + NH_3$$

to give acrylic acid. The acids with 3 and 4 methylene groups cyclise to give pyrolidones (XXVI) and piperidones (XXVII)

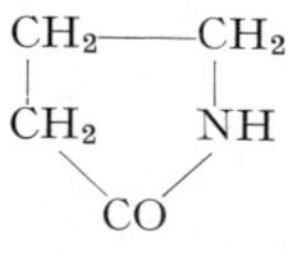

(XXVI) 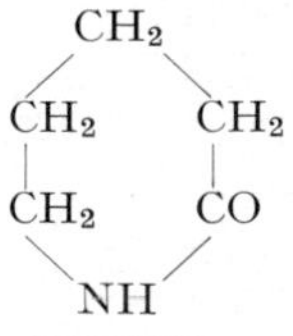　　　　　　　　　　(XXVII)

(2) From the lactam. The classical case of this reaction is the ring opening of caprolactam

$$\text{NH(CH}_2)_5\text{CO} \quad \rightarrow \quad -[\text{NH(CH}_2)_5\text{CO}]_n-$$

(3) Condensation of the diamine and dicarboxylic acid

$$\text{NH}_2\text{RNH}_2 + \text{HOOCR}_1\text{COOH} \rightarrow$$
$$\rightarrow \text{NH}_2\text{RNH}[\text{COR}_1\text{CONHRNH}]_{n-1}\text{COR}_1\text{COOH} + \text{H}_2\text{O}$$

Instead of the acid, an ester may be used or the amine may be reacted with the acid to form a salt which is then condensed. This is described for the preparation of nylon 66. In general the repeat unit (i.e.—NHRNHCOR$_1$CO—) of the polymer should have more than nine atoms in order to avoid the formation of a cyclic product. If R is a phenyl group, the diamine is less reactive than the primary aliphatic amines. In this case acid catalysts e.g. sulphuric, p-toluenesulphonic acids may be added.

The acid chloride may be used instead of the free acid and it has been shown that adipyl chloride will react almost instantaneously with hexamethylenediamine[41]. This can be carried out at the interface of two liquids (e.g. adipyl chloride in chlorobenzene and hexamethylenediamine in water). The polymer forms at the interface and can be drawn off.

(4) Reaction of the formyl derivative (XXVIII) of a diamine with the dicarboxylic acid

$$\text{OHCNHRNHCHO} \mid \text{HOOCR}_1\text{COOH} \rightarrow$$
$$\rightarrow -[\text{RNHCOR}_1\text{CONH}]_n- + \text{HCOOH}$$

(XXVIII)

(5) From nitriles. Nitriles will react with alcohols in 85% sulphuric acid in the cold to form amides. The mechanism is an ionic one where an alcohol will form a carbonium ion which will react with the nitrile groups thus

$$\text{R}_1\text{R}_2\text{R}_3\text{COH} \rightarrow \text{R}_3\overset{+}{\text{C}} + \text{RCN} \rightarrow [\text{R}_1\text{R}_2\text{R}_3\text{CN}=\overset{+}{\text{CR}}] \xrightarrow{\text{H}_2\text{O}} \text{R}_1\text{R}_2\text{R}_3\text{CNHCOR} + \text{H}^+$$

This reaction when carried out with glycols and dinitriles will lead to linear polyamides[42] e.g.

$$\text{HOCHCHOH} + \text{NCR}_1\text{CN} \rightarrow -[\text{CH}-\text{CH NHCOR}_1\text{CONH}]_n-$$
$$\quad\quad\;\; \text{R} \;\; \text{R} \quad\quad\quad\quad\quad\quad\quad\quad\quad\quad \text{R} \quad\;\; \text{R}$$

The reaction occurs in the cold and is very suitable when tertiary and secondary alcohols are used.

(6) From amino nitriles or dinitriles and diamines on heating with water to a temperature of 150–300°C

$$NCRCN + NH_2R_1NH_2 + H_2O \rightarrow$$
$$\rightarrow HOOCRCO[NHR_1NHCORCO]_{n-1}NHR_1NH_2 + NH_3$$

(7) From cyclic imides and diamines

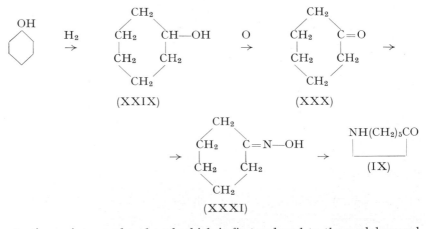

$$NCRCOOH + NH_2R_1NH_2 \rightarrow$$
$$\rightarrow NCRCO[NHR_1NHCORCO]_{n-1}NHR_1NH_2 + NH_3 + H_2O$$

Two polyamides will be discussed here: nylon 6 and nylon 66.

Nylon 6. This polymer may be produced from the amino acid or ε-caprolactam[44]. ε-and ζ-Amino acids readily form lactams which have the advantage of being more easily purified than the free acids. ε-Caprolactam is made in considerable quantities and is used for the preparation of plastics as well as fibres.

Caprolactam may be prepared from the oxime of cyclohexanone. The

starting point may be phenol which is first reduced to the cyclohexanol (XXIX) then oxidised to cyclohexanone (XXX). The oxime (XXXI) is prepared under aqueous conditions from hydroxylamine sulphate and the ketone when it comes out as an oil. The oxime undergoes a Beckmann rearrangement on treatment in oleum (24%) and yields the lactam, which separates as an oil and is purified by vacuum distillation (b.p. 120°C/10 mm). This rearrangement is exothermic and may be violent if not controlled.

The hydroxylamine sulphate used in this process may be prepared from sodium bisulphite, sodium nitrite and sulphur dioxide,

$$NaHSO_3 + NaNO_2 + SO_2 \rightarrow HON(SO_3Na)_2$$

(XXXII)

giving hydroxylamine disodium sulphonate (XXXII) which hydrolyses on warming. By using this reaction mixture directly to form the oxime the expensive process of isolation of hydroxylamine may be obviated.

A second possible route is by catalytic reduction of nitrocyclohexanone a process which gives the lactam directly. This is done by passage of the nitrocyclohexane vapour over a catalyst e.g. borophosphoric acid at a temperature of 150–450°C[45].

Caprolactam will yield the polymer on heating and there are several ways by which this polyamide has been made[47]. Many reagents assist the reaction e.g. water, alcohols, organic acids etc. and even metallic sodium[46]. In Germany, where nylon 6 has been mainly developed, a process is carried out in which the lactam with 10–20% of water is heated and water is removed as the polymerisation proceeds[29]. Alternatively, molten caprolactam containing 1–5% of catalyst (ε-aminocaproic acid or other nonstabilising compounds) is heated for periods of up to 8 hours at about 240–280°C. Water is allowed to escape. A molecular weight (number average) of 17,000 may be obtained at a temperature of 265°C. This is an equilibrium value and the melt still contains about 10% of the unreacted monomer and higher cyclic oligomers (XXXIII)[48]. The cyclic oligomers may be synthesised from the amino acids by the methods of peptide synthesis[49]. The quantity of "monomer" present in the melt varies with the reaction temperature as is shown by the results given in Table 5.

$$\begin{matrix} NH(CH_2)_5CO \\ | \qquad\qquad | \\ [CO(CH_2)_5NH]_n \end{matrix} \qquad n = 1,2,3 \ldots 8$$

(XXXIII)

It is possible to produce nylon 6 of very high mol. wt. by ionic polymerisation (using sodium hydroxide or carbonate as catalyst) at temperatures below the melting-point thereby reducing the monomer content to 2–3%. The product is not stable as far as its mol. wt. is concerned and has to be melted for many hours before being stabilised, presumably by transamidation reactions[50]. This process of achieving a stable molecular weight distribution may be speeded up by introducing an agent which promotes hydrolysis *e.g.* water, aminocaproic acid, acetic acid etc.[51]. The polymerisation of ε-caprolactam and depolymerisation will lead at equilibrium to the same mixture of the linear polymer and its cyclic oligomers[52]. The molecular weight may be controlled by monitoring the vapour pressure of water in the reactor, or by the addition of a mono-functional viscosity stabiliser (see later). The molten polymer is extruded into ribbon and then broken into chips. Excess "monomer" in the product (usually 6–11%) may be reduced to less than 1% by treatment with hot water.

TABLE 5

EQUILIBRIUM COMPOSITION OF MELT

Reaction temperature	Composition of product (in %)	
	Monomer	Polymer
160	3	97
220	10	90
250	12.5	87.5
280	15	85

Nylon 66. This is prepared from two components, hexamethylenediamine, $NH_2(CH_2)_6NH_2$ and adipic acid, $HOOC(CH_2)_4COOH$, giving a polymer with a repeat unit of

$$-NH(CH_2)_6NHCO(CH_2)_4CO-$$

The chemical name of such a polymer is polyhexamethylene adipamide.

The preparation of the intermediates may be carried out as follows: (1) Adipic acid. There are many routes possible to this key substance. Cyclohexanol can be prepared readily by the catalytic hydrogenation of phenol and oxidised to adipic acid (XXXIV) by treatment with 68% nitric acid or in air in the presence of a catalyst.

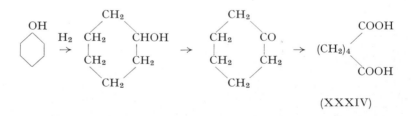

(XXXIV)

Alternatively, cyclohexane obtained from the petroleum industry or from catalytic hydrogenation of benzene is oxidised through to the acid or in two stages by air oxidation to give cyclohexanol and cyclohexanone which may be oxidised to adipic acid. The acid crystallises in white crystals (m.p. 152°C).

(2) Hexamethylenediamine (XXXV). This can be prepared from adipic acid by transformation first to the nitrile. The latter can be made by passing the acid vapour together with ammonia over a substance which will take out water *e.g.* silica gel. The ammonium salt (XXXVI) first formed is dehydrated to the amide and thence to the nitrile which can then be hydrogenated to the diamine using suitable catalysts (*e.g.* Raney nickel).

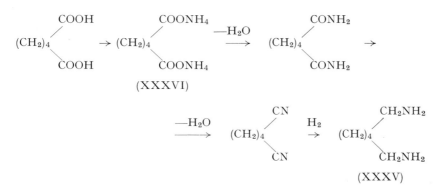

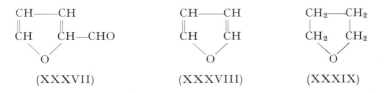

An excess of ammonia is necessary to avoid the formation of imines. The diamine can be purified by vacuum distillation. In the U.S.A. this diamine can be made from furfuraldehyde obtained from pentosan waste products (corn cobs or oat hulls)[52]. Furfuraldehyde (XXXVII) is treated with lime water to give furan (XXXVIII) which in turn is hydrogenated to the five-member ring compound tetrahydrofuran (XXXIX).

$$
\begin{array}{ccc}
\text{CH——CH} & \text{CH——CH} & \text{CH}_2\text{——CH}_2 \\
\parallel \qquad \parallel & \parallel \qquad \parallel & \mid \qquad \mid \\
\text{CH} \quad \text{CH—CHO} & \text{CH} \qquad \text{CH} & \text{CH}_2 \qquad \text{CH}_2 \\
\diagdown \quad \diagup & \diagdown \quad \diagup & \diagdown \quad \diagup \\
\text{O} & \text{O} & \text{O} \\
\text{(XXXVII)} & \text{(XXXVIII)} & \text{(XXXIX)}
\end{array}
$$

Tetrahydrofuran will open its ring when heated with hydrochloric acid in the presence of sulphuric acid to give 1,4-dichlorobutane (XL). The chlorine atoms may be replaced by nitrile groups by treatment with sodium cyanide. The adiponitrile so produced may then be hydrogenated to the diamine (XXXV).

References p. 64

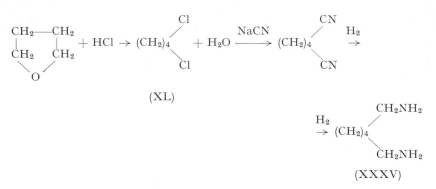

(XL)

(XXXV)

An interesting preparation has been described by Bannerman and Magat[53]. Chlorination of butadiene (XLI) yields the two dichlorides[54] (1,2- and 1,4-isomers).

$$CH_2=CH—CH=CH_2 + Cl_2 →$$
$$→ CH_2Cl—CH=CH—CH_2Cl + CH_2=CH—CHCl—CH_2Cl$$

(XLI)

Both these isomers on treatment with hydrogen cyanide[55] in the presence of cuprous halides yield 1,4-dicyano-2-butene ($CNCH_2CH=CHCH_2CN$). Hexamethylenediamine is then produced by hydrogenation. The diamine forms white crystals (m.p. 40.9°C).

(3) Formation of the polymer. In theory at least, it is possible to polymerise the components (amine and acid) in equimolar proportions; however if the proportions are not balanced, the product will have a low molecular weight due to the formation of an excess of one kind of end group over the other. With nylon 66 this problem is overcome by first forming "nylon salt". The two components dissolved in methanol react to precipitate a salt which chemically would be described as hexamethylene diammonium adipate, a water soluble powder of m.p. 190–191°C.

To prepare the polymer, the salt in aqueous solution (60%) is heated in an autoclave with the necessary amount of end group stabiliser (acetic acid)[56]. The rôle of this is discussed later. The temperature is raised to 220°C and after 1–2 hours to 270–280°C. Steam is bled off and the pressure inside the autoclave reduced to one atmosphere. The ebullition of the water acts as a means of agitation of the molten mass. To ensure equilibrium is maintained, the product at the end of the reaction is kept at a high temperature for an hour. The polymer is extruded into a ribbon and cut into chips (m.p. ca. 264°C). Oligomers (XLII) have been identified in nylon 66 but the quantity of these products is only about 1%[57].

$$NH(CH_2)_6NHCO(CH_2)_4CO$$
$$[CO(CH_2)_4 \ CONH(CH_2)_6NH]_n$$

(XLII) $\qquad\qquad\qquad\qquad n = 0,1,3$

Other polyamides

Other nylons have been seriously considered *viz.* 3, 4, 5, 7, 10 and 11[58,59]. Polyamides have been made from linear diamines and oxalic acid. It has been suggested that nylon 7 and nylon 9[59] be made via the amino acid which may be prepared from the teleomer of ethylene and carbon tetrachloride followed by hydrolysis. The chloroacid is then reacted with ammonia.

$$CCl_4 + nC_2H_4 \rightarrow Cl(CH_2CH_2)_nCCl_3 \rightarrow Cl(CH_2CH_2)_nCOOH \rightarrow \text{animo acid}$$

Nylon 11, already developed in France[60], is made from the self condensation of ω-aminoundecanoic acid, (XLIII), the acid arising from castor oil by pyrolysis followed by treatment first with hydrobromic acid and secondly by ammonia.

$$\text{Castor oil} \rightarrow CH_2{=}CH(CH_2)_8COOH \xrightarrow{\text{HBr}} Br(CH_2)_{10}COOH$$
$$\downarrow NH_3$$
$$\text{nylon 11} \leftarrow NH_2(CH_2)_{10}COOH$$

(XLIII)

Nylons made from dicarboxylic acids have also been the object of considerable study. The most notable is nylon 610 made from hexamethylenediamine and sebacic acid (XLV). The latter is made from castor oil (glyceryl ricinolcate) by treatment with strong caustic soda solution at a high temperature (250°C) giving first ricinoleic acid (XLIV) which breaks down further to the acid (XLV) and octanol-2

$$\text{Castor oil} \xrightarrow{\text{NaOH}} \text{glycerol} + CH_3(CH_2)_5CHOHCH_2CH{=}CH(CH_2)_7COOH$$

(XLIV)

$$\rightarrow CH_3(CH_2)_5CHOHCH_3 + HOOC(CH_2)_8COOH$$

(XLV)

or by electrolysis of the sodium salt of the half ester of adipic acid,

$$2NaOOC(CH_2)_4COOCH_3 \rightarrow 2Na^+ + CH_3OOC(CH_2)_4(CH_2)_4COOCH_3 + 2CO_2$$

(c) Polyurethans

This group of polymers was developed largely in Germany not only for use as fibres but also in the fields of adhesives, coating, foams etc. The polyurethans having a linear structure are fibre-forming, the urethan group —NHCOO— bearing a certain resemblance to the amide. They generally have melting-points lower than the corresponding polyamides. Chemically urethans are esters of carbamic acids either derived from acids of the form $R(NHCOOH)_2$ or $HORNHCOOH$. There are many general reactions which form esters of this kind.

(1) Phosgene will react with a glycol to give a bischloroformate (XLVI)

$$R(OH)_2 + 2COCl_2 \rightarrow R(OOCCl)_2 + 2HCl$$

$$(XLVI)$$

The chloroformate is capable of reacting with a diamine to give a linear polymer *e.g.*

$$R(OOCCl)_2 + NH_2R_1NH_2 \rightarrow -[OCONHR_1NHCOOR]_n- + HCl$$

This is a condensation reaction which eliminates hydrochloric acid.

(2) Phosgene will react with an amino alcohol to give a chloroformate (XLVII)

$$NH_2ROH + COCl_2 \rightarrow NH_2ROCOCl + HCl$$

$$(XLVII)$$

which in turn is capable of condensation to a polymer eliminating hydrochloric acid

$$NH_2ROCOCl \rightarrow NH_2(ROCONH)_{n-1}RCOCl + HCl$$

(3) Phosgene will react with diamines to give, in the presence of a phenol, a biscarbamic ester or urethan (XLVIII)

$$NH_2RNH_2 + PhOH + COCl_2 \rightarrow PhOCONHRNHCOOPh$$

$$(XLVIII)$$

This ester can undergo an exchange reaction with a glycol eliminating the phenol

$$PhOCONHRNHCOOPh + HOR_1OH \rightarrow -[R_1OOCNHRNHCOO]_n-$$
$$+ PhOH$$

(4) Amino alcohols may be transformed into the carbamic ester (XLIX) by reaction with phenyl chloroformate

$$NH_2ROH + ClCOOPh \rightarrow HORNHCOOPh + HCl$$

$$(XLIX)$$

This compound can undergo a "self exchange" to eliminate phenol

$$HORNHCOOPh \rightarrow -[RNHCOO]_n- + PhOH$$

(5) By reaction of a bisurethan (L) with a diamine

$$NH_2COOROOCNH_2 + NH_2R_1NH_2 \rightarrow -[ROOCNHR_1NHCOO]_n- + NH_3$$
(L)

(6) From isocyanates. A diisocyanate (LI) will readily react with water, alcohols, amines etc. and in particular, with a dihydric alcohol

$$OCNRNCO + HOR_1OH \rightarrow -[OOCNHRNHCOOR_1]_n-$$
(LI)

This reaction is an extremely versatile one and, in many instances, carried out by mixing the two reagents giving the possibility of a wide variety of polyurethans. The only polyurethan manufactured commercially as a fibre is "Perlon U" made from the glycol, 1,4-butanediol, and hexamethylene diisocyanate

$$HO(CH_2)_4OH + OCN(CH_2)_6NCO \rightarrow -[(CH_2)_4OOCNH(CH_2)_6NHCOO]_n-$$

The glycol, a solid of m.p. 19.7°C, can be synthesised from formaldehyde and acetylene to give 1,4-butenediol which is then hydrogenated catalytically. Hexamethylene diisocyanate may be prepared by the reaction of phosgene on hexamethylenediamine as the hydrochloride, carbonate or free base. When using the last, the diamine is dissolved in dichlorobenzene and treated at 0°C with phosgene (1 mole) to form the monocarbamyl chloride (LII)

$$NH_2(CH_2)_6NH_2 + COCl_2 \rightarrow HClNH_2(CH_2)_6NHCOCl$$
(LII)

Addition of a second mole of phosgene and raising the temperature to 140–150°C forms the second group accompanied by a loss of hydrochloric acid

$$HClNH_2(CH_2)_6NHCOCl + COCl_2 \rightarrow OCN(CH_2)_6NCO + 4HCl$$

To polymerise, the two intermediates are introduced into a cone shaped vessel with a special agitator. It is essential to ensure that the mixing is efficient. The diol is heated to 85–90°C and the diisocyanate is added

References p. 64

over a period of 1 h. The reaction is exothermic and the melt temperature is controlled at 190–198°C until the reaction is complete. The molten polymer is extruded, cut into chips and dried.

"Perlon U" is a hard polymer similar to nylon 6 and 66 but with a m.p. of 184°C (Table 3).

(d) Other Polymers

Fibre forming polyureas (polyamides of carbamic acid) are not of great practical interest because of low thermal stability. Nevertheless linear polyureas form fibres and may be prepared from
(1) a diisocyanate and a diamine

$$OCNR_1NCO + NH_2RNH_2 \rightarrow -[R_1NHCONHRNHCONH]_n-$$

(2) the diisocyanurate via the diurethan[61]

$$OCNRNCO + H_2O \rightarrow [HOOCNHRNHCOOH] \rightarrow$$
$$\rightarrow NH_2RNH_2 + CO_2 \rightarrow -[RNHCONH]_n-$$

(3) from azides of dicarboxylic acids by boiling in water[62]

$$N_3CORCON_3 \xrightarrow{H_2O} [OCNRNCO] \rightarrow -[RNHCONH]_n-$$

(4) by heating a thiocarbamate to 150°C in vacuo[63]

$$NH_2RNHCOSH \rightarrow NH_2[RNHCONH]_nRNH_2 + H_2S$$

The thiocarbamate was made from carbonyl sulphide and an aliphatic amine

$$COS + NH_2RNH_2 \rightarrow NH_2RNHCOSH$$

(e) Control of the Polymerisation

For commercial use, the polymer must have a consistent molecular weight. This property may be monitored by viscosity determinations of the polymer in a solvent[64]. In some instances such as polyamides, determination of the end groups may be made[65].

To obtain a product of high molecular weight in a condensation polymerisation, the reactants should be present in equimolecular amounts. If this condition be obtained, as indeed is so when an amino acid is condensed, the product would have an infinitely large molecular weight when the reaction is complete. This result would not normally be obtained since, in practice, it is not easy to remove all traces of the condensation products or to have no losses of the reagents or to avoid completely all side reactions. If, for example when a diamine is condensed with a carboxylic acid, one of the reagents is in excess then molecules will be produced with two similar end groups and further reaction will be stopped.

$$(n+1)NH_2RNH_2 + nHOOCR_1COOH \rightarrow NH_2[RNHCOR_1CONH]_nRNH_2$$

The action of the stabiliser mentioned earlier is to form an acetamido group at the end of the molecule

$$-NH_2 + CH_3COOH \rightarrow -NHCOCH_3$$

This group will remove an amino group from further reaction and hence act as a chain stopper or, since viscosity of a solution of the polymer is used for monitoring the process, as a "viscosity stabiliser". The addition of acetic acid made in the polymerisation of "nylon salt" is of an amount adequate to control the molecular weight at the desired value. Accurate control of this is important since fibre properties e.g. dyeing with acid dyes may be modified. In practice a nylon 66 of a molecular weight around 12,000 may be made by an addition of about 2% excess of the diacid. This discussion stresses the importance of obtaining the original reactants in a highly purified state.

With these condensations, water is evolved and an equilibrium set up

$$-COOH + NH_2- \rightarrow -CONH- + H_2O$$

Formally it is possible to write down a mass law equation in terms of the concentrations of each of the groups i.e.

$$[COOH][NH_2] = k[CONH][H_2O]$$

$$= k_1[H_2O]$$

since the number of amide groups is almost constant. The equation is interesting as it shows how the product of the concentrations of the end groups varies with the amount of water present and emphasises the fact that the molecular weight of the polymer in the melt varies with the quantity of water. With nylon 66, the molten polymer is in equilibrium with 0.16% of water. If the polymer is re-fused, care must be taken to ensure the material is dry[47] otherwise the equilibrium may be pushed to the left-hand side and the molecular weight decreased. This problem is of more importance with the polyesters since these are more susceptible to hydrolysis when molten than polyamides. In the formation of polyethylene terephthalate, the molecular weight of the product may be controlled by the amount of glycol removed.

References p. 64

Any side reactions which may occur in the condensation will effectively remove one of the components and upset the balance. With amines it is possible for ammonia to be liberated to form an imine

$$-NH_2 + NH_2- \rightarrow -NH- + NH_3$$

This secondary amino group will complicate matters by reacting further with a carboxylic acid group and giving a branched chain

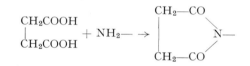

The diamine used in nylon 66 may form a cyclic imine which when reacted with a carboxyl group will have the effect of stopping the chain growing

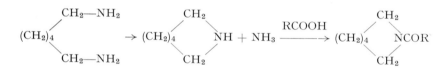

Succinic acid may form a cyclic imine

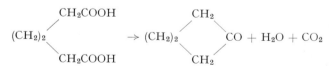

The carboxyl groups may eliminate water and carbon dioxide to form a ketone

$$(CH_2)_2 \begin{array}{c} CH_2COOH \\ \\ CH_2COOH \end{array} \rightarrow (CH_2)_2 \begin{array}{c} CH_2 \\ \\ CH_2 \end{array} CO + H_2O + CO_2$$

In polyesterification the glycol may form an ether

$$2\,HOCH_2CH_2OH \rightarrow HOCH_2CH_2OCH_2CH_2OH + H_2O$$

or an aldehyde

$$HOCH_2CH_2OH \rightarrow CH_2{=}CHOH + H_2O \rightarrow CH_3CHO$$

4. Kinetics of Polymerisation

Attention has been devoted to the preparation of polymers. The products so obtained must be reproducible in character and the reaction controllable so as to produce a material of the correct molecular weight in a time which is reasonable. To understand the factors controlling these variables, studies have been made of the rates of reaction; these kinetic studies are concerned with not only such questions as how fast will the reaction go but also what kind of mechanisms are involved, or conversely given a possible reaction mechanism what is the dependence of the rate on the concentrations of the various reactants.

Polymerisations are distinguished from other chemical reactions in that the reaction produces not a single chemical entity but a range of products of different molecular weights. Thus consider the condensation of an ω-hydroxy acid, HORCOOH. This will react first with another molecule to give a dimer

$$\text{HORCOOH} + \text{HORCOOH} \rightarrow \text{HORCOORCOOH} + \text{H}_2\text{O}$$

This dimer can react with a monomer or other dimers to give trimers or tetramers. These in turn can react with monomer, dimer, trimer and tetramers and so on. Hence, the reaction mixture at any time will contain molecules of different sizes. The reaction is stepwise and kinetic studies aim therefore at characterisation of the reactions in terms of physico-chemical constants as well as attempting to answer the question what is the range of sizes of molecules present when the reaction has proceeded to a certain extent. Further, the rate constants form an excellent way to summarise quantitatively a huge quantity of data.

The basic data necessary for any kinetic study are measurements of how far the reaction has gone after predetermined intervals of time. In many examples of kinetic investigations the reaction mixture or a sample of the mixture is cooled very rapidly to prevent any further reaction and the "frozen" mixture analysed for the concentration of the various components. For some reactions physical properties such as changes in volume (dilatometry), absorption spectrum, viscosity etc. may be measured. For the condensation reactions studied in this chapter, it is possible to take samples and titrate the residual carboxyl groups, follow the changes in the viscosity of the reaction mixture or melt or to determine the quantity of water liberated

(a) Reactivity of Polymers

In the earlier days arguments were put forward to show that, because of their high molecular weights, the chemical reactivities of polymers would be low. On the basis of the kinetic theory of gases, the rate constant k of a reaction between molecules in the gaseous phase is proportional to the number of collisions between molecules. The rate constant k is proportional to $pNZ \exp -(E/RT)$ where p is an orientation or steric factor, N is the number of molecules and E is the energy of the molecules. For the reaction between 2 kinds of molecules A and B, the frequency factor Z has been shown to be given by

$$Z = 2^{3/2} \left[\pi RT \left(\frac{1}{M_A} + \frac{1}{M_B} \right) \right]^{1/2} \sigma_{AB}^2 n_A n_B \qquad (1)$$

where M_A and M_B are the molecular weights of the molecules, n_A and n_B the numbers per cc and σ_{AB} the mean molecular diameter. This equation shows that, in the gas phase, increase of molecular weight reduces the number of collisions and hence the reaction constant. For reactions in solution, calculations of the collision frequency are more difficult but statistical reasoning[66] indicates that the solvent alters not the number of collisions but the manner in which they occur with respect to time. The solvent tends to form a "cage" causing the molecules to be held in the vicinity of each other so that many collisions occur before separation[67] Collisions in the liquid phase are to a certain extent between the same neighbours[68]. The purely intuitive application of equation 1 to polymer systems would indicate a reduction in reactivity since a polymer molecule would have a low kinetic velocity and hence a low collision frequency. In addition, it has been suggested that the functional group would be shielded by coiling up in the molecule[69], a fact which would lessen the probability of the group itself colliding. In terms of kinetic theory, this means a low "steric" factor. The increase in viscosity which occurs during polymerisation has been invoked as causing a decrease in rate[70].

These arguments in favour of a decreased reactivity of the polymer molecule arise from consideration of the mechanics of interaction of two functional groups attached to large molecules and not from reduction in the reactivity of the functional groups themselves. However, this picture does not take into account very important properties of a polymer molecule. The backbone of the molecule is made up of a series of atoms joined by covalent bonds; free rotation may occur around any one of these with the only proviso that the valency angles are not disturbed. The molecule could be regarded as composed of a series of segments and may take up an exceedingly large number of configurations in space. This means that the range of movements of the functional group will differ from that of the molecule as a whole. The latter will move very slowly as may be indicated by the high viscosity of polymer solutions or melts whereas the oscillations of the functional group may occur at frequencies of the order to be expected in liquids whose molecules are considerably smaller.

In addition, the work of Rabinowitch and Wood mentioned above shows that, when molecules in the liquid state collide, they will undergo repeated collisions before separating. In a system with a small diffusion rate, the functional groups will therefore undergo many collisions before separating *i.e.* the duration of the "collided" state will be increased. Flory[19] has also argued the case for the high reactivity of polymer molecules on the basis of the transition state theory[71] where the equilibrium is set up with a transition complex *i.e.* reactants $\rightleftharpoons$ transition complex. The rate of reaction is dependent on the concentrations of the complex set up and, from consideration of the factors determining the concentration of the complex, has concluded that the rate of reaction is not affected by the mobility of the molecules.

Nevertheless, there are extreme cases where the mobility is exceptionally low and the rate of reaction extremely high and the equilibrium concentration may not necessarily be maintained. In such a state the reaction may be controlled by diffusion. In general, polycondensation reactions do not suffer from this complication.

This discussion points to the idea that the reactivity of groups (*e.g.* COOH) is not modified by their attachment to a polymer molecule. The point may be exemplified by studying the rates of esterification and hydrolysis in homologous series where the reactivity of the carboxyl group in an acid such as $CH_3(CH_2)_nCOOH$ should change only for small values of n.

Rates of esterification of aliphatic acids in methanol or ethanol in the presence and absence of hydrochloric acid as catalyst[72,73] have been determined

$$CH_3(CH_2)_nCOOH + C_2H_5OH \rightarrow CH_3(CH_2)_nCOOC_2H_5 + H_2O$$

In the presence of a catalyst, the kinetics of this reaction will be

$$-\frac{d[COOH]}{dt} = k[COOH][OH][H^+] \qquad (2)$$

In the absence

$$-\frac{d[COOH]}{dt} = k_1[COOH]^2[OH] \qquad (3)$$

Equations 2 and 3 are written in terms of the concentrations of carboxyl and hydroxyl groups. The constants k and k_1 are different since in equation 3 the supply of hydrogen ions comes from the acid being esteri-

TABLE 6

Acid or chain length	k for esterification (a) HCl + ethanol [73] ($\times 10^4$ at 25°C)	(b) using H$^+$ methanol [74] ($\times 10^2$ at 20°C)	(c) using acid + ethanol [74] ($\times 10^6$ at 100°C)	k for esterification [72] of dibasic acids ($\times 10^4$ at 25°C)	k for saponification [74] at 50°C	k for etherification [75] ($\times 10^4$ at 30°C)
0	—	4.42	5.70	—	—	—
1	22.1	3.84	4.47	—	38.7	26.6
2	15.3	2.28	3.00	6.0	24.7	2.37
3	7.5	—	—	8.7	12.2	0.923
4	7.45	—	—	8.4	13.3	0.669
5	7.42	2.08	3.39	7.8	14.5	—
6	—	—	—	7.3	12.7	—
7	—	—	—			0.668
8	7.5	—	—		13.3	0.667
9	7.47	—	—			
> 9	7.6	—	—			0.690
Pelargonic	—	1.98	3.80			
Myristic	—	—	3.99			
Palmitic	—	2.21	4.27			
Behenic	—	—	4.27			

fied. The rates of esterification of dibasic acids have also been measured

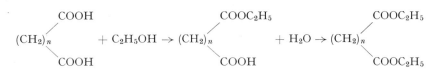

The hydrolysis of the esters with alkalis[74] was carried out in 85% ethyl alcohol at 50°C

$$CH_3(CH_2)_n COOC_2H_5 + KOH \rightarrow CH_3(CH_2)_n COOK + C_2H_5OH$$

A similar kind of experiment[75] is to react the alkyl diiodide with the sodium derivative of benzyl alcohol in ethanol. A summary of the data is given in Table 6. The figures given in the four columns bear out the argument that the reactivity does not depend on the value of n greater than 1 or 2. In polymer reactions this situation is usually the case. It must be noted, however, that substitution on the α-carbon atom will have an inhibiting effect[76] and modify the reaction constant.

These results are in accord with those generally found in homologous series in that, in any hydrocarbon chain, the effect of increasing the chain length falls off very rapidly. It must be noted, however, that the chains act so as to dilute the system so that the rate constants are calculated in terms of concentrations of functional groups per unit volume and not mole fractions. The values of k quoted in Table 6 are given in $(g \, equiv./l)^{-1} sec^{-1}$.

The data add confirmation to the principle that the reactivities of the functional groups are independent of chain length of the growing polymer.

(b) Kinetic Scheme

Consider for simplicity esterification of an hydroxy acid of formula HORCOOH. This molecule reacts with itself to give a dimer

$$HORCOOH + HORCOOH \rightarrow HORCOORCOOH + H_2O$$

The dimer will react with monomer or a second dimer to give trimers and tetramers. The products can be written with the symbols P_n to refer to a polymer of n units.

$$P_1 + P_1 \rightarrow P_2$$
$$P_2 + P_1 \rightarrow P_3$$
$$P_2 + P_2 \rightarrow P_4$$
$$\cdot$$
$$\cdot$$
$$\cdot$$
$$P_n + P_m \rightarrow P_{n+m}$$

The reaction has been shown to be catalysed by acid[77] so that in writing down the equations for the kinetics a term for the hydrogen ion must be taken into account. Each of the reactions above is assumed to have the same rate constant; in each reaction carboxyl and hydroxyl groups are lost and the overall rate of consumption of carboxyl or hydroxyl groups will be the sum of the rates at which they are consumed by each step. In kinetic terms this means that equations 2 and 3 may be used; this says that the rate of consumption of carboxyl groups is dependent only on the concentration of the hydroxyl, carboxyl and hydrogen ions in the system. If carboxyl and hydroxyl groups are present in equal amounts and if each is equal to c, equation 2 can be written as

$$-\frac{dc}{dt} = k'c^2 \tag{4}$$

k' is written as a constant equal to $k\,[\mathrm{H^+}]$.

If the system does not contain acid added as a catalyst, a second molecule of acid undergoing esterification functions as a catalyst and equation 3 becomes

$$-\frac{dc}{dt} = k''c^3 \tag{5}$$

Integrating equations 4 and 5 gives

$$\frac{1}{c} - \frac{1}{c_0} = k't \tag{6}$$

$$\frac{1}{c^2} - \frac{1}{c_0^2} = 2k''t \tag{7}$$

where c_0 is the concentration at the commencement of the experiment.

However, it is convenient in kinetic work of this kind to express the results in terms of the extent of the reaction rather than in terms of the concentration of groups present at any time. The extent of the reaction, p, is the concentration of the functional groups which have undergone reaction in time t expressed as a fraction of those present initially. Thus if there were N_0 present at time $t = 0$ and N at time t then the extent of reaction is

$$p = \frac{N_0 - N}{N_0} \quad \text{or} \quad N = N_0(1-p) \tag{8}$$

or in terms of concentration

$$c = c_0\,(1 - p)$$

The two equations for the rate of reaction in terms of the extent of reaction become

$$\frac{1}{1-p} - 1 = N_0 k' t \tag{9}$$

$$\frac{1}{(1-p)^2} - 1 = 2N_0 k'' t \tag{10}$$

A plot of $1/(1-p)$ (equation 9) or $1/(1-p)^2$ (equation 10) against time should give a straight line. The data for esterification[76,77] plotted in Fig. 6

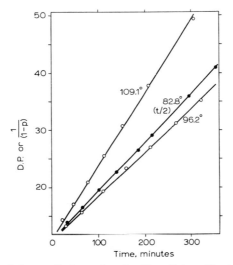

Fig. 6. Reaction of decamethylene glycol with adipic acid at the temperatures indicated, catalysed by 0.10 equivalent percent of p-toluenesulphonic acid. The time scale for the results at 82.8°C is to be multiplied by 2. (Courtesy American Chemical Society)[76]

show that the system follows the second order kinetics given by equation 9. Formation of polyamides has been shown also to follow a second order law in a manner paralleling the behaviour of monofunctional compounds. These second order kinetics are followed satisfactorily certainly up to molecular weights of *ca.* 10,000. This is a very large increase in the size of molecules in the condensation and is confirmation of the original hypothesis of independence of reactivity on molecular size.

Data for the uncatalysed systems is given in Fig. 7[76]. The graphs are straight lines only after the reaction has proceeded for a certain period of time. Because of the non-linearity, comparison is made between the reaction which is giving the polymer (diethylene glycol and adipic acid) and one which leads to a simple ester (diethylene glycol and caproic acid). The graphs for both systems are of the same shape and indeed may be superimposed by adjustment of the time scale only. (This is necessary since the experiments with caproic acid were carried out at smaller con-

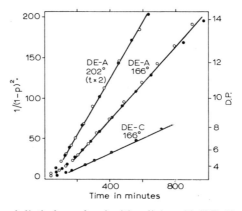

Fig. 7. Reactions of diethylene glycol with adipic acid (DE-A) and with caproic acid (DE-C). Time values at 202°C have been multiplied by 2. (Courtesy American Chemical Society)[76]

centrations.) Thus deviations from third order kinetics described by equation 10 occur in simple esterification to the same extent as in esterification reactions to form polymers. Again, this is taken as evidence that the assumption of equal reactivity is valid.

Nevertheless, the agreement with third order kinetics for the uncatalysed system is not very satisfactory. This is not immediately obvious from the graphs and arises from the mathematical form of the function $1/(1-p)^2$ which changes most rapidly as $p \to 1$. Values of $1/(1-p)^2$ vary from 1 to 25 when the range of esterification goes from 0 to 80%. The graphs show agreement with third order kinetics therefore for values of $1/(1-p)^2 > ca.$ 25 or values of p greater than 0.8. This disagreement with equation 10 for esterification is not entirely unexpected since in the first stages of reaction the removal of carboxyl and hydroxyl groups results in changes in the nature of the reaction medium. The cause of the change is not completely clear but could be connected with a change in dielectric constant or the shrinkage in volume due to the loss of water which is eliminated during the reaction.

Rates of hydrolysis of the dimer, trimer and mixtures of higher linear oligomers in the presence of hydrochloric acid have also been determined[78]. The rate constants in all cases were the same indicating that the hydrolysis reaction is independent of chain length as would be anticipated on the "equal reactivity" hypothesis.

(c) Molecular Weight of Polymer

In any polymerisation it is advantageous to follow the molecular weight (M.W.) or the degree of polymerisation (D.P.) For the simple case discussed above, the average D.P. will be given by the total number of the molecules N_0 which were present at the commencement of the reaction divided by the number at time t, i.e. N_0/N. This in terms of p becomes $1/(1-p)$.

If m_0 is the molecular weight of a structural unit, the average molecular weight of the polymer may be calculated. This average is based on the number of molecules and is referred to as the number average molecular weight $\bar{M}_n$

$$\bar{M}_n = \frac{m_0}{(1-p)} \tag{11}$$

The number of molecules which are present at any time is readily obtained in a system such as the one discussed by the number of carboxyl or hydroxyl groups remaining unreacted at any time.

If the D.P. be substituted in equations 9 and 10 for $1/(1-p)$, the following equations result

$$\text{D.P.} = N_0 k't + 1 \sim N_0 k't \text{ for long periods of reaction}$$

$$\text{D.P.} = (2N_0 k''t + 1)^{\frac{1}{2}} \sim (2N_0 k''t)^{\frac{1}{2}}$$

Hence, the D.P. for the acid catalysed reaction turns out to be approximately linearly dependent on t but on $t^{\frac{1}{2}}$ for the condensation in the absence of catalyst. In the latter case, the reaction must proceed for longer periods of time before a product having a high mol. wt. is obtained.

The molecular weight may be controlled if one of the components is present in excess or a "viscosity stabiliser" such as acetic acid used in the preparation of polyamides is introduced in the system. The decrease in molecular weight may be deduced as follows.

The degree of polymerisation is the average number of units in the molecule. The product of the D.P. and the total number of molecules N will equal the total number of units at the commencement of the reaction. Consider the formation of a polyamide obtained from a monomer, NH_2R_1COOH in the presence of a carboxylic acid R_2COOH. Let N_1 be the number of molecules of the monomer and N_2 of the acid. Then the number of amide groups or units which these substances will form is $N_1 + N_2$. When the extent of the reaction is p (*i.e.* the number of acid or amine groups used) the total number of molecules in the system will be $N_1(1-p) + N_2$.

The D.P. will be the ratio of these two quantities *i.e.*

$$\text{D.P.} = \frac{N_1 + N_2}{N_1(1-p) + N_2}$$

When there is no chain stopper present, $N_2 = 0$ and the D.P. becomes $1/(1-p)$.

For the polymerisation of a diamine $NH_2R_1NH_2$ and a dicarboxylic acid $COOHR_2COOH$ where the moles N_1 of the former is less than the moles N_2 of the latter, the formula is slightly modified. The total number of groups capable of forming amide linkages is $2N_1 + 2N_2$. The number of amide linkages is half this, *i.e.*, $N_1 + N_2$. When the amine or carboxyl groups have reacted to an extent p, $2N_1p$ amino and carboxyl groups will have reacted. The total number of free chain end groups will be $2N_1(1-p) + 2N_2 - 2N_1p = 4N_1(1-p) + 2(N_2 - N_1)$. As the condensation is bifunctional the number of molecules will be half this value. The degree of polymerisation is then given by

$$\text{D.P.} = \frac{N_1 + N_2}{2N_1(1-p) + N_2 - N_1}$$

If $N_2 = N_1$, this reduces to D.P. $= 1/(1-p)$ as before.

If the D.P. is calculated in terms of the number of repeating units (NHR_1NHCOR_2CO) the D.P. will be half this value.

These equations give the effect on the D.P. of an excess of carboxyl groups in the system but could apply equally when the amino groups are in excess.

One special case is when the reaction has gone almost to completion *i.e.* $p \sim 1$. The equations reduce in this case to

$$\frac{N_1 + N_2}{N_2} \quad \text{and} \quad \frac{N_1 + N_2}{N_2 - N_1}$$

showing that introduction of 0.5% mole of acetic acid in the polymerisation of an amino acid (such as caproic acid to give nylon 6) or an excess of 0.5% of the diacid limits the D.P. of the system to 200. These equations demonstrate how sensitive the molecular weight of a polymerisation is to the presence of monofunctional reagents which may be added or produced as a by-product, or in the second example to addition of an excess, of one of the components.

(d) Distribution of Molecular Weights

Previously, mention has been made of the degree of polymerisation and the molecular weight of the products. Clearly reactions, in which an n-mer can react at random with an m-mer will give rise, not to a compound with a unique molecular weight but to a product whose molecules will have molecular weights which are different from one another and vary over a range of values. The degrees of polymerisation discussed so far are average ones. For many purposes considerable value comes from knowing the number of molecules with particular degrees of polymerisation. The distribution of molecular weights can vary widely and the resulting polymer will have properties which will depend on this distribution. An example of a distribution of this kind is given in Fig. 8 where the mole

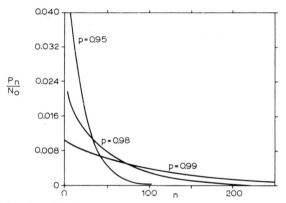

Fig. 8. Mole fraction distribution of chain molecules in a linear condensation polymer for several extents of reaction p. (Courtesy American Chemical Society)[87]

fraction of molecules with a certain D.P. is plotted against the D.P. (the molecular weight may be used equally well) for different values of p. This kind of curve is only one method of describing the distribution; another is in terms of the weight of material $i.e.$ the quantity of the polymer which has a D.P. of any given value. The corresponding weight distribution curve is given by Fig. 9. These methods of describing the system can be seen to be markedly different.

An average molecular weight may be assigned to the polymer. This is found from the data of Fig. 8; the average will be given by the total weight of the polymer divided by the number of molecules. This average is known as the number average molecular weight, $\bar{M}_n$, and in mathematical terms is defined as follows:

If there are n_i molecules in the polymer having a molecular weight of

m_i then the total weight is $\sum n_i m_i$ and the number of molecules is $\sum n_i$. Hence the number average molecular weight $\bar{M}_n$ is

$$\bar{M}_n = \frac{\sum n_i m_i}{\sum n_i}$$

The second method of plotting data given in Fig. 9 also enables an average molecular weight to be calculated. The average from this data is calculated in the same way as the number average except that the numbers of

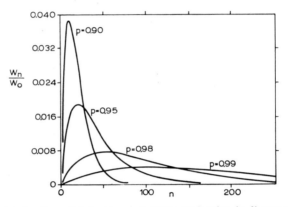

Fig. 9. Weight fraction distributions of chain molecules in linear condensation polymers for several extents of reaction p. (Courtesy American Chemical Society)[87]

molecules n_i is replaced by the weights w_i of the molecules having molecular weight m_i. Hence, the average molecular weight is given by

$$\bar{M}_w = \frac{\sum m_i w_i}{\sum w_i} = \frac{\sum n_i m_i{}^2}{\sum n_i m_i}$$

since

$$w_i = n_i m_i$$

The value of the molecular weight is described as the "weight average". This distinction is of importance for, when the molecular weights of polymers are measured by the colligative properties such as osmotic pressure, the number average is obtained whereas determination based on the amount of light scattered when a beam of light is passed through a solution gives a "weight average".

From these definitions the weight average molecular weight will turn out to be larger than the number average except in the case when the sample contains only one kind of molecule when the two are equal. This difference may be shown from consideration of a simple example.

Consider a polymer made up of equal numbers of molecules of molecular weight 5,000 and 10,000. The number average molecular weight is given by $15,000/2 = 7,500$. The weight fractions of the two kinds of molecules of the polymer are $\frac{1}{3}$ and $\frac{2}{3}$ and hence the weight average molecular weight is

$$\frac{1}{3} \times 5,000 + \frac{2}{3} \times 10,000 = \frac{25,000}{3} = ca.\ 8,300$$

Not all kinds of measurements used for the determination of molecular weights give these well defined averages; a very common (since it is rapid) method of determining the molecular weight is by viscosity. This method normally gives a different average as is discussed in Chapter 5.

Unfortunately in practice the determination of a distribution curve of the kind just discussed is very laborious. The polymer sample can be split into fractions of different molecular weights. This may involve dissolution in a solvent followed by fractional precipitation. The molecular weights of the fractions so obtained must be determined and hence a distribution curve constructed. There are other methods of carrying out this fractionation. For example, polymer is eluted from an inert support by a solvent mixture of increasing solvent power and various fractions collected.

However the kinetic scheme as written down should throw some light on what kind of molecular weight distribution is achieved in a condensation polymerisation. Consider the kinetics of polymerisation of an acid ARB with reactive groups A and B. (ARB could be an amino or hydroxy acid.) For simplification it is easier to refer to the products in terms of the number of monomer units; thus a product containing n units is simply referred to as P_n. The general condensation reaction can therefore be written as

$$P_n + P_m \rightarrow P_{n+m}$$

The reaction constant appropriate may be taken simply as k, independent of the values of n and m. If P_n refers to the concentration of n-mers in the reaction mixture, the loss of monomer will occur by reaction with all other species present and its rate of consumption may be written as

$$\frac{dP_1}{dt} = -kP_1 \sum_r P_r \tag{12}$$

The change of concentration of dimers increases from the interaction of two monomer molecules but is reduced by the reaction of dimers with all the other species in the system

$$\frac{dP_2}{dt} = \tfrac{1}{2}kP_1^2 - kP_2 \sum_r P_r \tag{13}$$

The value $\frac{1}{2}$ arises from the fact that two molecules of monomer are used up to produce one dimer. In a similar way the changes in concentration of trimers may be written as

$$\frac{dP_3}{dt} = \tfrac{1}{2}k(P_2 P_1 + P_1 P_2) - kP_3 \sum_r P_r \tag{14}$$

In general the change in concentration of n-mers is given by

$$\frac{dP_n}{dt} = \tfrac{1}{2}k \sum_s P_s P_{n-s} - kP_n \sum_r P_r \tag{15}$$

The second terms of the right-hand side of all these equations (12–15) have the common factor $\sum_r P_r$ which may be taken out leaving $k \sum P_r$. This group of terms therefore add up to $-k(\sum P_r)^2$. With the first set of terms the addition may be seen by setting them out as follows for the various values of n

$$n = 2 \qquad \tfrac{1}{2}kP_1{}^2$$

$$n = 3 \qquad \tfrac{1}{2}kP_1 P_2 + \tfrac{1}{2}kP_2 P_1$$

$$n = 4 \qquad \tfrac{1}{2}kP_1 P_3 + \tfrac{1}{2}kP_2{}^2 \ + \tfrac{1}{2}kP_3 P_1$$

$$n = 5 \qquad \tfrac{1}{2}kP_1 P_4 + \tfrac{1}{2}kP_2 P_3 + \tfrac{1}{2}kP_3 P_2 + \tfrac{1}{2}kP_4 P_1$$

and so on.

Addition of the first column gives $\tfrac{1}{2}kP_1(P_1 + P_2 + P_3 + P_4 \ldots)$ the second $\tfrac{1}{2}kP_2(P_1 + P_2 + P_3 + P_4 \ldots)$, the third $\tfrac{1}{2}kP_3(P_1 + P_2 + P_3 \ldots)$ so that in the limit each expression has a common factor $\sum_r P_r$. When this is taken out of each, $\tfrac{1}{2}k \sum_r P_r$ is left. The first terms of the right-hand side of these equations therefore sum to $\tfrac{1}{2}k(\sum P_r)^2$.

These equations therefore may be added to give

$$\frac{d \sum P_r}{dt} = -\tfrac{1}{2}k(\sum P_r)^2 \tag{16}$$

But $\sum P_r$ is the total number of molecules in the system at time t, *i.e.* N. Equation (16) then becomes

$$\frac{dN}{dt} = -\tfrac{1}{2}kN^2$$

an equation which may be integrated to give $1/N = +\tfrac{1}{2}kt +$ constant. Since at $t = 0$, $N = N_0$, the number of molecules at the commencement of the reaction, the value of the constant may be found and hence

$$\frac{1}{N} = \tfrac{1}{2}kt + \frac{1}{N_0} \tag{17}$$

In terms of the extent of reaction, p, since $N_0/N = 1/(1-p)$

$$p = \frac{N_0 kt}{2 + N_0 kt} \tag{18}$$

Equation 18 shows how the extent of the reaction varies with time.
    Equation 12 may be rewritten to give

$$-\frac{dP_1}{dt} = kP_1 N = kP_1 N_0(1-p) \tag{19}$$

The value of N may be substituted by equation 18 to give

$$\frac{dP_1}{P_1} = -\frac{2kN_0}{2 + N_0 kt}\, dt \tag{20}$$

Integrating equation 20 gives

$$\ln P_1 = -2\ln (2 + N_0 kt) + \text{constant}$$

$$\text{or } P_1 = \frac{\text{Constant}}{(2 + N_0 kt)^2} = \frac{4N_0}{(2 + N_0 kt)^2} = N_0(1-p)^2 \tag{21}$$

since $P_1 = N_0$ when $t = 0$.
    Equation 13 for the changes in concentration of P_2 may be rewritten,

$$\frac{dP_2}{dt} = \tfrac{1}{2}kP_1^2 - kP_2 N = \tfrac{1}{2}kN_0^2(1-p)^4 - kP_2 N_0(1-p) \tag{22}$$

The simplest mode of integration of this equation is to change the independent variable to p. Equation 16 may be rewritten in terms of p since $N = N_0(1-p)$

$$\frac{d(1-p)}{dt} = -\tfrac{1}{2}kN_0(1-p)^2 \quad \text{or} \quad \frac{dp}{dt} = \tfrac{1}{2}kN_0(1-p)^2 \tag{23}$$

A change of the variable from t to p may be done as follows

$$\frac{d}{dt} = \frac{dp}{dt}\frac{d}{dp}$$

Hence from equation 23

$$\frac{d}{dt} = \tfrac{1}{2}kN_0(1-p)^2 \frac{d}{dp}$$

Equation 22 thus becomes

$$\tfrac{1}{2}kN_0(1-p)^2\frac{dP_2}{dp} + kN_0(1-p)P_2 = \tfrac{1}{2}kN_0^2(1-p)^4$$

or

$$\frac{dP_2}{dp} + \frac{2}{1-p}P_2 = N_0(1-p)^2 \tag{24}$$

To integrate equation 24, both sides are multiplied by an integrating factor given by

$$e^{\int\frac{2}{1-p}dp} = e^{-2\ln(1-p)} = \frac{1}{(1-p)^2}$$

When this is done equation 24 integrates to

$$\frac{P_2}{(1-p)^2} = N_0p \quad \text{or} \quad P_2 = N_0p(1-p)^2 \tag{25}$$

the constant of integration being zero since when $p = 0$, $P_2 = 0$.
From equation 14, P_3 is given by

$$\frac{dP_3}{dt} = kP_1P_2 - kP_3N_0(1-p) \tag{26}$$

Substituting for P_1 and P_2 in equation 26 gives on change of independent variable

$$\tfrac{1}{2}kN_0(1-p)^2\frac{dP_3}{dt} + kN_0(1-p)P_3 = kN_0^2(1-p)^4$$

or

$$\frac{dP_3}{dt} + \frac{2}{1-p}P_3 = 2kN_0p(1-p)^2 \tag{27}$$

The integrating factor is again $1/(1-p)^2$ so that equation 27 integrates to

$$\frac{P_3}{(1-p)^2} = N_0p^2 \quad \text{or} \quad P_3 = N_0p^2(1-p)^2 \tag{28}$$

This procedure may be carried out with equations for P_4, P_5 ... P_n to give the general result

$$P_n = N_0p^{n-1}(1-p)^2 \tag{29}$$

Equation 29 gives the number of n-mers in terms of the extent of the reaction, since the concentration P_n has been tacitly assumed throughout to be in terms of the number of moles in the system. It is therefore the number distribution and in terms of the time becomes

$$P_n = N_0 \left(\frac{N_0 kt}{2 + N_0 kt} \right)^{n-1} \left(\frac{2}{2 + N_0 kt} \right)^2 \qquad (30)$$

Equation 30 shows that, at a certain time, the number of n-mers in the reaction mixture builds up to a maximum given by the time required for $dP_n/dt = 0$. The value for this is $t_{max} = (n-1)/N_0 k$ and the number of P_n molecules at the maximum is given by

$$P_n = \frac{4N_0(n-1)^{n-1}}{(n+1)^{n+1}}$$

The distribution can also be calculated by simple statistical reasoning bearing in mind the principle of equal reactivity of all functional groups. This principle states that the opportunities for reaction of any reactive group is equal to that of any other, independent of the extent of reaction and of the size of molecule to which it belongs. Consider the simple example of the condensation of an ω-amino or ω-hydroxy acid. Allow N_0 molecules of this acid to polymerise to an extent p when there are present N molecules. The probability of withdrawing at random a molecule which is an n-mer will be equal to the fraction of n-mers in the reaction mixture i.e. P_n/N_0. This probability will be related to the probability that $n-1$ carboxyl groups have reacted with the hydroxyl or amino groups. In the same way, the probability that a carboxyl group chosen at random in the mixture will have reacted will be equal to the fraction that have reacted. This latter is the extent of reaction p.

In a molecule containing two units there will be one carboxyl group condensed and another one free. The probability of finding such a molecule will be the product of the probabilities that a monomer unit picked at random will have a reacted carboxyl group which is connected via an amide or ester linkage to just one other monomer unit with an unreacted carboxyl group. The probability that these two events shall occur independently is p for the reacted and $1-p$ for the unreacted group; the chance that both groups will be together in the same molecule will be $p(1-p)$. In this argument, the probability of reaction of the hydroxyl or amino group will automatically be taken into account since reaction of the carboxyl group involves the complementary group and, in the system discussed here, the reactive groups are in equimolecular proportions so that if one carboxyl group is unreacted there must be a free hydroxyl or amino group to compensate.

References p. 64

In an n-mer such as

$$NH_2RCO^1NHRCO^2NH \ldots CO^{n-1}NHRCOOH$$

the probability that amide group 1 will be formed will be p, the probability of group 1 and 2 being formed will be p^2 and so on giving the probability for forming $n-1$ linkages as p^{n-1}. Taking into account the probability of the presence of the unreacted carboxyl group, the probability of formation of the n-mer will be $p^{n-1}(1-p)$.

Hence

$$P_n = Np^{n-1}(1-p) = N_0p^{n-1}(1-p)^2 \tag{31}$$

Equation 31 is the number distribution identical with equation 29 derived from the kinetic scheme.

It should be noted that in a condensation reaction interchange between terminal groups and those already condensed may occur $e.g.$

$$NH_2R_1CONHR_2COOH + NH_2R_3COOH \rightarrow$$
$$\rightarrow NH_2R_1COOH + NH_2R_3CONHR_2COOH$$

This kind of interchange does not alter the number of molecules in the systems and hence the number average degree of polymerisation will remain unchanged.

The effect of interchange reactions on the distribution of molecular sizes is of no importance in this kind of system since it can be shown that this distribution will be reached by random scission of infinitely long polymer molecules[79]. Further if interchange reactions proceed under conditions of constant extent of reaction $i.e.$ no further polymerisation is allowed to occur, the different species in the system will be formed at a rate equal to that at which they are destroyed. In other words, a state of dynamic equilibrium will be reached, and in such circumstances the distribution will be that derived above. This distribution may be referred to as the most probable[80,81].

The distribution given by the equation may be transferred into a molecular weight distribution by multiplication of the amount of each species present by its molecular weight. It is however simpler to take the molecular weight of the n-mer as being n times that of the structural unit. This procedure of course ignores the fact that the two end groups are not condensed but only a very small error is introduced as the molecular weight of the molecule differs from n times the molecular weight m_0 of the structural unit by 18, the molecular weight of a water molecule.

These distributions are better described in terms of mole fractions giving for the number distribution

$$\frac{P_n}{N_0} = p^{n-1}(1-p)^2 \tag{32}$$

and for the weight fractions distribution

$$\frac{w_n}{w_0} = np^{n-1}(1-p)^2 \tag{33}$$

Equations 32 and 33 are described in the Figs. 8 and 9, and indicate that the monomers and material of low molecular weight are in excess throughout the reaction as far as numbers are concerned although their contribution to the weight distribution is naturally considerably less. The equations apply equally well to the condensation of monomers of the type A.R.A and B.R.B provided that the components are present in equimolecular proportions. The resulting distribution for the system when one component is in excess is rather complex and will not be discussed here[53,81,82].

Equation 33 has a maximum value for a particular value of n which can be found by logarithmically differentiating with respect to n.

$$\ln \frac{w_n}{w_0} = \ln n + (n-1) \ln p + 2\ln(1-p)$$

$$\frac{d}{dn} \ln \frac{w_n}{w_0} = \frac{1}{n} + \ln p$$

or

$$\frac{d}{dn} \frac{w_n}{w_0} = np^{n-1}(1-p)^2 \left(\frac{1}{n} + \ln p\right) \tag{34}$$

Equation 34 is zero when

$$n = -\frac{1}{\ln p} \tag{35}$$

This value of n may be approximated by putting

$$\ln p = \ln \left\{1 - (1-p)\right\} = -\left\{(1-p) + \frac{(1-p)^2}{2} + \frac{(1-p)^3}{3} \cdots\right\} \sim -(1-p)$$

Hence the maximum occurs approximately when $n = 1/(1-p)$, this is the value of the number average degree of polymerisation.

The average molecular weights may be calculated from equations 32 and 33. Thus the number average is given by

$$\overline{M}_n = \frac{\sum_1^\infty m_r P_r}{\sum_1^\infty P_r} = \frac{m_0 \sum_1^\infty r p^{r-1}(1-p)^2}{\sum_1^\infty p^{r-1}(1-p)^2} = \frac{m_0}{1-p} \tag{36}$$

The weight average is given by

$$\bar{M}_w = \frac{\sum\limits_{1}^{\infty} m_r w_r}{\sum\limits_{1}^{\infty} w_r} = \frac{\sum r m_0 r p^{r-1}(1-p)^2}{\sum r p^{r-1}(1-p)^2} = m_0 \frac{1+p}{1-p} \tag{37}$$

The ratio of $\bar{M}_w/\bar{M}_n = 1+p$. This value tends to 2 as the reaction reaches completion i.e. as $p \to 1$.

As mentioned earlier, the practical determination of the molecular weight distribution involves the rather laborious procedure of separation of the polymer into fractions followed by measurement of the molecular weights of these fractions. Taylor[83] fractionated nylon 66 into 46 cuts by precipitation of the polymer by addition of water to solutions in phenol. Some of his results are reproduced in Fig. 10 and compared with the

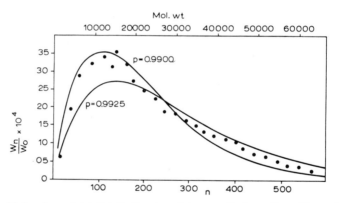

Fig. 10. Molecular weight distribution in polyhexamethyleneadipamide as obtained by fractionation (points) compared with curves calculated from equation 33 for two values of p. (Courtesy American Chemical Society)[83]

theoretical curve. The comparison is satisfactory. This has been confirmed more recently[84]. A different confirmation of the "most probable distribution" has been made by Flory[81,82]. In these experiments one kind of average (e.g. the weight average) molecular weight has been calculated from another (e.g. number average) by means of the distribution. The results are in agreement with theory.

That the results show agreement between theory and practice may be also taken as demonstrating the validity of the principle on which these calculations have been made i.e. of the principle of equal reactivity.

(e) Kinetics of Polymerisation of Caprolactam

The kinetics of the formation of nylon 6 from caprolactam are not as straightforward as those discussed above but make an interesting contrast. Addition of water to caprolactam opens the ring to give ε-aminocaproic acid which reacts with a second molecule of the lactam to give a dimeric acid which in turn reacts with a third molecule of the lactam and so on.

$$NH(CH_2)_5CO + H_2O \rightarrow NH_2(CH_2)_5COOH$$

$$NH(CH_2)_5CO + NH_2(CH_2)_5COOH \rightarrow NH_2(CH_2)_5CONH(CH_2)_5COOH$$

$$NH_2(CH_2)_5CONH(CH_2)_5COOH + NH(CH_2)_5CO \rightarrow$$

$$\rightarrow NH_2(CH_2)_5CONH(CH_2)_5CONH(CH_2)_5COOH \text{ etc.}$$

In such a reaction scheme, the number of molecules or chains in the system is decided by the number of water molecules introduced so that, if N moles of caprolactam are used in the reaction and x is the number of moles of water used, the number average D.P. would be given by the ratio N/x.

If M refers to the concentration of caprolactam and $P_1, P_2, P_3 \ldots P_n$ to that of the polymer according to the number of caproic acid units, then the reaction can be written as

$$M + H_2O \xrightarrow{k_1} P_1$$

$$P_1 + M \xrightarrow{k_2} P_2$$

$$P_2 + M \xrightarrow{k_3} P_3 \quad \text{etc.}$$

and the kinetics may be written as

$$-\left(\frac{dM}{dt}\right)_{\substack{\text{Due to the} \\ \text{ring opening}}} = k_1 M[H_2O] \tag{38}$$

$$-\left(\frac{dM}{dt}\right)_{\substack{\text{Due to reaction to} \\ \text{form } n\text{-mers}}} = k_n P_{n-1} M \tag{39}$$

If all reaction constants k_2, k_3 etc. are identical as might be expected for reactions involving aminocarboxylic acids of different chain length, equations 38 and 39 may be added to obtain the rate of consumption of caprolactam

References p. 64

$$-\frac{dM}{dt} = M\{k_1[H_2O] + k\sum P_n\} \qquad (40)$$

where $k = k_2 = k_3$ etc.

Equation 40 may be written in terms of the concentration of the chains $\sum P_n$. This may be put equal to P to give

$$-\frac{dM}{dt} = M\{k_1[H_2O] + kP\} \qquad (41)$$

A second kinetic equation may be written in terms of the number of chains or free carboxyl groups in the system; since the addition reaction does not alter the number and they are all started by the reaction of the lactam with water, the following equation holds

$$\frac{dP}{dt} = k_1[H_2O]\,M \qquad (42)$$

The system of caprolactam polymerisation initiated by water has been analysed in some detail[85] and the rate of change of the various components in the system measured. The results show that equation 41 is not completely obeyed. When the concentration of the chains is determined and H_2O and M are measured, it is found that the values of k_1 calculated by substitution of these numerical values into equation 42 are not constant but k_1 increases linearly with increasing numbers of carboxyl groups in the system $i.e.$ with the value of P. This means that the ring opening is catalysed presumable by the end groups of the chains, most likely the carboxyl groups[86]. If this is so the increase in the number of chains could be given by

$$-\frac{dP}{dt} = \{k_1 + k_1'P\}\,M\,[H_2O] \qquad (43)$$

In practice k_1 turns out to be small and hence except at low values of P the equation may be written as

$$-\frac{dP}{dt} = k_1'PM\,[H_2O] \qquad (44)$$

Further it has been shown that the rate of caprolactam usage is determined within a relatively small error by the polyaddition reaction (equation 40); a knowledge of the rate of usage of caprolactam and the concentration of carboxyl groups, if the terms $k_1[H_2O]$ be ignored, enable k to be calculated. Again it turns out that k is approximately linear with the concentration of carboxyl groups. Equation 40 may approximately be written as

$$-\frac{dM}{dt} = \{k + k'P\}MP \sim k'P^2 M \tag{45}$$

since the value of k as found experimentally is small.

Summarising the picture so far it has been shown by measurement of the rates that the action of water on caprolactam to give ε-aminocaproic acid is catalysed by the presence of the acid so produced as are the subsequent addition reactions.

Unfortunately these additional complications do not complete the picture. On prolonged heating, the system will reach an equilibrium state in which unconverted lactam is present as well as oligomers. In kinetic terms this means that a back reaction must be allowed for and the reaction should be written as

$$NH(CH_2)_5CO + H_2O \rightleftharpoons NH_2(CH_2)_5COOH$$

Even allowing for this, other reactions must be considered. Polycondensation may occur with the elimination of water

$$P_n + P_m \rightleftharpoons P_{m+n} + H_2O$$

Transamidation will also be possible. In this the lengths of the chains are altered

$$P_{n+r} + P_m \rightleftharpoons P_{m+r} + P_n$$

These last two reactions will have the effect of modifying the molecular weight distribution.

A reaction where monomer molecules are adding on to a fixed number of chains without termination gives rise to a sharp distribution of molecular weight. The weight fraction is given by

$$w_n = \frac{n}{\nu + 1} \frac{e^{-\nu} \nu^{n-1}}{(n-1)!}$$

where ν is the ratio of the number of moles of monomer per mole of water. This distribution is a sharp one and quite different from the broad one for the most probable distribution expected for a nomal polycondensation. In Fig. 11 (p. 64) is compared this distribution (curve a) with that of the most probable (curve b) with the same number average. The last two reactions have the effect of changing the expected sharp molecular weight distribution to a broad one and if the polymer is heated for a sufficient length of time, the system will approach the most probable.

References p. 64

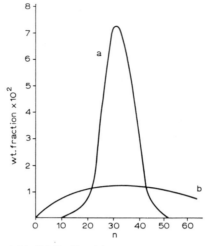
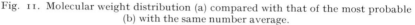

Fig. 11. Molecular weight distribution (a) compared with that of the most probable (b) with the same number average.

REFERENCES

1 E. FISCHER, *Ber.*, 34 (1901) 2868; 39 (1906) 551; 40 (1907) 1754.
2 E. FISCHER, *Ber.*, 41 (1908) 2875; *Ann.*, (1910) 372.
3 C. A. BISCHOFF, *Ber.*, 35 (1902) 2455, 4076.
4 H. STAUDINGER, *Die hochmolecularen organischen Verbindungen*, Springer, Berlin, 1932.
5 Collected Papers of W. H. CAROTHERS. Edited by H. MARK and G. S. WHITBY, Interscience, New York, 1940.
6 W. H. CAROTHERS and J. A. ARVIN, *J. Am. Chem. Soc.*, 51 (1929) 2560.
7 W. H. CAROTHERS and F. J. VAN NATTA, *J. Am. Chem. Soc.*, 52 (1930) 314.
8 W. H. CAROTHERS, J. A. ARVIN and G. L. DOROUGH, *J. Am. Chem. Soc.*, 52 (1930) 3292.
9 E. HOLLO, *Ber.*, 61 (1928) 895.
10 J. VON BRAUN, *Ber.*, 40 (1907) 1840; S. GABRIEL and T. A. MAASS, *Ber.*, 32 (1899) 1266.
11 J. VON BRAUN, *Ber.*, 40 (1907) 1834; O. WALLACH, *Ann.*, 312, 205; 309 (1899) 18; A. MANASSE, *Ber.*, 35 (1902) 1367.
12 W. H. CAROTHERS and G. J. BERCHET, *J. Am. Chem. Soc.*, 52 (1930) 5289.
13 W. H. CAROTHERS and E. W. SPANAGEL, *J. Am. Chem. Soc.*, 57 (1935) 929.
14 M. STOLL and A. ROUVÉ, *Helv. Chim. Acta*, 17 (1934) 1283.
15 M. STOLL and A. ROUVÉ, *Helv. Chim. Acta*, 18 (1935) 1087.
16 W. H. CAROTHERS and J. W. HILL, *J. Am. Chem. Soc.*, 55 (1933) 5043; W. H. CAROTHERS, *Chem. Revs.*, 8 (1931) 353.
17 W. H. CAROTHERS, *Chem. Revs.*, 8 (1931) 353.
18 E. GUTH and H. MARK, *Monatsh.*, 65 (1934) 93.
19 P. J. FLORY, *Chem. Revs.*, 39 (1946) 137.
20 W. H. CAROTHERS, G. L. DOROUGH and F. J. VAN NATTA, *J. Am. Chem. Soc.*, 54 (1932) 761.
21 W. H. CAROTHERS, J. W. HILL and F. J. VAN NATTA, *J. Am. Chem. Soc.*, 56 (1934) 455.
22 R. DIETZEL and R. KRUG, *Ber.*, 58B (1925) 1307.

23 J. W. HILL, *J. Am. Chem. Soc.*, 52 (1930) 4110.
24 W. H. CAROTHERS and J. W. HILL, *J. Am. Chem. Soc.*, 57 (1935) 925.
25 C. N. HINSHELWOOD, *Kinetics of Chemical Change*, Oxford Clarendon Press, 1940.
26 W. H. CAROTHERS and J. W. HILL, *J. Am. Chem. Soc.*, 54 (1932) 1579.
27 W. H. CAROTHERS and F. J. VAN NATTA, *J. Am. Chem. Soc.*, 55 (1933) 4714.
28 H. BATZER and B. MOHR, *Makromol. Chem.*, 23 (1957) 270.
29 *B.I.O.S.* file No. 33, 50.
30 J. R. WHINFIELD, *Endeavour*, 11 (1952) 29.
31 R. HILL and E. E. WALKER, *J. Polymer Sci.*, 3 (1948) 609.
32 E. J. BOURNE et al., *J. Chem. Soc.* (1949) 2976.
33 G. O. CURME and F. JOHNSTON, *Glycols*, Reinhold, New York, 1952.
34 T. SKWARSKI, *Zeszyty Nauk. Politechn. Lodz. Chem.*, see *Chem. Abstr.*, 51 (1957) 1650^f.
35 J. R. WHINFIELD, *Chem. and Ind.*, London, (1953) 226.
36 J. D. ROSS, E. R. COBURN, W. A. LEACH and W. B. ROBINSON, *J. Polymer Sci.*, 13 (1954) 406.
37 C. E. BURR, *J. Polymer Sci.*, 15 (1955) 591.
38 K. YAMAGUCHI et al., *J. Chem. Soc. Japan, Ind. Chem. Sect.*, 58 (1955) 358; *Chem. Abstr.*, 49 (1955) 14373^g.
39 H. HOLTSCHMIDT, *Makromol. Chem.*, 13 (1954) 141. `
    H. BATZER and H. LEVY, *Makromol. Chem.*, 15 (1955) 211.
    K. W. DOCK and H. N. CAMPBELL, *J. Polymer Sci.*, 18 (1955) 218.
40 E. K. BOLTON, *Ind. Eng. Chem.*, 34 (1942) 43.
41 E. E. MAGAT and R. D. STRACHOU, *U.S.P.* (1955) 2, 708, 617.
42 See *Polyamides and Polyesters* by D. E. BANNERMAN and E. E. MAGAT in the series *High Polymers*, Vol. X., Interscience, New York, 1956.
43 D. D. COFFMAN, N. L. COX, E. L. MARTIN, W. E. MOCHEL and F. J. VAN NATTA, *J. Polymer Sci.*, 3 (1948) 85.
44 W. E. HANFORD and R. M. JOYCE JNR., *J. Polymer Sci.*, 3 (1948) 167.
45 D. C. ENGLAND, *U.S.P.* 2,634,269.
46 F. WILOTH, *Angew. Chem.*, 69 (1957) 271; *Z. physik. Chem. Frankfurt*, 11 (1957) 78.
    A. MATTHES, *Kolloid-Z.*, 153 (1953) 28.
    H. YUMOTO and N. OGATA, *Makromol. Chem.*, 25 (1957) 71, 91.
47 P. SCHLACK, *J. Polymer Sci.*, 3 (1947) 167.
48 H. ZAHN et al., *Angew. Chem.*, 68 (1956) 229, 498, 616, 628; 69 (1957) 239, 270; *Chem. Ber.* 90 (1957) 320, 2176.
    M. ROTHE, *Angew. Chem.*, 69 (1957) 730; *Ann.*, 609 (1957) 88.
    P. H. HERMANS, *Chem. and Ind.*, London, (1955) 347.
49 M. ROTHE, *J. Polymer Sci.*, 30 (1958) 227.
50 W. GRIEHL, *Faserforsch. u. Textiltech.*, 6 (1955) 260.
    F. WILOTH, *Kolloid-Z.*, 145 (1956) 203.
    J. SEBENDA, *Kunststoff – Rundschau* (1957) 245.
    T. G. MAJURY, *J. Polymer Sci.*, 24 (1957) 488.
51 J. SAUNDERS, *J. Polymer Sci.*, 30 (1958) 479.
52 O. W. CASS, *Ind. Eng. Chem.*, 40 (1948) 216.
53 *Polymer Processes*, Vol. X, Interscience, New York, 1956.
54 I. E. MUSKAT and H. E. NORTHRUP, *J. Am. Chem. Soc.*, 52 (1930) 4043.
55 J. R. JOHNSON and G. M. WHITMAN, *U.S.P.*, 2 (1949) 477617.
56 D. D. COFFMAN, G. J. BERCHET, N. R. PETERSON and E. W. SPANAGEL, *J. Polymer Sci.*, 2 (1947) 306.
57 C. S. BROWN, A. HILL and P. V. YOULE, *Nature*, 177 (1956) 127.
58 ARNOLD HOFFMAN and Co., *B. P.* 731, 294.
    F. WILOTH, *Makromol. Chem.*, 15 (1955) 98.
    T. SHONO et al., *J. Chem. Soc. Japan, Ind. Chem. Sect.*, 57 (1954) 76a.
    D. S. BRESLOW, G. E. HULSE and A. S. MATLOCK, *J. Am. Chem. Soc.*, 79 (1957) 3766.
59 Abstract in *Faserforsch. u. Textiltech.*, 7, (1956) 323, 422.
    A. B. PAHSHVER, *Tekstil Prom.*, 16 (1958) No. 7, 18.

A. A. Shepikkeev, V. N. Topchikasheva and T. I. Shein, *Tekstil. Prom.*, 16 (1956) No. 1, 33.

A. N. Nesmeyanov et al., *Chem. Tech. (Berlin)*, 9 (1957) 139; *Zhur. Obshcheĭ Khim.*, 27 (1957) 2, 418.

60 R. Aelion, *Fibres*, 17 (1956) No. 3, 79.

61 Y. Iwakura, *Chem. Abstr.*, 45 (1951) 2711.

61a P. J. Flory, *U.S.P.* 224 (1941) 192.

62 T. Leiser and H. Gehln, *Ann.* 556 (1944) 127.

63 G. J. M. van der Kerk, H. G. J. Overmars and G. M. van der Want, *Rec. trav. chim.*, 74 (1955) 1301.

64 G. B. Taylor, *J. Am. Chem. Soc.*, 69 (1947) 635.

65 J. E. Waltz and G. B. Taylor, *Anal. Chem.*, 19 (1947) 448.

S. Basu, *J. Polymer Sci.*, 5 (1950) 735.

66 R. H. Fowler and E. A. Guggenheim, *Statistical Thermodynamics*, Cambridge University Press, 1939, pp. 530–6.

67 E. Rabinowitch and W. C. Wood, *Trans. Faraday Soc.*, 32 (1936) 1381.

68 R. H. Fowler and M. B. Slater, *Trans. Faraday Soc.*, 34 (1938) 81.

69 H. Mark and R. Raff, *High Polymeric Reactions, Their Theory and Practice*, Interscience, New York, 1941, pp. 139, 151, 176 (*High Polymers*, Vol. III).

70 H. Dostal and H. Mark, *Oesterr. Chemiker-Ztg.*, 40 (1937) 25; *Angew. Chem.*, 50 (1937) 348.

71 S. Glasstone, K. J. Laidler and H. Eyring, *Theory of Rate Processes*, McGraw Hill, New York, 1941.

72 B. V. Bhide and J. J. Sudborough, *J. Indian Inst. Sci.*, 8A (1925) 89.

73 R. A. Fairclough and C. N. Hinshelwood, *J. Chem. Soc.*, (1939) 593.

74 D. P. Evans, J. J. Gordon and H. B. Watson, *J. Chem. Soc.*, (1938) 1439.

75 D. C. Haywood, *J. Chem. Soc.*, 121 (1922) 1904.

76 P. J. Flory, *J. Am. Chem. Soc.*, 61 (1939) 334; 62 (1940) 2261.

77 A. C. Rolfe and C. N. Hinshelwood, *Trans. Faraday Soc.*, 30 (1934) 935.

N. Ivanoff, *Bull. soc. chim. France*, [5], 17 (1950) 347.

78 D. Heikens, *J. Polymer Sci.*, 22 (1956) 65.

79 W. Kuhn, *Ber.*, 63 (1930) 1503.

80 W. H. Stockmayer, *J. Chem. Phys.*, 11 (1943) 45.

81 P. J. Flory, *J. Am. Chem. Soc.*, 64 (1942) 2205.

82 P. J. Flory, *J. Am. Chem. Soc.*, 58 (1936) 1877.

83 G. B. Taylor, *J. Am. Chem. Soc.*, 69 (1947) 638.

84 G. J. Howard, *J. Polymer Sci.*, 37 (1959) 310, 548.

85 P. H. Hermans, D. Heikens and P. F. van Velden, *J. Polymer Sci.*, 30 (1958) 81.

86 D. Heikens, P. H. Hermans and S. Smith, *J. Polymer Sci.*, 38 (1959) 265.

87 P. J. Flory, *J. Am. Chem. Soc.*, 63 (1941) 3083.

CHAPTER 3

ADDITION POLYMERS

1. Formation

The polymerisation of ethylene derivatives can be induced under many conditions. The monomers which most readily polymerise are those where ethylene is substituted on one carbon atom only; compounds of formulae $CH_2=CXY$ are used extensively for the manufacture of many common polymers e.g. polyvinyl chloride, polymethyl methacrylate etc. Usually one (X) of the substituents is polar—typical compounds are vinyl chloride $(CH_2=CH \cdot Cl)$ and acrylonitrile $(CH_2=CH \cdot CN)$; the second (Y) is often hydrogen but may be a non-polar group e.g. methyl in methyl methacrylate $(CH_2=C(CH_3)COOCH_3)$ or sometimes a polar group e.g. chlorine in vinylidiene chloride $(CH_2=CCl_2)$. In general ethylenes substituted on both carbon atoms i.e. of formula $CHX=CHY$ are more difficult to polymerise although, under rather special conditions, polymers can be made from the parent ethylene (X = Y = H) and its tetrafluoro derivative.

Polymerisation of ethylene derivatives may be carried out in the gas phase when the polymer is deposited as a solid or in the liquid phase when the monomer may be used alone or diluted with a solvent. An alternative method is to disperse the monomer in an aqueous medium and polymerise the emulsion so formed.

Addition polymerisation is initiated through the presence of an activated molecule introduced into the system by the following agencies,

(a) *Thermal Means*
(b) *Free Radical Initiation*
(c) *Light*
(d) *Ionic Catalysts*

(a) Thermal Means

If two monomer molecules M collide and the energy transfer is sufficiently large, a "hot" molecule M* will be produced. This molecule may react with a monomer molecule and transfer the reactive centre; further reaction occurs with other monomer molecules

$$M^* + M \rightarrow MM^* + M \rightarrow MMM^*, \text{ etc.}$$

Hence a chain is built up at the end of which resides the reactive centre.

Growth ceases when the reactive end is deactivated. Not all ethylenic compounds will polymerise by thermal means alone[1,2].

The reaction has been considered to occur when two molecules collide perhaps to give a diradical

$$2CH_2{=}CHX \rightarrow \dot{C}HX{-}CH_2{-}CH_2{-}\dot{C}HX$$

This radical is more likely to be formed on energetic grounds than the transfer of a hydrogen atom from one molecule to another

$$2CH_2{=}CHX \rightarrow CH_3{-}\dot{C}HX + CH_2{=}\dot{C}X$$

The formation of a diradical by opening of the double bond *i.e.*

$$CH_2{=}CHX \rightarrow \dot{C}H_2{-}\dot{C}HX$$

would require again a large amount of energy (*ca.* 50 kcal) and is unlikely. However, the means by which thermal initiation is brought about is not completely resolved.

(b) *Free Radical Initiation*

Polymerisation may be initiated by substances which decompose to give free radicals which in turn react with the double bond of the monomer. This produces a molecule with a radical end which is capable of reacting with a further monomer molecule, a process which is repeated many times.

$$\dot{R} + CH_2{=}CHX \rightarrow RCH_2{-}\dot{C}HX + CH_2{=}CHX \rightarrow$$
$$\rightarrow RCH_2CHXCH_2\dot{C}HX + CH_2{=}CHX, \text{ etc: to polymer}$$

Free radicals are entities in which one or more of the normal valencies is not satisfied; examples of such electron deficient substances are methyl, ethyl, phenyl etc. By virtue of their unsatisfied valency, free radicals are in general extremely reactive although one or two are sufficiently stable to be isolated and analysed chemically, for example tridiphenylmethyl[3] (I) or diphenylpicrylhydrazyl[4] (II)

(I)　　　　　　　　　　　　　　　　　(II)

The presence of an unpaired electron is responsible for the property of paramagnetism which free radicals possess and which serves as a possible means of detection. In some instances, free radicals may be detected in the emission spectrum of the light arising from an electrical discharge through a gas. By this means, the OH radical has been shown to exist.

Again, it is possible to irradiate substances for short periods with light of high intensity and to determine the absorption spectrum immediately after the light is shut off. By such means, known as "flash photolysis", it is possible to detect certain radicals by their absorption spectra[5].

For the most part, however, the presence of free radicals is deduced from qualitative and quantitative analyses of chemical reactions. For example[6], lead tetraethyl may be thermally decomposed and the decomposition products passed over metals such as zinc when the volatile zinc diethyl is formed.

The reaction presumably follows the course

$$Pb(C_2H_5)_4 \rightarrow Pb(C_2H_5)_2 + 2CH_3\dot{C}H_2$$

$$2CH_3\dot{C}H_2 + Zn \rightarrow Zn(C_2H_5)_2$$

Alternatively, 2-azobisisobutyronitrile (III) decomposes to give nitrogen and the nitrile radical (IV)

$$(CH_3)_2C-N=N-C(CH_3)_2 \rightarrow N_2 + 2(CH_3)_2\dot{C}$$
$$\underset{CN}{|} \qquad \underset{CN}{|} \qquad\qquad\qquad \underset{CN}{|}$$
$$\text{(III)} \qquad\qquad\qquad\qquad \text{(IV)}$$

The reaction carried out in the presence of a quinone gives mono- and di-ethers (V)

$$2(CH_3)_2\dot{C} + O-\langle\rangle-O \rightarrow (CH_3)_2CO\langle\rangle OC(CH_3)_2$$
$$\underset{CN}{|} \qquad\qquad\qquad\qquad\qquad \underset{CN}{|} \qquad \underset{CN}{|}$$
$$\text{(V)}$$

Again, in the decomposition of diacetyl peroxide in acetic acid solution intermediate free radical products are most likely formed. The reaction in acetic acid may be represented according to the following scheme

$$(CH_3COO)_2 \rightarrow 2CH_3\overline{C}O\dot{O} \rightarrow 2\dot{C}H_3 + 2CO_2$$
$$\dot{C}H_3 + CH_3COOH \rightarrow CH_4 + \dot{C}H_2COOH$$
$$2\dot{C}H_2COOH \rightarrow (CH_2COOH)_2$$

The polymerisation reaction being a chain reaction can in some instances be employed as a sensitive test for the detection of free radicals[7].

In general, the reactions which radicals undergo depend on the urge for electrons to form pairs with spins in opposite directions. Thus two radicals may form a covalent bond

$$\dot{R}_1 + \dot{R}_2 \rightarrow R_1R_2$$

or lose or gain an electron by a transfer (redox) reaction producing ions.

$$\dot{R} + X \rightarrow \bar{R}: + X^+$$

Reactions of this kind give products which are no longer radicals. In some instances the product may be a radical

$$\dot{R} + AB \rightarrow RA + \dot{B}$$

and in particular if the second molecule is an ethylenic compound, the radical may add and produce a new radical

$$\dot{R} + CH_2{=}CHX \rightarrow RCH_2\dot{C}HX$$

Radical reactions are usually rapid processes. Some of the radical initiators or catalysts used for polymerisation are discussed below.

(i) *Peroxides.* The decomposition of peroxides such as dibenzoyl peroxide would indicate a split at the O—O bond to give acyl radicals which may further lose carbon dioxide[8]

$$(RCOO)_2 \rightarrow 2RCO\dot{O} \rightarrow 2\dot{R} + 2CO_2$$

The kinetics for the first step in this reaction may be written as conforming to a first order law

$$\frac{-d[I]}{dt} = k[I] \qquad (1)$$

where $[I]$ is the concentration of peroxide and k is the rate constant. In a peroxide such as dibenzoyl, the dipoles associated with the benzoate groups repel one another as indicated by the charge separations $\delta+$ and $\delta-$

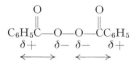

This diagram suggests that the introduction of electron repelling substituents into one or both of the phenyl residues will increase the electron density between the two oxygen atoms, increase the repulsion between them and hence the rate of cleavage at the O—O bond; electron attracting substituents on the other hand will increase the stability. Measurements of the rate constants of the decomposition would indicate this to be so[9]. The electron repelling methoxyl group in p,p'-dimethoxydibenzoyl peroxide raises the rate constant to 7.06×10^{-3} min^{-1} as against 2.52×10^{-3} min^{-1} for the unsubstituted peroxide, whereas the electron attraction substituent in p,p'-dicyanodibenzoyl peroxide reduces it to 1.22×10^{-3} min^{-1}. The decomposition of the peroxide in solution may not necessarily be as simple as predicted by the first order decomposition discussed above and has been found[10] in some systems to have the order of 1.3 or even[11] 2.

This could arise from attack by the benzoyl radicals of the initiator on the solvent; the order of the decomposition reaction may be modified according to the solvent[12]. In the presence of a radical acceptor such as styrene[13], the order of reaction is very near to unity suggesting that, in a polymerisation reaction, the free radicals produced from the initiator are virtually all captured. For polymer studies therefore the reaction may be taken as first order.

There are peroxides other than dibenzoyl which are suitable for initiation. Di-t-butyl peroxide (VI) is valuable since thermal decomposition is appreciable only above 100°C as compared with dibenzoyl peroxide which is active above 60°C. Peresters such as t-butyl perbenzoate (VII) are intermediate in properties between dibenzoyl and dibutyl peroxides, whereas other peresters may initiate polymerisation at room temperatures.

$$(CH_3)_3CO \qquad \langle \rangle - COO \qquad R-N=N-R$$
$$(CH_3)_3CO \qquad (CH_3)_3CO$$
$$(VI) \qquad\qquad (VII) \qquad\qquad (VIII)$$

(ii) *Azo compounds*[14,15]. These initiators decompose more readily than the peroxides and their efficiency as chain initiators for the polymerisation of styrene is very high. They have the general formula $R-N=N-R$ (VIII) breaking down to $2\dot{R} + N_2$, where R is an aliphatic group. In contrast, the aromatic azo compounds are stable and used as dyes. Some of the simple aliphatic compounds are unsuitable since they may be too unstable to handle. Azomethane (VIII) $(R = CH_3)$ is very unstable but its reactivity can be reduced by the introduction of polar groups. 2-Azobisisobutyronitrile (III) is sufficiently stable to be of great utility as an initiator. The kinetics of decomposition are first order and not very dependent on the solvent used[16].

(iii) *Redox systems*. In aqueous systems, hydrogen peroxide and salts of peracids are effective in initiating polymerisation but, if reducing bodies such as aldehydes or ferrous ions are added to the system, the efficiency of these initiators is much enhanced. The reagent prepared from hydrogen peroxide and ferrous ions is known as Fenton's reagent[17] and is considered to react[18] in the following manner

$$Fe^{++} + H_2O_2 \rightarrow Fe^{+++} + OH^- + \dot{O}H$$
$$\dot{O}H + H_2O_2 \rightarrow H_2O + H\dot{O}_2$$
$$H\dot{O}_2 + H_2O_2 \rightarrow H_2O + O_2 + \dot{O}H$$
$$\dot{O}H + Fe^{++} \rightarrow Fe^{+++} + OH^-$$

References p. 116

This chain gives rise to hydroxyl and perhydroxyl radicals capable of initiating polymerisation[19,20,21] although, in the presence of adequate amounts of monomer, only the first step will be operative as all the OH radicals produced will initiate polymerisation.

Polymerisation in aqueous media is often carried out with ammonium persulphate as a catalyst[22], a substance which will decompose to $\dot{S}O_4^-$ radicals. The rate of polymerisation is increased by the addition of a reducing agent. A convenient agent to add to the system is another sulphur acid; in the case of addition of thiosulphate a reaction scheme has been worked out[23].

$$\dot{S}_2O_8^{--} + S_2O_3^{--} \rightarrow SO_4^{--} + \dot{S}O_4^- + \tfrac{1}{2}(S_4O_6)^{--}$$

The free radical $\dot{S}O_4^-$ can in addition react with water to give hydroxyl radicals

$$\dot{S}O_4^- + H_2O \rightarrow SO_4^{--} + H^+ + \dot{O}H$$

The system thus produces a supply of free radicals capable of initiating polymerisation. The activity of a reduction activation system can be increased by the addition of certain metal ions (*e.g.* Fe^{+++} or Cu^{++}) in very small amounts[24]. Indeed, the rate of production of radicals is significantly increased if the concentration of metal ions is of the order of parts per million. With care this increase in the rate of production in such a promoted reduction system can be employed to increase the rate of polymerisation.

There are many possible redox systems capable of liberating free radicals *e.g.* organic peroxides with reducing agents (*e.g.* phenylsuphinic acid or ferrous ions[25]). The reaction with ferrous ions may be written as

$$Fe^{++} + ROOR \rightarrow Fe^{+++} + RO^- + R\dot{O}$$

giving rise to the radical $R\dot{O}$. The technical importance of redox systems in polymerisation lies, to some extent, in their ability to produce radicals at lower temperatures than many other initiating systems.

(iv) *Other systems.* N-nitrosoacylarylamines[26] (IX) decompose according to the reaction below giving free radicals

$$R_1NCOR \rightleftharpoons R_1N \quad C{=}O \rightarrow RCO\dot{O} + \dot{R}_1 + N_2$$

with NO and N—O R substituents

(IX)

These initiators have not yet been used to a great extent.

(c) Photochemical Initiation[27,28,29]

Irradiation of most of the ethylenic monomers causes polymerisation. The absorption of light by the double bond may cause excitation of the less strongly held π-electrons to form a diradical. However some difficulties may be raised against the formation of diradicals since, when these have reacted with monomer molecules, the growing radical might tend to form a cyclic molecule once a certain size is reached. In certain circumstances, it has been postulated that scission of the monomer may occur as in the irradiation in the gaseous phase of methyl vinyl ketone (X)[30].

$$CH_2{=}CHCOCH_3 \rightarrow \dot{C}H_3 + CH_2{=}\dot{C}H + CO_2$$
$$(X)$$

The vinyl radicals are not active in initiating polymerisation but combine to form butadiene (XI)

$$2CH_2{=}\dot{C}H \rightarrow CH_2{=}CH{-}CH{=}CH_2$$
$$(XI)$$

At present the question of the actual mechanism has not been fully resolved, although kinetic work on the polymerisation of methyl methacrylate and styrene would favour the formation of monoradicals[31,32].

(d) Ionic Initiators

A number of unsaturated compounds e.g. butadiene, styrene, vinyl alkyl ether will polymerise with the help of metallic halides of the Friedel-Crafts type e.g. BF_3, $TiCl_4$, $SnCl_4$, $AlCl_3$ etc.; all, on the Lewis definition, are strong acids. The polymerisation reaction takes place rapidly at very low temperatures (e.g. $-100°C$ for isobutylene with BF_3) and proceeds through a mechanism involving ions. In most instances, the reaction requires the presence of traces of substances such as water, hydrochloric acid which act as cocatalysts. The monomers polymerised by these substances contain electron releasing substituents so that the doubly bonded carbon atoms tend to share a pair of electrons with these electron acceptors. This would indicate that their mode of action involves carbonium ions[33]. Evidence for this comes from the fact that triphenylmethyl chloride is a catalyst for the polymerisation of vinyl ethers in m-cresol. In this case the catalyst ionises to give the carbonium ion Ph_3C^+.

A possible mechanism for their mode of action is

$$BF_3 + CH_2{=}CHXY \rightarrow F_3\bar{B}CH_2\overset{+}{C}XY + CH_2{=}CXY \rightarrow$$
$$\rightarrow F_3\bar{B}CH_2CXYCH_2\overset{+}{C}XY \rightarrow polymer$$

or, since a cocatalyst is required, a mechanism is possible which may involve a proton transfer[34,35]. BF_3 will initiate polymerisation of iso-butylene in the present of water. The first reaction is to form a hydrate $BF_3 \cdot OH_2$ which will transfer a proton

$$BF_3OH_2 + CH_2{=}C(CH_3)_2 \rightarrow (CH_3)_3C^+ + BF_3OH^-$$

$$(CH_3)_3C^+ + CH_2{=}C(CH_3)_2 \rightarrow (CH_3)CCH_2C^+(CH_3)_2 \rightarrow \text{polymer}$$

In an analogous way, it is possible with some monomers *e.g.* methacrylo-nitrile to polymerise by an anionic mechanism. For example metallic sodium, dissolved in liquid ammonia, will react with the double bond to produce an anion which can further polymerise

$$CH_2{=}CXY + \overset{-}{N}H_2 \rightarrow NH_2CH_2\overset{-}{C}XY + CH_2{=}CXY \rightarrow$$

$$\rightarrow NH_2CH_2CXYCH_2\overset{-}{C}XY \rightarrow \text{polymer}$$

2. Polymer Structure

Addition polymerisations have a characteristic feature namely, they are chain reactions. The polymer molecules grow rapidly at the expense of the monomer and reach high molecular weights very quickly. Uncon-sumed monomer molecules are present throughout the course of the reaction until the final polymer chains are produced. In addition poly-merisation, the conversion of monomer to polymer is not accompanied by a corresponding increase in the degree of polymerisation of the polymer; there are present a small and constantly renewed population of active chain ends which grow to full length and then die. This distinguishes such systems from condensation reactions where large numbers of chains slowly increase in molecular weight as reaction proceeds.

In this chapter polymerisation using free radical initiators is discussed. The process may be regarded as being in three parts, initiation, propaga-tion and termination. The evidence for the ability of radicals to initiate polymerisation is indirect but it has been shown[30] that introduction of methyl radicals, formed by photochemical decomposition of acetone, into gaseous vinyl chloride, for example, produces a deposit of polymer on the walls of the vessel. Alternatively polymerisation may be caused by the well established triphenylmethyl radical[8].

Other evidence which goes to confirm the free radical initiation is the effect of solvents such as carbon tetrachloride. The latter is known to be very readily attacked by free radicals[8] and it will curtail the growth of polymer chains, the reaction being the abstraction of a chlorine atom and formation of a trichloromethyl radical

$$\overset{\cdot}{R} + CCl_4 \rightarrow RCl + \overset{\cdot}{C}Cl_3$$

This point is elaborated in the discussion on transfer reactions. Inhibitors for free radical reactions will reduce the growth of a polymer chain. Quinonoid compounds, polyhydroxyphenols, aromatic aminonitroso and nitro compounds act as inhibitors. The mechanism of the reaction of a radical with quinone may be written as

$$\dot{R} + Q \rightarrow R\dot{Q}$$

The reactivity of the new radical $R\dot{Q}$ will be different from $\dot{R}$ and, if the new radical is sufficiently stabilised by resonance, it will not react so readily. Finally, the equations of the kinetics deduced on the basis of a free radical mechanism of polymerisation do fit many of the known facts.

The propagation reaction of radical initiated polymerisation may be written as

$$—CH_2\dot{C}HX + CH_2{=}CHX \rightarrow —CH_2CHXCH_2\dot{C}HX \qquad (2)$$

where the monomer molecules are adding to the chain radical in a head to tail fashion. However, there is an alternative mechanism of growth

$$—CH_2\dot{C}HX + CHX{=}CH_2 \rightarrow —CH_2CHXCHX\dot{C}H_2 \qquad (3)$$

If the polymer chain grows exclusively according to equation 2, a polymer results with the group X attached to each alternate carbon atom; if according to equation 3 the groups X are attached to adjacent carbon atoms. If both proceed simultaneously, some groups will be on adjacent and others on alternate atoms

$$—CH_2—CH—CH_2—CH—CH_2—CH—CH—CH_2—$$
$$\qquad\quad |\qquad\qquad |\qquad\qquad |\quad\ |$$
$$\qquad\quad X\qquad\quad X\qquad\quad X\ \ X$$

Hence more than one structure is possible.

Fortunately the orthodox methods of chemical analysis shed some light on the structure of the polymer. If the polymer is polyvinyl alcohol, attack by periodic acid is diagnostic of the presence of two adjacent hydroxyl groups in an aliphatic chain. The reaction gives two aldehyde groups

$$—CH—CH—$$
$$\quad\ |\quad\ |\qquad + HIO_4 \rightarrow —CHO\ OHC—$$
$$\quad OH\ \ OH$$

Marvel and Denvon[36] showed that polyvinyl alcohol was not oxidised by this reagent, and hence presumed it contained no 1,2-glycol units. Again reaction of zinc with polyvinyl halides[37] removes the halogen to an extent of 84–87% to yield a polymer which does not decolourise aqueous potassium permanganate. This is a result which would be expected on the basis of random attack by the zinc along a regularly spaced array of halogen atoms[38]. The reaction will proceed to give, assuming the 1,3-structure, the result below,

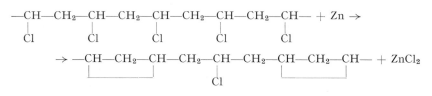

The final product will, on the basis of a random attack by the zinc, always leave a number of residual chlorine atoms unable to pair up to form cyclopropane rings. The residual halide atoms do not liberate iodine from potassium iodide, a reaction which is specific of the 1,2-dihalides.

Other systems show the 1,3 structure *e.g.* poly-*o*-bromostyrene[39], methyl vinyl ketone[40]. Destructive distillation[41] of polystyrene yielded products 1,3,5-triphenylbenzene, 1,3,5-triphenylpentane and 1,3-diphenyl-propane. The characteristic feature of these products is that none of them have adjacent phenyl groups. With polyvinyl methyl ketone (XII)

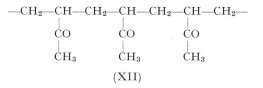

(XII)

an internal aldol condensation is possible to give a series of condensed cyclohexane rings (XIII)

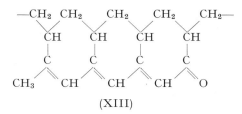

(XIII)

This condensation process eliminates 79–85% of the oxygen compared with the theoretical of 81–86%[42]. Head to head arrangements will give rise to furan rings(XIV)

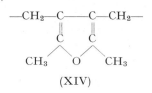

(XIV)

a process which eliminates 50% of the total amount of oxygen. A random distribution of the groups down the chain will lead to a value of oxygen loss intermediate between the two.

Absorption spectra have been used in this connection. Thus, it has been shown that the infra-red spectrum of polyvinyl acetate (XV) is near that of isopropyl acetate (XVI) and that of polymethyl methacrylate (XVII) is near that of methyl isobutyrate[43] (XVIII)

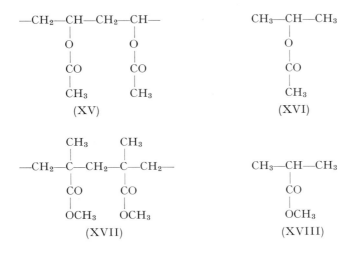

The 1,3 structures have been confirmed by the comparison of ultra-violet spectra of the polymers with that of a simple compound; thus the spectrum of polyvinyl alcohol agrees with 2,4-dihydroxypentane (XIX, R = OH) and that of polyvinyl chloride with 2,4-dichloropentane (XIX, R = Cl).

$$H_3C—CHR—CH_2—CHR—CH_3$$
$$(XIX)$$

The evidence both chemical and spectroscopic is, with few exceptions, in favour of a head to tail structure. One exception is the polymer[44] produced from monomers of the form $CH_2=CBrCOOCH_3$ which will dehalogenate to an extent of 97% with zinc and liberate iodine from potassium iodide. If the halogen atoms are distributed in pairs down the polymer chain there is no reason why all the halogen should not be removed.

Nevertheless, chemical techniques do not rule out the possibility of a small number of linkages which are head to head. The detection of a small number of head to head groups in the molecule requires techniques more sensitive than normal chemical methods. Head to head arrangements may be shown up if the chain is broken; in these circumstances the molecular weight will drop sharply. It has been shown[45] that the reaction of polyvinyl alcohol with periodate gives a notable decrease in viscosity indicating a very small number of adjacent hydroxyl groups (*ca.* 1–2%). The position has been reviewed by Marvel[46].

Of the two modes of propagation, that given by equation 2 is to be preferred since the radical $RCH_2\dot{C}HX$ will be stabilised by resonance with the substituent *e.g.* for styrene there are many cannonical states of the type

This possibility is not allowed in the second mode of propagation and, since such resonance possibilities will lead to a lower energy for the system, the mechanism 2 is more likely. These arguments apply equally to the initiation as to the individual steps of propagation. It follows that the more stable the initial radical $RCH_2\dot{C}HX$, the more likely is the propagation to proceed through the more stable radicals with $-CH_2\dot{C}HX$ at the end. Thus, a most important factor in the addition of monomer to a radical is the resonance stabilisation of the radical which arises from the addition[47]. If the radical is stabilised to a large degree, the reaction will be dependent to a considerable extent on the reactivity of the monomer. Such is the case for styrene. On the other hand vinyl chloride gives chains whose radical ends are not stabilised to a large extent, so that the reaction will be dependent on the radical reactivity rather than on that of the monomer.

The indications are that a benzyl radical of equation 2 (X = phenyl) is favoured by resonance stabilisation to the extent of 20–25 kcal. The other kind of radical is phenylethyl type and will not differ greatly in stability from methyl or ethyl radicals. Resonance stabilisation will be less but not negligible when the group X is CH_3COO, CH_3CO etc.

The series given below gives the decreasing order of reactivity for a series of substituted ethylenes (*i.e.* X in the formula $CH_2=CHX$)

$$p\text{-}C_6H_4 > CH=CH_2 > C_6H_5 > CN \sim COOR > Cl > CH_2R \sim OOCCH_3 > H$$

3. Termination Reactions

The growing polymer chains once started will continue to grow until some mechanism is invoked to prevent them. The most obvious method of stopping the chains is by mutual termination

$$\dot{M}_r + \dot{M}_s \rightarrow M_{r+s}$$

This annihilation will give a "dead" polymer molecule containing initiating radical fragments as the end units[48]. Confirmation of this is possible by detection of end groups by chemical analysis or by use of initiator containing bromine or its radioactive isotope, and detection of the latter in the resultant polymer[49]. Thus if hydroxyl radicals derived from the ferrous ion/hydrogen peroxide reagent are used to initiate the polymerisation of methyl methacrylate and styrene in aqueous media, the presence of two hydroxyl groups has been shown in each molecule[50] of the polymer; azobisisobutyronitrile labelled with radioactive ^{14}C gives a polystyrene with two radical fragments per molecule[51]. Using potassium persulphate labelled with ^{35}S as initiator, polystyrene has resulted with two initiator residues per molecule[52]. From these examples, the conclusion may be made that mutual termination is in the main responsible for termination in many systems.

However, mutual termination is not the only possible reaction. It is possible, if the reaction is carried out in a solvent SX, for the growing radical to attack the latter abstracting an atom from it

$$\dot{M}_r + SX \rightarrow M_rX + \dot{S}$$

This reaction gives rise to a "dead" polymer and a solvent radical $\dot{S}$ which can be capable of initiating growth of another polymer chain. An example of this behaviour is found if the solvent is carbon tetrachloride. The polymer chain will abstract a chlorine atom and give rise to a radical $\dot{C}Cl_3$

$$\dot{M}_r + CCl_4 \rightarrow M_rCl + \dot{C}Cl_3$$

This procedure will mean that one chain is stopped and another started; the number of chains is thereby increased but they will naturally be of shorter length (lower D.P.). Transfer reactions of this kind mean that polymerisations carried out in different solvents will lead to products whose D.P. is dependent on the solvent, as has been demonstrated for the polymerisation of styrene. The ability of the radical $\dot{S}$ to start a chain may differ from that of the polymer radical. If the reactivity of the radical $\dot{S}$ is low, the polymerisation rate will be reduced in addition to decreasing the molecular weight of the polymer.

It is possible to get chain transfer with the monomer. This reaction may be written as

$$\dot{M}_r + M \rightarrow M_r + \dot{M}$$

where a new radical is produced. In general, chain transfer with monomer not of major importance although in one or two instances it may be obvious particularly if the new radical does not start a new chain. In this connection the free radical (XX) produced by hydrogen abstraction from a carbon atom adjacent to an allylic double bond is one which will fail to initiate polymerisation since it is resonance stabilised[53]. The two possible resonance forms are given (XXI)

$$—CH_2\dot{C}HX + CH_2{=}CH—CHR \rightarrow —CH_2CH_2X + CH_2{=}CH—\dot{C}HR$$

$$(XX)$$

$$CH_2{=}CH—\dot{C}HR \qquad \dot{C}H_2—CH{=}CHR$$

$$(XXI)$$

The fate of this radical is not known for certain; it may disappear through dimerisation or by reaction with other radicals. However, there is no doubt that such a reaction occurs since polymerisation of allyl compounds leads to products of low D.P. This kind of reaction has been referred to as degradative chain transfer.

A further possibility of transfer must be mentioned. The radical may abstract a hydrogen atom from the polymer thereby setting up a centre from which a further chain may grow. This reaction may be represented diagrammatically,

$$—CH_2CHXCH_2CHXCH_2— + \dot{M}_r \rightarrow —CH_2CHXCH_2\dot{C}XCH_2— + M_r$$

Transfer reaction with the polymer will materially alter the shape of the latter since the linear chain now carries a branch. If two of the branches were to join together two polymer chains would be linked and, if such a procedure were carried to its limit, a cross-linked material would result.

It is not always the case that interaction of the polymer radical with another radical leads to mutual termination; a hydrogen atom may be transferred

$$—CH_2\dot{C}HX + \dot{C}HXCH_2— \rightarrow —CH_2CH_2X + CHX{=}CH—$$

This disproportionation reaction gives rise to a saturated and an unsaturated terminal group.

The growing radical may be terminated by one of the radicals produced from the catalyst. However there is little evidence from kinetic data that this occurs. The reason undoubtedly lies in the fact that, except when the polymerisation has gone close to completion, the number of monomer molecules present in the polymerising system outweighs the number of radicals; hence the probability of the radical colliding with a second radical is much less than the probability of meeting a monomer molecule.

4. Polyethylene

In the fibre field there are many suitable vinyl type polymers. The parent chemically speaking is polyethylene or rather polymethylene. This substance may be formed by the decomposition of diazomethane[54]

$$n CH_2 N_2 \rightarrow (CH_2)_n + n N_2$$

This reaction is catalysed by metallic copper, silver or boron trifluoride[55]. The polymers so produced are of high molecular weight. Commercially, polyethylene or polythene is made by polymerising ethylene. A temperature of 300°C and a pressure of 100–200 atm are conditions giving some polymerisation, the polymer having a low molecular weight; to obtain a molecular weight of the order of 10,000, high pressures (ca. 1,000 atm) and temperatures around 100°C are necessary. The essential requirement is that, in the polymerising system, there should be a high concentration or density of ethylene. The polymerisation is carried out using free radical catalysts and the mechanism is similar to other vinyl types. The reaction, in addition to being controlled by temperature and catalyst concentration, is also affected by pressure variations. In manufacture one of the difficulties which had to be overcome is the heat which is liberated. The reaction $C_2H_4 \rightleftharpoons 1/n(C_2H_4)_n$ (gas) liberates 22.35 kcal per mole at 227°C and if carried out adiabatically, a large rise in temperature would result (1% polymerisation at 100°C and 1000 atm will cause a 20°C rise[56]).

At room temperatures the free energy of polymerisation is in favour of the polymer. At high temperatures ethylene undergoes a breakdown to carbon and methane or hydrogen.

In the earlier investigations of high pressure polymerisation, oxygen was found to be a catalyst probably as it oxidises ethylene to produce free radicals. However, it is possible to use a wide range of free radical catalysts. The estimates of the heat and free energy changes[57] in the reaction of a methyl radical with ethylene $\dot{C}H_3 + CH_2{=}CH_2 \rightarrow CH_3CH_2\dot{C}H_2$ are 27 kcal and 16.7 kcal at room temperature, suggesting that the polymerisation proceeds in this way. The kinds of catalysts are organic peroxides used in aqueous or organic solvents; hydrogen peroxide/persulphate in aqueous solution as well as the azo class have been used.

To obtain a product suitable for forming filaments i.e. of a molecular weight in the region of 10–20,000 the reaction is carried out at 1000 atm pressure and 100–300°C. At these temperatures ethylene is above its critical temperature but, at these very high pressures, the density of the compressed gas is approaching that of the liquid at boiling point. The polymerisation of compressed ethylene bears some relation to polymerisation of liquid monomers although its greater compressibility makes greater concentration variations possible.

References p. 116

Although the chains are in the main terminated mutually, transfer reactions do occur *e.g.*

$$—\dot{C}H_2 + RH \rightarrow —CH_3 + \dot{R}$$

This naturally reduces the D.P. and, in order to control the reaction, care must be taken to avoid impurities which will enter into such chain reactions. It is possible to produce polyethylenes of low mol. wt. by adding a second component *e.g.* addition of HCl gives[58,59]

$$—\dot{C}H_2 + HCl \rightarrow —CH_3 + Cl$$

$$Cl + C_2H_4 \rightarrow ClCH_2\dot{C}H_3 \rightarrow \text{polymer}$$

On the basis of thermodynamic arguments[58], chain transfer to another ethylene molecule is not as likely as transfer to the polymer

$$—\dot{C}H_2 + CH_2— \rightarrow —CH_3 + —\dot{C}H—$$

This reaction leads to a branched structure, a fact which seems likely in view of the lower melting-point and density of high pressure polythene as compared with other paraffins of high molecular weight. Branches in polythene chains have been demonstrated by infra-red spectroscopy[60,61]. An average value for the methyl content is 1 in 30–50 carbon atoms along the chain. This value is higher than the expected number of two per molecule. The methyl groups lie on chains which grow from active centres produced by the transfer reaction. The polymer is thus of the form

$$
\begin{array}{ccc}
—CH—(CH_2—CH_2)_n—CH— \\
\mid \qquad\qquad\qquad \mid \\
(CH_2)_l \qquad\qquad (CH_2)_m \\
\mid \qquad\qquad\qquad \mid \\
CH_3 \qquad\qquad\quad CH_3
\end{array}
$$

For textile uses, polythene made in this way suffers from a low m.p. (110–120°C). Of recent years, however, changes have been made in the method of manufacture so that the product has a higher m.p. (*ca.* 135°C). This higher melting is a consequence of less branching in the polymer molecules thereby permitting a closer and more regular packing of the chains giving a material with a more crystalline structure and higher density. These points are discussed in a later chapter.

According to the patent literature high density polythenes may be prepared using either supported catalysts such as nickel or cobalt on charcoal or metal alkyls. When using the supported catalysts the polymerisation takes place at temperatures above 100°C with pressures around 1000 lb./in.² (*ca.* 70 atm) in the presence of liquid hydrocarbons which dissolve the polymer and help to maintain the activity of the catalyst. The metal alkyl catalysts[62] e.g. aluminium alkyls have been shown to be effective.

Subsequently catalysts obtained from the reaction of alkyls of metals in groups I–III with compounds of transition metals in groups IV–VI have been found to be effective. An example is the catalyst produced from titanium tetrachloride and aluminium triethyl dissolved in n-heptane. The polymerisation reaction which occurs is heterogeneous, taking place on the surface of the solid particles of catalyst. Monomer is probably adsorbed on to active sites which distort the electron distribution in the molecules so that some charge separation occurs. The mechanism of polymerisation is thought to be ionic rather than due to radicals and is perhaps best classified separately as "polymerisation by coordination complex"[108]. Indeed, it is to be expected, since the reaction conditions are so much milder, that the mechanism of polymerisation will be different from that of the normal high pressure method. Using these catalysts ethylene is polymerised at atmospheric pressure at room temperature. The density of the low pressure polythene will be around 0.96 as compared to the high pressure product[63] of 0.92. It is a more suitable product for fibres.

5. Polyvinyl Chloride

Vinyl chloride was described by Regnault[64] as long ago as 1838 and polymerised by Baumann[65] in 1872 but it is only in the last three decades that commercial production of it and its polymer have been developed. Vinyl chloride can be made on a commercial scale by the reaction of acetylene with hydrochloric acid. This may be done by passage of the gases over a catalyst such as activated carbon impregnated with mercuric chloride[66].

Heat is developed during this reaction and cooling is necessary. The products are condensed by cooling and impurities — acetylene, ethylidene chloride and acetaldehyde are removed by fractionation. Removal of the impurities and, in particular, acetylene is necessary.

The monomer is polymerised by free radical initiators (acyl peroxides, aliphatic azo compounds) at temperatures in the range 30–80°C. The reaction is exothermic (ca. 22 kcal/mol[56]) and, as it proceeds, the polymer is precipitated. The polymerisation therefore is heterogeneous, a fact which modifies the characteristics of the reaction. Thus Bengough and Norrish[67] suggest that initiation occurs in the monomer phase but that chain transfer occurs with the precipitated polymer. A chain therefore could start to grow from the dead polymer. The mobility of such a growing chain is much reduced, the probability of chain termination occurring by collision with another radical is reduced and hence the rate of polymerisation increases. Confirmation of this comes from the fact that addition of polymer to the system increases the rate of reaction, presumably by supplying more possible points where chains may be started. This is in accordance with the rate of polymerisation curves measured by Jenkel et al.[68] (Fig. 12) who found that the rate increased up to about 50%

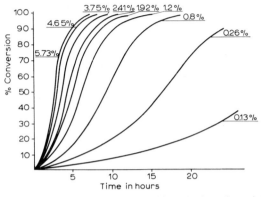

Fig. 12. Percentage conversion of vinyl chloride as a function of time at 50°C in the presence of different concentrations of dibenzoyl peroxide[68].

conversion and then decreased. An alternative explanation is that the precipitated polymer is in fact swollen and hence readily accessible to monomer. If polymerisation occurs in the swollen gel, again the termination reaction will be less probable and hence the rate will increase until the monomer supply begins to fail when it will decrease again[69]. In kinetic terms, it is possible to explain the rate of polymerisation in terms of the rate constants of the system by making that for the termination abnormally small[70]. The characteristics of bulk polymerisation are not shown if the reaction is carried out in a solvent in which the polymer is soluble i.e. there is no acceleration nor increased rate on addition of the polymer[71].

However, the polymerisation of vinyl chloride in bulk is not practicable since the heat liberated during the reaction would cause substantial temperature increases, giving rise to an uncontrolled reaction and possible decomposition of the polymer; moreover bulk polymerisation would give large masses of material which would not be easy to break down for further processing. These difficulties are avoided if the polymerisation is carried out using the monomer dispersed in an aqueous medium. The heat evolved during the polymerisation is dissipated in the large volume of water and the product obtained in a fine state of division. There are two methods available: (a) emulsion polymerisation and (b) granular or suspension polymerisation. At first sight, these two techniques are similar since the monomer is dispersed as discrete particles usually in water, a medium in which the monomer is not appreciably soluble. However, in emulsion polymerisation the emulsifying agent forms micelles which contain some monomer. The catalyst is usually a water soluble one. In suspension polymerisation, the monomer droplets are stabilized by a suitable additive and the catalyst is soluble in the monomer. For process (a), the monomer is dispersed in water which contains an emulsifying agent and a suitable free radical initiator (*e.g.* potassium persulphate alone or with an activator). Polymerisation is carried out at temperatures ranging from 30–80°C depending on the D.P. required; a dispersion or emulsion of particles of polymer commonly known as a latex is formed. The diameter of the latex particles falls in the range 0.01–0.3 μ and the latex usually has a concentration of 30–50% by weight.

In the earlier stages of the reaction, the system is considered to be made up of emulsifier micelles containing monomer and an aqueous dispersion of monomer droplets. The droplets are very much larger in size than the emulsifier micelles but the latter present a large interfacial area. The micelles because of their large area are able to capture most of the radicals generated in the aqueous phase. The polymerisation, once commenced in the micelle, must be supplied with monomer by either diffusion of monomer molecules from the droplets to the micelles via the aqueous phase[72] or diffusion of the growing radicals into the monomer droplets. The former hypothesis is adequate to account for the practical observations[73]. The polymerisation differs from the homogeneous one in that live chains are individually isolated in the micelles and hence the random collisions between the ends of growing chains normally occurring in a homogeneous polymerisation are restricted. This means that the termination step occurs less frequently and hence the overall reaction rates are faster.

In the above brief discussion, it has been assumed that the micelles are the sole centres of initiation; however, if the monomer has appreciable water solubility or the initiator any solubility in the monomer liquid, reaction may be started in the aqueous phase or in the droplets.

For suspension or granular polymerisation, the monomer is dispersed by vigorous agitation in water with a stabiliser which may be a hydrophilic colloid such as gelatin, starch etc.; these compounds hinder the monomer globules coalescing by modification of the interfacial tension[74]. The particle size of the droplets varies roughly from 0.1 to 5 mm. There is a danger in this kind of system that, as polymerisation proceeds and the droplets become viscous, they may adhere to each other; once this is avoided the final product is in the form of spherical beads. The stabiliser in this system does not affect significantly the reaction mechanism. Sus-

pension polymerisation can be regarded as a convenient way of carrying
out bulk polymerisations under conditions of ready dissipation of heat.
The initiator can be a free radical one which is soluble the in monomer
(*e.g.* dibenzoyl peroxide) and hence polymerisation occurs in the monomer
phase (not in the aqueous one as with the emulsion process). The polymerisation is carried out at temperatures ranging from 40--70°C, temperature being used to control the reaction. The size of the polymer
particle obtained by this technique depends of stabiliser employed as
well as on the degree of agitation. The particles may be separated from
the aqueous phase by filtration or centrifuging.

In the fibre field, copolymers of vinyl chloride are of considerable importance. Polymerisation of vinyl chloride can be carried out in the presence of a second monomer to give a product with some of the desirable
properties prepared from the monomers alone. Diagrammatically the
polymerisation of two monomers $CH_2=CHX$ and $CH_2=CHY$ gives a
product of formula (XXII)

$$-CH_2-CH-CH_2-CH-CH_2-CH-CH_2-CH-CH_2-CH-$$
$$\quad\quad\ \ X\quad\quad\quad\ \ X\quad\quad\quad\ \ Y\quad\quad\quad\ \ X\quad\quad\quad\ \ Y$$

(XXII)

The first synthetic fibres of this kind were made from vinyl chloride
copolymerised with a small amount of vinyl acetate. Polyvinyl chloride is
a hard tough water-white resin; polyvinyl acetate is a clear polymer
which is soluble in acetone but its softening point is low. The vinyl acetate
component was introduced for the reasons of solubility in acetone and
hence as an aid in transformation of the substance into fibre form.
Further it helps to plasticise. Vinyon HH was produced on a semi commercial scale in the U.S.A. in 1935 but such fibres suffered from a low softening point and a high shrinkage when placed in hot water. Nowadays
commercial fibres are made from vinyl chloride and acrylonitrile. The
two fibres "Dynel" and "Vinyon N" are chemically of this kind, the
former is marketed as staple fibre and the latter as continuous filament.
The fibres differ also in their modes of extrusion. At present the staple
fibre "Dynel" is successful whereas the continuous filament form has
been discontinued. The use of the second monomer to form a copolymer
enables the properties of the polymer to be modified. In this case the
fibre Vinyon N has a higher softening point than the earlier Vinyon HH.
A different technique adopted in Germany to obtain a polymer soluble in
acetone was to chlorinate polyvinyl chloride; the fibres produced from
this polymer were called PeCe. Polyvinyl chloride is capable of being

chlorinated to give a polymer with desirable solubility properties in solvents such as esters, ketones etc. Chlorination may be carried out in tetrachloroethane when the polymer is in solution, or as a suspension in chloroform; the reaction is exothermic. The product so made is suitable for conversion into fibres which have a high resistance to chemical attack. The low solubility of the parent polyvinyl chloride polymer in a solvent suitable for extrusion has been overcome in France by the use of a mixture of acetone and carbon disulphide. Fibre produced in this way is marketed under the name of Rhovyl. However it still suffers from a low softening point and contracts at temperatures greater than 78°C. It seems that the optimum fibre strength[75] is given if the D.P. is about 1,250–1,450.

Vinyon N is a fibre which is prepared from the copolymer of vinyl chloride with acrylonitrile, Saran a fibre made from a copolymer of vinyl chloride and vinylidene chloride, the latter component being present in the larger quantities. The copolymers are claimed to have a greater range of physical and mechanical properties, better heat stability and solubility in organic solvents.

6. Vinylidene Chloride

This material again goes back to the time of Regnault[76]. Later a white solid polymer was shown to be formed from it under the influence of light[77]. Commercially the material was not developed until the 1930's. The monomer (XXIII) can be prepared by removing hydrochloric acid from 1,1,2-trichloroethane

$$CH_2Cl—CHCl_2 \rightarrow CH_2{=}CCl_2$$
$$(XXIII)$$

or by direct chlorination of vinyl chloride followed by removal of hydrochloric acid by treatment with alkali. Vinylidene chloride boils at 31.7°C/760 mm and will readily polymerise on exposure to light or by free radical initiators. Polymerisation in bulk gives an insoluble polymer and the reaction when initiated by dibenzoyl peroxide[78] shows the same acceleration as vinyl chloride; in contrast, measurements of the rates of polymerisation initiated photochemically do not show increased rates[79]. However, this fact has been shown not to be an anomaly since accelerated rates are compensated in the photochemical case by an automatic reduction in initiation; this reduction arises from the fact that the insoluble polymer which is produced scatters light and hence reduces the effective intensity of illumination[80]. The polymer, which may be formed by emulsion or granular polymerisation, is a crystalline material with a high softening point and is insoluble in most solvents. Vinylidene chloride is usually used to form copolymers which are suitable for fibre formation.

With vinyl chloride as the second comonomer, the fibre Saran has been made; with vinyl chloride (13%) and acrylonitrile (2%), the Germans made the fibre Durit and the fibre P.C. 120 contains ethyl acrylate (7.5%).

7. Polyvinyl Acetate and Alcohol

Fibres may be made from polyvinyl acetate but the softening points are too low to make them interesting for this purpose. However polyvinyl acetate may be hydrolysed to the alcohol and treated with formaldehyde to give a polymer, developed as the fibre Vinylon. The raw materials for this fibre are cheap. Acetylene may be converted to acetic acid in the presence of water and oxygen; reaction with a further molecule of acetylene using zinc acetate as a catalyst gives vinyl acetate (XXIV)

$$C_2H_2 + H_2O + O \rightarrow CH_3COOH + C_2H_2 \rightarrow CH_3COOCH{=}CH_2$$
$$(XXIV)$$

Vinyl acetate may be polymerised using radical catalysts in methanol. The acetic acid groups are hydrolysed by addition of caustic soda to the methanol solution. Polyvinyl alcohol precipitates, is filtered off and dissolved in water. This aqueous solution is extruded into a bath containing sodium sulphate when fibres are produced and, since polyvinyl alcohol is soluble in water, these fibres are insolubilised by treatment with formaldehyde.

8. Polyacrylonitrile

Perhaps the monomer of overriding importance in the fibre field is acrylonitrile. Polyacrylonitrile, like many other polymers, has been known for a long time but, for making fibres, this material suffered from the defect of being insoluble in common solvents and unable to be extruded from a melt because softening occurs at temperatures approaching the decomposition point.

However, it was found that hydrotropic solvents such as concentrated solutions of calcium thiocyanate would dissolve polyacrylonitrile and polar organic solvents[81] (dimethylformamide and tetramethyl sulphone) were suitable. Since this time (1943) polyacrylonitrile and its copolymers have been manufactured in fibre form. Materials such as Orlon, Courtelle, Acrylan etc. are of this kind.

Acrylonitrile (XXVI) may be prepared from ethylene oxide by reaction with hydrocyanic acid to form the cyanohydrin (XXV) which in turn can be dehydrated,

$$\begin{matrix} CH_2 \\ | \quad \diagdown \\ \quad \quad O + HCN \rightarrow HOCH_2CH_2CN \rightarrow CH_2{=}CHCN \\ | \quad \diagup \\ CH_2 \quad \quad \quad (XXV) \quad \quad \quad (XXVI) \end{matrix}$$

An alternative method is direct addition of hydrocyanic acid to acetylene.

$$C_2H_2 + HCN \rightarrow CH_2 = CHCN$$

In the former case, the two reactants may be run into a vessel containing water and diethylamine and caustic soda as catalysts. After acidification and removal of the water, the cyanohydrin is dehydrated using magnesium carbonate. In the latter, acetylene and hydrocyanic acid are passed into an aqueous solution of cuprous chloride and ammonium chloride. A dilute solution of acrylonitrile is formed which can be concentrated while the unreacted materials are recirculated.

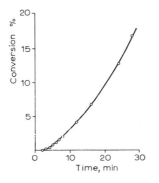

Fig. 13. Bulk polymerisation of acrylonitrile at 60°C using dibenzoyl peroxide (2.7×10^{-2} mole per cent)[112].

Polymerisation of acrylonitrile can be initiated by free radicals. The reaction is exothermic (17.3 kcal/mol) so that polymerisation in bulk is not feasible on a large scale. As with many polymerisations in bulk, the polymer is insoluble in the monomer and separates in an essentially unswollen condition. The reaction shows the features of other polymerisations where the polymer separates i.e. the rate of conversion increases over the initial period[82] up to about 20% conversion (Fig. 13). Polymerisation commences at a rate not dissimilar from that in a lower concentration. This auto-acceleration leads to an increase in the degree of polymerisation as compared with homogeneous systems but may be removed by addition of a small molecule capable of reaching and reacting with the terminal radical ends. n-Butyl mercaptan is such a substance and reacts as follows[80,99]

$$—CH_2\dot{C}HX + BuSH \rightarrow —CH_2CH_2X + Bu\dot{S}$$

The radicals produced by this reaction are small, capable of diffusing out of the solid polymer and hence are mutually annihilated,

$$Bu\dot{S} + Bu\dot{S} \rightarrow BuSSBu$$

Again the auto acceleration is removed if the polymerisation is carried out in N,N-dimethylformamide (Figs. 13 and 14). In this system it has been possible to show that polymer produced photochemically contains occluded radicals. Trapped radicals to the extent of 1–10% have been detected by reaction with N,N-diphenyl-N'-picrylhydrazyl (II)[82] and by

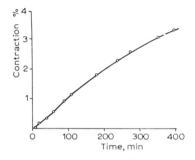

Fig. 14. Polymerisation of acrylonitrile in N,N-dimethylformamide solution at 60°C using dibenzoyl peroxide (2.7 × 10⁻² mole per cent on monomer). Concentration of monomer 2.88 mol/l (Contraction is proportional to conversion.)[112].

measurements of paramagnetic resonance[83]. It would seem therefore that, when the polymer precipitates, any radical ends occluded in the polymer will not be as accessible as in solution; this means that the termination reaction is reduced in speed whereas the propagation is not much affected since small monomer molecules will relatively easily reach the trapped radicals. Only in extreme cases would occlusion be expected to reduce the progagation reaction. However, the polymerisation is best carried out on a large scale in an aqueous medium, the polymer precipitating out in a fine granular form. The manufacture may be carried out by flowing into a vessel streams of the monomer and an aqueous solution of ammonium persulphate containing an activator such as sodium thiosulphate. In order that the rate of reaction may be reproducible, an amount of a promoter e.g. copper sulphate is added so as to overcome any adventitious impurities which may enter the system, thereby swamping any natural variations which may arise due to the presence of traces of heavy metal ions in the materials used. Buffers may be used to control the pH of the system since the action of the reduction activator with the persulphate depends on the acidity. The detailed conditions for the reaction e.g. temperature, pH etc. as well as the degree of conversion of monomer to polymer depends on the activator pair used. The D.P. of the polymer varies with the temperature of polymerisation as well as the nature of the initiator, increasing with activity of the initiator and with lowering of temperature. For solution spinning, a molecular weight in the range 35,000–50,000 is desirable.

The polymerisation of acrylonitrile is complicated by the possibility of transfer to the dead polymer leading to a branched polymer. For this reason, the reaction is not run at high degrees of conversion so that unused acrylonitrile must be recovered.

Acrylonitrile is often polymerised to give polymers for modern fibres in the presence of a comonomer. The polymer so formed may only contain a small amount of the second component but it is sufficient to modify the properties of the fibre. The modifications of considerable practical importance have been those designed to produce fibres which are readily dyeable since polyacrylonitrile itself is extremely difficult in this respect. Unfortunately, little definite knowledge is available as to the extent and nature of the second monomer, although vinyl acetate and vinylpyridine have been mentioned in the patent literature.

9. Polyvinylidene Dinitrile

This polymer is made from vinylidene dinitrile by free radical or anionic initiators to give a white infusible resin[84]. The copolymer with vinyl acetate has given a material suitable for fibres and marketed under the name "Darvan" (originally named Darlan[85]).

10. Tactic Polymers

Polymer molecules made from α-olefins (alk-1-enes of formula $CH_2=CHX$) will have structures of the type (XXVII)

$$-CH_2-\overset{*}{C}H-CH_2-\overset{*}{C}H-CH_2-\overset{*}{C}H-CH_2-$$
$$\qquad\quad | \qquad\qquad | \qquad\qquad |$$
$$\qquad\quad X \qquad\qquad X \qquad\qquad X$$

(XXVII)

From this structure, it will be deduced that the groups attached to the carbon atoms marked with the asterisks are capable of assuming two stereospecific configurations. Vinyl polymers are normally formed from the monomers using initiators which are free radicals or positive or negative ions. The products so made possess a random distribution along the chain of the two asymmetric types of carbon atoms. Diagrammatically the situation may be represented in Fig. 15a; such polymers are described as atactic.

In recent years, however, catalysts have been discovered which not only initiate growth of the chain but also exert a directing effect on the configuration of the atoms composing the chain. A regular arrangement of the substituent groups is possible as is indicated in Fig. 15b where all groups R are disposed in the same fashion. Such a polymer is defined as isotactic. A further possible variation of a regular arrangements is that where the groups R are disposed alternately along the chain in the two configurations. Such polymers are described as syndiotactic (Fig. 15c).

Of the many possible catalysts the one most described is that formed from titanic chloride and triethyl aluminium in heptane or aliphatic

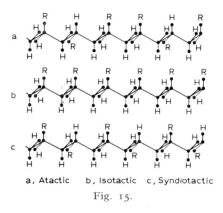

a, Atactic   b, Isotactic   c, Syndiotactic

Fig. 15.

hydrocarbon solvents. This catalyst was shown suitable for the preparation of low pressure polyethylene discussed earlier[62,86] and has been shown to give isotactic polyolefins[87].

The isotactic polymers are of considerable interest from the practical point of view since they have higher melting-points than the normal atactic materials as may be seen from Table 7. They are in general highly crystalline (see Chapter X).

TABLE 7

Monomer	Melting-point of polymer	
	Atactic	Isotactic
Styrene	85	230
But-1-ene	—42	120–130
Propene	—35	160–170

Isotactic polypropylene has attracted attention as a fibre; its properties are very good being comparable to those of the polyamides and polyesters. It is however degraded by light and is very difficult to dye. Both these defects have been overcome in some measure by additives or modifications of the fibre; there is also the added advantage that the raw material is particularly cheap. The mechanism of polymerisation[88] by these catalysts will not be discussed here. It must be added however that isotactic polymers may not be perfectly arranged and it may be that they contain long runs of stereospecific carbon atoms interspersed with atactic material. Such details of structure have not been thoroughly worked out.

11. Kinetics of Polymerisation

The kinetics of polymerisation of the various monomers vary considerably according to the chemical character of the monomers as well as the conditions of polymerisation. When polymerised in bulk, the polymer may precipitate hence producing conditions different from those of the homogeneous reaction. In emulsion polymerisation the reaction occurs in micelles supplied by the emulsifying agent. Reaction conditions may be such as to slow the rate of termination down and hence increase both the rate of reaction and molecular weight of the polymer. Polymerisation under these conditions is heterogeneous in character and it is not surprising that the system is more complicated than that under homogeneous conditions. Reaction kinetics of homogeneous systems, nevertheless, form the basis which can be extended to heterogeneous conditions.

Discussion of the kinetics will be confined to polymerisation initiated by free radicals and restricted owing to shortage of space to reactions in homogeneous solution. As previously discussed, there are three aspects to consider, initiation, propagation and termination.

(a) Initiation

The first step is the decomposition of the initiator, I, into two radicals $\dot{R}$.

$$I \rightarrow 2\dot{R}$$

If the reaction constant for this reaction may be written as k_i, the rate of production of radicals may be written as

$$\frac{d[\dot{R}]}{dt} = 2k_i[I] \tag{4}$$

The factor 2 is introduced to take care of the fact that the radicals must be produced in pairs. The radical $\dot{R}$ is able to initiate the reaction chain

$$\dot{R} + M \rightarrow \dot{M}_1 \tag{5}$$

where M refers to the monomer and $\dot{M}_1$ to the first member of the propagation chain. The rate of initiation v_i i.e. of formation of chain radicals can be written in the form

$$v_i = \frac{d[\dot{M}]}{dt} = 2fk_i[I] \tag{6}$$

where f is a factor which represents the fraction of primary radicals, $\dot{R}$, which initiate chains. This is tantamount to saying that the reaction 5 is fast for, if it is not, the factor f will be dependent on the monomer concentration. However, a large fraction of the primary radicals may react with the other molecules in the system to give an inactive product *e.g.*

$$\dot{R} + S \rightarrow \dot{S} \text{ (inactive)}$$

Such a reaction will make f less than unity. Another possibility is that the radicals which are formed in pairs can recombine before they escape from one another[89]. This "cage" effect is a first order combination and will make f less than unity and a function of monomer concentration.

It is possible, in a case such as the polymerisation of acrylonitrile with redox catalysts[24], to show that the radical concentration is maintained constant when the rate determining step must be taken as reaction 5 giving the velocity of initiation as

$$v_i = \frac{d[\dot{M}]}{dt} = k_i [\dot{R}][M] \tag{7}$$

This state of affairs corresponds to the factor f being linearly dependent on the monomer concentration.

The initiator efficiency, f, may in some instances be determined by comparison of the amount of initiator decomposed with the number of initiator fragments which start the polymer chains. The number of initiator fragments has been determined by Evans[20] for styrene polymerised by OH radicals or by using a catalyst which contains a radioactive atom. Azobisisobutyronitrile labelled with ^{14}C has been used[90]. Efficiencies ranging from 0.6–1.0 were found for methyl methacrylate, vinyl acetate, styrene, vinyl chloride and acrylonitrile.

A second method is to determine the number average molecular weight of the polymer and hence calculate the number of molecules formed. If the reaction involves no transfer and termination is by coupling of radicals, the number of combined primary radicals is twice the number of molecules. This method, although dependent on a knowledge of the reaction mechanism, has given results in agreement with other observations for styrene initiated by dibenzoyl peroxide[31,32].

A third method is to use inhibitors. These substances in some instances have been shown to react stoichiometrically with the chain radicals giving products of very short chain lengths[91], one molecule of inhibitor being used per chain initiated. Thus in the inhibition period, the number of chains started is assumed to be equivalent to the number of inhibitor molecules used; and hence from the knowledge of the rate of decomposition, the efficiency may be calculated. It is assumed in this argument that the chain radicals which react with the inhibitor are not the primary ones. This is likely since the monomer molecules are in such excess[92]. This technique has been adopted using the stable free radical, 2,2-diphenyl-1-picrylhydrazyl (I) in the polymerisation of vinyl acetate and styrene[93].

Initiation of polymerisation by irradiation of the monomer solution must be mentioned. Absorption of light by a monomer molecule will give rise to a radical of some kind and may be written formally as

$$M + h\nu \rightarrow \dot{M}$$

The rate of production of the radicals will be dependent on the amount of light energy absorbed; the quantum yield now corresponds to the efficiency f. If irradiation of intensity I_0 passes through the solution of thickness x with concentration of monomer $[M]$, the energy absorbed is given according to the Beer/Lambert law by $I_0 (1 - e^{-\varepsilon(M)x})$ where ε is the extinction coefficient. The rate of radical production will be

$$\frac{d[\dot{M}]}{dt} = 2fI_0(1 - e^{-\varepsilon(M)x}) \sim 2fI_0\varepsilon x[M] \tag{8}$$

Initiation in such a system is thus dependent on the monomer concentration.

Another method is to put into the system a photochemical initiator which releases free radicals at a wavelength where the monomer is unaffected. Such a substance may be benzoin or azobisisobutyronitrile which are decomposed to free radicals on irradiation with light from a mercury arc in the region of 3600 Å. In this instance the velocity of initiation will be dependent on the intensity, the absorption of light by the initiator and the concentration of initiator. The reaction may be represented as

$$I + h\nu \rightarrow 2\dot{R}$$
$$\dot{R} + M \rightarrow \dot{M}$$

Photochemical techniques may be carried out at low temperatures when thermal polymerisation is absent and moreover have the advantage for fundamental studies that the production of radicals may be instantaneously controlled by variations of light intensity.

(b) Propagation

The reaction of the monomer molecules with the reactive centres at the end of the chains may be written as

$$\dot{M}_1 + M \rightarrow \dot{M}_2$$
$$\dot{M}_2 + M \rightarrow \dot{M}_3$$
$$\dot{M}_3 + M \rightarrow \dot{M}_4$$
$$\cdot$$
$$\cdot$$
$$\cdot$$
$$\dot{M}_n + M \rightarrow \dot{M}_{n+1}$$

where $\dot{M}_n$ refers to a chain radical containing n units.

Each of these steps could be described by means of the rate of loss of monomer

$$\left(\frac{\mathrm{d}\,[M]}{\mathrm{d}t}\right)_1 = -k_1[\dot{M}_1][M]$$

$$\left(\frac{\mathrm{d}\,[M]}{\mathrm{d}t}\right)_2 = -k_2[\dot{M}_2][M]$$

$$\vdots \text{ etc.}$$

where $\{(\mathrm{d}[M])/\mathrm{d}t\}_n$ refers to the monomer concentration change due to reaction of $\dot{M}_n$ with monomer. The overall rate of change of monomer concentration is measurable in practice and these equations can be added up to give the velocity of propagation, v_p

$$v_p = \frac{\mathrm{d}\,[M]}{\mathrm{d}t} = -[M]\,\{k_1[\dot{M}_1] + k_2[\dot{M}_2]\ldots\} \tag{9}$$

The loss of monomer is a measure of the rate of polymerisation or the velocity of polymerisation. However the question must be asked as to whether the reactivity of the growing chain is modified as the chain grows[94,28]. Decrease in reactivity may however arise for steric reasons[95]; in other words, although the radical ends are unchanged in reactivity, the probability of their coming to a position suitable for reaction may be reduced. To compensate however for this, the longer chain will experience more collisions with other molecules than a shorter one. Before two reactants can react, they must diffuse towards each other and, when close enough, they will be in equilibrium with an activated complex on the concentration of which depends the rate of reaction. In the reaction under consideration, they react to form a single molecule so that only the diffusion and reaction steps need be considered. When a small molecule and a large molecule are considered, the rate of meeting of the two will depend mainly on the speed of diffusion of the smaller one so that it would seem that the polymerisation rate would depend on the movement of the monomer molecule. However, a polymer molecule is made up of many segments each capable of independent motion so that the movement of the active head of the chain is very much greater than that of a rigid molecule. The mobility of the radical end may not in fact be very much less than that of a small radical. It seems therefore that the process controlling the rate is the opening of the double bond of the monomer. This means that there is almost no effect of molecular weight on the rate of growth of the polymer chain.

The kinetic treatment may be rendered possible if it is assumed that the reaction constants are identical *i.e.* $k_1 = k_2 \ldots = k_n = k_p$, the propagation constant. Equation 9 then becomes

$$\frac{\mathrm{d}[M]}{\mathrm{d}t} = -k_p[M]\{[\dot{M}_1] + [\dot{M}_2] + [\dot{M}_3]\ldots\} \qquad (10)$$

The quantity in the braces is the total concentration of the radicals taking place in the reaction and may simply be written as $\dot{M}$. Equation 10 then becomes

$$\frac{\mathrm{d}[M]}{\mathrm{d}t} = -k_p[M][\dot{M}] \qquad (11)$$

(c) Termination

On the assumption that the termination of the reaction is the union of two radical ends to annihilate both, the equation can be written

$$\dot{M}_n + \dot{M}_m \rightarrow M_{n+m}$$

and the loss in radicals is

$$\frac{\mathrm{d}[\dot{M}]}{\mathrm{d}t} = -2k_{mn}[\dot{M}_n][\dot{M}_m] \qquad (12)$$

where k_{mn} is the termination constant.

Again a kinetic scheme in which each coupling reaction has a different constant would be impossible of solution. The reaction between two radicals is fast; the rate will be determined by the number of times per second that the reactive heads are in the correct position. It is difficult to calculate the rate at which small radicals collide in a liquid and any calculation with a polymer radical will be further complicated by the fact that each segment of the polymer chain is capable of free rotation around the single bonds comprising the backbone of the polymer. This means that the mobility of the radical head will be much larger than for a rigid molecule and the mobility may not be much less than that of a small radical. Thus the rate of termination may be taken to be independent of molecular weight and equation 12 may be written in terms of a single termination constant, k_t, as

$$\frac{\mathrm{d}[\dot{M}]}{\mathrm{d}t} = -2k_t[\dot{M}]^2 \qquad (13)$$

This step would seem justified on the basis of the fit of the overall kinetics to the data.

However, the rate at which the growing chain ends collide need not under all conditions be independent of molecular weight. Since the diffusion of large radicals may be slow, it is to be expected that a point may be reached when the termination step is diffusion controlled. A reduction in the rate of the termination step would give more time for the radicals to grow and hence give a product of higher molecular weight. Since the diffusion coefficient is inversely proportional to the viscosity, the effect is to be expected in polymerisations in bulk when a considerable quantity of monomer has been converted and the reaction mass has become very viscous. This is referred to as the gel effect. An alternative way of causing the reaction to be diffusion controlled is to reduce the mobility of the active head by causing the growing molecule to coil itself up[69],[96]. This shields the radical end and may be done by carrying the reaction out in the presence of a precipitant such as methanol. When the rate of termination is reduced the overall rate of polymerisation is consequently increased. It should be noted that the termination step differs from the propagation one since both reacting species are large molecules. With the propagation reaction, the supply of monomer units is governed by the diffusion of small molecules even if the movement of the large one is restricted.

(d) Steady State

Consider a polymerisation initiated by irradiation so that the formation of radicals occurs at a constant rate v_i. When the light is switched on, the radicals formed will combine with monomer and, as the live polymer molecules increase in concentration, so will their rate of destruction. A stage will be reached when the rate of production of radicals is approximately equal to their rate of destruction. Under such conditions, the concentration of radicals and the rate of reaction vary very little with time except for effects produced by changes in the concentrations of reactants. The rate of change of radical concentration is given by the difference between their rate of formation and their rate of destruction

$$\frac{d[\dot{M}]}{dt} = v_i - 2k_t[\dot{M}]^2 \tag{14}$$

Since v_i is constant, equation 14 may be integrated to give

$$[\dot{M}] = \left(\frac{v_i}{2k_t}\right)^{\frac{1}{2}} \text{Tanh}(2k_t v_i)^{\frac{1}{2}} t \tag{15}$$

provided that $[\dot{M}] = 0$ when $t = 0$.

Now Tanh x is a function which increases rapidly from zero and approaches unity asymptotically. When t approaches infinity $[\dot{M}]$ approaches a maximum value $[\dot{M}]_s$. In practice then, the radical concentration rapidly approximates to the value $[\dot{M}]_s$ and approaches within 1%

of this value when $(2k_t v_i)^{\frac{1}{2}} t$ is $\geqslant 3$. When this situation is reached, the concentration of $\dot{M}$ does not substantially change and the system may be described as being in the "steady state". The steady state principle was first enunciated by Bodenstein[97] and says that a reaction involving a transient species is characterised by rates of formation and disappearance of this species which are equal. The previous discussion would indicate that this is an approximation but one which has been amply justified by the consistency of the results obtained. The condition for this stationary state is $d[\dot{M}]/dt = 0$ and hence from equation 14

$$[\dot{M}]_s = \left(\frac{v_i}{2k_t}\right)^{\frac{1}{2}} \tag{16}$$

In accepting the stationary state principle, the rate of destruction of radicals should be fast.

The rate of radical decay can be determined by stopping the initiation, when v_i now equals zero, and equation 14 becomes

$$\frac{d[\dot{M}]}{dt} = -2k_t[\dot{M}]^2 \tag{17}$$

This equation integrates to

$$2k_t t = \frac{1}{[\dot{M}]} - \frac{1}{[\dot{M}]_0} \tag{18}$$

where $[\dot{M}]_0$ is the radical concentration at the time when v_i became zero and equals $[\dot{M}]_s$ if the stationary concentration had been attained prior to shutting off the light. A knowledge of k_t again shows that the change of $[\dot{M}]$ is rapid. Thus in this system the radical concentration is rapidly built up and will decay rapidly when the source of initiating radicals is removed.

It can further be shown that the steady state concentrations of the individual radicals will be constant[98]. The rate of change of the concentration of the radical $\dot{M}_n$ is given by

$$\frac{d[\dot{M}_n]}{dt} = k_p[\dot{M}_{n-1}][M] - k_p[\dot{M}_n][M] - k_t[\dot{M}_n] \sum [\dot{M}_m] \tag{19}$$

Equation 19 may be equated to 0 for all values of n. A more complete discussion of the steady state is given elsewhere[99].

When this steady state is reached the concentration of radicals in the system is given by equation 16. Substituting this into equation 11 and using the value of v_i for the radical initiated polymerisation, the rate of polymerisation becomes

$$\frac{d[M]}{dt} = -\frac{f^{\frac{1}{2}} k_i^{\frac{1}{2}}}{k_t^{\frac{1}{2}}} k_p[I]^{\frac{1}{2}} [M] \tag{20}$$

This equation shows the interesting point that the rate of build up of polymer (or loss of monomer) is first order with respect to the monomer concentration but only of half order with respect to the concentration of initiator.

When studying the polymerisation kinetics, it is usual to measure the propagation rate $d[M]/dt$ over the first stages of the reaction where it is possible to regard $[I]$ and $[M]$ as constant. By confining attention to analysis of values of $d[M]/dt$ and their relation with conditions, a large amount of information may be obtained on polymerisation mechanisms without recourse to the very much larger problem of deducing the relation between $[M]$ and t as is done in much kinetic work.

The dependence of the rate of polymerisation on initiator and monomer concentration has been shown experimentally to be followed in numerous monomer/initiator systems. Typical examples are the polymerisations of methyl methacrylate using azobisisobutyronitrile[100], and dibenzoyl peroxide[101], styrene with dibenzoyl peroxide[102] and azobisisobutyroni-

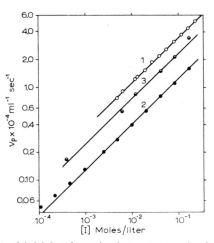

Fig. 16. Log-log plot of initial polymerisation rates v_p (moles l^{-1} sec^{-1}) against initiator concentration (moles l^{-1}). 1. Methyl methacrylate using azobisbutyronitrile at 50°C[100]. 2. Styrene with dibenzoyl peroxide at 60°C[102]. 3. Methyl methacrylate with dibenzoyl peroxide at 50°C[101].

trile[31]. An example of the results is given in Fig. 16; an alternative way of expressing the data is to calculate the ratio

$$\frac{d[M]}{dt}\bigg/[I]^{\frac{1}{2}}[M]$$

Both the straight lines in Fig. 16 and the constancy of the ratio confirm the validity of equation 20.

In the case of photochemical initiation, the rate of initiation is given by $2f\varepsilon x I_0 [M]$ whence the rate of polymerisation will be

$$v_p - \frac{d[M]}{dt} = -k_p(f\varepsilon x I_0)^{\frac{1}{2}}[M]^{\frac{3}{2}} \tag{21}$$

i.e. proportional to the square root of the intensity of illumination. This has been shown to hold for methyl methacrylate[103] and vinyl acetate[28].

However, although a large number of systems obey this kinetic scheme, it does depend on the initiation reaction being independent of monomer concentration. These kinetics are therefore most likely to be followed when the initiator efficiency is high. If f be considerably < 1 and hence possibly dependent on $[M]$, the first order kinetics may change to a dependence on monomer concentration of greater than 1. For the important case of the polymerisation of acrylonitrile in aqueous media using for example ammonium persulphate as a catalyst, it has been shown that the supply of free radicals $\dot{R}$ arising from the decomposition of the initiator is approximately constant during the polymerisation[22]. This suggests that the reaction of the primary radical with monomer is a rate controlling one. The kinetics of the initiation will be given by

$$\frac{d[\dot{M}]}{dt} = k_i[\dot{R}][M]$$

Applying the steady state theory to this system gives a rate of polymerisation

$$v_p = \frac{d[M]}{dt} = -k_p\left(\frac{k_i}{k_t}\right)^{\frac{1}{2}}[\dot{R}]^{\frac{1}{2}}[M]^{\frac{3}{2}} \tag{22}$$

Since $\dot{R}$ is a constant, equation 22 may be integrated to give

$$\frac{1}{[M]^{\frac{1}{2}}} - \frac{1}{[M]_0^{\frac{1}{2}}} = k_p\left(\frac{k_i}{k_t}\right)^{\frac{1}{2}}[\dot{R}]^{\frac{1}{2}}t \tag{23}$$

where $[M] = [M]_0$ when $t = 0$.

The reciprocal of the (monomer concentration)$^{\frac{1}{2}}$ *vs.* t is a straight line.

As has been mentioned this kind of system is conducive to the use of the redox initiators. This may be exemplified by the persulphate/thiosulphate system. The reaction may be written as

$$S_2O_8{}^{--} + S_2O_3{}^{--} \xrightarrow{k_1} SO_4{}^{--} + \dot{S}O_4{}^{--} + \tfrac{1}{2}S_4O_6{}^{--}$$

$$\dot{S}O_4{}^{--} + S_2O_3{}^{--} \xrightarrow{k_2} SO_4{}^{--} + \tfrac{1}{2}S_4O_6{}^{--}$$

References p. 116

The free radical $\dot{S}O_4{}^{--}$ or the hydroxyl obtained from reaction of the latter with water is responsible for initiation

$$H_2O + \dot{S}O_4{}^{--} \rightarrow \dot{O}H + SO_4{}^{--} + H^+$$

In the first equation $\dot{S}O_4{}^{--}$ radicals are produced and lost by the second and by initiation of radical chains either directly or via the hydroxyl radicals. Confining attention to the radical $\dot{S}O_4{}^{--}$ the rate of production of this radical is $k_1 [S_2O_8{}^{--}][S_2O_3{}^{--}]$ and its rate of loss

$$\{k_2[S_2O_3{}^{--}][\dot{S}O_4{}^{--}] + k_i[\dot{S}O_4{}^{--}][M]\}$$

These may be equated to find the stationary concentration of $\dot{S}O_4{}^{--}$ radicals

$$[\dot{S}O_4{}^{--}] = \frac{k_1[S_2O_8{}^{--}][S_2O_3{}^{--}]}{k_2[S_2O_3{}^{--}] + k_i[M]} \sim \frac{k_1}{k_2}[S_2O_8{}^{--}] \tag{24}$$

Since most of the free radicals are destroyed by reaction with the thiosulphate the quantity $k_i[M]$ may be ignored. The concentration of $[\dot{S}O_4{}^{--}]$ may be substituted in equation 20 in place of $f\,k_i[I]$ to give

$$-\frac{d[M]}{dt} = k_p\left(\frac{k_1 k_i[S_2O_8{}^{--}]}{k_t k_2}\right)^{\frac{1}{2}}[M]^{\frac{3}{2}} \tag{25}$$

The rate is independent of thiosulphate concentrations but is dependent on the persulphate and will fall as the persulphate is used.

When there is a promotor present e.g. Cu^{++} ions[56] the kinetics are modified and the polymerisation rates depend on the promotor concentration.

(e) Degree of Polymerisation

The equations discussed above enable a picture of the rate of usage of the monomer to be described in terms of three constants. They say nothing explicit about the very important question of the length of the chain produced in the polymerisation. One way of looking at this question is to ask how many units of monomer are used (on average) for every radical which starts a chain. This quantity will be given by the ratio of the rate at which the monomer is used up to the rate at which the chains are started and is called the kinetic chain length, usually written as ν, i.e.

$$\nu = \frac{\nu_{prop}}{\nu_{init}}$$

At the steady state the velocity of initiation is identical to that of termination so that

$$\nu = \frac{\nu_{prop}}{\nu_{term}}$$

Substituting the values from equations 11 and 13 gives

$$v = \frac{k_p[M][\dot{M}]}{2k_t[\dot{M}]^2} = \frac{k_p}{2k_t}\frac{[M]}{[\dot{M}]} \tag{26}$$

Since it is the steady state which is considered, the radical concentration may be eliminated by equations 6 and 16 to give

$$v = \frac{k_p}{2(fk_ik_t)^{\frac{1}{2}}}\frac{[M]}{[I]^{\frac{1}{2}}} \tag{27}$$

Or in terms of the rate of propagation (equation 20) to give

$$v = \frac{k_p^2}{2k_t}\frac{[M]^2}{v_p} \tag{28}$$

The kinetic chain length is therefore calculable from a knowledge of the constants and initiator and monomer concentrations. Moreover, the average degree of polymerisation P_n is equal to the rate of polymerisation/ rate of termination of radicals and hence the kinetic chain length is related to P_n by $P_n = 2v$. From equation 28 if the D.P. were plotted against the polymerisation rate v_p for constant monomer concentration, a

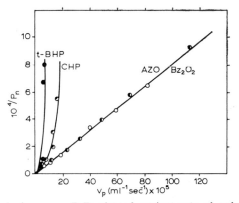

Fig. 17. Reciprocal of average D.P. plotted against rate of polymerisation v_p at 60°C for undiluted methyl methacrylate using azobisisobutyronitrile (AZO), diben-zoyl peroxide (Bz₂O₂), cumene hydroperoxide (CHP) and t-butyl hydroperoxide (t–BHP)[32].

straight line should result. The results for methyl methacrylate are shown in Fig. 17 and found to be satisfactorily in agreement with this theory for some initiators and not others. More generally $P_n < 2v$. A reduction in D.P. from that calculated may arise if the termination step is one of disproportionation *i.e.*

$$-CH_2-\dot{C}HX + \dot{C}HX-CH_2- \xrightarrow{k_d} -CH_2CH_2X + CHX{=}CH-$$

In this reaction, one radical abstracts a hydrogen atom from the other giving one molecule with a saturated and another with an unsaturated terminal group. This mode of chain termination is difficult to detect since the group which might be characteristic *i.e.* the unsaturated one is present in the polymer in too small a quantity. Disproportionation however does reduce the D.P. as compared with mutual termination. If all radicals were terminated by this method, two molecules will be produced at every reaction so that the D.P. will be equal to the kinetic chain length *i.e.* $P_n = \nu$. Thus, depending on the proportion of mutual termination to disproportionation, P_n lies between ν and 2ν. Chain termination by disproportionation does not alter the kinetics since the reaction may be written as

$$\dot{M}_n + \dot{M}_m \xrightarrow{k_d} M_n + M_m$$

This process is essentially a bimolecular one *i.e.*

$$-\frac{d[\dot{M}]}{dt} = 2k_d[\dot{M}]^2 \tag{29}$$

assuming k_d to be independent of the size of the molecules.

(f) Transfer Reactions

It has been assumed that, when a growing radical collides with a monomer, propagation occurs. This may not necessarily always happen; a hydrogen atom may be transferred to a monomer molecule ending one chain and producing a radical which will initiate another.

$$-CH_2-\dot{C}HX + CH_2{=}CHX \rightarrow -CH{=}CHX + CH_3\dot{C}HX$$

When polymerisation is carried out in a solvent, transfer of an atom from the solvent to the growing radical may occur. Again the radical may react with the initiator thereby finishing one chain and starting another. These reactions may be written as

$$\dot{M}_n + M \xrightarrow{k_{tr_M}} M_n + \dot{M} \quad \text{transfer to monomer}$$

$$\dot{M}_n + S \xrightarrow{k_{tr_S}} M_n + \dot{S} \quad \text{transfer to solvent}$$

$$\dot{M}_n + I \xrightarrow{k_{tr_I}} M_n + \dot{I} \quad \text{transfer to initiator}$$

Any of these reactions will have the effect of increasing the number of molecules and hence decreasing the D.P. None of them alter the number of radicals in the system provided the radicals formed in these reactions set new chains going. The rate of polymerisation is therefore unchanged.

Termination reactions of the type

$$\dot{S} + \dot{M}_n \rightarrow M_n S$$

$$\dot{S} + \dot{S} \rightarrow S_2$$

are considered to play little part and are ignored in this discussion. Nevertheless each transfer reaction will terminate a chain so that, for the purpose of calculating the rate of chain termination, each is making its contribution. The average degree of polymerisation P_n is given by the ratio

$$\frac{\text{rate of growth}}{\text{rates of termination by all processes}}$$

$$P_n = \frac{k_p[M][\dot{M}]}{k_t[\dot{M}]^2 + k_{tr_M}[M][\dot{M}] + k_{tr_S}[\dot{M}][S] + k_{tr_I}[\dot{M}][I]} \tag{30}$$

where $[\dot{M}]$ is the concentration of all the radicals. No allowance has been made in the above equation for transfer to polymer and, in the discussion, this is assumed absent as it leads to modification of a chain molecule rather than an increase in the number of molecules. The most important of these transfer processes is that to solvent. If all others are ignored equation 30 may be written as

$$\frac{1}{P_n} = \frac{k_t[\dot{M}]}{k_p[M]} + \frac{k_{tr_S}[S]}{k_p[M]} \tag{31}$$

To use this equation in a simple fashion, the first term on the right-hand side may be maintained constant provided $[I]^{\frac{1}{2}}/[M]$ is kept constant. Under these conditions 1/D.P. may be plotted against $[S]/[M]$ to give a straight line of slope k_{tr_S}/k_p. The case of thermal initiation is specially useful in this connection. Thermal initiation is bimolecular

$$M + M \rightarrow M^* + M$$

giving for the rate of production of radicals (hot molecules)

$$\frac{d[M^*]}{dt} = k[M]^2$$

and hence in the steady state the concentration of activated molecules will be given by

$$[M^*] = \frac{k}{k_t} [M]$$

If this value replaces $[\dot{M}]$ in equation 31 the first term of the right-hand side becomes constant independent of monomer concentration. Equation 31 for this case may be written as

$$\frac{1}{P_n} = \frac{1}{P_0} + \frac{k_{tr_S} [S]}{k_p [M]} \qquad (32)$$

where P_0 is the D.P. in the absence of a transfer reagent. Equation 32 is suitable for the determination of the transfer constant k_{tr_S}/k_p.

An alternative method for determination is to measure the change of solvent and monomer concentrations.

Monomer is used by the propagation reaction and by the reaction of the solvent radical $\dot{S}$. The reactions are

$$\dot{M}_n + M \rightarrow \dot{M}_{n+1}$$

$$\dot{S} + M \rightarrow \dot{M} + S$$

The loss of solvent is due to

$$\dot{M}_n + S \rightarrow M_n + \dot{S}$$

Hence

$$-\frac{d[M]}{dt} = k_p[M][\dot{M}] + k_s[M][\dot{S}]$$

and

$$-\frac{d[S]}{dt} = k_{tr_S}[S][\dot{M}]$$

But in such a system there will be a stationary concentration of solvent radicals hence

$$k_s[M][\dot{S}] = k_{tr_S}[\dot{M}][S]$$

Thus

$$\frac{d[M]}{dt} \bigg/ \frac{d[S]}{dt} = \frac{k_p[M][\dot{M}] + k_{tr_S}[S][\dot{M}]}{k_{tr_S}[S][\dot{M}]} = \frac{k_p}{k_{tr_S}} \frac{[M]}{[S]} + 1 \qquad (33)$$

Measurements of the change of concentrations of monomer and solvent have been used to determine the constant k_{tr_S}/k_p[109].

The plot of equation 32 has been carried out using data for the polymerisation of styrene. The results are given in Fig. 18[104]. This shows the possibility of producing a polymer of controlled molecular weight according to the ratio of $[S]/[M]$ chosen. The effect of solvent transfer on the rate of polymerisation is small[104,105], in most cases indicating that transfer reactions to solvents start new chains.

The effectiveness with which the radicals attack the solvent molecules will be related to the strength of bond which is broken as well as the

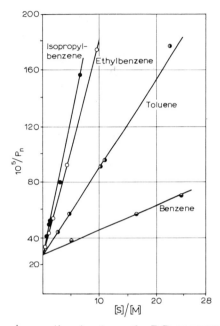

Fig. 18. Effects of aromatic solvents on the D.P. of styrene at 100°C[104].

TABLE 8

Radical	Solvent	Temperature	$k_{tr_S}/k_p \times 10^5$
Polystyrene[110]	Benzene	60°	0.18
	Toluene	60°	1.25
	Ethylbenzene	60°	6.7
	Diphenylmethane	60°	23
	n-Butyl chloride	60°	0.4
	Methylene chloride	60°	1.5
	Benzyl chloride	60°	15.6
	Carbon tetrachloride	60°	920
	Carbon tetrabromide	60°	136,000
Polymethylethacrylate[111]	Benzene	80°	0.75
	Toluene	80°	5.25
	Ethylbenzene	80°	13.5
	Butyl chloride	80°	12.0
	Carbon tetrachloride	80°	23.9

References p. 116

reactivity of the radical. Using the same radical and a variety of solvents, the transfer reactions may be regarded as a measure of the bond strengths in the solvent. Solvents differ markedly in this respect to different radicals[106]; some transfer constants are given in Table 8 where a wide range of reactivity is shown.

(g) Effect of Temperature

When making polymers, one of the most important properties requiring control is the degree of polymerisation. Some aspects of the D.P. in relation to the reaction constants have already been discussed and also how this property depended on transfer reaction. However reaction constants are temperature dependent; it is to be expected that changes of temperature will modify their values and bring about a change in the D.P. In general an increase in temperature will reduce the length of the chain as is shown below.

The changes in rate constants with temperature are given by the Arrhenius equation

$$k = Ae^{-E/RT} \tag{34}$$

where A = the collision frequency factor
E = the energy of activation
T = the absolute temperature
R = the gas constant.

The equation for the D.P. is

$$P_n = \frac{k_p{}^2}{k_t} \frac{[M]^2}{v_p} = \frac{k_p}{k_t{}^{\frac{1}{2}} k_i{}^{\frac{1}{2}} f^{\frac{1}{2}}} \frac{[M]}{[I]^{\frac{1}{2}}} \tag{35}$$

From equations 20 and 35 the value of $k_p/k_t{}^{\frac{1}{2}}$ may be obtained. Both these constants obey equation 34 so that, in terms of the activation energies for the propagation and termination reactions (E_p and E_t), the relationship of this quantity with temperature may be written as

$$\frac{k_p}{k_t{}^{\frac{1}{2}}} = \frac{A_p}{A_t{}^{\frac{1}{2}}} \exp - \frac{(E_p - \dfrac{E_t}{2})}{RT} \tag{36}$$

Thus a plot of log $k_p/k_t{}^{\frac{1}{2}}$ against $1/T$ gives the values of ($E_p - E_t/2$) and this latter turns out to be 5–6 kcal/mol which corresponds to an increase in $k_p/k_t{}^{\frac{1}{2}}$ of around 30–35% for a temperature rise of 10°C. Photochemical polymerisations, having initiation reactions which are independent of temperature, have a temperature dependence which is determined by the changes in k_p and k_t.

The situation is different for the radical initiated reactions. In this system the reaction velocity is determined by $(k_i/k_t)^{\frac{1}{2}} k_p$ and hence the activation energy is

$$\frac{E_i}{2} + E_p - \frac{E_t}{2}$$

where E_i is the activation energy for the decomposition of the initiator. The value of E_i for dibenzoyl peroxide is of the order of 30 kcal; translated to polymerisation rates, this means that a 10°C temperature rise will increase the reaction rates by roughly a factor of 2–3.

The D.P. is given by equation 35; substituting into this equation, the D.P. may be written in terms of activation energies

$$P_n = \frac{A_p}{(A_i A_t f)^{\frac{1}{2}}} \frac{[M]}{[I]^{\frac{1}{2}}} \exp - \frac{[E_p - \frac{E_i + E_t}{2}]}{RT} \tag{37}$$

so that the changes in D.P. are dependent on the value of $E_p - (E_i + E_t)/2$. This quantity is negative so that increases in temperature are accompanied by decreases in D.P.

Moreover, some polymers can decompose by a stepwise loss of monomer units provided the temperature is high enough; this reaction is the reverse of polymerisation. Depolymerisation is normally very slow at room temperatures so may be ignored but, since the activation energy is high, the importance of the depolymerisation increases at a rate faster than that of polymerisation. A temperature (the ceiling temperature) may be reached at which the two rates are equal. Above this temperature the polymer free radicals depolymerise instead of increasing in size.

(h) Determination of the Rate Constants

In the discussion no mention has been made of the values of the constants in the equations. For a system with initiation, propagation and mutual termination, equations 20 and 35 may be used to obtain a knowledge of the initiation rate k_i but not k_p and k_t separately since both equations are dependent on $k_p/k_t^{\frac{1}{2}}$. Although for any reaction numerical values of this ratio may be assigned, a further measurement is necessary to obtain the reaction constants themselves. One able to meet this need is the average life time τ of the active centre *i.e.* the period over which the radical exists from initiation to annihilation. The value of τ will be equal to the concentration of radicals divided by the rate of destruction *i.e.*

$$\tau = \frac{[\dot{M}]}{2k_t[\dot{M}]^2} = \frac{1}{2k_t[\dot{M}]} = \frac{k_p}{2k_t} \frac{[M]}{v_p} \quad \text{at the steady state} \tag{38}$$

τ is the time during which the radical concentration $[\dot{M}]$ disappears so that $v_i\tau = [\dot{M}]$. Since τ is the average lifetime of the kinetic chain, during time τ each radical consumes v monomer molecules. Hence v is related to τ

$$v = -\frac{\tau}{[\dot{M}]}\frac{d[M]}{dt} \tag{39}$$

τ itself is a quantity which must be deduced from a knowledge of $[\dot{M}]$ and is not directly measurable. Direct measurements of the concentration of radicals by techniques such as paramagnetic resonance are unfortunately not practical as yet and, since the concentrations involved are extremely small, $[\dot{M}]$ must be deduced from sector disc techniques described below.

Thus the three measurements would give k_i, and $k_p/k_t^{\frac{1}{2}}$ and k_p/k_t; hence the individual rate constants could be calculated. The method most amenable to the determination of τ is photochemical; irradiation of monomer systems has the advantage that, during a period of illumination, radicals are being created and their creation can be controlled at will.

Consider now a monomer contained in a vessel and irradiated by a lamp. On illumination radicals are produced which initiate chains which in turn are annihilated. The number of these radicals will grow until the steady state is reached when their concentration will remain constant. The rate of production of radicals is given by equation 14 which, combined with equation 8 for a photochemically initiated polymerisation, gives

$$\frac{d[\dot{M}]}{dt} = 2fI_0\varepsilon x[M] - 2k_t[\dot{M}]^2 \tag{40}$$

The intensity term may be removed by expressing equation 40 in terms of the steady state value given by equations 8 and 16; $[\dot{M}]_s$ is the maximum value of the radical concentration (*i.e.* the concentration at the steady state). Substituting this value gives

$$\frac{d[\dot{M}]}{dt} = 2k_t\{[\dot{M}]_s^2 - [\dot{M}]^2\} \tag{41}$$

Integration of equation 41 gives

$$\frac{1}{[\dot{M}]_s}\text{Tanh}^{-1}\frac{[\dot{M}]}{[\dot{M}]_s} = 2k_t t + C \tag{42}$$

C is a constant of integration which is zero if, at the start of illumination $t = 0$, the number of radicals $[\dot{M}]$ is also zero. From equation 38 the term $2k_t[\dot{M}]_s$ may be replaced by $1/\tau$. Hence

$$\text{Tanh}^{-1}\frac{[\dot{M}]}{[M]_s} = \frac{t}{\tau} + C[\dot{M}]_s \tag{43}$$

The rate of growth of the radical concentration is given by the curve OA in Fig. 19 where the ratio $[\dot{M}]/[\dot{M}]_s$ is plotted against t/τ. For this curve the reaction is commenced with no radicals present so that the value of C in equation 43 will be zero. When the light is shut off the number of radicals is decreased by the termination reaction. In the absence of illumination the rate of destruction of radicals is given by

$$-\frac{d[\dot{M}]}{dt} = 2k_t[\dot{M}]^2 \tag{13}$$

which integrates to

$$\frac{1}{[\dot{M}]} = 2k_t t + C'$$

The integration constant C' is $1/[\dot{M}]_s$, if the illumination is switched off $(t = 0)$ when the system is in the steady state.

Hence

$$\frac{1}{[\dot{M}]} - \frac{1}{[\dot{M}]_s} = 2k_t t$$

or

$$\frac{[\dot{M}]_s}{[\dot{M}]} - 1 = 2k_t[\dot{M}]_s t = \frac{t}{\tau}$$

The decay of the radical concentration is given by the curve AB. The rate of polymerisation is proportional to the concentration of radicals and hence the values of $[\dot{M}]$ are proportional to the rate. Hence if the polymerisation could be measured during the build-up or decay periods, equations 42 and 43 would enable τ or $[\dot{M}]_s$ to be calculated. Unfortunately the measurement of polymerisation rates over the very short periods of time required for the build-up or decay of radicals is extremely difficult, and most workers in this field have approached the problem in a different way.

Illumination of the system may be allowed for periods which are long, when the radical concentration builds up according to curve OA (equation 42), remains stationary and then decreases according to curve AB (equation 43). In such circumstances, the rate of polymerisation will reach that given by the steady state equation during the illumination and rapidly drops to zero during the period of darkness. Periods of illumination and darkness may be achieved by interposing a circular disc with a sector removed between the light source and the reaction vessel. The periods of illumination may be varied according to the speed of rotation of this sector disc, although the ratio of the periods of darkness to light remains constant. For slow speeds the situation is the one just discussed and the effect on the polymerisation of introducing the sector disc is to reduce the period of illumination. If the ratio of the dark to light periods is a, then the reaction vessel will be illuminated for a period which is

$1/(1 + a)$ times that of the steady illumination. The rate of polymerisation is therefore reduced according to this ratio.

Speeding up the rotation of the sector disc reduces the periods of illumination until a point is reached, when the radical concentration has insufficient time to reach the steady state value during the light period and is unable to reach zero in the dark. When this happens, the radical concentration will not have time to grow to the steady state value but will begin to decay before this is reached. This situation is depicted by the saw tooth curve FGE in Fig. 19. Clearly for such speeds of rotation the individual changes in radical concentration cannot be followed but the average value can be determined. Increasing the rate of rotation of the

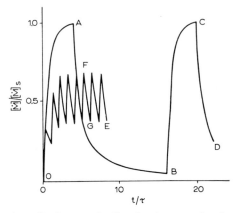

Fig. 19. Variation in radical concentration for two speeds of a sector with a 1,3-opening[113].

sector shortens the time of flash and in the limit, if the speed is fast enough, the radicals are no sooner formed than they begin to decay. This is tantamount to a reduction in intensity of the light instead of a reduction in the period of illumination. Since from the previous calculation (equation 21) the rate of reaction is proportional to the square root of the intensity, the rate is decreased from that of steady illumination by the factor $1/(1 + a)^{\frac{1}{2}}$. Thus the two extreme conditions are
(a) for slow speeds of rotation a reduction in the time of illumination and
(b) at high speeds a reduction in intensity of illumination.

Between these extremes the rate changes according to the curve given in Fig. 20, where the concentration of radicals, relative to the stationary value, is plotted against the time of flash deduced from the sector speed. The curve shows that the rate of polymerisation is determined by the radical concentration changes from that at the fast speed to that at the slow speed, the two with rates varying by a factor $(1 + a)^{\frac{1}{2}}$. The shape of the curve between the extremes depends on the values of τ and a as is expected from the equations for the build-up and decay of radicals. In practice to measure τ for a fixed value of a, polymerisation is carried out at varying sector speeds and the graph of polymerisation rate plotted against the sector speed. The data are then compared with theoretical curves for different values of τ and the value of τ is found by matching the practical curve with the theoretical.

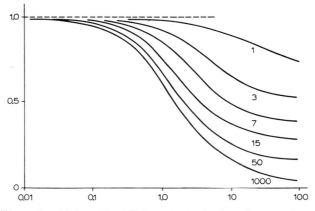

Fig. 20. The ratio of intermittent light rate to steady value as a function of the duration of the flash for different values of a[113].

At any sector speed between the two extremes, calculation of the rate of polymerisation or concentration of radicals may be done by calculation of the average concentrations of the radicals over the dark and light periods. The details of the calculation are discussed elsewhere[99].

Some values of the rate constants for propagation and termination are given in Table 9.

TABLE 9

Monomer	k_p	$k_t \times 10^{-7}$
Vinyl acetate	1240	3.1
Styrene	55	2.5
Methyl methacrylate	143	0.61
Methyl acrylate	720	0.22
Butyl acrylate	14	0.0009
Methacrylonitrile	21	2.7

(i) *Initiation Rates*

Although k_i may be determined from a knowledge of the rate of the polymerisation and the D.P. under steady state conditions, independent values may be found from a knowledge of the kinetic chain length using the equation $v = v_p/v_i$. The measurements of v could be made by determining the number of initiator fragments in the polymer; the method naturally relies on initiator fragments starting a chain. One of the simplest ways experimentally is to label the catalyst with a radio-active atom when the degree of radio-activity in the polymer may be measured[107].

Another possible technique is by means of inhibitors. These substances, when added to a monomer suppress the formation of polymer until they are consumed, when the rate of propagation becomes normal. It is assumed that inhibitors react with initial radicals to give products incapable of initiating polymerisation. The kind of result is given in Fig. 21 for the

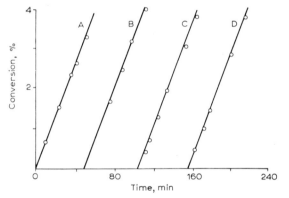

Fig. 21. Inhibition of photo polymerisation of vinyl acetate by *p*-benzoquinone at 25°C. Curves A, B, C, D refer to inhibitor concentrations of 0, 1.86, 3.86 and 5.80 × 10⁻³ moles l⁻¹ [114].

polymerisation of vinyl acetate in the presence of different quantities of *p*-benzoquinone. Extrapolation of the conversion curve gives an induction period. The rate of initiation is given by the consumption of inhibitor provided it is known how many radicals react with each inhibitor molecule. The weakness of this method lies often in lack of knowledge of this number and indeed of the actual reaction of the radical with the inhibitor. Inhibitors used include *p*-benzoquinone and diphenylpicrylhydrazyl.

12. Molecular Weight Distributions

The discussion on kinetics of addition polymerisation shows that the rates of polymerisation and the number average D.P. are dependent on the constants k_i, k_p and k_t as well as the possibility of transfer reactions and more than one termination reaction. Calculations of the molecular weight distribution curves are thus intrinsically more difficult to deduce than those for condensation polymerisations, and hence only a brief mention will be made as to how the problem might be tackled.

Consider a system where the monomer concentration remains constant. Radicals are produced at a constant rate and the termination is by disproportionation. In such simple conditions for a chain containing r units to be formed, one termination and $r - 1$ propagation steps must have occurred. For simplicity termination by disproportionation has been chosen since, by this kind of termination, radical growth ceases without an increase in r as would happen for mutual termination. There is a probability q which determines whether the chain radical will add on to the monomer. The probability of forming a chain of r units will be the probability that the propagation reaction will have occurred $r - 1$ times *i.e.* q^{r-1}. The probability that the chain will terminate since only two possibilities are considered – propagation and termination – will be $1 - q$. Hence the probability p_r that the initial radical will produce a molecule of r units will be

$$p_r = q^{r-1}(1 - q) \tag{44}$$

If, at a certain stage in the polymerisation, the quantity of monomer converted is ΔM (assumed small) and the polymer produced has an average D.P. of $\bar{P}_n$, the number of molecules of polymer will be given by $\Delta M/\bar{P}_n$. The probability of finding a molecule containing r units in the polymer will be given by its fractional concentration, *i.e.*

$$p_r = \frac{P_r}{\text{number of moles}} = \frac{P_r}{\Delta M/\bar{P}_n} \tag{45}$$

Substitution for p_r from equation 44 gives

$$P_r = \frac{\Delta M}{\bar{P}_n} q^{r-1}(1 - q) \tag{46}$$

$\bar{P}_n$ may be calculated from p_r; since each molecule contains r units, the total fractional number of units in molecules containing r units is rp_r. Hence

$$\bar{P}_n = \Sigma rp_r = \Sigma rq^{r-1}(1 - q) = (1 - q)\frac{d}{dq} \Sigma q^r = \frac{1}{1 - q}$$

Substitution for $\bar{P}_n$ into equation 46 gives

$$P_r = \Delta Mq^{r-1}(1 - q)^2 \tag{47}$$

This gives the number distribution of molecules. For the weight distribution the weight fractions w_r will be $rP_r/\Delta M$ and hence $w_r = rq^{r-1}(1 - q)^2$.

q may be calculated as follows. Let τ_p be the average time interval between the formation of a radical and its entry into a reaction with monomer and τ_d the time interval between the formation of a radical and its annihilation at termination. The mean life time of a radical is given by

$$\frac{1}{\tau} = \frac{1}{\tau_p} + \frac{1}{\tau_d}$$

The probability that a radical will undergo a propagation reaction will be determined by the inverse of the time it spends between creation and reaction so that

$$q = \frac{1}{\tau_p} \Big/ \frac{1}{\tau}$$

In terms of the reaction constants, the values of τ_p and τ_d will be given by the concentration of radicals divided by the rate at which the radicals react. Hence,

$$\tau_p = [\dot{M}] \Big/ \frac{\mathrm{d}[M]}{\mathrm{d}t} = \frac{1}{k_p[M]} \; ; \; \tau_d = [\dot{M}] \Big/ \frac{\mathrm{d}[\dot{M}]}{\mathrm{d}t} = \frac{1}{2k_d[\dot{M}]}$$

Substitution gives

$$q = \frac{k_p[M]}{k_p[M] + 2k_d[\dot{M}]}$$

The system discussed is a hypothetical one and in more complicated systems, where termination can occur in other ways or the concentration of monomer may vary, the distribution of molecular weight differs from the most probable one discussed above. If the monomer concentration changes, then q alters and a broader distribution may be obtained; on the other hand, if termination is by combination of radicals the distribution is narrower. In general the kind of distribution obtained varies according to the importance of the various reactions taking place. A detailed discussion of the problem is given elsewhere[99].

REFERENCES

[1] P. J. Flory, *J. Am. Chem. Soc.*, 59 (1937) 241.
[2] F. R. Mayo, *J. Am. Chem. Soc.*, 65 (1943) 2324.
[3] F. Muller *et al.*, *Ann.*, 520 (1935) 248.
[4] S. Goldschmidt and K. Renn, *Ber.*, 55 (1922) 628.
[5] N. K. Bridge, *J. Chem. Phys.*, 32 (1960) 945.
[6] J. H. Baxendale in *Polymer Processes*, ed. C. E. Schildknecht, Interscience, New York, 1955.
[7] N. Uri, *Chem. Revs.*, 50 (1952) 375.
[8] D. H. Hey and W. A. Waters, *Chem. Revs.*, 21 (1937) 179.
[9] C. G. Swain, J. T. Clarke and W. H. Stockmeyer, *J. Am. Chem. Soc.*, 72 (1950) 5426.

[10] D. S. Brown, *J. Am. Chem. Soc.*, 62 (1940) 2657.
[11] B. Barnett and W. E. Vaughan, *J. Phys. Chem.*, 51 (1947) 926.
[12] P. D. Bartlett and K. Nozaki, *J. Am. Chem. Soc.*, 69 (1947) 2299; 68 (1946) 1686.
[13] C. G. Swain, W. H. Stockmayer and J. T. Clark, *J. Am. Chem. Soc.*, 72 (1950) 5426.
[14] F. M. Lewis and M. S. Matheson, *J. Am. Chem. Soc.*, 71 (1949) 747.
[15] C. G. Overberger, M. T. O'Shaughnessy and H. Shalit, *J. Am. Chem. Soc.*, 71 (1949) 2661.
[16] D. C. Blackley and H. W. Melville, *Makromol. Chem.*, 18 (1956) 16.
[17] H. J. H. Fenton, *J. Chem. Soc.*, (1894) 899.
[18] F. Haber and J. Weiss, *Naturwissenschaften*, 20 (1932) 248; *Proc. Roy. Soc. London*, 147A (1934) 332.
[19] J. H. Baxendale, M. G. Evans and G. S. Park, *Trans. Faraday Soc.*, 42 (1946) 155.
[20] M. G. Evans, *J. Chem. Soc.*, (1947) 266.
[21] C. S. Marvel, R. Deanin, C. J. Claus, M. B. Wyld and R. L. Seitz, *J. Polymer Sci.*, 3 (1948) 350.
[22] L. Morgan, *Trans. Faraday Soc.*, 42 (1946) 169.
[23] R. C. Houtz, *Textile Research J.*, 20 (1950) 786.
[24] L. Morgan, *Trans. Faraday Soc.*, 42 (1946) 169.
  C. H. Sorum and J. O. Edward, *J. Am. Chem. Soc.*, 74 (1952) 1206.
[25] E. J. Vandenberg and G. E. Hulse, *Ind. Eng. Chem.*, 40 (1948) 932.
[26] A. T. Blonquist, J. R. Johnson and H. J. Sykes, *J. Am. Chem. Soc.*, 65 (1943) 2446.
[27] H. W. Melville, *Proc. Roy. Soc. London*, 167A (1938) 99.
[28] G. M. Burnett and H. W. Melville, *Proc. Roy. Soc. London*, 189A (1947) 456.
[29] C. H. Bamford and M. J. S. Dewar, *Proc. Roy. Soc. London*, 192A (1948) 309.
[30] G. D. Jones and H. W. Melville, *Proc. Roy. Soc. London*, 187A (1946) 19.
[31] D. H. Johnson and A. V. Tobolsky, *J. Am. Chem. Soc.*, 74 (1952) 938.
[32] B. Baysal and A. V. Tobolsky, *J. Polymer Sci.*, 8 (1952) 529.
[33] D. D. Eley and A. W. Richards, *Trans. Faraday Soc.*, 45 (1949) 425, 436.
[34] R. G. W. Norrish and K. E. Russell, *Trans. Faraday Soc.*, 48 (1952) 91.
[35] F. S. Dainton and G. B. B. M. Sutherland, *J. Polymer Sci.*, 4 (1949) 37.
[36] C. S. Marvel and C. E. Denoon, *J. Am. Chem. Soc.*, 60 (1938) 1045.
[37] C. S. Marvel, J. H. Sample and M. F. Roy, *J. Am. Chem. Soc.*, 61 (1939) 324.
[38] P. J. Flory, *J. Am. Chem. Soc.*, 61 (1939) 1518.
[39] C. S. Marvel and N. S. Moon, *J. Am. Chem. Soc.*, 62 (1940) 45.
[40] C. S. Marvel and C. L. Levesque, *J. Am. Chem. Soc.*, 60 (1938) 280.
[41] H. Staudinger and A. Steinhofer, *Ann.*, 517 (1935) 35.
[42] P. J. Flory, *J. Am. Chem. Soc.*, 64 (1942) 177.
  F. T. Wall, *J. Am. Chem. Soc.*, 64 (1942) 269.
[43] H. W. Thompson and P. Torkington, *J. Chem. Soc.*, (1944) 597.
[44] C. S. Marvel and J. C. Cowan, *J. Am. Chem. Soc.*, 61 (1939) 3156.
[45] P. J. Flory and F. S. Lentner, *J. Polymer Sci.*, 3 (1948) 880; 5 (1950) 267.
[46] C. S. Marvel, in *Chemistry of Large Molecules*, R. E. Burk and O. Grummitt (eds.), Interscience, New York, 1943.
[47] K. Nozaki, *J. Polymer Sci.*, 1 (1946) 455.
[48] C. C. Price and R. W. Kell, *J. Am. Chem. Soc.*, 63 (1941) 2798.
  C. C. Price, R. W. Kell and E. Kreb, *J. Am. Chem. Soc.*, 64 (1942) 1103.
  C. C. Price and B. E. Tate, *J. Am. Chem. Soc.*, 65 (1943) 517.
  C. C. Price and D. A. Durham, *J. Am. Chem. Soc.*, 14 (1942) 2508.
  P. D. Bartlett and S. G. Cohen, *J. Am. Chem. Soc.*, 65 (1943) 543.
  W. Kern and H. Kämerer, *J. prakt. Chem.*, 161 (1942) 81.
[49] H. F. Pfann, D. J. Salley and H. Mark, *J. Am. Chem. Soc.*, 66 (1944) 983.
  H. F. Pfann, V. Z. Williams and H. Mark, *J. Polymer Sci.*, 1 (1946) 14.
[50] J. H. Baxendale, S. Bywater and M. G. Evans, *J. Polymer Sci.*, 1 (1946) 237.
[51] J. C. Bevington, H. W. Melville and A. P. Taylor, *Symposium on Macromols*, Stockholm, 1953.

[52] W. V. Smith, *J. Am. Chem. Soc.*, 71 (1949) 4077.

[53] P. D. Barlett and R. Altschul, *J. Am. Chem. Soc.*, 67 (1945) 812.

[54] E. Bamberger and F. Tschirner, *Ber.*, 33 (1900) 955.

[55] G. D. Buckley, L. H. Cross and M. A. Ray, *J. Chem. Soc.*, (1950) 2714.
G. D. Buckley and M. H. Ray, *J. Chem. Soc.*, (1952) 3701.

[56] R. Hill, *Fibres from Synthetic Polymers*, Elsevier, Amsterdam, 1953.

[57] W. M. D. Bryant, *J. Polymer Sci.*, 6 (1951) 359.

[58] K. Nozaki, *Discussions Faraday Soc.*, 2 (1947) 337.

[59] R. B. Richards, *J. Appl. Chem. London*, 1 (1951) 370.

[60] J. J. Fox and A. J. P. Martin, *Proc. Roy. Soc. London*, 175A (1940) 208.

[61] L. H. Cross, R. B. Richards and H. A. Willis, *Discussions Faraday Soc.*, 9 (1950) 235.

[62] K. Ziegler, *Angew. Chem.*, 64 (1952) 323.

[63] A. Clark, J. P. Logan, R. L. Banks and W. C. Lanning, *Ind. Eng. Chem.*, 48 (1956) 1152.

[64] V. Regnault, *Ann.*, 69 (1838) 151.

[65] E. Baumann, *Ann.*, 163 (1892) 127.

[66] *B.I.O.S.*, No. 104–32; *F.I.A.T.*, No. 867, *B.I.O.S. Miscellaneous Report*, No. 1.

[67] W. I. Bengough and R. G. W. Norrish, *Proc. Roy. Soc. London*, 200A (1950) 301.

[68] E. Jenckel, H. Eckmans and B. Rumbach, *Makromol. Chem.*, 4 (1949) 15.

[69] R. G. W. Norrish and R. R. Smith, *Nature*, 150 (1942) 336.

[70] M. Magat, *J. Polymer Sci.*, 16 (1955) 491.

[71] G. M. Burnett and W. W. Wright, *Proc. Roy. Soc. London*, 221A (1954) 28.

[72] R. G. Fordyce and E. C. Chapin, *J. Am. Chem. Soc.*, 69 (1947) 581.
R. G. Fordyce and E. C. Chapin, *J. Am. Chem. Soc.*, 69 (1947) 695.
R. G. Fordyce, *J. Am. Chem. Soc.*, 69 (1947) 1903.
I. M. Kolthoff and N. J. Dale, *J. Am. Chem. Soc.*, 69 (1947) 441.
I. M. Kolthoff and F. A. Bovey, *J. Am. Chem. Soc.*, 69 (1947) 2143.
I. M. Kolthoff and F. A. Bovey, *J. Am. Chem. Soc.*, 70 (1948) 791.
W. P. Hohenstein and V. S. Fülette, *J. Polymer Sci.*, 3 (1948) 22.
J. H. Baxendale, M. G. Evans and J. K. Kilham, *J. Polymer Sci.*, 1 (1946) 466.

[73] R. S. Vinograd, L. L. Fong and W. M. Sawyer, *Am. Chem. Soc.*, *Mts*, 1944.

[74] W. P. Hohenstein and H. F. Mark, *High Molecular Weight Compounds*, Interscience, New York, 1944.
C. F. Fryling, *Ind. Eng. Chem.*, *Anal. Ed.*, 16 (1944) 1.
H. P. Hohenstein and H. F. Mark, *J. Polymer Sci.*, 1 (1940) 127, 549.

[75] K. Shura *et al.*, *Chem. Abstr.*, 51 (1957) 9165.

[76] V. Regnault, *J. prakt. Chem.*, 18 (1839) 80.

[77] E. Baumann, *Ann.*, 163 (1872) 308.

[78] W. I. Bengough and R. W. Norrish, *Proc. Roy. Soc. London*, 218A (1953) 149.

[79] J. D. Burnett and H. W. Melville, *Trans. Faraday Soc.*, 46 (1950) 976.

[80] C. H. Bamford and A. D. Jenkins, *Proc. Roy. Soc. London*, 216A (1953) 515.

[81] R. C. Houtz, *Textile Research J.*, (1950) 786.

[82] C. H. Bamford and A. D. Jenkins, *Proc. Roy. Soc. London*, 222A (1955) 220.
W. M. Thomas and J. J. Pallow, *J. Polymer Sci.*, 13 (1954) 329.

[83] C. H. Bamford, D. S. E. Ingram, A. D. Jenkins and M. P. Symons, *Nature*, 175 (1955) 898.

[84] H. Gilbert *et al.*, *J. Am. Chem. Soc.*, 78 (1957) 1669.
G. E. Ham, *J. Polymer Sci.*, 24 (1957) 349.

[85] J. A. Somers, *Man-Made Textiles*, 33 (1957) No. 394, 32.

[86] K. Ziegler, *Angew. Chem.*, 67 (1955) 541.

[87] G. Natta, P. Pino, G. Mazzanti, P. Corradini and U. Giannini, *Atti accad. nazl. Lincei. Rend. Classe sci. fis. mat. e. nat.*, 19 (1955) 397.
G. Natta, P. Corradini and I. W. Bassi, *ibid.*, 404.
F. P. Reding, *J. Polymer Sci.*, 21 (1956) 547.
G. Natta and P. Corradini, *Angew. Chem.*, 68 (1956) 615.
G. Natta, *Angew. Chem.*, 68 (1956) 393.

[88] C. E. H. BAWN, *Proc. Chem. Soc.* (1958) 139.
H. UELZMAN, *J. Polymer Sci.*, 32 (1958) 457.
[89] A. S. MATHESON, *J. Chem. Phys.*, 13 (1945) 584.
J. J. HERMANS and M. M. HORIK, *J. Polymer Sci.*, 11 (1953) 325.
F. R. MAYO, R. A. GREGG and M. S. MATHESON, *J. Am. Chem. Soc.*, 73 (1951) 1691.
[90] L. M. ARNETT and J. H. PETERSON, *J. Am. Chem. Soc.*, 74 (1952) 2031.
[91] S. G. COHEN, *J. Am. Chem. Soc.*, 69 (1947) 1057.
[92] P. J. FLORY, *Principles of Polymer Chemistry*, Cornell Univ. Press, Ithaca, 1953, p. 119.
[93] M. S. MATHESON, E. E. AUER, E. B. BEVILACQUA and E. J. HART, *J. Am. Chem. Soc.*, 73 (1951) 1700.
[94] J. H. BAXENDALE, M. G. EVANS and J. K. KILHAM, *Trans. Faraday Soc.*, 42 (1946) 668.
[95] C. E. H. BAWN, *Trans. Faraday Soc.*, 32 (1936) 178.
H. DOSTAL, *Monatsh.*, 67 (1935) 63; 70 (1937) 324; 70 (1937) 409.
[96] H. W. MELVILLE, *Proc. Roy. Soc. London*, 189A (1947) 494.
[97] M. BODENSTEIN, *Z. phys. Chem.*, 85 (1913) 329; *Z. Electrochem.*, 42 (1938) 443.
[98] E. M. FRITH and R. F. TUCKETT, *Linear Polymers*, Longmans, Green, 1951.
[99] C. H. BAMFORD, W. G. BARB, A. D. JENKINS and P. F. ONYON, *The Kinetics of Vinyl Polymerisations by Radical Mechanisms*, Butterworth, 1958.
[100] L. M. ARNETT, *J. Am. Chem. Soc.*, 74 (1952) 2027.
[101] G. V. SCHULZ and F. BLASCHKE, *Z. physik. Chem.*, B51 (1942) 75.
[102] F. R. MAYO, R. A. GREGG and M. S. MATHESON, *J. Am. Chem. Soc.*, 73 (1951) 1691.
[103] KH. S. BAGDASARYAN, *Zhur. Fiz. Khim.*, 21 (1947) 25.
[104] R. A. GREGG and F. R. MAYO, *Discussions Faraday Soc.*, No. 2 (1947) 328.
[105] R. A. GREGG and F. R. MAYO, *J. Am. Chem. Soc.*, 70 (1948) 2373; 75 (1953) 3530.
[106] B. BAYSAL and A. V. TOBOLSKY, *J. Am. Chem. Soc.*, 74 (1952) 938.
[107] J. C. BEVINGTON, S. H. BRADBURY and G. M. BURNETT, *J. Polymer Sci.*, 12 (1954) 469.
[108] M. SZWARC, *Advances in Chemical Physics*, Vol. II, p. 156, Interscience, New York, 1959.
[109] R. A. GREGG and F. R. MAYO, *J. Am. Chem. Soc.*, 70 (1948) 2373.
R. A. GREGG, D. M. ALDERMAN and F. R. MAYO, *J. Am. Chem. Soc.*, 70 (1948) 3740.
J. L. O'BRIEN and F. GORMICK, *J. Am. Chem. Soc.*, 77 (1955) 4757.
[110] R. A. GREGG and F. R. MAYO, *J. Am. Chem. Soc.*, 75 (1953) 3530. *Discussions Faraday Soc.*, No. 6, (1947) 329.
[111] S. BASU, J. N. SEN and S. R. PALIT, *Proc. Roy. Soc. London*, A202 (1950) 485.
[112] C. H. BAMFORD and A. D. JENKINS, *Proc. Roy. Soc. London*, 216A (1953) 515.
[113] W. A. NOYES and P. A. LEIGHTON, *The Photochemistry of Gases*, Reinhold, New York, 1941.
[114] G. M. BURNETT and H. W. MELVILLE, *Proc. Roy. Soc. London*, 189A, (1947) 456, 481, 494.

CHAPTER 4

COPOLYMERS

1. General

Synthetic fibres introduced the possibility of manufacturing textiles with specified properties but, even with the large range of different monomers available, it may not always be possible to meet every specification. However, by polymerising one monomer in the presence of a second, a copolymer which may have in some degree the desirable properties of both homopolymers may be prepared. In a copolymer, the two or more kinds of monomer units are chemically joined and both form part of the chain. This is a feature which distinguishes a copolymer from a mixture of two homopolymers. Thus polyvinyl chloride does not give fibres with adequate suppleness, polyvinyl acetate gives fibres having a low softening point and poor mechanical properties. On the other hand, the copolymer of vinyl acetate (12%) and vinyl chloride (88%) is a material well suited for fibre manufacture (Vinyon). The introduction of a certain amount of vinyl acetate also has the advantage of making the polymer soluble in acetone, a cheap solvent suitable for dry spinning. Polyvinylidene chloride is an infusible and intractable material but the copolymer of vinylidene chloride with vinyl chloride (85/15) is suitable for transformation into the fibre Saran. The copolymer has better resistance to solvents and a slightly higher softening point than fibres made from vinyl chloride.

Fibres made from acrylonitrile are used to a considerable extent. The first fibres were produced from the homopolymer but suffered from defects, the most notable of which were perhaps its intractability to dye absorption and its insolubility in almost all common solvents. To overcome these difficulties and yet retain the desirable properties of polyacrylonitrile fibres (e.g. high strength, resistance to light etc.) small amounts of a comonomer have been used in the polymerisation. Typical of these are vinyl acetate, vinylpyrolidine, methylvinylpyridine, vinylpyridine or vinyl chloride. These copolymers have in general improved solubility and ability for dyeing although some other properties may suffer. In Table 10 are given some of the acrylic fibres manufactured.

It should be noted that the true composition of these copolymers is a little uncertain since their composition is mainly deduced from patent literature. Condensation copolymers may be prepared via the reactions discussed for condensation polymers but using more than one kind of acid, diamine

TABLE 10

Fibre	Probable composition	Manufacturer
Orlon	Acrylonitrile Methyl methacrylate	DuPont U.S.A.
Acrilan	Acrylonitrile Vinyl acetate or vinylpyridine	Chemstrand U.S.A.
Courtelle	Comonomer not known	Courtaulds U.K.
Creslan	Acrylonitrile Vinyl acetate Methylvinylpyridine	Cyanamid U.S.A.
Dynel	Acrylonitrile (40%) Vinyl chloride (60%)	Carbide U.S.A.
Vinel	Acrylonitrile and vinyl chloride Vinylidene chloride	Tennessee Eastman U.S.A.
Darlan	Vinylidene dinitrile (50%) Vinyl acetate (50%)	Goodrich U.S.A.

or glycol. It is even possible by heating more than one condensation polymer (*e.g.* nylon 66 and nylon 610) at sufficiently high temperatures to obtain random copolymers by interchange reactions. Copolymers have in general lower melting-points and higher solubilities and are finding uses as adhesives etc. (*e.g.* the copolymer made from nylon 66, 610 and 6).

Fibres have been made in East Germany from condensation copolymers namely, Eftrelon and Wetrelon. The former is a copolymer of nylon 6 and 66 in the proportion of 10/90; the latter is made from caprolactam (43%) and hexamethylene terephthalamide (57%)[2]. In their mechanical properties, both resemble nylon 6 and 66 but they are considered to be softer and more pliable. The melting-point of Eftrelon is about 15°C lower than nylon 66 whereas that of Wetrelon is considerably higher than that of nylon 6 and about equal to the melting-point of nylon 66.

Copolymers in the polyester field have not been as successful as polyamides although one – a polyethylene terephthalate fibre believed to contain a certain amount of isophthalic acid – has been marketed (Vycron)[3]. This fibre is easier to dye than the homopolymer.

The properties of copolymers depend not only on the chemical nature of the comonomers but also on their relative proportions in the product. In condensation copolymerisations where the monomers or homopolymers are heated together until equilibrium is reached, the copolymer composition will be directly determined by that of the starting mixture. In addition polymerisation, the reactivities of the monomers to the free radical chain ends which are propagating the reaction are in general different, and the composition of the copolymer can be very different from that of the mixture of monomers from which it is formed. It is therefore important that the kinetics of the reaction be studied in order to obtain knowledge of the composition of the copolymer.

An example of the differences in reactivities of the monomers comes from the formation of Vinyon N (acrylonitrile/vinyl chloride) where the acrylonitrile is used more rapidly. To counterbalance this and to obtain a copolymer with the monomers present in the ratio 40/60, the ratio of acrylonitrile/vinyl chloride in the monomer mixture may be as low as 8/92. The difference between the composition of the copolymer and that of the monomer mixture is accounted for in terms of the relative reactivities of the different radicals and monomers by the copolymerisation equation discussed below.

In this chapter the kinetics of copolymerisation of addition reactions is discussed. Condensation copolymers have not been considered since they have not achieved significant importance in the fibre field compared with addition copolymers.

2. Kinetics

A mixture of two monomers may be polymerised using initiators of the kind discussed in Chapter 3. Attention here will be devoted to free radical initiation; naturally the copolymerisation reaction can involve chain transfer, termination by disproportionation etc. but for simplicity it is assumed that the system is initiated by radicals and terminated by mutual combination. Further, the assumption is made that the reactivity of the growing radicals is determined not by the chain length but by the reactivity of the terminal group only. The propagation steps are therefore decided by which of the two monomers M_1 and M_2 is carried at the reactive end of the chain and the chemical nature of the monomer which is adding. The growing chain may be denoted by the radical end as $\dot{m}_1$ and $\dot{m}_2$, independent of the length or composition of the rest of the chain. Reaction of $\dot{m}_1$ with the monomers M_1 or M_2 will give rise to radicals $\dot{m}_1$ or $\dot{m}_2$ respectively.

Thus, there are four propagation steps

$$\dot{m}_1 + M_1 \rightarrow \dot{m}_1 \qquad k_{11}$$
$$\dot{m}_1 + M_2 \rightarrow \dot{m}_2 \qquad k_{12}$$
$$\dot{m}_2 + M_1 \rightarrow \dot{m}_1 \qquad k_{21}$$
$$\dot{m}_2 + M_2 \rightarrow \dot{m}_2 \qquad k_{22}$$

Each of these steps will have its own reaction constant. These have been written with two suffixes, the former of which refers to the kind of reacting radical, the latter to the kind of monomer being added to the chain.

The chains may be initiated by activating either monomer but this step is not of great importance if the primary radicals react equally efficiently with both monomers. The mutual termination reactions will be three in number each with its own reaction constant. Fortunately much information can be obtained from consideration of the propagation step only since, if the chains are long, the important question of the composition and arrangement of units in the copolymer will be determined by the relative rates of the propagation reaction.

The kinetic scheme for propagation gives the rate of consumption of the two monomers

$$-\frac{d[M_1]}{dt} = k_{11}[\dot{m}_1][M_1] + k_{21}[\dot{m}_2][M_1] \tag{1}$$

$$-\frac{d[M_2]}{dt} = k_{12}[\dot{m}_1][M_2] + k_{22}[\dot{m}_2][M_2] \tag{2}$$

These equations may be simplified by the assumption of steady state conditions applied to each kind of radical. The equation for the build-up of radicals of the first kind will be given by

$$\frac{d[\dot{m}_1]}{dt} = -k_{12}[\dot{m}_1][M_2] + k_{21}[\dot{m}_2][M_1] \tag{3}$$

Equation 3 contains the cross propagation constants only, since the other "homo" propagation steps do not involve any change in concentration of the radicals $\dot{m}_1$ or $\dot{m}_2$. Equating equation 3 to zero gives

$$k_{12}[\dot{m}_1][M_2] = k_{21}[\dot{m}_2][M_1] \tag{4}$$

This is the same as saying that the rate of production of radicals $\dot{m}_2$ from $\dot{m}_1$ will be equal to that of $\dot{m}_2$ by reaction with M_1 and hence a stationary state for radicals $\dot{m}_1$ implies a stationary state for radicals $\dot{m}_2$. Implicit in this is the assumption that the chains are long and that initiation and termination reactions are not frequent events.

If equations 1 and 2 are divided and the steady state condition (equation 4) introduced, the concentration of radicals may be eliminated to give

$$\frac{d[M_1]}{d[M_2]} = \frac{[M_1]}{[M_2]} \frac{\frac{k_{11}}{k_{12}}[M_1] + [M_2]}{\frac{k_{22}}{k_{21}}[M_2] + [M_1]} = \frac{[M_1]}{[M_2]} \frac{r_1 \frac{[M_1]}{[M_2]} + 1}{\frac{[M_1]}{[M_2]} + r_2} \tag{5}$$

where r_1 and r_2 are called the monomer reactivity ratios. Equation 5 gives the composition of the copolymer formed at any instant and is known as the copolymerisation equation[4,5]. If the initial stages of reaction only are considered, this equation gives the ratio of the molar concentrations of the two monomers in the copolymer. The values of the monomer reactivity ratios are important. Thus if $r_1 > 1$ there is a greater tendency for $\dot{m}_1$ to react with M_1 than with M_2; if $r_1 < 1$ the reverse is true. In Table II a number of values of r_1 and r_2 are given. Equation 5 is one which does not contain the initiation or termination constants; for this reason therefore the manner in which the composition of the copolymer is built up during the propagation reaction is independent of initiator and the overall reaction rate. Further, values of r_1 and r_2 do not in general change to any significant extent in the presence of solvents or transfer agents.

Equation 5 shows that the composition of the copolymer will depend on the feed ratio, M_1/M_2, and that, unless this ratio is maintained constant by further additions of the monomers, the composition of the resulting copolymer will change continuously as the feed ratio alters. Further, the constants r_1 and r_2 in the equation express the reactivity of the radical towards its parent monomer relative to that towards a different monomer.

Special Cases

(a) Ideal. Copolymerisation is classified as ideal when the reactivity ratios are related according to equation 6

$$r_1 = \frac{1}{r_2} \quad \text{or} \quad \frac{k_{11}}{k_{12}} = \frac{k_{21}}{k_{22}} \tag{6}$$

The copolymerisation equation reduces to

$$\frac{d[M_1]}{d[M_2]} = r_1 \frac{[M_1]}{[M_2]} \tag{7}$$

This means that the two radicals have the same preference for adding to one of the monomers as the other. Because of this the units in the copolymer will be arranged in a random fashion in relative amounts determined by the composition of the feed and the relative reactivities of the two monomers. Ideal polymerisation is the exception rather than the rule. In Table II three pairs of monomers, styrene with (a) butadiene and (b) p-methoxystyrene, and methyl methacrylate with 2,5-dichlorostyrene approach this behaviour.

(b) Alternating. This term arises from the fact that, when each radical reacts exclusively with the other monomer, a copolymer results with the monomer units alternating down the chain. In terms of reactivity ratios this means $r_1 = r_2 = 0$ and equation 5 reduces to

$$\frac{d[M_1]}{d[M_2]} = 1 \tag{8}$$

In Table 11 the pairs of monomers maleic anhydride/isopropenyl acetate, vinyl acetate/diethyl maleate and styrene/maleic anhydride with very low values of r_1 and r_2 approximate to this state.

These cases (a) and (b) represent extremes of behaviour, one where the distribution of the two comonomers in the copolymer chain are random and the other, where they turn up in an alternating sequence. Between these lie a variety of arrangements. In some pairs r_1 is greater than unity and r_2 is very much less; the radical $\dot{m}_1$ therefore has a tendency to add on monomer M_1 whereas the radical $\dot{m}_2$ has a tendency to add the monomer M_1 rather than M_2. Sequences of M_1 molecules will therefore occur in the copolymer chain to an extent determined by the values of r_1 and r_2.

An unusual case of this kind is that of styrene and vinyl acetate with r_1 very large and r_2 very small. In this system styrene will be used up very much more rapidly and, because of this tendency, will not allow the vinyl acetate to polymerise to any large extent; in other words, styrene tends to inhibit the polymerisation of vinyl acetate.

In many instances r_1 and r_2 are less than unity so that there is a tendency for both kinds of radicals $\dot{m}_1$ and $\dot{m}_2$ to react with monomers of a different kind i.e. $\dot{m}_1$ with M_2 and vice versa. This means that there is again a tendency to alternate. Some measure which indicates the degree of alternation in the pairs of comonomers would be useful and from the practical point of view such a measure is the value of $r_1 r_2$ given in the last column of Table 11.

TABLE 11

EXAMPLES OF MONOMER REACTIVITY RATIOS[17]

Monomer 1	Monomer 2	r_1	r_2	$r_1 r_2$
Styrene	Butadiene	0.78	1.39	1.08
Styrene	p-Methoxystyrene	1.16	0.82	0.95
Styrene	Vinyl acetate	55	0.01	0.55
Acrylonitrile	Styrene	0.05	0.40	0.02
Acrylonitrile	Vinyl acetate	4.05	0.06	0.24
Acrylonitrile	Vinyl chloride	3.28	0.02	0.66
Vinyl acetate	Diethyl maleate	0.17	0.043	0.007
Vinyl acetate	Vinyl chloride	0.23	1.68	0.39
Methyl methacrylate	Styrene	0.46	0.52	0.24
Methyl methacrylate	Methacrylonitrile	0.67	0.65	0.42
Methyl methacrylate	Vinyl acetate	20	0.015	0.30
Methyl methacrylate	2,5-Dichlorostyrene	0.44	2.25	1.08
Styrene	Maleic anhydride	0.01	0	0
Vinyl acetate	Vinyl ethyl ether	3.0	0	0
Acrylonitrile	Vinylidene chloride	0.91	0.37	0.34
Acrylonitrile	Diethyl fumarate	8	0	0
Acrylonitrile	Diethyl maleate	12	0	0
Maleic anhydride	Isopropenyl acetate	0.002	0.032	very small

In many instances monomers of the type CHX=CHY do not homo-polymerise but will form copolymers. One or two examples are maleic anhydride (I), methyl fumarate (II), cinnamyl nitrile (III) and the methyl ester (IV) of cinnamic acid. Even stilbene (V) has been reported to copoly-merise with maleic anhydride[5]. In general 1,2-disubstituted derivatives will add on to 1,1-disubstituted chain radicals as in the copolymerisation of vinylidene chloride and diethyl maleate.

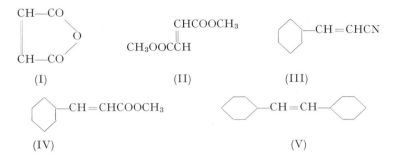

3. The Polymer

(a) *Instantaneous Composition of the Polymer and the Feed*

The changes in the composition of the polymer formed at any instant may be deduced in terms of the feed ratio. This is most easily shown by trans-forming the equation to one in which mole fractions are used. Thus let

$$F_1 = 1 - F_2 = \frac{d[M_1]}{d([M_1] + [M_2])} \tag{9}$$

where F_1 and F_2 are the mole fractions of monomers 1 and 2 in the co-polymer being formed at any instant. Similarly the mole fractions of the monomers in the feed may be written as

$$f_1 = 1 - f_2 = \frac{[M_1]}{[M_1] + [M_2]} \tag{10}$$

The copolymerisation equation may be written in terms of f_1 and f_2 when it becomes

$$F_1 = \frac{r_1 f_1^2 + f_1 f_2}{(r_1 f_1^2 + 2 f_1 f_2 + r_2 f_2^2)} \tag{11}$$

Hence F_1 may be plotted against f_1; in Fig. 22 this has been done for pairs of ideal copolymers with different values of r_1. The graph shows how widely the composition of the copolymer changes with the compo-sition of the feed.

In Fig. 23 some curves for non-ideal mixtures are given and, excluding the case where $r_1 = r_2 = 1$, the composition of the polymer is not equal to the feed ratio except for a unique value of the feed. This is the point where the curve crosses the line $F_1 = f_1$, called the azeotropic line. For points on this line

$$\frac{d[M_1]}{d[M_2]} = \frac{[M_1]}{[M_2]} \qquad (12)$$

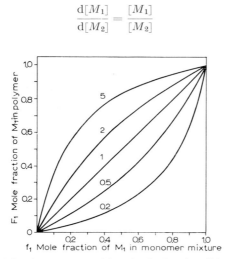

Fig. 22. Incremental polymer composition (mole fraction F_1) plotted against the monomer composition (mole fraction f_1) for ideal copolymerisations ($r_1 = 1/r_2$). Values of r_1 are indicated[32].

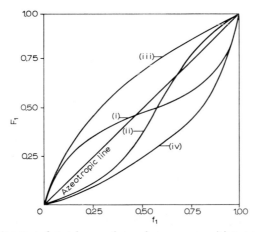

Fig. 23. Instantaneous dependence of copolymer composition on monomer feed composition; F_1, f_1 are the mole fractions of monomer 1 in copolymer and in monomer mixture, respectively. Reactivity ratios: curve (i), $r_1 = 0.2$, $r_2 = 0.3$; curve (ii), $r_1 = 2$, $r_2 = 3$; curve (iii), $r_1 = 2$, $r_2 = 0.3$; curve (iv), $r_1 = 0,2$, $r_2 = 3$[33].

References p. 139

From equation 5 this condition means that the feed ratio must be fixed by the reactivity ratios

$$\frac{[M_1]}{[M_2]} = \frac{1 - r_2}{1 - r_1} \tag{13}$$

At this value of the feed the instantaneous composition of the polymer is equal to that in the feed; this situation is analogous to a distillation of a binary mixture of two liquids[6] and, because of this, such mixtures are described as azeotropic. At all other values of the feed the polymer will be richer in one or the other components than the feed.

The condition for the azeotropic mixture means, since the feed ratio must be positive, that r_1 and r_2 are both less or greater than unity. For systems of this kind, then, the graph of F_1 vs. f_1 must cut the azeotropic line. This situation is shown in Fig. 23 where curve i is the case when r_1 and $r_2 < 1$ and curve ii when they are both > 1. When $r_1 > 1$ and $r_2 \leqslant 1$ or $r_1 < 1$ and $r_2 \geqslant 1$ (curves iii and iv) there is no possibility of an azeotropic mixture.

(b) Composition of the Polymer

Attention has been devoted to the instantaneous relation between the composition of the copolymer and the feed ratio. To investigate the overall composition of the copolymer formed during a polymerisation, an integrated form of the copolymerisation equation must be discussed.

The copolymerisation equation gives the instantaneous relation between the concentrations of the monomers in the system and the increments of each which are polymerised. It has been shown to be possible to carry out integration of the equation to obtain the relation between the concentration of monomers at any instant and their starting concentrations M_1^0 and M_2^0.

The equation deduced is

$$\log \frac{[M_1]}{[M_1^0]} = \frac{r_1}{1 - r_1} \log \frac{[M_1^0][M_2]}{[M_1][M_2^0]} - \frac{1 - r_1 r_2}{(1 - r_1)(1 - r_2)} \log \frac{\frac{(r_1 - 1)}{(r_2 - 1)} \frac{[M_2]}{[M_1]} - r_1 + 1}{\frac{[M_2^0]}{[M_1^0]} - r_1 + 1} \tag{14}$$

This equation is not the usual kind of equation found in kinetic studies since the time variable does not appear explicitly. The equation enables the concentration of monomer 1 to be determined if that of monomer 2 is known at any instant in the polymerisation. The composition of the copolymer formed is then given by $M_1^0 - M_1$ for monomer 1 and $M_2^0 - M_2$ for monomer 2. However, this equation suffers from the disadvantage that the concentration of one monomer must be known before the concentration of the other can be calculated.

Often the composition of the copolymer is required in terms of the conversion of both monomers rather than of one only. To achieve this a semi-graphical solution has been set up[8].

F_1 in the system may be assumed to be greater than f_1 when dM moles of a total of M moles of the two monomers have polymerised. The number of moles of M polymerised is given by $-F_1d[M]$. Whilst this happens f_1 changes by df_1 and the number of unreacted M_1 moles changes from $f_1[M]$ to $(f_1 + df_1)(M + dM)$.

For a balance of material in the system, the decrease in the number of moles of M_1 must equal the number in the newly formed polymer i.e.

$$f_1[M] - (f_1 + df_1)([M] + d[M]) = - F_1 d[M]$$

giving

$$\frac{d[M]}{[M]} = \frac{df_1}{F_1 - f_1}$$

or

$$\log \frac{[M]}{[M_0]} = \int_{(f_1)_0}^{f_1} \frac{df_1}{(F_1 - f_1)} \tag{15}$$

For given values of r_1 and r_2, F_1 may be found from equation 11 as a function of f_1. From this, the integral may be evaluated by graphical means. The value of the integral gives $\log [M]/[M^0]$ and from this the degree of conversion or number of moles of the comonomers used –

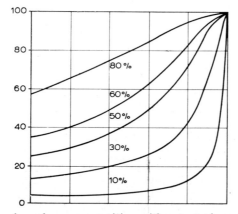

Fig. 24. Variation of copolymer composition with extent of reaction for styrene–2-vinylthiophene; $r_1 = 0.35$ and $r_2 = 3.1$, $(r_1 r_2 = 1.09)$. Ordinate mole percent of styrene in polymer. Abscissa extent of reaction. Different feed ratios put in mole percent styrene[9].

$[1 — (M/M_0)]$ – may be found for a change in composition of the monomer in feed from $(f_1)_0$ to f_1.

Thus it is possible to construct a curve relating the connection between f_1 and degree of conversion. The changes occurring in f_1 can then be used to give the composition of the polymer. The average composition of the copolymer can be calculated from graphical integration of the curve of F_1 against M_1. In Fig. 24 are given the results of the polymer composition as a function of the extent of reaction for different feed ratios for the pair styrene – 2-vinylthiophene[9] ($r_1 = 0.35$, $r_2 = 3.10$, $r_1 r_2 = 1.09$). This pair approximates to the ideal case. The curves show that the greater reactivity of the vinylthiophene causes both feed and polymer to approach pure styrene at high extents of reaction until, when the reaction has neared completion, almost pure styrene is left.

In commercial preparations, it is very desirable to produce a polymer which is homogeneous. The above discussion suggests two ways this may be achieved (a) by stopping the reaction short of complete conversion or (b) feeding in controlled amounts of monomers in order to maintain the feed composition at a constant value.

4. Reactivity of Monomer

(a) Evaluation of Monomer Reactivity Ratios

The determination of these ratios usually requires carrying out the polymerisation to low degrees of conversion. The monomers free from dissolved air are sealed in an evacuated tube together with the initiator. Polymerisation is allowed to proceed at a fixed temperature and the polymer is isolated from the reaction mixture at the end of a suitable time. If the polymers are insoluble, the reaction is best carried out in a suitable solvent. After isolation often by precipitation with a solvent such as ether or methanol, the polymer may be analysed e.g. by chemical means for elements[10,11,12] (e.g. nitrogen) or characteristic groups (e.g. acetoxy in vinyl acetate). Some polymers are amenable to physical methods of analysis such as refractive index[13], ultra-violet spectra[14] or infra-red spectra[15].

The data so obtained may be analysed by

1. Fitting directly to the plots of polymer/monomer composition curves. This method is insensitive to small changes in r_1 and r_2.

2. The copolymerisation equation may be re-arranged to

$$r_2 = \frac{[M_1]}{[M_2]} \left\{ \frac{\mathrm{d}[M_2]}{\mathrm{d}[M_1]} \left(1 + \frac{[M_1]}{[M_2]} r_1\right) - 1 \right\} \tag{16}$$

The experimental data gives $\mathrm{d}[M_2]/\mathrm{d}[M_1]$ from the composition of the copolymer for low conversions. Putting in values of $d[M_2]/d[M_1]$ and $[M_1]/[M_2]$ this equation defines a straight line when r_1 and r_2 are treated as the variables. Each experiment, using different values of the feed ratio, will give one line so that the true values of r_1 and r_2 for the system will be those given at the intersection. In practice there will be some error so that

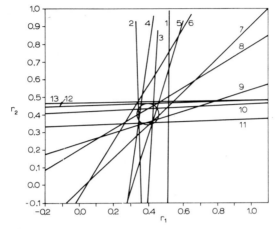

Fig. 25. Estimation of reactivity ratios by the method of intersections. The circle represent the most probable value for the r_1, r_2 value[17].

the lines may not necessarily intersect at a point but give an area contained by these lines. Such data are given in Fig. 25. The size of this area gives information about the accuracy of the results.

3. From plots of F_1 vs. f_1[16]. Equation 11 can be rearranged to

$$\frac{f_1(1 - 2F_1)}{(1 - f_1)F_1} = r_2 + \frac{f_1{}^2(F_1 - 1)}{(1 - f_1)^2 F_1} r_1 \tag{17}$$

Equation 17 is that of a straight line with slope r_1 and intercept r_2.

(b) Relative Reactivities of Monomers

The examples of reactivity ratios given in Table 11 indicate that two types only need be considered (a) those where r_1 and r_2 are less than 1 and (b) r_1 is > 1 and r_2 is very small. A value of the reactivity ratio of less than 1 means that $k_{11} < k_{12}$ and hence the chain with radical $\dot{m}_1$ at its end has a preference for reacting with the monomer M_2. Then if both r_1 and r_2 are less than unity there will be a preference for the monomers in the growing copolymer chain to alternate. In case (b) where r_1 is greater than unity $i.e.$ $k_{11} > k_{12}$, alternation in the growing chain arises because the reactivity of the second monomer for itself is very low $i.e.$ $k_{22} \ll k_{21}$.

References p. 139

TABLE 12

PRODUCTS OF MONOMER REACTIVITY RATIOS[18]

	α-methylstyrene	butadiene	styrene	isopropenyl acetate	vinyl acetate	vinyl chloride	2-chlorobutadiene	2,5-dichlorostyrene	methyl methacrylate	vinylidene chloride	methyl acrylate	methyl vinyl ketone	β-chloroethyl acrylate	methacrylonitrile	acrylonitrile	diethyl fumarate	maleic anhydride
butadiene	1.0																
styrene																	
isopropenyl acetate			1.0														
vinyl acetate			0.55	0.63													
vinyl chloride		0.2	0.34		0.4												
2-chlorobutadiene		0.2	0.16			0.5											
2,5-dichlorostyrene	0.07	0.19	0.24		0.12		0.75										
methyl methacrylate		0.1	0.16			0.7		1.0									
vinylidene chloride			0.14			0.9		0.5	0.61								
methyl acrylate		0.04	0.10				0.75	0.9	0.8								
methyl vinyl ketone			0.06						0.9								
β-chloroethyl acrylate			0.06									0.9					
methacrylonitrile	0.006	0.01	0.06	0.24	0.24			0.43									
acrylonitrile	0.006	0.02	0.02	0.25	0.13	0.24	0.13	0.015	0.34				0.24	1.1			
diethyl fumarate		0.02	0.02	0.004	0.06	0.17			0.56						0.56		
maleic anhydride	0.00006	0.0002	0.002	0.0002	0.002		0.13	0.13	0.6							0.6	

As mentioned earlier, the ability to alternate is best indicated by the product $r_1 r_2$. It has been shown possible to tabulate pairs of monomers according to the values of the product $r_1 r_2$[17]. Data of this kind is given in Table 12 where the values of $r_1 r_2$ tend to be smaller the farther apart they are in the list. This separation might in fact be due to a sequence of polarities, species differing in polarity having a greater tendency to react with each other.

Although it is impossible from the reactivity ratios to obtain the individual constants, k_{11}, k_{12} etc., the relative reactivity of a monomer towards different radicals can be assessed.

The inverse of the ratio r_1 or r_2 is a measure of the relative reactivity of the radical with a second monomer compared with reactivity with its own. A list of values of $1/r_1$ will therefore give a table of relative reactivities of monomers with respect to a "standard" monomer *i.e.* a figure which is proportional to k_{12}. Examples using styrene, methyl methacrylate and vinyl chloride as the reference radicals are given in Table 13. From such

TABLE 13

RELATIVE REACTIVITIES OF MONOMERS WITH DIFFERENT POLYMER RADICALS[9]

Radical	Styrene	Vinyl chloride	Methyl methacrylate
Styrene	1.0	30	2.2
Butadiene	1.3	—	4.0
Methyl vinyl ketone	3.5	10	—
Acrylonitrile	2.4	>15	0.74
Methyl acrylate	1.3	12	—
Vinyl chloride	0.05	1.0	0.07
Alkyl acetate	0.01	0.9	0.04
Vinyl acetate	0.02	0.5	0.05
Vinyl ethyl ether	0.61	0.5	—

data[18] the effects of substituents X in the vinyl derivative $CH_2{=}CHX$ fall in an order which is roughly the same for all radicals and is that expected if the radicals derived from the monomers are placed in order of decreasing resonance energies. For example the radical from styrene is stabilised as shown by the resonance energy of 20 kcal whereas the radical from vinyl chloride is stabilised to a much smaller degree of the order of 1–2 kcal. In other words the reactivity is related to the resonance possibilities in the radicals which arise from the structures of the form

$$CH_2{-}CH$$
$$\overset{|}{\underset{|}{C}}{-}\overset{..}{O}$$
$$CH_3$$

for the substituent $X = COCH_3$ and

for $X = C_6H_5$.

However, any substituents which stabilise the radicals will be likely to stabilise the monomers themselves. If such stabilisation occurs to any extent the reactivity of the monomers will be reduced. Resonance stabilisation in the monomer will act in the opposite sense to that in the radical. Studies of the resonance energies of the monomers arising from the introduction of different substituents have been shown to vary in the same sequence as that in the radicals but of considerably less magnitude. For example the resonance stabilisation in styrene or butadiene monomers due to conjugation is only of the order of 3 kcal. It is this low degree of stabilisation which allows the statement that the reactivity depends to a large degree on resonance of the radical rather than of the monomer. The reactivity ratios discussed above give information about the reaction of one radical with different monomers. To obtain a broader picture, information as to the reactivities of the same monomer with different radicals is necessary. This data may be obtained from knowledge of r_1 and the rate constant k_{11} determined by the methods described in Chapter 3. Some values of the rate constants of monomers with different radicals are given in Table 14.

TABLE 14

PROPAGATION RATE CONSTANTS AT 60°C

$(l\ mole^{-1}\ sec^{-1})$[18]

Monomer	Radical			
	Styrene	Methyl methacrylate	Methyl acrylate	Vinyl acetate
Styrene	176	789	11,500	~ 370,000
Methyl methacrylate	338	367		~ 250,000
Methyl acrylate	235		2,100	~ 37,000
Vinyl acetate	3.2	18.3	233	3,700

The order of the reactivity of the radicals with the monomers is the reverse of that for the reactivity of monomers with radicals. In the table styrene is the least reactive and vinyl acetate the most; hence as anticipated resonance stabilisation of the radical depresses its activity.

In general the effect of a substituent in depressing the activity of the radical is greater than its effect in enhancing the activity of the monomer.

In a discussion of the reactivity of these radicals and monomers, some note must be taken of the polarity of the substituents as well as the possibility of steric interference. Referring back to Table 12, the polar effects in copolymerisation follow the general pattern found in other organic reactions. Indeed in a series of nuclear substituted styrenes, the reactivities have been shown to be dependent on the Hammett σ value of the substituent[19]. It has been suggested that the alternating tendency is due to the interaction of the permanent dipoles in the monomers but the extent of the polar contribution to the reactivities has not been completely resolved.

Steric effects also play a part in copolymerisation. A number of 1,2-disubstituted (CHX=CHY) are reluctant to copolymerise whereas the corresponding 1,1-compounds (CH₂=CXY) react easily; again the former compounds will not homopolymerise whereas the latter will. This behaviour may be attributable to steric hindrance. The two kinds of compounds may be expected to react with a growing radical according to reactions a and b

$$—CH_2—\dot{C}HZ + CHX{=}CHY \rightarrow —CH_2CHZCHX\dot{C}HY \tag{a}$$

$$—CH_2—\dot{C}HZ + CH_2{=}CXY \rightarrow —CH_2CHZCH_2—\dot{C}XY \tag{b}$$

It is likely therefore that in case (b) there will be less steric hindrance than in case (a) where the bulky Z and X groups are on adjacent carbon atoms.

5. Termination Reactions

To obtain a complete picture of addition copolymerisation, notice must be taken of the termination rates. The position of the overall kinetics may be simplified by the choice of initiator which releases radicals capable of combining equally efficiently with either monomer. The rate of initiation of both monomers will be given by $v_i = 2fk_i[I]$. Two steady state conditions may be applied; one to the total radical concentration, the other to the separate concentrations of $\dot{m}_1$ and $\dot{m}_2$. The first requires that the rate of initiation is equal to the termination rate. The termination reactions may be written as

$$
\begin{aligned}
\dot{m}_1 + \dot{m}_1 &\rightarrow M_{n+m} & k_{t_{11}} \\
\dot{m}_1 + \dot{m}_2 &\rightarrow M_{n+m} & k_{t_{12}} \\
\dot{m}_2 + \dot{m}_2 &\rightarrow M_{n+m} & k_{t_{22}}
\end{aligned}
$$

The first equation for the steady state then becomes

$$v_i = 2k_{t_{11}}[\dot{m}_1]^2 + 2k_{t_{12}}[\dot{m}_1][\dot{m}_2] + 2k_{t_{22}}[\dot{m}_2]^2 \tag{18}$$

The second steady state condition is the one used earlier (equation 4).

The total rate of use of the monomers (overall polymerisation rate) is given by

$$-\frac{d([M_1] + [M_2])}{dt} = k_{11}[\dot{m}_1][M_1] + k_{21}[\dot{m}_2][M_1] + k_{12}[\dot{m}_1][M_2] + k_{22}[\dot{m}_2][M_2]$$

Using equations 4 and 18 the radical concentrations can be eliminated to give

$$-\frac{d([M_1]+[M_2])}{dt} = \frac{(r_1[M_1]^2 + 2[M_1][M_2] + r_2[M_2]^2)\, v_i^{\frac{1}{2}}\, \delta_1}{\left(r_1^2[M_1]^2 + 2\phi r_1 r_2 \dfrac{\delta_2}{\delta_1}[M_1][M_2] + r_2 \dfrac{\delta_2}{\delta_1}[M_2]^2\right)^{\frac{1}{2}}}$$

where

$$\delta_1 = \left(\frac{2k_{t_{11}}}{k_{12}^2}\right)^{\frac{1}{2}}; \quad \delta_2 = \left(\frac{2k_{t_{22}}}{k_{12}^2}\right)^{\frac{1}{2}}; \quad \phi = \frac{k_{t_{12}}}{2k_{t_{11}}^{\frac{1}{2}} k_{t_{22}}^{\frac{1}{2}}}$$

Similarly, equations can be derived for the consumption of the separate monomers. ϕ compares the cross termination constants with those for pairs of like radicals. If $\phi > 1$ then cross termination is favoured; if < 1 the converse is true. Values of ϕ may be determined using the rate of copolymerisation equation and a knowledge of r_1 and r_2. The values of δ may be found from studies of homopolymerisation. In general, a value of ϕ greater than 1 is typical and it may be that such a preference for cross termination arises from differences in polarity analogous to the effects discussed for alternation.

6. Block Copolymers

The copolymerisation discussed in this chapter leads to materials in which the monomer units are arranged in (a) a random fashion (b) an alternating sequence along the chain or (c) an arrangement lying between the extremes (a) and (b). Ordered arrangements may be obtained in which the monomer units are in a "block" giving a copolymer made from two monomers X and Y a structure of the form

—XXXX YYY YY XXX YYY—

Thus a polyoxyethylene glycol of formula VI[20]

$$HO(CH_2CH_2O)_nH$$

(VI)

and mol. wt. 1000–6000 has been introduced into a polymer such as polyethylene terephthalate when a polymer of composition VII could be produced

—O[OCC$_6$H$_5$COOC$_2$H$_4$O]$_m$OCC$_6$H$_4$COO(C$_2$H$_4$O)$_n$OOCC$_6$H$_5$COO—

(VII)

so that at intervals down the chain there would be blocks of polyoxyethylene glycol units $(CH_2CH_2O)_n$.

These polymers may be prepared by condensing the components dimethyl terephthalate, ethylene glycol and the polyoxyethylene glycols. It is interesting to note that the homopolymers themselves are incompatible when melted together. The product made in fibre form has improved dyeability and flexibility with little or no alteration in the extensibility. Unfortunately as a fibre it suffers from instability to ultra-violet radiation.

Block copolymers exist to some extent in silk fibroin where units of glycine and alanine are grouped together. The composition of silk is discussed in Chapter 9. In the field of addition polymers[21], block copolymers have been made by flowing one monomer containing an initiator (azobiscyclohexanoic carbonitrile) along a tube where the monomer was irradiated and polymerisation commenced. The monomer containing a high concentration of growing radicals then ran into and was well dispersed in the second monomer. Thus the growing chains continued to grow in the second monomer and a copolymer was formed with part of its chain made from the first monomer and part from the second. Naturally, this kind of experiment gives some of the homopolymer from which the block copolymer must be separated. It is possible to produce a block copolymer by suspending droplets of styrene in an aqueous solution of methacrylic acid and polymerising in the aqueous phase when some of the growing radicals diffuse into the styrene droplets[22].

A further technique has been employed in which a polymer was formed in the presence of an efficient transfer reagent. Carbon tetrabromide was used in the presence of styrene. The polystyrene so made contained a large number of bromine and tribromomethyl groups; this polymer when dissolved in methyl methacrylate produced free radicals on irradiation by removal of a bromine atom; the radicals were then able to react with the monomer giving a block copolymer of styrene and methyl methacrylate[23].

Although block copolymers have not achieved great commercial significance, they are of considerable interest since the properties of these polymers are different from normal copolymers. An example of this is the block copolymer VII quoted above whose melting-point is not reduced to the extent anticipated for random copolymers. It is possible, in such copolymers, that a long sequence of units of one kind would allow the copolymer to have opportunities for forming crystallites which would be denied to the random material.

A possible and more subtle example of a block copolymer may be the isotactic materials referred to in Chapter 3. In this kind of polymer it seems likely that blocks of isotactic material may be interspersed with blocks of atactic.

7. Graft Copolymers

In some instances, it is possible to join or graft a polymer on to another as a side chain. The simplest way to form a graft is by transfer reaction with a dead polymer. Thus dibenzoyl peroxide will initiate reaction in polymethyl acrylate containing p-chlorostyrene[24]. The reaction may be written as

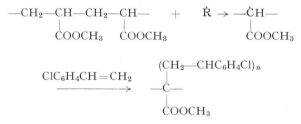

Other workers have used *e.g.* polymethyl methacrylate and vinyl chloride, polyvinyl chloride and methyl methacrylate[25]. Another example was a vinylidene chloride–styrene copolymer in the presence of which vinyl acetate was polymerised. In this instance chlorine atoms were abstracted from the copolymer; the resulting radicals acted as centres for polymerisation of the vinyl acetate. By this technique chains of vinyl acetate are grafted. There are very many variations of this[26]. Fibres made from graft copolymers of polyacrylonitrile and polyvinyl acetate, of polyacrylonitrile and polyvinyl alcohol have been examined[27]. Another possible means of forming an active centre in a dead polymer is by irradiation; using a source of radiation such as ^{60}Co, styrene has been grafted on to polyethylene fibres.

Graft copolymers usually may be separated from the homopolymers because of considerable differences in solubility. If the graft is a long one the polymer will vary in its properties according to the solvent. Thus methyl methacrylate chains can be grafted on to rubber molecules. When such a graft polymer is dissolved in benzene, the rubber chains will dissolve and remain extended whereas benzene, a poor solvent for methyl methacrylate, will cause the polymethyl methacrylate chains to coil up. Films cast from this solvent will be rubbery in character since the methyl methacrylate chains are virtually reduced to a very small volume and do not play a part. This graft copolymer will also dissolve in chloroform but in this instance the rubber chains coil themselves so that films cast from this solvent have the properties of polymethyl methacrylate[31].

In the fibre field, polymers of improved dyeability have been made by polymerising acrylonitrile in the presence of a water soluble high molecular weight material *e.g.* polyvinyl alcohol, polyvinylpyridine etc.[28].

Graft copolymers may be made in the field of condensation polymers. Thus reaction of nylon 6 or 66 yields a graft with a polyethylene oxide side chain of about 6 units[29]. Alternatively the polyamide may be made the side chain by reacting polymethyl acrylate with caprolactam[30].

REFERENCES

1 C. W. AYAS, *J. App. Chem. London*, 4 (1954) 444.
2 H. LUDEWIG, *Faserforsch. u. Textiltech.*, 6 (1955) 277.
3 V. C. EHRLICH, *Modern Textiles Mag.*, 39 (1958) 59.
4 T. ALFREY, JR. and G. GOLDFINGER, *J. Chem. Phys.*, 12 (1944) 205.
  F. R. MAYO and G. LEWIS, *J. Am. Chem. Soc.*, 66 (1944) 1594.
5 F. M. LEWIS and F. R. MAYO, *J. Am. Chem. Soc.*, 70 (1948) 1533.
6 F. T. WALL, *J. Am. Chem. Soc.*, 66 (1944) 2050.
7 F. R. MAYO and F. M. LEWIS, *J. Am. Chem. Soc.*, 66 (1944) 1594.
8 I. SKEIST, *J. Am. Chem. Soc.*, 68 (1946) 1781.
9 G. M. BURNETT, *Mechanisms of Polymer Reactions*, Vol. 3 of the series *High Polymers*, Interscience, New York, 1954.
10 F. M. LEWIS, C. WALLING, WM. CUMMINGS, E. R. BRIGGS and F. R. MAYO, *J. Am. Chem. Soc.*, 70 (1948) 1519.
11 K. NOZAKI, *J. Polymer Sci.*, 1 (1946) 455.
12 C. WALLING, E. R. BRIGGS, K. B. WOLFSTIRN and F. R. MAYO, *J. Am. Chem. Soc.*, 70 (1948) 1537.
13 F. M. LEWIS, C. WALLING, WM. CUMMINGS, E. R. BRIGGS and W. I. WENISCH, *J. Am. Chem. Soc.*, 70 (1948) 1527.
14 R. SIMHA and L. A. WALL, *J. Research Nat. Bur. Standards*, 41 (1948) 521.
15 C. S. MARVEL *et al.*, *Ind. Eng. Chem.*, 40 (1948) 2371.
16 M. FINEMAN and S. D. ROSS, *J. Polymer Sci.*, 5 (1950) 259.
17 T. ALFREY, JR., J. J. BOHRER and H. MARK, *Copolymerisation*, Vol. 8 of the series *High Polymers*, Interscience, New York, 1952.
18 F. R. MAYO and C. WALLING, *Chem. Revs.*, 46 (1950) 191.
19 C. WALLING, E. R. BRIGGS, K. B. WOLFSTIRN and F. R. MAYO, *J. Am. Chem. Soc.*, 70 (1948) 1537.
20 D. COLEMAN, *J. Polymer Sci.*, 14 (1954) 15.
21 J. A. HICKS and H. W. MELVILLE, *J. Polymer Sci.*, 12 (1954) 461.
  G. GOLDFINGER and C. HEFFELFINGER, *J. Polymer Sci.*, 13 (1954) 123.
  H. W. MELVILLE and B. D. STEAD, *J. Polymer Sci.*, 16 (1955) 565.
22 A. S. DUNN and H. W. MELVILLE, *Nature*, 169 (1952) 699.
23 A. S. DUNN, B. D. STEAD and H. W. MELVILLE, *Trans. Faraday Soc.*, 50 (1954) 279.
24 R. B. CARLIN and N. E. SHAKESPEARE, *J. Am. Chem. Soc.*, 68 (1946) 876.
25 G. SMETS and M. CLAESON, *J. Polymer Sci.*, 8 (1952) 289.
26 R. A. HAYES, *J. Polymer Sci.*, 11 (1953) 531.
  J. SCHMETS and G. SCHMETS, *Bull. soc. chim. Belges*, 63 (1954) 59.
27 *Faserforsch. u. Textiltech.*, 7 (1956) 213.
28 E. I. JONES, L. B. MORGAN, J. F. L. ROBERTS and S. M. TODD, *B.P.* 715, 194.
29 A. C. HAAS, S. G. COHEN, A. C. OGLESBY and E. R. KARLIN, *J. Polymer Sci.*, 15 (1955) 427.
30 *U.S.P.* 2,524,045.
31 F. M. MERRETT, *Brit. Rubber Producers Research Assoc.*, No. 264.
32 P. J. FLORY, *Principles of Polymer Chemistry*, Cornell Univ. Press, Ithaca, 1953.
33 C. H. BAMFORD, W. G. BARB, A. D. JENKINS and P. F. ONYON, *The Kinetics of Vinyl Polymerisations by Radical Mechanisms*, Butterworths, London, 1958.

CHAPTER 5

MOLECULAR WEIGHT DETERMINATION

In the previous chapters, some emphasis has been placed on the calculation of the molecular weight of polymers. There is more than one reason for regarding the molecular weight of a polymer as important. In manufacture, this property may be used as a criterion of reproducibility of production or as a means of characterisation of the polymer. In physicochemical or physical studies, although knowledge of the chemical nature may come from the mode of synthesis, it is necessary to have some measure of the size of molecules or better still of the distribution of sizes. However, even though the molecular weight is basic for work on polymers, it is impossible to discuss exhaustively molecular weight determinations here and the reader is referred to standard works[1].

In general, techniques for molecular weight determination are of two kinds — (a) mainly chemical based on end group analysis and (b) physical, based on studies of the properties such as osmotic pressure, light scattering etc.

1. Chemical Methods: End-Group Analysis

Simple methods of chemical analysis may be used to determine the molecular weights of polymers provided that the molecule possesses one or more groups capable of undergoing chemical reaction and distinct in character from the main chain units.

The number of such groups per molecule must be known unambiguously; such knowledge may come from the mode of formation of the polymer. Usually the method is confined to analysis of linear polymers carrying characteristic end groups, when the number of active ends per molecule is measured. In this case the molecular weight can be calculated from the end-group analysis to be

$$\bar{M}_n = \frac{\text{(weight of polymer)} \times \text{(number of end groups per molecule)}}{\text{total number of end groups determined}}$$

Since it is the number of end groups which has been measured, the molecular weight must be the number average. Erroneous molecular weights will arise if the polymer has branches carrying the reactive groups or if the polymer contains any unreacted groups left in the polymer, by virtue for example of the reaction not following completely the accepted equation.

End-group analysis relies on the detection of a group attached to a molecule of high molecular weight. Hence the higher the molecular weight the larger the quantity of polymer required for analysis and the more difficult is the chemical reaction to carry out. For this reason chemical methods are restricted to the analysis of polymers of molecular weights up to the order of 20,000.

End-group determinations have been of great value for polyesters and polyamides[2,3,4]. With the former compounds, the carboxyl end groups have been titrated particularly for the esters made from ω-hydroxy acids e.g. polyundecanates (I), which carry one carboxyl group per molecule.

$$HO[(CH_2)_9OCO]_n(CH_2)_9COOH$$

(I)

Polyesters made from two difunctional reactants are somewhat more difficult since it is necessary to know the ratio of the number of hydroxyl ends to carboxyl. In a system such as that studied by Flory[3] in which decamethylene glycol was heated with excess of adipic acid, it could be safely assumed that the polymer had two carboxyl groups per molecule. Polymers having an excess of one component over the other would require both hydroxyl and carboxyl groups to be determined, in which case the sum would be twice the total number of ends. Analysis of polyethylene terephthalate is possible by dissolution in hot benzyl alcohol and titration with sodium benzylate as the alkali[5].

Reaction of the polymer with succinic anhydride (II) gives rise to further carboxyl groups in place of hydroxyl

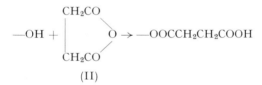

(II)

Titration of the treated material will give the total number of end groups whereas the difference in the titration of the treated and untreated will give the number of hydroxyl groups. Another possibility[6] is to immerse the polymer in heavy water several times until the OH and the COOH interchange their hydrogen atoms for deuterium. The deuterated polymer can be burnt and the water so produced analysed for deuterium[7].

For polyamides, titration of a solution of the polymer is possible using an alkali or acid according to whether it is the carboxyl or amino groups to be estimated[4]. The titration is carried out in a solvent such as phenol, or m-cresol and the end-point may be determined by use of an indicator or conductometrically. End-group analysis of fibres made from condensation polymers is particularly valuable since they have molecular weights in the range 10,000–20,000, a region too high for the methods of molecular weight determination used for small molecules and too low for easy use of osmometry.

Analysis of the end groups in addition polymers comes down to detection of the group arising from the initiator, and may be successful in cases where the reaction is well defined and there is no chain transfer as in some vinyl polymerisations[9,10,11]. A particular case of an acrylonitrile polymer using hydroxyl radicals as initiator has been successfully carried out by analysis for the hydroxyl groups in the polymer[8]. Generally end-group analysis is more difficult with addition polymers, since the number of possible ways of terminating a chain radical is large and the polymer structure may not be accurately known. If the vinyl polymerisation is carried out when the predominant reaction is chain transfer (in the presence of transfer agents *e.g.* mercaptans or carbon tetrachloride[12,13]) it may be assumed that the elements of one molecule of the chain transfer reagent will be present per molecule of polymer so that the number of polymer molecules may be estimated from the number of fragments of the chain transfer agent.

2. Physical Methods

(a) Colligative Properties

The most common methods of measuring molecular weights depend on the colligative properties of solutions — depression of freezing point, elevation of boiling-point, lowering of vapour pressure and osmotic pressure.

In making use of these properties, it may be assumed that the vapour pressure of the solute is negligible so that the vapour pressure lowering due to the solute is a measure of the change in activity of the solvent. The relation between the changes in activity is given by Raoults Law which equates the fractional lowering of the solvent vapour pressure to the mole fraction of the solute,

$$\frac{p_0 - p}{p_0} = \frac{m_2}{m_1 + m_2} = N_2 \tag{1}$$

where p_0 is the vapour pressure of the pure solvent, p, the vapour pressure of the solution made up of m_1 moles of solvent and m_2 of solute. The mole fraction is N_2. In a dilute solution, the activity a_1 of the solvent is p/p_0 and the left-hand side of equation 1 is $1 - a_1$. For dilute conditions, a_1 may be written as the mole fraction so that

$$1 - a_1 = 1 - \frac{m_1}{m_1 + m_2} = \frac{m_2}{m_1 + m_2} = a_2 \tag{2}$$

Thus the measurement of the depression of the activity of the solvent enables the mole fraction of the solute to be found and hence, from its weight concentration, the molecular weight.

The depression in activity may be found from the boiling-point elevation when the temperature increase necessary to restore the vapour pressure of the solution to atmospheric is determined, or by the observation of the freezing-point depression when the temperature is lowered until the activity of the solvent in the solution equals that of the pure crystalline solvent.

Both these temperature differences, ΔT, are related to the molecular weights; for an ideal system

$$\frac{\Delta T}{c} = \frac{RT^2}{\Delta H \varrho M} \tag{3}$$

where ΔH is the latent heat of fusion or evaporation, and ϱ the density of the solvent; c is the concentration of solute of molecular weight M.

The accuracy with which small temperature differences can be measured limits the maximum molecular weight which can be determined by these two methods.

Using benzene as solvent the value of $\Delta T/c$ may be calculated from the constants in the equation. In Table 15 are given some results for substances of molecular weights ranging from 5,000–100,000. These figures indicate that measurement of changes of temperature of the order of 0.001 °C will have to be made in an experiment; this kind of difference is difficult to determine experimentally, so that this method is restricted to compounds whose molecular weights are 5,000 or less.

TABLE 15

M	$\Delta T/c$ in °C/g/100 ml		π/c in g/cm²/g/100 ml
	for boiling-point	for freezing-point	
5,000	0.0062	0.0116	50
10,000	0.0031	0.0058	25
50,000	0.0006	0.0012	5
100,000	0.0003	0.0006	2.5

The difficulties of obtaining accurate molecular weights are made more exacting with polymer solutions because of the deviations from the limiting dilution behaviour exhibited by their solutions even at low concentrations. Any measurements made on polymer solutions must therefore be conducted at low concentrations and the results be extrapolated to infinite dilution.

A polymer molecule may be regarded as made up of segments each of

References p. 158

which is capable of free rotation at the joints. The molecule is capable therefore of taking up numerous configurations in solution. This is diagrammatically shown in Fig. 26 where the segments are given by the arrows and the distance between the ends of the molecule by r. The polymer molecule is capable of coiling up to a degree which will depend on the restrictions placed on free rotation of the bonds and the interac-

Fig. 26. Freely jointed chain[1].

tion of the polymer with solvent molecules. In a "good" solvent where polymer/solvent contacts are favoured, the chains will tend to take up the fully extended form. In a "poor" solvent the molecule will tend to form a coiled configuration. The volume which the polymer molecule in this randomly coiled condition occupies will be very much larger than the molecule itself $e.g.$ the average "density" of the segments composing the dissolved polymer molecule may be as small as 10^{-2} g/cm^3. The configuration of these molecules is one which can be derived by a statistical treatment which shows that the molecule may be approximated by a symmetric statistical distribution of chain elements about their collective centre of gravity. The simplest way to characterise the chain is by the root mean square distance between the ends. The volume which the dissolved polymer molecule exerts is therefore many times its molecular volume and, since the colligative properties used for molecular weight determinations require that molecules make individual contributions, the measurement must be determined under conditions sufficiently dilute to allow the individual polymer molecules to occupy separate volumes. Thus in determinations of polymer molecular weights, restrictions are introduced both by the fact that the molecular weights themselves are high as well as by the shape which a molecule may have in solution.

Equation 3 refers to an ideal system where the simple law given in equation 1 holds. In practice, deviations from this simple picture occur; to enable this formula to be used, it may be necessary for the measurements to be made at several values of c and the values of $\Delta T/c$ extrapolated to zero concentration to obtain $(\Delta T/c)_{c=0}$. This limiting value at "infinite" dilution or zero concentration can then be regarded as the ideal and used for calculations using equation 3. Further all polymers, unless specially fractionated, are made up of molecules of more than one molecular weight. Hence any value for the molecular weight of such materials will be an average one. The colligative properties just discussed are measures of $1 - a_1$ when the system is so dilute that $a_1 = N_1$. N_2 in this system now is the sum of the mole fractions of all the different molecular weight species in the polymer. The mole fraction N_i of each species will make its contribution so that the value of N_2, the mole fraction of the solute, will be the sum of the fractions of each species

$$N_2 = \sum_i N_i$$

In a dilute solution the mole fraction of the solute may be approximated to m_2/m_1. This may be put in terms of concentrations *i.e.* in moles per unit volume. The concentration c in g/ml will become c/M moles/ml; if the molar volume of the solvent is v_1 then the number of moles in 1 ml is given by $1/v_1$ so that m_2/m_1 becomes $v_1(c/M)$. If there are a number of species, the number of moles will be the sum so that N_2 approximates to $v_1 \sum_i c_i/M_i$ where c_i is the concentration of the ith species of molecular weight M_i. If now a solution of concentration c is made of average molecular weight $\bar{M}$, the mole fraction $N_2 \sim v_1(c/\bar{M})$.

Comparing these equations for N_2 shows that

$$\bar{M} = \frac{c}{\sum_i c_i/M_i} = \frac{\sum c_i}{\sum c_i/M_i} \tag{4}$$

The number of moles/ml of each specie is given by $N_i = c_i/M_i$ and hence this average is obtained by dividing the total weight of material c by the total number of moles. It is therefore the number average $\bar{M}_n$. The expression in terms of the symbols given in Chapter 2 becomes

$$\bar{M}_n = \frac{\sum N_i M_i}{\sum N_i} \quad (c \text{ per unit volume is } \sum N_i M_i)$$

With osmotic pressure measurements, the activity of the solvent in solution is restored to that of pure solvent by applying a pressure to the solution; now the rate of change of activity with pressure is given by

$$\left(\frac{\partial \ln a_1}{\partial P}\right)_{v,N} = \frac{v_1}{RT} \tag{5}$$

where v_1 is the partial molar volume of the solvent. In the osmotic experiments, the pressure is increased from atmospheric to the value of the osmotic pressure plus the atmospheric *i.e.* from P_0 to $P_0 + \pi$; this equation will give the relation, if integration of both sides is carried out from P_0 to $P_0 + \pi$ or o to π,

$$\int_0^\pi \frac{\partial \ln a_1}{\partial P} \, dP = \int_0^\pi \frac{v_1}{RT} \, dP$$

or

$$\int_{a_1}^1 d \ln a_1 = \int_0^\pi \frac{v_1}{RT} \, dP \tag{6}$$

The limits of the integral on the left-hand side are a_1 the activity of the solvent corresponding to an osmotic pressure of zero, a situation which would exist if the solution were on both sides of the membrane. When solvent is put on the other side, the osmotic pressure builds up so that the activity of the solvent in the solution becomes unity, and equal to that of the pure liquid.

In dilute solutions, the partial molar volume may be put equal to the molar volume v_1 of the solvent and treated as constant; equation 6 can then be integrated to

$$- \ln a_1 = \frac{v_1}{RT} \pi \tag{7}$$

In terms of mole fractions in very dilute solutions, $a_1 = N_1 = 1 - N_2$ hence

$$- \ln a_1 = - \ln N_1 = - \ln (1 - N_2) \sim N_2 + \frac{N_2{}^2}{2} + \frac{N_2{}^3}{3} \ldots \sim N_2 \sim \frac{cv_1}{M} \tag{8}$$

The expansion of the logarithm in the form of a series is possible since $N_2 \ll 1$.

Replacing $- \ln a_1$ by cv_1/M in equation 7 gives

$$\frac{\pi}{c} = \frac{RT}{M} \tag{9}$$

As before, this discussion has assumed ideal solutions; for real ones and in particular polymer solutions, osmotic pressures must be determined at several concentrations and the data extrapolated to infinite dilution. In these circumstances equation 9 becomes

$$\left(\frac{\pi}{c}\right)_{c=0} = \frac{RT}{M} \tag{10}$$

Again osmotic pressure is a property dependent on the number of molecules and hence the value of M for a polymer is the number average.

The values of π/c have been calculated from equation 10 for a range of concentrations (column 4, Table 15) and can be seen to show an effect which is more easy to measure than the temperature changes in columns 2 and 3.

Osmotic pressure measurements thus have a considerably wider range of application and it is possible under favourable circumstances to work up to molecular weights of the order of 10^6. The osmometer[14] (Fig. 27)

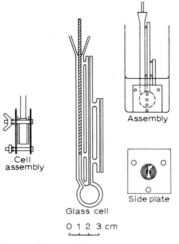

Fig. 27. Zimm.-Myerson osmometer[1].

consists essentially of a device for separating a polymer solution from the solvent by means of a membrane permeable only to the solvent. The common membrane materials used include collodion, regenerated cellulose[15], bacterial cellulose[16], rubber, etc. To the compartment containing the solution is attached a capillary tube and the hydrostatic rise, when equilibrium is reached, may be measured.

In practice the determination of molecular weights by osmometry requires considerable care in order to avoid leaks around or through the membrane. Membranes are available with a range of pore sizes but, even with this choice, it is possible for some of the molecules with the smaller molecular weights to diffuse through and hence lead to erroneous readings. This sets a lower limit to the applicability of osmotic methods which may be 5,000–20,000 depending on the membrane chosen and the kind of polymer being studied.

The results must be extrapolated to infinite dilution before the molecular weight of the polymer can be calculated. This can be done either by an empirical extrapolation of the π/c vs. c graph, which is usually linear or slightly convex towards the concentration axis at the dilutions employed, or by fitting the experimental points to a curve predicted by one of the statistical thermodynamic theories of polymer solutions and using this as a guide in making the extrapolation.

The expression for the reduced osmotic pressure (π/c) may be written as a power series in terms of concentration

$$\frac{\pi}{c} = \frac{RT}{M} + Bc + Cc^2 + \dots \tag{11}$$

The coefficients B and C are known as virial coefficients and theories of polymer solutions relate these to the relative sizes of the polymer and solvent molecules, and the strengths of the interactions between them. In general, the π/c vs. c graph will have a different slope for the same molecular weight polymer specimen in different solvents, but will extrapolate to the same limiting value at infinite dilution as equation 11 requires. This is shown in Fig. 28.

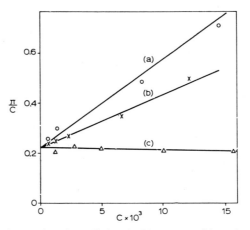

Fig. 28. Plot of π/c vs. c for nitrocellulose in (a) acetone, (b) methanol and (c) nitrobenzene[23].

(b) Light Scattering

When a beam of light — essentially an electromagnetic wave — encounters a molecule, its electrical field polarises the molecule. The degree of polarisation will be proportional to the magnitude of the electrical field of the light wave, and hence changes in the same manner as the electromagnetic wave. This is tantamount to saying that the molecule, provided its dimensions are small with respect to the wavelength of light, behaves as if it were a dipole oscillating in phase with the electrical field. Such a dipole will act as a source of radiation and will emit or scatter light.

In Fig. 29 the light beam of intensity I_0 encounters a molecule placed at the origin of a set of coordinates. The dipole induced in the molecule has a strength which is proportional to the intensity of the electric field,

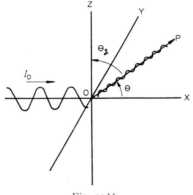

Fig. 29[14].

E, of the light beam given by αE where α is the polarisability. Consider a point P, distant r from O and in a direction so that OP makes an angle θ_z with the axis OZ. On the basis of the electromagnetic theory of light, the intensity of the scattered beam reaching P will be given by

$$i_{\theta_z} = \frac{16\pi^4\alpha^2 I_0}{\lambda^4 r^2} \sin^2\theta_z \qquad (12)$$

where λ is the wavelength. So far it has been tacitly assumed that the light beam is plane polarised with the direction of the electric field in the direction OZ. In practice unpolarised light is used in light scattering experiments; to calculate the scattering from the molecule when unpolarised light is used, it is considered that the latter can be replaced by two beams of light of equal intensity $I_0/2$ but plane polarised at right angles with their electric fields in the directions OZ and OY. If θ_y is the angle which OP makes with OY, the incident beam will induce two dipoles of strengths αE; at right angles to one another in the molecule these two dipoles will radiate and give at the point P intensities i_{θ_y} and i_{θ_z},

$$i_{\theta_y} = \frac{8\pi^4\alpha^2 I_0}{\lambda^4 r^2} \sin^2\theta_y \; ; \quad i_{\theta_z} = \frac{8\pi^4\alpha^2 I_0}{\lambda^4 r^2} \sin^2\theta_z \qquad (13)$$

so that the total intensity of light reaching P is

$$i_{\theta_y} + i_{\theta_z} = i_\theta = \frac{8\pi^4\alpha^2 I_0}{\lambda^4 r^2}(\sin^2\theta_y + \sin^2\theta_z) = \frac{8\pi^4\alpha^2 I_0}{\lambda^4 r^2}(1 + \cos^2\theta) \quad (14)$$

θ is now the angle which OP makes with the direction OX.

Further for a substance like a gas containing a number of molecules, N, contained in a volume V, the quantity of scattered light may be found by adding the contributions from the individual molecules. For such a case

$$i_\theta = \frac{8\pi^4\alpha^2 I_0}{\lambda^4 r^2}\frac{N}{V}(1 + \cos^2\theta) \quad (15)$$

For a solution under extreme conditions of dilution, the scattering may be regarded as arising from the difference in polarisability of the solute molecules as compared with those of the solvent. The excess polarisability is related to the dielectric constants ε and ε_0 of the solution and solvent by the equation

$$\frac{4\pi N}{V}\alpha = \varepsilon - \varepsilon_0 \quad (16)$$

The dielectric constants can be replaced by the squares of the refractive indices ($\varepsilon = n^2$)

$$\alpha = \frac{V}{4\pi N}(n^2 - n_0^2) \quad (17)$$

n may be treated as a function of concentration and expanded in terms of its differential coefficients according to Taylor's Theorem

$$n = f(c) = n_0 + c\left(\frac{df(c)}{dc}\right)_{c=0} + \dots$$

$$\sim n_0 + c\frac{dn}{dc} \quad (18)$$

Hence

$$n^2 = n_0^2 + 2cn_0\left(\frac{dn}{dc}\right)_{c=0} + c^2\left(\frac{dn}{dc}\right)^2_{c=0} \dots$$

$$\sim n_0^2 + 2cn_0\left(\frac{dn}{dc}\right)_{c=0} \quad (19)$$

The polarisability given in equation 17 may be rewritten

$$\alpha = \frac{n_0 c V}{2\pi N}\left(\frac{dn}{dc}\right)_{c=0} \quad (20)$$

When substituted in equation 15

$$\frac{i_\theta}{I_0} = \frac{2\pi^2 c^2 n_0^2 V}{N r^2 \lambda^4}\left(\frac{dn}{dc}\right)^2_{c=0}(1 + \cos^2\theta) \quad (21)$$

Equation 21 may be simplified to some extent by noting that, when c is put equal to $NM/\underline{N}V$ where $\underline{N}$ is Avogadros number, the equation reduces to

$$\frac{i_\theta}{I_0} = \frac{2\pi^2}{\underline{N}\lambda^4 r^2} n_0^2 \left(\frac{\mathrm{d}n}{\mathrm{d}c}\right)^2 Mc\,(1 + \cos^2\theta) \tag{22}$$

This is an equation which enables the molecular weight M to be calculated. However, it involves the variable r which may be difficult to measure. It may, therefore, be simpler to use an integrated form in which the total amount of light scattered is calculated. The turbidity τ is calculated by integrating i_θ/I_0 over all directions *i.e.*

$$\tau = \int \frac{i_\theta}{I_0} 2\pi r^2 \sin\theta\, \mathrm{d}\theta \tag{23}$$

When this is done the equation leads to the simple result

$$\tau = HcM \tag{24}$$

where

$$H = \frac{32\pi^3}{3\lambda^4 \underline{N}} n^2 \left(\frac{\mathrm{d}n}{\mathrm{d}c}\right)^2$$

The molecular weight can therefore be calculated from a knowledge of the reduction of light intensity when a beam passes through a solution. This is the relative loss in light per unit volume of solution containing N particules of solute in a volume V. The changes in intensity of light from I_0 to I when a beam of light passes through the same solution of thickness x may be written as

$$\frac{I}{I_0} = \mathrm{e}^{-\tau x} \sim 1 - \tau x$$

or

$$\tau = \frac{1}{x}\left(\frac{I_0 - I}{I_0}\right) \tag{25}$$

Unfortunately the loss of light which a beam suffers on passage through a solution is very small so that it is not feasible to measure it directly. To measure the intensity of scatter at a fixed angle say 90° is simpler since, although the value may be small, a direct measurement of intensity is made and not the difference of two large intensities. The value of i_{90} can be found from equation 22

$$\frac{i_{90}}{I_0} = \frac{2\pi^2}{\underline{N}\lambda^4 r^2} n_0^2 \left(\frac{\mathrm{d}n}{\mathrm{d}c}\right)^2 Mc = \frac{H}{r^2}\frac{3Mc}{16} \tag{26}$$

so that

$$\tau = HMc = \frac{16}{3}\pi r^2 \frac{i_{90}}{I_0}$$

References p. 158

This method of measurement re-introduces the value of r but measurements of i_{90} can be simply translated to τ, if the instrument used is standardised previously with a substance of known turbidity.

The kind of apparatus used in this measurement is indicated in Fig. 30 and consists of a light source L preferable monochromatic. The mercury

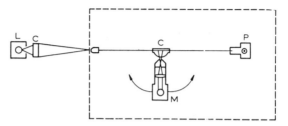

Fig. 30. Light scattering machine with two photomultipliers[1].

arc lamp gives a suitable line of high intensity in the green region ($\lambda = 5350$ Å) of the spectrum. The light beam is collimated and passed through a cell C and the scattered beam allowed to fall on an electron multiplier M. The incident beam may be monitored by allowing a fraction of it to fall on a second multiplier P. The ratio of the signals from the multipliers gives a value proportional to i_{90}/I_0, which can be converted to τ once the instrument has been standardised. The light scattering method requires absolute cleanliness in working since, in the preparation of the solution for test, all dust particles must be eliminated.

Light scattering theory is more complicated than that just discussed by reason of two factors:

(i) The size of the molecules may be too large for a simple dipole to suffice as a representation of the molecule. The molecule must be regarded as a set of dipoles each of which is in phase with the incident wave but, because of this, are out of phase with one another. In Fig. 31 the molecule is

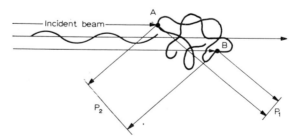

Fig. 31. Mutual interference of light scattered by different parts of the same polymer molecule[14].

represented as a coiled structure; at two points A and B for example, radiation from the induced dipoles will be in different phases and hence on reaching points P_1 and P_2 will interfere either destructively or constructively. To show this, scattering envelopes may be constructed where the distance from the origin to the envelope is proportional to the intensity of scattered light. Fig. 32 shows the relative shapes of the scattering envelopes for a large spherical particle placed at the origin of coordinates

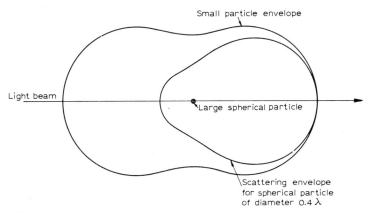

Fig. 32. Scattering envelope of a small particle compared with a large spherical one.

as compared to the shape of the envelope for a small particle. For the small particle (say of size $\lambda/20$), the scattering envelope is symmetrical and dumb-bell in shape; for the large, the forward scattering exceeds the back scattering. The scattering envelope has lost its symmetry and in practice a correction must be made for this. The dissymmetry is characterised by the ratio of the intensities at $45°$ and $135°$ (i_{45}/i_{135}) and, if an assumption is made about the shape of the scattering molecule, it is possible to calculate from this ratio the value of i_{90} which would have been observed had the scattering been of the simple kind for small particles.

(ii) The discussion so far has been concerned with the scattering produced from a number of molecules which are at such large distances apart that each can be regarded as an independent scattering centre so that there is no interference between the scattered beams. However, when the molecules get closer together, interference between the scattered beams will occur; when the molecules are sufficiently close together as in a liquid or a perfect crystal, the interference will be extreme and it is possible to show that, at any point P, the light scattered from one part of the system will be exactly $180°$ out of phase from light from another part. In such circumstances, the amount of light scattered is zero since destructive interference is complete. Scattering from a solution of finite concentration is subject to the same argument so that again complete interference occurs.

Nevertheless liquids and solutions do scatter light; scattering centres exist due to the inhomogeneities which occur from fluctuations in density and concentration. If a small volume element of solution be considered, the concentration on average will be constant but, at any instant of time due to the random thermal motion of the particles, it will be different from the average concentration. Density fluctuations are responsible for the scattering from pure solvents, but need not be considered since their contribution may be eliminated by deducting the intensity observed for the solvent from that of the solution.

For a solution the random fluctuation of concentration of solute in a volume δV causes an increase in the polarisability above the average value. This increase $\Delta \alpha$ replaces α in equation 15 and, in terms of the changes of the dielectric constant, is given by

$$\Delta \alpha = \frac{\Delta \varepsilon \delta V}{4\pi} \tag{27}$$

The original equation is also modified by the fact that instead of a number of molecules N in a volume V there are $1/\delta V$ scattering elements in a unit volume. N/V is thus replaced by $1/\delta V$. The scattering equation becomes with these modifications

$$\frac{i_\theta}{I_0} = \frac{\pi^2 (\Delta \varepsilon)^2 \delta V}{2\lambda^4 r^2} (1 + \cos^2 \theta) \tag{28}$$

The average change in dielectric constant can be replaced by the average change in the square of the refractive index. This procedure changes the fluctuations $\overline{(\Delta \varepsilon)^2}$ into fluctuations in concentration, $\overline{(\Delta c)^2}$

$$\overline{(\Delta \varepsilon)^2} = \left(\frac{\partial \varepsilon}{\partial c} \right)^2 \overline{(\Delta c)^2} = \left[2n_0 \left(\frac{dn}{dc} \right)_{c=0} \right]^2 \overline{(\Delta c)^2} \tag{29}$$

The random fluctuations in concentration are related to the thermo-dynamic properties of the system by the equation

$$\overline{(\Delta c)^2} = \frac{kT}{\dfrac{\partial^2 G}{\partial c^2}} = kT \frac{v_1 c}{\delta V \dfrac{\partial \mu_1}{\partial c}} \tag{30}$$

where G is the free energy of the solvent and μ_1 its chemical potential. The chemical potential may be translated to osmotic pressure

$$-\frac{\partial \mu_1}{\partial c} = v_1 \frac{\partial \pi}{\partial c} \tag{31}$$

Substituting for $(\overline{\Delta\varepsilon})^2$ in terms of osmotic pressure gives

$$\tau = Hc \, \frac{RT}{\dfrac{\partial\pi}{\partial c}} \tag{32}$$

The intensity of light scattered therefore depends on concentration in a manner similar to that of osmotic pressure.

If the dependence of osmotic pressure on concentration is given by a power series (equation 11) then equation 32 becomes

$$\frac{Hc}{\tau} = \frac{1}{M_2} + 2Bc \tag{33}$$

where B is the second virial coefficient. Plots of Hc/τ vs. c may be either linear or curved, and depend on polymer–solvent interactions in the same way as osmotic pressure graphs but, when a satisfactory extrapolation has been made, the value of Hc/τ when $c \to 0$ may be equated to $1/M_2$ (Fig. 33).

Weight average molecular weight. With polymers which are composed of molecules of different sizes, the molecular weight obtained is an average value. Molecular weights found by light scattering techniques are weight

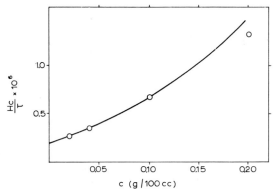

Fig. 33. Hc/τ vs. c plot for high molecular weight polystyrene in benzene[14].

averages. This arises from the fact that the quantity of light irradiated depends on the square of the polarisation α which is in turn dependent on the size of the molecule. If there are in the system molecules of molecular weight M_i at a concentration c_i, the turbidity of the solution will be the sum of those arising from each molecular size

$$\tau = \sum_i \tau_i \tag{34}$$

Now from equation 24 $\tau_i = Hc_iM_i$ and, if it be assumed for such a series of compounds of differing molecular weight that $(dn/dc)_{c=0}$ is the same for all, then

$$\tau = H \sum c_iM_i \tag{35}$$

In terms of the average value of the molecular weight

$$\tau = Hc\bar{M}_w \tag{36}$$

Comparison of equations 35 and 36 gives

$$c\bar{M}_w = \sum_i c_iM_i$$

or

$$\bar{M}_w = \frac{\sum c_iM_i}{c} = \frac{\sum N_iM_i^2}{\sum N_iM_i} \tag{37}$$

(c) Viscosity

The viscosity of a solution has been shown by Einstein[18] to depend on the size of the solute molecules relative to those of the solvent. For a suspension or dilute solution of spheres whose size is large compared with the size of the solvent molecules, the relationship becomes

$$\frac{\eta - \eta_0}{\eta_0} = \frac{5}{2} V \tag{38}$$

where η and η_0 are the viscosities of the solution and solute and V is the volume fraction of the solute. Although equation 38 refers to hard spherical particles, it does give reason to anticipate that the presence of voluminous polymer molecules would give substantial increases in the viscosity

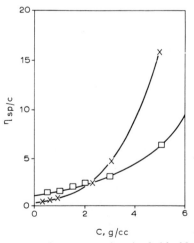

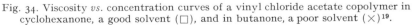

Fig. 34. Viscosity *vs.* concentration curves of a vinyl chloride acetate copolymer in cyclohexanone, a good solvent ($\square$), and in butanone, a poor solvent ($\times$)[19].

of a solvent. The viscosity of a solution is basically related to the size or extension in space of the polymer molecules. The viscosity will therefore depend on the shape of the molecules and this may be altered according to whether the solvent is good or not. Some results for the viscosity of a copolymer in good and bad solvents are shown in the Fig. 34[19]. Theoretical calculations[20] have shown that the intrinsic viscosity $[\eta]$ should be related to the molecular weight of a polymer by an equation of the form

$$\lim_{c \to 0} \left(\frac{\eta - \eta_0}{c \eta_0} \right) = [\eta] = KM \tag{39}$$

(For this limit on the left-hand side, the intrinsic viscosity, the concentrations are expressed in g of solute/100 ml.)

Unfortunately this equation is not a good representation of the facts. A better and widely used relation is

$$[\eta] = KM^\alpha \qquad \text{or} \qquad \ln [\eta] = \ln K + \alpha \ln M \tag{40}$$

The values of K and α depend on the properties of solvent and solute molecules and on their interactions. It can be shown that the value of α would be 2 for rod-like solute molecules and unity for spherical ones. Randomly kinked linear molecules should have the index α less than unity.

To measure the molecular weight of a polymer, the viscosity of solutions of different concentrations are measured and $(\eta - \eta_0)/c\eta_0$ plotted against the concentration after which extrapolation to $c = 0$ gives $[\eta]$: substitution in equation 40 enables M to be determined. Values of K and α have to be found from measurements on samples of known molecular weight which are as homogeneous as possible. For determination of molecular weights of heterodisperse systems, this method gives an average value which lies between the number and weight average. The kind of average may be deduced as follows. Consider a very dilute solution where the individual molecules can be taken to make independent contributions to the viscosity

$$\frac{\eta - \eta_0}{\eta_0} = \eta_{sp} = \sum_i (\eta_{sp})_i \tag{41}$$

where η_{sp} is the specific viscosity and the suffix i refers to the species of molecular weight M_i. If each species contributes to the specific viscosity and the concentrations are very small, equation 40 leads to

$$(\eta_{sp})_i = KM_i^\alpha c_i \tag{42}$$

whence

$$\eta_{sp} = K \sum M_i^\alpha c_i$$

Hence

$$[\eta] = K \left(\frac{\sum M_i^\alpha c_i}{c} \right)_{c=0} = K\bar{M}_v^\alpha \tag{43}$$

References p. 158

Hence the viscosity average molecular weight

$$\bar{M}_v = \frac{\sum M_i^\alpha c_i}{c} = (\sum w_i M_i^\alpha)^{1/\alpha} = \left(\frac{\sum N_i M_i^{1+\alpha}}{\sum N_i M_i}\right)^{1/\alpha} \tag{44}$$

Thus the viscosity average molecular weight is a special one. Care must be taken in the calibration of this method since, if unfractionated samples are used in the determination of K and α, the calibration curve of ln $[\eta]$ *versus* ln M by which α is determined will be higher than it should be.

The viscosity method of measuring molecular weights is rapid in practice once the K and α values are known. In some instances it can be used as a control test in industry. An example of this comes from the textile field, where the viscosities of solutions of cellulose in cuprammonium hydroxide[22] or cupriethylenediamine[21] are determined and used as a parameter for estimating the extent of chemical degradation or damage to the fibres in a yarn or fabric which may have occurred during processing.

The methods described in this chapter are the main ones employed in work on polymers. Others do exist such as sedimentation, diffusion etc. but they are not so universally used as osmotic pressure, light scattering or viscosity.

REFERENCES

1   P. J. FLORY, *Principles of Polymer Chemistry*, Cornell Univ. Press, Ithaca, 1953. F. W. BILLMEYER, JR., *Textbook of Polymer Chemistry*, Interscience, New York, 1957. C. E. H. BAWN, *The Chemistry of High Polymers*, Butterworth, London, 1948. E. M. FRITH and R. F. TUCKETT, *Linear Polymers*, Longmans, London, 1951.
2   W. O. BAKER, C. S. FULLER and J. H. HEISS, JR., *J. Am. Chem. Soc.*, 63 (1941) 2142. W. H. CAROTHERS and F. J. VAN NATTA, *J. Am. Chem. Soc.*, 52 (1930) 3222; 62 (1940) 1057; 63 (1941) 2142.
3   P. J. FLORY, *J. Am. Chem. Soc.*, 61 (1939) 3334.
4   J. E. WALTZ and G. B. TAYLOR, *Anal. Chem.*, 19 (1947) 448.
5   A. CONIX, *Makromol. Chem.*, 26 (1958) 226.
6   I. M. WARD, *Nature*, 180 (1957) 141.
    I. M. WARD, *Trans. Faraday Soc.*, 53 (1957) 1406.
7   J. GAUNT, *Analyst*, 29 (1954) 580.
8   M. G. EVANS, *J. Chem. Soc.*, (1947) 272.
9   K. L. BERRY and J. H. PETERSON, *J. Am. Chem. Soc.*, 73 (1951) 5195.
10 J. C. BEVINTON, H. W. MELVILLE and R. P. TAYLOR, *J. Polymer Sci.*, 12 (1954) 449.
11 U. CROATTO and G. GIACOMELLO, *Gazz. chim. ital.*, 82 (1952) 712.
12 R. A. GREGG and F. R. MAYO, *J. Am. Chem. Soc.*, 70 (1948) 2373.
13 C. H. BAMFORD and M. J. S. DEWAR, *Proc. Roy. Soc. London*, 192A (1948) 329.
14 P. J. FLORY, *Principles of Polymer Chemistry*, Cornell Univ. Press, Ithaca, 1953.
15 R. E. MONTONNA and L. T. JILK, *J. Phys. Chem.*, 45 (1941) 1374.
16 C. R. MASSON, R. F. MENZIES, J. CRUICKSHANK and H. W. MELVILLE, *Nature*, 157 (1946) 74.
17 M. L. HUGGINS, *Ann. N.Y. Acad. Sci.*, 44 (1943) 431.
18 A. EINSTEIN, *Ann. Physik*, 19 (1908) 289; 34 (1911) 591.
19 A. G. JANSSEN and CALDWELL, *Polymer Bull.*, 1 (1945) 120.
20 M. L. HUGGINS, *Physical Chemistry of High Polymers*, Wiley, New York, 1958.
21 *Norme Français* NF, T 12/005, March (1953).
22 F. MARSH, *An Introduction to Cellulose Chemistry*, Chapman & Hall, London, 1938.
23 G. GEE, *Trans. Faraday Soc.*, 38 (1942) 276.
24 R. F. BOYER, *J. Polymer Sci.*, 8 (1952) 73; 9 (1952) 197.

CHAPTER 6

COTTON AND FLAX

In the earlier chapters, attention has been devoted to the manner by which and the rates at which monomers react to form polymers. The constitution of the resulting synthetic materials may be deduced not only from chemical and physical investigations on the polymer but also from the knowledge of the reactions involved in its preparation. By contrast, natural polymers such as cellulose or proteins can not be synthesised; their structure must be deduced from chemical and physical analysis.

There are many natural fibres; some are animal in origin (wool, mohair, silk etc.), others come from vegetable sources (cotton, flax, jute etc.). This chapter is concerned with the growth and morphology of two vegetable fibres — cotton and flax. These two fibres are examples from the many vegetable fibres which exist. One of them is in reality a seed hair and the other is found as part of the stem of a plant and is classified as a bast fibre. Chemically their major constituent is the carbohydrate cellulose, a polymer which is the cheapest available and is an essential constituent of plant tissue.

1. Cotton

The fibres grow as single cells which emerge from the epidermic or outer layer of the cotton seed and form a dense cover over the surface. Cotton is a hair attached to the seed of several species of the botanical genus *Gossypium* which belongs to the order Malvaceae. The cotton plant is a shrub which is indigenous to many sub-tropical countries but its cultivation is best carried out in warm humid climates. It is grown extensively in North and South America, India, China, Russia and Egypt and to a lesser extent in countries such as Turkey and the Sudan. Not only are there many forms of cultivated cotton plants but there are many wild ones. The cotton plant grows to a height which may be up to 4–6 ft; its cultivation varies widely depending on climate, soil etc.[1].

Before the plant reaches its full height, it throws off flower stalks at the extremity of which the blossom pods subsequently appear. These expand until they reach about the size of a bean when they burst and display the blossom. The latter lasts for only 24 hours. When the blossom falls, a small dark green triangular pod forms which in turn increases to the size of a walnut. This is termed a boll and may contain 20 or more seeds. When maturity is reached the boll bursts to display the cotton seeds covered in a "downy" mass of cotton. These features are shown on the stem of a cotton plant in Fig. 35.

The cotton fibres grow in a tubular form; through the centre runs a canal known as the lumen. Naturally when the boll opens and the fibres

Fig. 35. Cotton plant. (Courtesy B.C.I.R.A.)

are exposed to air, moisture evaporates. This in turn causes the seed hair to shrink making the lumen smaller and flatter until finally the walls collapse. A drastic change of shape of this kind naturally causes stresses to be set up and the collapsed fibres show convolutions arising from this. The appearance of cotton fibres under the microscope is very typical (Fig. 36).

The tip of the fibres is characterised by the absence of both lumen and convolutions and its tapering rod-like end. The base of the fibre may naturally be irregular in shape since, in the ginning process, it may have been torn away from the coat of the seed. The collapse of the walls is accompanied by changes in the shape of the cross section of the fibre, the originally circular cross section being transformed to one which may be of a variety of shapes ranging from linear, elliptical to dumb-bell. Some may

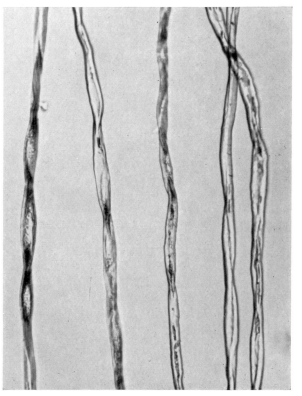

Fig. 36. Cotton fibres. (Courtesy B.C.I.R.A.)

be U shaped — often the immature ones. The shapes are shown in Figs. 37 and 38.

In very many varieties of cotton, the seed has not only the long fibres (lint) used for spinning into yarn but also there grow, from the seed, an undergrowth of short coarser fibres (fuzz) which may be coloured whereas the lint fibres are near white. The distribution of the lint and fuzz fibres is not uniform over the seed; the epidermal cells near the base of the seed give mainly lint fibres whereas those at the tip give more fuzz fibres. The

References p. 175

distribution of the two kinds of fibres is different for different varieties of cotton but it is only in rare instances that fuzz fibres are absent. Naturally not all the cotton fibres produced are perfect. Due to unfavourable climatic conditions or attack by pests or diseases, the growth of the seed hair inside the boll may be stopped or slowed down before maturity. Such

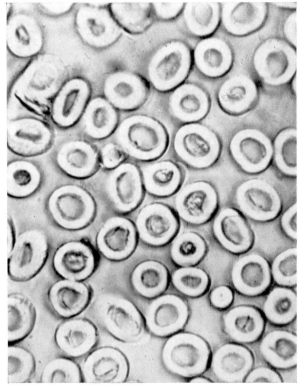

Fig. 37. Cross section of cotton fibres (uncollapsed). (Courtesy B.C.I.R.A.)

fibres are classified as immature and consist of a hollow tube in which the secondary wall (see later) has been deposited to only a small degree. Such fibres naturally collapse when the boll opens and assume a ribbon like appearance with the absence of the convolutions characteristic of mature fibres. Because of the lack of secondary walls, such fibres lack rigidity and tend to form knots known as "neps" which are difficult to remove. This immature or dead cotton also causes defects in dyeing, showing up as light specks.

To obtain the cotton fibres, the hairs are cut from the seed by means of knives, the process being called ginning. The residue left behind will consist of the seed and hairs of a short length which remain attached to the seed coat. These short hairs are referred to as cotton linters and form a valuable source of cellulose for chemical purposes such as produc-

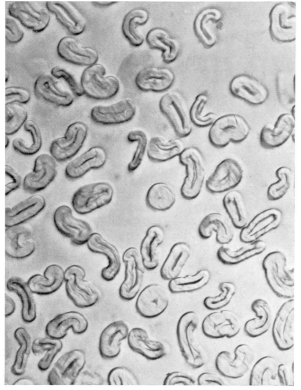

Fig. 38. Cross section of cotton fibres (collapsed). (Courtesy B.C.I.R.A.)

tion of nitrocellulose or cellulose acetate. They are removed by passage through a specially constructed gin. The ginning process is an important one and, if not carried out well, may cause the more stringy fibres to matt and cause neps.

Cotton from the various sources will differ in its length, fineness, colour, etc. The range in average lengths of cotton fibres suitable for spinning into yarn is from 12–36 mm but, in any one sample of fibres, the fibre lengths will vary considerably and methods have been developed in which the numbers of fibres in the different length groups may be determined[2].

The range of fibre lengths is shown in Fig. 39 where a sample of cotton has been separated according to this property. .

Fineness of the fibres is also very important and will have a considerable bearing on the fineness of the yarn which may be spun. The finest

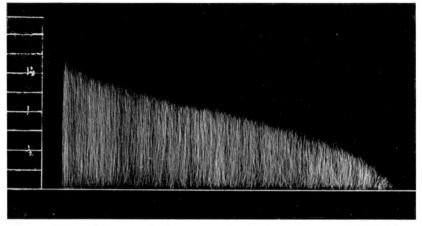

Fig. 39. Different fibre lengths from a sample of cotton. (Courtesy B.C.I.R.A.)

cottons are the Sea Island and Egyptian varieties with an average staple length of $1-2\frac{1}{2}$ in. The next group are those such as American Upland of staple $\frac{1}{2}-1\frac{5}{16}$ in. whilst as an example of coarse cottons some of the Indian and Asiatic varieties have lengths from $\frac{3}{8}-1$ in. Although in a brief classification of this kind, it would seem that fineness and staple length go hand in hand, this is not necessarily so and length and fineness must be regarded as two distinct properties of the fibre.

Examination of the cotton fibre under the microscope shows it to be a single cell, an irregularly collapsed tube with a central canal or lumen running throughout its length. A more detailed examination reveals three further parts to the fibre. The hair is covered with a thin layer of tightly moulded material — the cuticle. Inside this comes the primary wall followed by the secondary wall. To some extent these complications are not unexpected. The cotton fibre develops in two phases; some of the epidermal cells of the seed sprout and continue to grow lengthwise for a period of approximately 25 days after flowering. In this stage the fibre consists of the primary wall bounded by the cuticle. The second phase consists of deposition of the secondary wall on the interior of the primary. This process begins several days before the hair reaches its full length and continues for some 35–50 days being almost complete after 40 days. Growth usually ceases a few days prior to the opening of the boll. The periods quoted here depend on the conditions of growth of the plant as well as its variety.

The four characteristic regions of the fibre are discussed separately.

2. Characteristic Regions of Cotton Fibre

(a) Cuticle

This consists of a very thin outer layer of tightly moulded material. Its true composition is not known with certainty but would seem to consist of a deposit of cotton wax and pectic material. This wax is a complex mixture of waxes, fats and resins. Although the cuticle is moulded to the primary wall during growth it is not an integral part of it. In the first phase of growth of the cotton hair, when the fibre is increasing in length, the cuticle shows as an oily film. During the phase when the secondary wall is being deposited, this layer hardens and appears more like a varnish. One of the functions of the cuticle is to protect the fibre from atmospheric oxidation which possibly arises from the action of the ultra-violet component of strong sunlight.

(b) Primary Wall

In the first phase of growth, the cotton fibre consists of the primary wall enclosing the nucleus and protoplasm. These latter two materials are essential for every living cell. Chemically, the primary wall consists mainly of cellulose and, with fibres at this stage, it is possible to dissolve out the primary wall with a solution which is a solvent for cellulose (cuprammonium hydroxide) leaving the cuticle behind. The primary wall has a thickness of only $0.1-0.2$ mμ as compared to the over-all width of the fibre of 20 mμ. The cellulose material of this wall is laid down from the initiation of growth. Microscopical examination with the aid of suitable swelling techniques shows that the cellulose has been laid down in the form of fine threads or fibrils. (Fig. 40 shows such fibrils for the secondary wall.) These fibrils are laid down in such a way that those on the outside of the wall are mainly in a longitudinal direction to the fibre axis whereas those on the inside are transverse. Between these inner and outer layers, the fibrils are laid down in a spiral fashion probably making an angle of about 70° to the fibre axis. There is evidence that these spirals may be twisting both in left-handed (S) and a right-handed (Z) fashion.

This kind of pattern of formation of the fibrils will give a fibre with less strength in a longitudinal than in a transverse direction. Hence the fibre has a high peripheral strength which will restrict lateral swelling.

References p. 175

The lower strength in the longitudinal direction may be the cause of the low tensile strength of immature fibres.

Although the primary wall consists mainly of cellulose, it is in this network of fibrils that quantities of impurities are to be found. These are mainly pectic substances but include fatty ones.

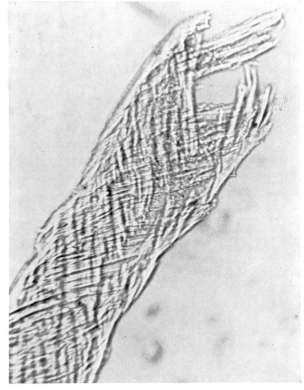

Fig. 40. Fibrils in secondary wall. (Courtesy B.C.I.R.A.)

(c) Secondary Wall

This part of the fibre is laid down in the second phase of growth and forms roughly 90% of the total weight. The wall is composed of successive layers of cellulose deposited on the inner side of the primary wall without increase in fibre diameter. These layers can be observed in cross sections of the fibre when correctly swollen[6] and have been referred to as daily growth rings (Fig. 41). The formation, size and pattern of such rings has been shown to be dependent on fluctuations in light and temperature during growth[5]; indeed the growth rings may be absent if the plant is grown under conditions of constant temperature and illumination[3]. The growth of the secondary wall is important for the tensile strength of the fibres, which for young fibres increases with the formation of the second-ary wall reaching a limit about 35 days after flowering[4].

Again more detailed microscopical examination of the secondary wall

Fig. 41. Daily growth rings. (Courtesy B.C.I.R.A.)

reveals a network of fibrils (Fig. 40). The presence of units which are long and thin may be shown up by the light microscope when the fibre is swollen or mechanically disintegrated. Unfortunately the size of such fibrils appears to vary with the method of preparation of the sample. Average diameters vary from $0.1\ \mu$ to $1.4\ \mu$[7]. The higher resolutions which are obtainable with the electron microscope indicate that the fibrils are not the smallest structural units observable and it is possible that the latter may have a width of $100-250$ Å. This latter is known as a micro-fibril[8].

The fibrils in the secondary wall are aligned in layers or lamellae and follow a spiral path around the fibre axis. The first layer of the wall *i.e.* that deposited on to the primary wall, has its spiral making an angle of $20-30°$ with the fibre axis. The fibrils in subsequent layers spiral at an angle which ranges between $20-45°$. The fibrils in the secondary wall change direction at frequent intervals along the fibre length; at the points where these reversals occur, the fibrils may bend round in a curve or be discontinuous, one set of fibrils ending and another starting in the opposite sense.

The reversals in the directions of the spirals has its bearing on the convolutions of the fibre. When the boll opens and the fibre dries out, there is a greater shrinkage in the direction perpendicular to the fibrils than parallel to them. Hence because of the spiral structure and its reversals, the collapse of the fibre is accompanied by a twisting of the fibre about its axis. The convolutions appear with directions of rotation which change at the points where the reversals in the directions of the spirals in the secondary wall occur.

(d) Lumen

This canal, which stretches from the base of the fibre to the tip where it is closed, varies in dimensions over a wide range. In the fibre before the boll opens, it may occupy as much as a third of the cross sectional area of the fibre, reducing to a twentieth or less in the dried out fibre where it appears as little more than a slit. The luminia are shown in the cross-sections in Figs. 37 and 38. The lumen contains the protoplasmic material essential for cell growth so that when the fibre dries out a residue is left in the lumen after evaporation. The contents in the lumen will contain protein as well as mineral salts and a certain amount of colouring matter which is mainly responsible for the creamy colour of most raw cultivated cotton.

3. Flax

In contrast to cotton, flax is found in the stem of the plant, *Linium usitatissimum*. It is classified with other fibres such as Ramie, Jute etc., as a bast fibre. Bast fibres are found in the stalks of dicotyledenous plants, the name implying that from the seed emerges a pair of leaves. This distinguishes such plants from monocotyledons where from the seed emerges a single leaf. The leaves of dicotyledons have distinctive characteristics in that the system of veins is much branched, monocotyledons meeting usually at the base of the leaf. Fibres such as esparto grass (used in the manufacture of paper) or sisal are derived from monocotyledons.

There are many species of the flax plant (genus *Linium*) but only a few are cultivated for the fibre and, with the exception of the species mentioned above, not cultivated to any great extent. The plant is an annual, which, when grown for its fibre, has erect, slender, pale green stalks of diameter 0.10–0.15 in. reaching a height of 3–4 ft. The plant has attenuated narrow, lance shaped leaves, and gives blue or white flowers. For fibre production, it is sown thickly and may be harvested (a) when flowering is almost over and the stalk is green (b) when the fruit has set or (c) when the seed pods have ripened and the stalk is yellowish brown. (b) is the best condition since (a) gives a soft fibre but poor yield and (c)

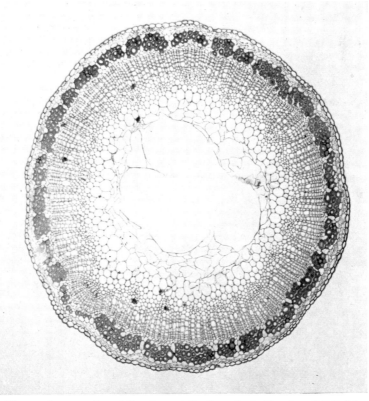

Fig. 42. Cross section of the stem of the flax plant. (Courtesy L.I.R.A.)

gives a coarse fibre. Some varieties of the flax plant are grown for their seed (linseed) in which case the plants are widely spaced to encourage branching and seed formation.

The flax fibre in the stem of the plant forms about 25% by weight although the amount of fibre recovered after isolation is much smaller than this (up to about 15%). Examination of the cross-section of the stalk shows many components (Fig. 42). There are six annular regions:

(1) Epidermis. This consists of a layer of thick walled cells covered by an external cuticle. There are about 40 openings, known as stomata, per mm². These openings are sufficiently large for retting bacteria to enter.

(2) Cortex. One or two layers of approximately circular cells form the cortex. These cells contain colouring matter and substances known as pectins.

(3) Fibre bundles. The bast fibres are found in this layer which is the ring of dark cells in Fig. 42. Each stem contains up to 40 bundles of some 12–40 fibres per bundle. Roughly speaking there are about 1000 flax fibres in each stem.

(4) Cambium. A ring of thin-walled cells separating the wood from the fibres.

(5) Wood. Towards the centre of the stem is a ring of very short, thick, woody cells which give mechanical support to the plant.

(6) Pith. Down the length of the stem runs a chamber known as the pith cavity. It is surrounded by thin walled cells.

From the foregoing, it is clear that the extraction of flax fibres from the stem involves the removal of much extraneous material and separation of the fibres from other parts of the stem to which they are gummed by pectic materials. The process of extraction of the fibres from the stem is known as "retting" and may be carried out under many different conditions.

4. Processing of Flax

(a) Retting

The bast fibre bundles (Fig. 43) can be freed from the surrounding cellular tissue by the combined action of moisture and bacteria, these being found on the flax straw. Correct retting is of great importance; underretting will mean that the required fibre bundles are not easily separated from the wood and excess retting results in a weakened fibre. The main methods are dew and water retting.

For the former process, the stalks are spread on grass and allowed to stay there until bacterial action with the aid of sun, dew and air dissolve the cellular tissue and the larger part of the gummy substances. Two to three weeks is usually allowed for this process to be completed as judged by the ease with which the fibres are separated from the stalk. This process obviously relies on a heavy dew falling at night and is of value where water supplies are short.

The second process i.e. water retting is more common and is carried out in slow moving rivers, bogs or dams. Nowadays tanks are being used and in these the bundles of straw are placed root downwards. Water heated to about 30 °C is pumped in to cover the straw and the temperature maintained. During the first 6–8 hours, sometimes termed the "leach", dirt and colouring matter are dissolved from the fibre. In fermentation processes involved in the bacterial action, acids are formed which may be

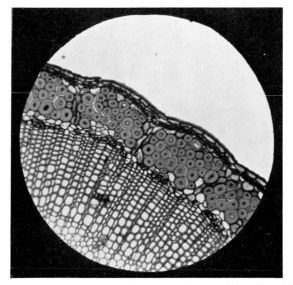

Fig. 43. Part cross section showing compact rounded bundles of fibres.
(Courtesy L.I.R.A.)

harmful. They are removed by allowing a slow trickle of water to run in and out of the tank to waste. The time required for the retting to be complete is about 4–6 days. Retting in ponds, bogs etc. is not so easily controlled and takes longer.

After retting, the bundles of stalks (straw) must be dried and stored for a month or so to cure, when the fibre is supposed to become stronger and easier to remove from the wood. The different retting processes give flaxes of different qualities.

(b) Scutching

The woody portions and the bark (shive) are removed by this process which may be carried out by hand but more usually nowadays by machine. In the latter, the straw passes between fluted rollers which break the shive in many places throughout its length. The broken pieces of shive are next removed in a "scutching" mill where straw is brought into contact with wide flat blades which scrape or beat off the unwanted shive. The blades may be made of wood or steel. In many parts nowadays, breaking and scutching are carried out in one machine. In this process, there is always some waste consisting of pieces of shive and short pieces of fibre; this rejected material is usually submitted to a second scutching operation to recover the fibre, producing "re-scutched tow". This product gives rather coarse yarns on spinning and is sometimes used for the manufacture of paper.

(c) *Spinning*

The raw material for the spinner is flax and "re-scutched tow". In a spinning mill the product is "hackled". Hackling is a combing operation where the flax is combed intermittently with combs of increasing fineness. In this operation, the long fibres are separated from the shorter ones as well as removing any remaining pieces of shive. The finest strands from this process are known as line. Broken fibres which must arise from this kind of combing process give rise to a second quality known as machine tow.

The flax strands which are extracted from the straw are fibre bundles, adhering to which is some cortical tissue. This gives the fibre a characteristic colour. The spinners and weavers prefer to work with the flax in "bundle" form rather than to break it down to the separate fibres. The bundle will contain many ultimate fibres since their length may range from 6–40 in.; the length of the ultimate fibre is roughly 0.2–2.6 in. with an average around 1.0–1.25 in.

Because of the gummy material holding the fibres together, flax is usually spun wet by passing the material in the form of a roving through a trough on the spinning frame containing water heated to 150–200°F. The hot water softens the gummy (pectinous) materials and allows a finer yarn to be obtained than if spun in the usual way *i.e.* dry.

5. Structure of Flax Fibres

Raw flax has a creamy colour, the intensity of which depends on the skill and quality of its preparation. The fibre contains 1% of wax and this helps to give a high lustre; it is also a very strong fibre.

The ultimate fibres are 10–36 mm long (av. 25 mm) with a width of 10–20 mμ; the length to breadth ratio is about 1,100–1,200 to 1. They are single cells which normally taper to a point; the walls are very thick and as a consequence the lumen is very small or almost obliterated. The cell is cylindrical with a smooth surface except for the numerous faint "discolourations" or "dislocations" (nodes) which run transversely across the fibre (Fig. 44). Cross sections of the mature fibres are polygonal in shape (Fig. 45) with a very small lumen. The immature fibres are more oval in shape and possess large luminia.

The nodes in the flax fibre are numerous and there may be as many as 800 in a single fibre. They show up when flax fibres are viewed under the polarising microscope or can be made more apparent by staining with zinc chloroiodide or methylene blue. Several explanations have been advanced for the cause of the nodes; they may be due to minute fissures

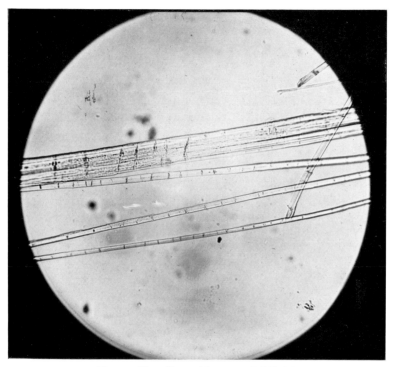

Fig. 44. Flax fibres. (Courtesy L.I.R.A.)

or local separation of the fibrils which make up the cell walls or could be points at which the direction of the fibrils is modified. Either of these postulates would explain the fact that on stretching the nodes disappear, since in the former case the fibrils would be pulled together and in the latter adlineated. Release of tension brings the fibre back to its original unstretched state and the nodes reappear. Swelling treatments also reduce the intensity of these "dislocation" marks, a fact which may be explained on these hypotheses.

Mounting the flax fibre in water and compressing the fibre with the tip of a scalpel reveals under the microscope numerous fissures; the fibre wall is found to be made up of fibrils, a fact which has been assumed for the above discussion. The wall structure has been shown[9], with the help of the electron microscope, to be in three layers. The inner and outer of these are thin and have fibrils laid down in a spiral with a Z twist. The thick middle wall has its fibrils spiralling with an S. In contrast to cotton, there are no reversals of the direction of the spirals. It has been

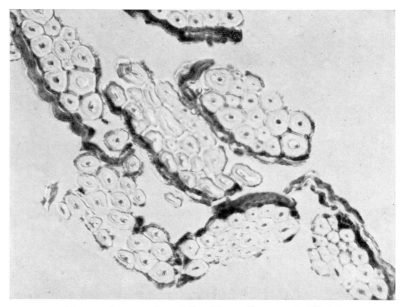

Fig. 45. Cross section of flax fibres. (Courtesy L.I.R.A.)

suggested that the points of reversal of the direction of the fibrils are points of mechanical weakness in cotton fibres. The lack of reversals in flax suggest that flax is stronger than cotton. The angle which the spirals of the fibrils of flax make with the fibre axis is less than in cotton, a fact which may have a bearing on the relative inextensibility of flax.

Although emphasis has been placed on the fact that both cotton and flax are constructed from fibrils which are chemically composed of cellulose, all fibres do contain certain quantities of non-cellulosic impurities. The quantity of cellulose will vary from over 90% for cotton to more like 60% for flax, the exact values depending on the source of the cotton or flax. The impurities in cotton fall into the following classes — protein, pectic substances, waxes, mineral and colouring matter. Flax, with a larger amount of impurity than cotton, contains in addition lignin and hemicelluloses. The impurities contribute very important properties to these fibres and must be taken into account in the subsequent treatments (such as bleaching, scouring) to which the fibre may be subjected. The removal of these impurities is a subject dealt with in a later volume. As far as this volume is concerned, attention is devoted to the chemistry of cellulose, the main constituent.

REFERENCES

[1] H. R. MAUERSBERGER, (Editor), *Matthews' Textile Fibres*, Chapman & Hall, London, 1954.

[2] Shirley Test.

[3] D. B. ANDERSON and J. H. MOORE, *Ann. J. Botany*, 24 (1937) 503.

[4] E. E. BERKLEY, *Textile Research*, 9 (1939) 355.

[5] T. KERR, *Protoplasma*, 27 (1937) 229.

[6] W. L. BALLS, *Proc. Roy. Soc. London*, 90B (1919) 452.

[7] A. J. BAILEY AND R. M. BROWN, *Ind. Eng. Chem.*, 32 (1940) 57; F. L. BARROWS, *Contrib. Boyce Thompson Inst.*, 11 (1940) 161.

[8] H. W. EMERTON, *Fundamentals of the Beating Process*, Brit. Paper & Board Ind. Research Assoc., Kenley, 1957.

[9] P. A. ROELOFSEN, *Textile Research J.*, 21 (1951) 412.

CHAPTER 7

CHEMISTRY OF CELLULOSE

Cellulose makes up about a third of all vegetable matter being the main constituent of the cell walls of higher plants. Cellulose never occurs in a pure form; in wood it constitutes about 40–50% of the weight, in flax 60–85%, whereas cotton seed hairs which are the purest source contain about 90%.

1. Purification of Cellulosic Materials

The purification of cellulosic materials consists of the removal of impurities with which the cellulose is associated in nature, a process which may require fairly drastic chemical treatment. Chemical treatments will cause degradation and care must be taken to reduce this to a minimum if a standard "pure" cellulose is to be obtained. Cotton is the most suitable source as the impurities may be removed by alkaline boiling followed by bleaching[1]. The cellulose of bast fibres is freed from much of the impurity by the fermentation which goes on in the retting process and to a greater extent by bleaching. However, much of the cellulose used industrially comes from wood. Wood is first made into chips of a size suitable for digestion in an autoclave with liquors containing (a) sulphur dioxide and certain bisulphites chiefly those of calcium, magnesium, sodium or ammonium or (b) caustic soda or (c) sodium sulphide and caustic soda.

Liquor (a) is acidic whereas (b) and (c) are alkaline; treatments using these materials are known as the sulphite, soda and sulphate (Kraft) processes. Digestion yields a fibrous pulp which may be further purified by bleaching.

The term sulphate is not obvious and arises as follows: the spent liquor from the digestion is normally evaporated to dryness and the organic material extracted from the wood burnt off to reclaim the alkali as sodium carbonate. To this liquor is added sodium sulphate which is reduced to sulphide during this process.

The degree of purification required in practice will depend on the end use. For making paper, the presence of some of the impurities is advantageous and may add to the strength of the paper sheet; for use in viscose manufacture, it is desirable to remove all impurities as far as possible. The products thus obtained will vary according to the source of cellulose, the extent and the kind of treatment the raw material undergoes and the extent of chemical attack which occurs in the treatment. They are commonly called cellulose even though they may not be chemically identical. For chemical as distinct from technological purposes, the cellulose derived from cotton may be taken as the standard and all other "celluloses" referred to this. This definition restricts the term to that part of the cell wall in the plant or tree which chemically and physically resembles the product from cotton. In the technological field, the use of cellulose may not be so tied to a product of fairly well defined chemical constitution and other definitions may be of considerable value. Thus, the term α-cellulose refers to the material in a pulp which remains insoluble after treatment with caustic soda solution of mercerising strength[1,2,3] (ca. 18%). This kind of cellulose cannot be regarded as being "pure" as the test was originally devised as a guide to the yield to be obtained from wood pulps after transformation into viscose rayon. Actually, α-cellulose obtained from a bleached pulp contains the cellulose fibrils together with small quantities of other polysaccharides. The alkali soluble fraction from this treatment deposits a second fraction on acidification referred to as β-cellulose, leaving a third fraction remaining in the liquor known as γ-cellulose. These two fractions are chemically distinct from cellulose.

2. Chemical Constitution of Cellulose

(a) Structure of the Molecule

Elementary analysis of cellulose classifies it as a carbohydrate of empirical formula $C_6H_{10}O_5$. Hydrolysis gives in high yield the sugar D-glucose. The yield of glucose varies according to the conditions of hydrolysis. Direct hydrolysis with cold 72% sulphuric acid has given 90.7% yield[4]. Better results are obtained by other methods. Acetylated cellulose was first prepared using sulphuric acid as a catalyst and then treated with hydrochloric acid in the presence of methanol. The methyl group was exchanged for acetyl, the process being one of methanolysis; 80.5% yield of the methyl derivatives of glucose[5] was obtained. Repetition of this using a different catalyst (chlorine and sulphur dioxide) gave a yield[6] of 95.5%. The techniques involved in these reactions are vigorous and it is not surprising that 100% yield cannot be achieved. The yield of 95.5% is therefore taken to show that cellulose, on hydrolysis, yields only glucose and hence is a polymer with the anhydroglucose residues as its building unit.

Glucose is a monosaccharide containing 6 carbon atoms. The simplest formula which may be written is given by (I), the numbering of the carbon atoms being written alongside. From formula (I), see the next page, it is seen that atoms 2, 3, 4 and 5 are asymmetric and, hence, give rise to optical activity. Because of this asymmetry in a monosaccharide, there are 16 possible configurations for the hydrogen and hydroxyl groups; eight of these are mirror images of the others and hence these compounds can be grouped into two series known as D- and L-isomers characterised

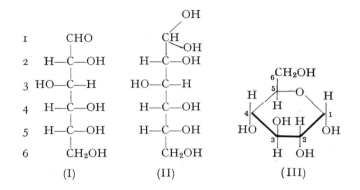

      (I)   (II)   (III)

by the position of the hydroxyl group on the penultimate carbon atom 5. The monosaccharide from cellulose, D-glucose, is characterised by the hydroxyl group being on the right-hand side when looking towards carbon atom number 1. It must be noted that D or L refers only to the configuration and not to the sign of the optical rotation. The dispositions of the hydroxyl and hydrogen atoms in D-glucose are those given in the formula.

Formula (I) shows the presence of a free aldehyde group but this is not easily detected by Schiffs' reagent. Reaction of glucose with hydrochloric acid in dry methanol does not yield a diacetal as would be anticipated, but two isomers known as α- and β-methyl-D-glucosides. The acetyl derivative (the pentaacetate) fails to react with hydroxylamine. Thus some of the expected reactions of the aldehyde group are not found. The explanation of these phenomena has been shown to lie in the condensation of the aldehyde group with the hydroxyl group at carbon atom 5 to form a cyclic hemiacetal. This can be imagined to occur in aqueous solution via addition of water at the aldehyde group to form the dihydroxy body (II) on the number 1 atom followed by elimination of water between two hydroxyl groups carried on atoms 1 and 5 (formula III). This formula has been written so that the plane of the ring appears to be at right angles to the plane of the paper; the thick lines are considered to project whereas the thin ones go into the paper. The ring closure has been written to occur between the 1 and 5 atoms to give the "pyranose" form. This has been shown to be mainly correct although, when glucose dissolves in water, a small amount of the "furanose" form, where the 1 and 4 atoms are linked, is produced. Although, in general, monosaccharides give reactions in which the three possible forms (open chain, furanose or pyranose) can be detected depending on conditions, the quantities of the first two are normally very small and hence, for the present discussion, glucose will be considered to be in the pyranose form (III). In the cyclic forms of glucose carbon atom 1 is asymmetric; the hydroxyl group and the hydrogen atom may be disposed in two different configurations, designated as α- and β- forms. The two forms have been isolated by crystallisation of glucose from aqueous solutions at room temperature and at the boiling-point[8]. These forms on dissolution equilibrate to give a mixture of both, a change which is reflected in the optical activity of the solutions; as the solutions equilibrate, the optical activity is altered to its equilibrium value due to the changes in configuration which occur at the carbon atom 1. This phenomenon is called mutarotation[9]. When methylated, glucose can form the methyl derivatives of the α- and β-forms; these are called α- and β-methylglucosides. They are now no longer interconvertible and therefore do not show mutarotation when dissolved.

If D-glucose is the structural unit for cellulose, it is reasonable to construct a polymer molecule by elimination of water between two of the five possible hydroxyl groups so that the sugar units are joined together through an oxygen bridge; this leaves three possible hydroxyl groups in cellulose capable of undergoing esterification or methylation. Acetylation or nitration of cellulose yields, when the reaction has gone to its maximum extent, triacetates[10] and trinitrates[11]. Evidence from methylation experiments did not disagree with the ultimate formation of a trimethyl ether, it being possible to obtain methylcellulose containing 45.0% methoxyl[12] (theoretical possible 45.6%). The reasons for the failure of the methoxyl content to reach the full theoretical value are not known with certainty; it may be due to the steric disposition of the groups or inaccessibility of some of the groups to the reagent. Confirmation that cellulose is composed of a long chain of anhydroglucose units came when the trimethylcellulose gave as its main hydrolysis product 2,3,6-tri-O-methyl-α-D-glucopyranose(IV)[12,13,14].

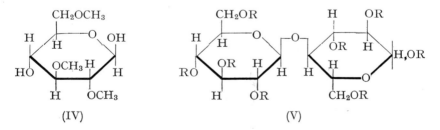

(IV)   (V)

This result is in agreement with the idea that the glucose units are joined through bridges involving the 1 and 4 carbon atoms.

References p. 220

Further evidence of structure comes from experiments in which cellulose is partially hydrolysed under carefully controlled conditions with acetic acid, acetic anhydride and sulphuric acid. Yields of 50–51% of cellobiose octaacetate[15] (V, R = $COCH_3$) have been obtained. Cellobiose is a disaccharide whose structure has been shown[7] to be that of two molecules of glucose joined through a 1,4-linkage with the glucose ring on the left in the β-configuration. The cellulose chain cannot be expected to give on hydrolysis much higher yields of cellobiose than those quoted since, if the links in the chain are equally susceptible to attack, glucose and higher sugars will also be produced. Higher sugars known as oligo-saccharides can be produced under less drastic conditions. The oligo-saccharides from cellotriose up to celloheptose have been identified. These are considered to be constructed from glucose units in the β-configuration[16].

This evidence does not show that all the linkages in the cellulose chain are 1,4 in the β-configuration. There may be a certain number of glucose rings which are in the α-configuration and linked together through atoms other than 1 and 4. The presence, in a chain of even a few linkages different from the 1,4 and a few units with configurations different from the β, would modify the shape of the polymer and hence have a marked effect on the physical properties of cellulose. Evidence [17] has accumulated to show that at least 99% of the glycosidic bonds are of the cellobiose type i.e. β-D-glucose-[1,4]-D-glucose. One argument in favour of this statement runs as follows.

If the cellulose chain be uniform, the optical rotation (molecular rotation) of a cellulose solution should be the sum of the rotations given by the individual sugar units. Hence for a polymer of D.P. equal to n, if the rotation is M_n, this statement says that $M_n = M_e + (n-2) M_i + M_a$ where M_e is the rotation of the non-reducing terminal sugar unit

   M_i is the rotation of the intermediate sugar units

   M_a is the rotation of the reducing terminal sugar unit,

The reducing and non-reducing terminal units, A and B in (VI), differ in properties from the intermediate ones as will be discussed later.

The rotation in terms of a unit is

$$\frac{M_n}{n} = \frac{M_e + M_a}{n} + \frac{n-2}{n} M_i \qquad (1)$$

If n is large as may be assumed in cellulose, the rotation per unit will be the limit of M_n/n as n tends to infinity; this equals M_i. The limit may be substituted into equation 1 to give

$$\frac{M_n}{n} = \frac{M_e + M_a}{n} + \frac{n-2}{n} \left(\lim_{n \to \infty} \frac{M_n}{n} \right) \qquad (2)$$

For a series of sugars with increasing number of units and of the identical configurations, equation 2 shows the relation between the measured value of the rotation and the number of units. From the series cellobiose, cellotriose etc. it is possible to calculate the limit by substitution. Comparison of this value with the observed one showed some agreement. For this purpose, the cellulose was dissolved in 51% sulphuric acid. Better results were obtained by comparing the limiting value derived from the fully methylated glucosides of the oligosaccharides with the rotation of trimethylglucose; chloroform, methanol, and 50% sulphuric acid were used as solvents.

The evidence gives a picture of the cellulose molecule as a linear polymer constructed from the condensation of β-glucose molecules linked together through the 1 and 4 positions (VI).

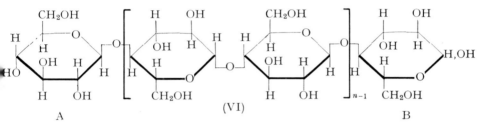

(VI)

This formula shows that cellulose contains in each glucose unit three free hydroxyl groups, one primary and two secondary; the glucose units are written so as to alternate spacially, a configuration which exists in the crystalline portion of cellulose but which may not necessarily be true for the amorphous. In the latter region, the residues may be capable of rotation around the C—O—C bonds. As written, the molecule appears to have a planar shape. This is only an approximation since the pyranose ring is puckered in such a manner as to reduce the strain in the bonds[18]. The pyranose rings are considered to exist in the "chair" form[19].

Further evidence of the cellulose structure is available. Cellulose on treatment with *p*-toluenesulphonyl chloride (tosyl chloride) reacts to form a *p*-toluenesulphonate[20](VII)

$$ROH + CH_3\langle\rangle SO_2Cl \rightarrow ROSO_2\langle\rangle CH_3 \xrightarrow{\text{NaI}} RI$$

(VII)　　　　(VIII)

The ester so formed, on reaction with sodium iodide in acetone, exchanges one *p*-toluenesulphonyl group for iodine giving an iodide (VIII). This reaction is characteristic of a primary alcohol and indicates that one of the three hydroxyls is a primary one.

The reaction of cellulose with periodate also lends confirmation to formula (VI). Periodate is a specific oxidant for α-glycols and potential α-glycols (*e.g.* α-diketones, which give α-glycols on reduction)[21]. α-Glycols themselves are oxidized to aldehydes with scission of the C—C bond and α-diketones or α-dialdehydes are oxidized to acids.

$$\begin{array}{c} R_1CHOH \\ | \\ R_2CHOH \end{array} \quad \xrightarrow{\ IO_4^-\ } \quad R_1CHO + R_2CHO + H_2O$$

$$\begin{array}{c} R_1C=O \\ | \\ R_2C=O \end{array} + H_2O \quad \xrightarrow{\ IO_4^-\ } \quad R_1COOH + R_2COOH$$

With three hydroxyl groups in neighbouring positions, the two molecules of aldehyde are produced together with one of formic acid.

$$R_1CHOHCHOHCHOHR_2 \quad \xrightarrow{\ IO_4^-\ } \quad R_1CHO + HCOOH + R_2CHO$$

Glucose reacts with 5 molecules of periodate to give 5 molecules of formic acid and one of formaldehyde

$$C_6H_{12}O_6 + 5IO_4^- \rightarrow 5HCOOH + HCHO + 5IO_3^-$$

The reaction proceeds in stages. Three molecules of periodate are reduced giving the formyl ester (X) which hydrolyses to formic acid and glyceraldehyde (XI).

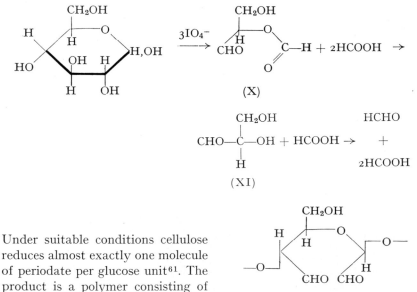

(X)

(XI)

(IX)

Under suitable conditions cellulose reduces almost exactly one molecule of periodate per glucose unit[61]. The product is a polymer consisting of dialdehyde units (IX) but it is important to remember that the end groups undergo more extensive oxidation owing to their larger number of adjacent hydroxyl groups. The end groups, A and B in formula (VI), are referred to as the non-reducing and reducing ends respectively. The two groups are differentiated by the fact that one is joined through carbon atom 1 to the fourth carbon of the penultimate unit. The aldehyde group is thus combined and not capable of exhibiting reduction properties. Group B is joined to the chain through carbon atom 4 leaving the aldehyde group exposed in the form of a hemiacetal and therefore capable of undergoing reactions such as the reduction of Fehlings solution. The non-reducing end group, A in (VI), consumes two molecules of periodate and yields one molecule of formic acid and the dialdehyde (XII)

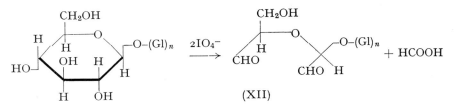

The reducing end group, B in (VI), behaves similarly to glucose in yielding a formyl ester (XIII) which is hydrolysed to a substance (XIV) able to be oxidized further to (XV)

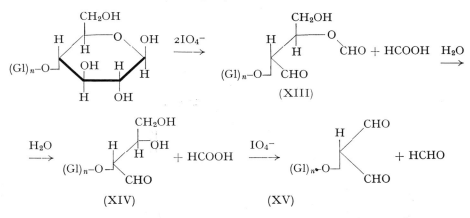

The amount of periodate consumed by oxidation of the end groups is very small compared with that used in oxidizing the very much larger number of intermediate chain units. However, in the presence of a moderate excess of periodate, the dialdehyde (XV) is oxidized further[103]. Two molecules of formic acid and one of carbon dioxide are formed and another normal reducing end group is exposed on the cellulose chain

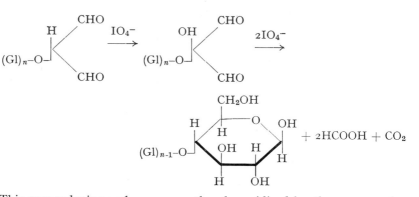

This new reducing end group can then be oxidized by the same mechanism, which therefore leads to the progressive oxidative scission of the chain-molecules. This is the phenomenon known as "over-oxidation". It explains the ease with which consumptions of periodate substantially greater than one molecule per glucose unit can be obtained and it vitiates the application of periodate oxidation as a method of measuring the chain length of cellulose.

(b) End Groups

The estimation of end groups may in some polymers be relatively simple *e.g.* amino groups in nylon[23] but for cellulose many difficulties arise. Methylation followed by hydrolysis should yield a small quantity of 2,3,4,6-tetramethylglucose arising from the non-reducing end group as well as a large quantity of the 2,3,6-trimethylglucose. Tetramethylglucose has been detected in the products in this treatment[24].

The presence of the reducing end groups shows up in the reducing properties of cellulose. It is most commonly shown by the ability of such a group to reduce copper from cupric to the cuprous state[25] or silver ions to the metal[26]. Cellulose will also react with phenylhydrazine[27], hydrazine[28], and ethyl mercaptan[29], all compounds capable of reacting with carbonyl groups. Oxidising agents also attack the reducing end. Alkaline iodine[27] and chlorous acid[30] have been used with varying success. To some extent, formula (VI) may be regarded as the "ideal" as the exact constitution of a sample of cellulose will depend on its source and hence mode of purification needed to isolate it from impurities. As will be discussed later, hydrolysis or oxidation of cellulose will occur to an extent depending on the vigour of the reagents used in the purification.

The formula as written is that of a polysaccharide. However, sugars are noted for their solubility in water whereas cellulose, a carbohydrate carrying a considerable number of hydroxyl groups, is insoluble. This is due to strong interchain forces which are produced by hydrogen bonding between the hydroxyl groups on neighbouring chains. X-ray studies (Chapter 12) show that the molecules are linear and roughly planar in shape and capable of packing together a regular structure. Thus the chains are able to adlineate themselves and be bonded at a large number of points and hence give rise to an insoluble structure.

(c) Degree of Polymerization (D.P.) of Cellulose

The choice of a solvent for cellulose is not easy and the few available are unusually difficult to work with. Benzyl triethylammonium hydroxide, Zincoxene[31] (a complex of zinc hydroxide and ethylenediamine), iron-sodium tartrate[32] and others have been suggested but the best and commonest used are cuprammonium hydroxide and cupriethylenediamine. These latter are alkaline and oxidation and degradation of cellulose can occur. It is possible to reduce the degradation to a negligible degree if the dissolution is carried out in the absence of oxygen and light with addition of a small quantity of glucose but, even so, they have not proved suitable solvents for the fractionation of cellulose[33], a necessary preliminary before establishing a relationship between D.P. and viscosity. Nevertheless, relationships between viscosity and D.P. have been established for solutions of cellulose in cuprammonium but it has been found necessary to determine the D.P. of the particular samples of cellulose by other techniques. Workers in this field have turned to studies of the derivatives of cellulose particularly the triacetates and trinitrates. These are soluble in organic solvents but, in this case, care must be taken to ensure that no degradation occurs during esterification. This last point has however been overcome since it has been shown that practically the same D.P. may be obtained for products made under different conditions of nitration. The triacetate can be deacetylated and nitrated again without noticeable degradation[34].

Two procedures have been adopted; (a) measurement of the D.P. of secondary cellulose acetate using acetone as a solvent followed by deacetylation and measurement of cuprammonium viscosities of the regenerated material, and (b) taking of samples of partially hydrolysed cellulose–hydrocellulose and obtaining their D.P. by measurements of the trinitrates[35]. Molecular weights of these derivatives have been made by viscometry, osmometry, light scattering etc.[36]. However, it must be stressed that it is essential to ensure that the cellulose is fully substituted and, in particular, that for samples of high D.P. the shear stresses in the measurement of the viscosity are not too high[37].

Molecular weight determinations via end group analysis are unsatisfactory with cellulose, since the high D.P. of the latter means that very small percentages of end groups have to be determined.

In general, the determination of the D.P. of cellulose is more complicated than for most polymers and it is not surprising that different values have been obtained. The position has been summarised by Harland[38]. The values quoted, it must be added, are measured on samples of "purified" cellulose; it is impossible to guarantee that, in the extraction of cellulose, no degradation occurs so that the D.P. of native cellulose may be considerably higher. The opinion reached is that native cellulose has a D.P. greater than 3000. The ultracentrifuge method has given different results for the D.P. of cellulose from different sources ranging from 36,000 for flax, 10,800 for cotton to 2–3000 for sulphite pulp and 460 for viscose rayon[39]. The values of the D.P. are naturally average ones, the kind of average depending on the method used. In the case of the viscosity work, fractionation of the trinitrates[40] and of secondary acetate[41] has been carried out. Naturally the molecular weight distribution is dependent on the source of cellulose, how well it has been purified and to what extent the lower molecular weight fractions have been extracted.

3. Derivatives of Cellulose

Cellulose is capable of forming esters and ethers which differ in their degree of esterification or substitution up to the maximum given by the reaction of the three hydroxyl groups attached to each anhydroglucose unit. Characterisation of an ester or ether requires not only a knowledge of the D.P. but also a knowledge of the degree of substitution (D.S.).

(a) Cellulose Esters

(i) *Cellulose nitrates*

Esters with nitric acid were first made in the earlier part of the nineteenth century. These products were responsible for many changes in industrial and military technology. Gun cotton replaced black powder as a propellant and the introduction of celluloid as a synthetic plastic initiated to a large extent the moulding and fabrication of plastics. The reaction is usually carried out with mixtures of nitric and sulphuric acids and water, the degree of substitution being modified by variation of the concentration of these three components as well as reaction conditions. The characteristics of cellulose nitrate differ according to its end use; for use as a lacquer, a D.P. around 200 and a D.S. of 1.9–2.3 will suffice whereas, for an explosive (gun cotton), the D.P. should be about 2000 and the D.S. 2.4–2.8. Solubility in solvents is also affected. Cellulose nitrates are made from a variety of raw materials *e.g.* cotton linters, wood pulp, waste cellulose sheet etc. These different sources of cellulose will have different D.P.'s. To obtain gun cotton, cellulose with a high D.P. is used and care taken to ensure a minimum of degradation during nitration. For plastics or lacquers, cellulose of a low D.P. may be used *e.g.* waste cellulose sheet. For the nitrates of low D.P., deliberate hydrolysis of the nitrate may be carried out to reduce the D.P. to the desired value. Dissolution of the cellulose does not occur during the nitration with these mixtures; indeed cotton retains its fibrous form with little apparent modification apart from a harsher handle and an increased density.

Other reaction mixtures have been tried. For example phosphoric acid has been used in lieu of sulphuric[43]; pure nitric acid, or nitric acid together with methyl nitrate yielded cellulose nitrates of fairly high D.P., the cellulose dissolving in these reaction mixtures. For studies of molecular weight where degradation is to be avoided, a mixture of acetic acid, acetic anhydride and nitric acid[34] should be used. Most of the reacting mixtures when employed under conditions of maximum reaction give nitrates which fall short of the full degree of substitution of 3 by a small amount (*e.g.* a nitrogen content of $13-14\%$ compared with the theoretical 14.14%). However, it has been shown possible to achieve a pure cellulose trinitrate by treatment of dry cotton with nitrogen pentoxide[44].

Cellulose nitrate does not react in the expected manner with alkali; instead of giving the alkali nitrate and cellulose the reaction gives the nitrite and a wide variety of decomposition products of cellulose[16]. For saponification to yield cellulose, alkali sulphide solutions are used.

(ii) *Esters with organic acids*

Cellulose can react with organic acids, anhydrides or acid chlorides. Apart from formic acid direct esterification leads to low degrees of substitution. The more usual procedure is to use the anhydride in the presence of an acid catalyst, but it is possible to employ the free acid in the presence of an impelling agent. The latter is a substituted anhydride which does not itself esterify cellulose but, presumably, transforms the acid to its anhydride which is then able to react. As impelling agents, monochloroacetic and trifluoroacetic anhydrides have been used. Acid chlorides will react with cellulose if pyridine is used as a reaction medium.

Cellulose acetate is the most important member of this class being used for fibre manufacture as well as plastics. Esterification is carried out with the fibrous material suspended in the reaction mixture. The reaction is a heterogeneous one but, in the later stages of the reaction, the cellulose usually passes into solution. The course of the reaction is governed by the rates of diffusion of catalyst and acetic anhydride into the fibre[45]. This means that, in order to obtain a product which is uniform, care must be taken to ensure the raw material is in a suitable form. This can to some extent be achieved by pre-treatment with acetic acid or acetic acid and the catalyst. The sulphuric acid employed as catalyst reacts faster than acetic anhydride. The reaction is accompanied by evolution of heat and care must be taken to control the temperature[46]. The reaction is complete when the cellulose is completely soluble in the reaction mixture. Sulphuric acid in the reaction mixture will esterify first the cellulose[47] presumably giving an ester of the type $ROSO_3H$; during acetylation, trans-esterification occurs leaving the sulphuric acid capable of reacting with other free hydroxyl groups. Trans-esterification continues reducing the amount of combined sulphuric acid. The presence of combined mineral acid is a disadvantage as it leads to a product which is easily degraded. Additions of water are made to the reaction mixture to destroy the residual anhydride and, in so doing, sulphuric acid is removed. However, this procedure removes some acetyl groups so that the acetyl content is less than the theoretical. Removal of the sulphuric acid and partial replacement by acetyl groups is best achieved by gradual additions of magnesium acetate and water[14].

Acetylation of cellulose is commercially of such importance that many processes have been patented. Catalysts such as perchloric acid, zinc chloride etc., solvents other than acetic acid, *e.g.* chlorinated hydrocarbons have been employed.

Methylene chloride with perchloric acid has been shown to be an effective medium for producing the triacetate. If a reaction medium in which cellulose acetate is not soluble *e.g.* carbon tetrachloride is used, the product retains its fibrous form.

Esters of organic acids such as propionate and butyrate etc. have been made. If the structure of the acid is changed by increasing the number of carbon atoms in the chain, the esters produced have markedly different physical properties from the acetate but they are not of great interest in the textile field.

Cellulose triacetate was made commercially as long as 50 years ago. It was suitable for spinning into fibres from chloroform solution but, because of the hazards associated with this solvent and the inability at that time to dye such a fibre, commercial production did not last. Also the material may have suffered from the difficulty of removing completely the catalyst with consequent instability to heat. Cellulose triacetate lay dormant until methylene chloride became readily available. The latter is an excellent solvent for the triacetate and can be used in the acetylation in conjunction with perchloric acid as catalyst. Perchloric acid does not combine with cellulose and this is advantageous. Fibres made from triacetate are now well established commercially. Dyeing, originally a stumbling block to the development of the fibre, can nowadays be done satisfactorily and the fibre itself has certain advantages such as the ability to hold pleats permanently.

The commercial exploitation of the triacetate as a fibre was not only held up by lack of suitable solvents but was also overshadowed by the discovery of Cross, Bevan and Miles that controlled hydrolysis of the triacetate (often referred to as primary acetate) led to a "secondary" acetate which was soluble in the non-toxic solvent acetone.

Partial hydrolysis is simply achieved by adding water to the reaction mixture after dissolution of the cellulose and allowing hydrolysis to proceed until the product is soluble in acetone. For textile purposes, the secondary cellulose acetate is hydrolysed until a degree of substitution of *ca.* 2.4 is reached. De-acetylation produces hydroxyl groups and transforms a product soluble only in non-polar solvents such as chloroform or methylene chloride into one soluble in polar solvents *e.g.* acetone. Naturally, it is possible to produce a wide range of cellulose acetates according to the degrees of polymerisation and substitution. For example by hydrolysing in an increasing amount of water, acetates which have 13–19.1% of acetyl groups can be produced. These are water soluble[48]. Analysis of the acetone soluble cellulose acetate has shown that the free hydroxyl groups which are liberated during the hydrolysis may be found on all three (2, 3 and 6) carbon atoms in the glucose residues. This has been demonstrated by reacting the cellulose acetate with tosyl chloride, and treating the product with pyrrolidine which replaced the tosyl with pyrrolidyl groups to give for example (XVI). Hydrolysis was then followed by analysis; the fragments showed D-glucose to be present together with 3 other products[49] arising from substitution in the 3-positions in the cellulose ring.

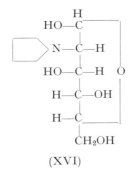

(XVI)

Acetylated cellulose has been produced for textile purposes by treatment of yarn with acetic anhydride vapour. Only the outer and more accessible parts of the fibre react and are completely acetylated but the product has properties similar to those of the triacetate. Partial acetylation of cotton goods has been investigated since such products show considerable resistance to heat and rotting by micro-organisms. This superficial treatment is done in a non-solvent using acetic anhydride[50].

A wide variety of cellulose esters have been studied. Cellulose propionate and butyrate have never achieved great commercial importance, but the mixed ester of butyrate with acetate is used for lacquers, moulding powder etc. Replacement of some of the acetyl groups by butyryl gives a product which has solubility in a wider range of solvents and a greater compatibility with solvents.

(b) Cellulose Ethers

Ethers of cellulose are normally prepared by the action of the etherifying agent on cellulose which has been treated with a swelling and solvating agent. Sodium hydroxide is most used for this purpose but other reagents are effective *e.g.* liquid ammonia, organic bases, etc. The raw material for this purpose is usually wood pulp of high α-cellulose content or cotton linters. The cellulose is first treated with caustic soda solutions to give "soda cellulose". The degree of substitution achieved is determined by the sodium hydroxide concentration near the end of the reaction, the etherification efficiency decreasing as the water concentration increases. The properties of cellulose ethers are very dependent on the degree of substitution. Samples of cellulose ethers of increasing D.S. show a transition from insolubility to solubility in aqueous alkali, water, water–alcohol mixtures, hydrocarbon–alcohol mixtures and finally aromatic hydrocarbons. Solubility in water is less when the ether has improved solubility in the non-polar solvent. The solubility of these ethers in water obtained at the lower values of the D.S. is considered to arise from the wedging apart of the cellulose chains, thereby allowing the hydroxyl groups to be available for hydration[51]. Naturally, as the number of the substituent non-polar groups increases and hence decreases the number of hydroxyl groups, solubility in organic solvents replaces that in water. Cellulose ethers also are thermoplastic in behaviour; the softening temperature decreases as the size of the substituent increases and depends on D.P. and D.S.

The reaction of soda or alkali cellulose with the reagent is heterogeneous. In the early stages, the solid soda cellulose is surrounded by aqueous caustic soda and the etherifying reagent must diffuse through this to the reaction centres. To obtain a uniform product demands, therefore, uniform distribution of the swelling agent which must provide alkalinity at every point throughout the reaction. Uniform swelling of the cellulose helps the diffusion of the etherifying reactions to the centres of reaction.

(i) Methylcellulose

This may be prepared commercially by reaction of soda cellulose with

methyl chloride or dimethyl sulphate. Its properties are naturally determined by the D.P. and D.S. Products of a low D.S. (0.1–0.9) are soluble
in aqueous sodium hydroxide. Those of higher D.S. (1.6–2.0) are soluble
in cold water but the solution gels on heating. The many commercial
kinds and viscosity grades of this material are generally water soluble
with a D.S. around 1.6. Clear solutions containing up to 5% of methylcellulose are viscous and have properties associated with protective
colloids. Films may be prepared which are tough and flexible and may be
rendered insoluble by reaction with a suitable cross-linking agent *e.g.*
formaldehyde.

Water soluble methylcelluloses do not show appreciable thermoplastic
behaviour but char when the temperature is raised to 220–230°C. This
is probably due to the lack of bulkiness of the methyl groups and failure
to give internal plasticisation. Methylcellulose finds applications as a
protective colloid or dispersing agent in emulsions, textile finishing and
printing.

(ii) *Ethylcellulose*

This material is prepared with ethyl chloride. Again products of low
D.S. (0.3–0.5) are alkali soluble, from 0.7–1.3 water soluble. Products of
higher D.S. (2.2–2.5) are soluble in organic solvents and are of value as
varnishes, adhesives, plastics etc.

(iii) *Carboxymethylcellulose*

Cellulose is treated with sodium hydroxide to produce alkali cellulose
which, in turn, is reacted with monochloroacetic acid or its sodium salt

$$ROH + ClCH_2COONa \xrightarrow{\text{NaOH}} ROCH_2COONa + NaCl + H_2O$$

In this system, a certain amount of sodium glycolate is formed as a by-
product

$$ClCH_2COONa + NaOH \rightarrow HOCH_2COONa + NaCl$$

Commercially, carboxymethylcellulose (C.M.C.) in the form of its sodium
salt is made with a low D.S. If D.S. is 0.7–1.2, the product is water
soluble; at D.S. 0.1–0.2 it is soluble in 3–10% aqueous caustic soda. The
free acid is not used to any great extent since it is not water soluble. The
solution behaves differently from methylcellulose in that no gelling occurs
on heating; it is not precipitated by addition of dilute alkali but is
precipitated by strong acids, heavy metal ions, etc. Carboxymethyl-
cellulose is of considerable value as a thickener, a protective colloid and is
used in the food industry. It is employed to a considerable extent with
detergents as a builder to prevent deposition of soil.

References p. 220

(iv) *Hydroxyethylcellulose*

This may be formed by reaction of alkali cellulose with ethylene oxide or chlorohydrin

$$ROH + CH_2\overset{\diagdown O \diagup}{-\!\!-}CH_2 \rightarrow ROCH_2CH_2OH$$

$$ROH + ClCH_2CH_2OH \xrightarrow{\text{NaOH}} ROCH_2CH_2OH + NaCl + H_2O$$

These reactions may not necessarily stop after one molecule has reacted. A second or greater number of molecules may react

$$ROCH_2CH_2OH + CH_2\overset{\diagdown O \diagup}{-\!\!-}CH_2 \rightarrow ROCH_2CH_2OCH_2CH_2OH \text{ etc.}$$

Thus more molecules may have combined than corresponds to the number of hydroxyl groups substituted.

Hydroxyethylcellulose is more hydrophilic than ethylcellulose as the substitution does not diminish the number of hydroxyl groups. This would seem to be reflected in the solubility — increase in temperature does not cause coagulation. This derivative of cellulose is made in relatively low ranges of degree of substitution (better M.S. — the number of moles introduced per glucose unit) of the order of 0.05–0.5. They are soluble in water or alkali.

(v) *Other ethers*

Ethers may be formed by addition of compounds containing activated double bonds. In the textile field, cotton has been modified by reaction with acrylonitrile producing a material known as cyano-ethylated cotton[52]. This treatment confers improved resistance to rot, heat and abrasion. The reaction between alcohol groups and acrylonitrile is

$$ROH + CH_2{=}CHCN \rightarrow ROCH_2CH_2CN$$

It may be carried out by impregnating the cotton material with 2% sodium hydroxide solution and treating with acrylonitrile at 55 °C. With care, high values of D.S. may be achieved. The cyano-ethylated cotton can be hydrolysed to the free acid *i.e.* carboxyethylcellulose. Other compounds of this type have been studied notably acrylamide ($CH_2{=}CHCONH_2$) but the results from the technical point of view have not been as useful as those using acrylonitrile.

(c) *Mechanism of Reaction*

Esterification is usually carried out in a strongly acid medium (mainly nitration, sulphation and acetylation). Nitration and sulphation are rapid reactions; acetylation is slower. In general the esterification reaction is ionic, *e.g.* nitration probably occurring via the NO_2^+ ion. In the reaction of carboxylic acid with an alcohol, the following steps must be considered[53]

$$RCOOH + H^+ \rightleftharpoons RCO\overset{+}{O}H_2 \rightleftharpoons R\overset{+}{C}O + H_2O$$

The reaction of hydrogen ions with the acid is to form the ion $R\overset{+}{C}O$ which is capable of reacting with the alcohol group

$$R\overset{+}{C}O + R_1OH \rightleftharpoons RCO\underset{H}{\overset{+}{O}}R_1 \rightleftharpoons RCOOR + H^+$$

For an anhydride the reaction scheme is the same, the ion being produced as follows

$$(RCO)_2O + H^+ \rightleftharpoons (RCO)_2\overset{+}{O}H \rightleftharpoons R\overset{+}{C}O + RCOOH$$

The ion $R\overset{+}{C}O$ has been shown to exist in the case of acetic anhydride[54].

Etherification is carried out in an alkaline medium with alkyl halides or less commonly alkylsulphates. The reaction course may be written as

$$R\bar{O} + R_1Cl \rightarrow R\bar{O}R_1Cl \rightarrow ROR_1 + \bar{C}l$$

For cellulose, the hydroxyl groups react to give an equilibrium state

$$ROH + OH^- \rightleftharpoons RO^- + H_2O$$

so that the acidity of the hydroxyl groups will determine the quantity of the ion formed and hence be one of the factors influencing reactivity. As the acidity of the hydroxyl in cellulose is about equal to that of water, there will be equal chances for etherification or hydrolysis.

These reactions are in fact no different from those undergone by aliphatic alcohols of low molecular weight but special features arise from the heterogeneous nature of reactions with cellulose. In carrying out these reactions, great care is taken to ensure that the fibrous material is uniformly accessible to the reagent. To produce a homogeneous product, it is essential that reaction occurs along the length of the cellulose chain. The penetration of reagent into the fibres must be determined by diffusion and the reaction rates of the groups in the fibre. However, the reaction is a relatively slow one for the formation of ethers and esters, so it would not be anticipated that the diffusion stage would be a rate determining step.

Cellulose ethers and esters to be of value in practice must be uniform in constitution. Samples will vary according to their D.P. and D.S. but further variants may occur due to the distribution of substituents between the various anhydroglucose units in the chain, as well as between the different hydroxyl groups in the glucose units themselves.

The latter point may be discussed by assuming that the reaction is a homogeneous one and that all the hydroxyl groups are of equal reactivity. Reaction will occur at random with any of the hydroxyl groups in the cellulose with the reagent to reach a certain value of D.S.; clearly some of the glucose units will have reacted to a high degree, whereas others will not have reacted at all. Thus a D.S. of unity does not mean that all glucose units will have one hydroxyl group substituted; some will have none while others have two or even three. Uniformity on this scale does not therefore exist. It is possible to calculate the numbers of unreacted glucose units and those substituted with one, two or three hydroxyl groups. For such calculations the anhydroglucose units are assumed to be equally available, the end groups are ignored and the reaction constants of the hydroxyl groups taken as constant throughout the reaction. This simple kinetic calculation may be done as follows.

Consider the reaction when there is present sufficient reagent to enable its concentration to remain constant during the reaction. The general equation for the reaction will in these circumstances be

$$-\frac{d[OH]}{dt} = k[OH] \tag{3}$$

This is a first order equation where the reaction constant k contains terms for the concentration of the reagent and catalyst. The concentration of unsubstituted glucose units in cellulose, S_0, will be reduced by reaction at hydroxyl groups on carbon atoms 2, 3 and 6 so that the rate of loss of S_0 is given by

$$-\frac{dS_0}{dt} = k_2 S_0 + k_3 S_0 + k_6 S_0 \tag{4}$$

where k_2, k_3 and k_6 refer to the reaction of the 2-, 3- and 6-hydroxyl groups respectively.

Equation 4 may be integrated to give

$$S_0 = S'_0 e^{-(k_2+k_3+k_6)t} \tag{5}$$

where S'_0 is the concentration of S_0 when $t = 0$.

In terms of fractions, $s_0 = S_0/S'_0$, equation 5 may be written

$$s_0 = e^{-(k_2+k_3+k_6)t} \tag{6}$$

The concentration of monosubstituted units S_6 is built up by reaction of unsubstituted units and is lost by reaction of units already substituted on the 6 carbon atom. Hence

$$\frac{dS_6}{dt} = k_6 S_0 - k_2 S_6 - k_3 S_6$$

or in terms of fractional concentration

$$\frac{ds_6}{dt} = k_6 s_0 - k_2 s_6 - k_3 s_6 \tag{7}$$

Substituting for s_0 from equation 6, equation 7 gives on rearrangement

$$\frac{ds_6}{dt} + (k_2 + k_3)s_6 = k_6 e^{-(k_2+k_3+k_6)t} \tag{8}$$

Equation 8 may be integrated by first multiplying by an integration factor $e^{(k_2+k_3)t}$ to give

$$e^{(k_2+k_3)t}\frac{ds_6}{dt} + e^{(k_2+k_3)t}(k_2 + k_3)s_6 = k_6 e^{-k_6 t} \tag{9}$$

On integration, equation 9 gives

$$s_6 e^{(k_2+k_3)t} = -e^{-k_6 t} + \text{Constant (say } A)$$

or

$$s_6 = -e^{-(k_2+k_3+k_6)t} + A e^{-(k_2+k_3)t} \tag{10}$$

But since $s_6 = 0$ when $t = 0$, $A = 1$.
Hence

$$s_6 = e^{-(k_2+k_3)t} - e^{-(k_2+k_3+k_6)t} \tag{11}$$

Similarly, for the groups substituted at the 2 and 3 atoms, equations for the fractions s_2 and s_3, may be written

$$s_2 = e^{-(k_3+k_6)t} - e^{-(k_2+k_3+k_6)t} \tag{12}$$

$$s_3 = e^{-(k_6+k_2)t} - e^{-(k_2+k_3+k_6)t} \tag{13}$$

The monosubstituted units may now react to give disubstituted. The fraction of units substituted in the 2,3-position $s_{2,3}$ will be produced from reaction of those units substituted in the 2- and 3-positions, and lost by further reaction

$$\frac{ds_{2,3}}{dt} = k_2 s_3 + k_3 s_2 - k_6 s_{2,3} \tag{14}$$

Substituting for s_2 and s_3 from equations 12 and 13 gives on rearrangement

$$\frac{ds_{2,3}}{dt} - k_6 s_{2,3} = k_2 \{e^{-(k_6+k_2)t} - e^{-(k_2+k_3+k_6)t}\} + k_3 \{e^{-(k_3+k_6)t} - e^{-(k_2+k_3+k_6)t}\}$$

$$(15)$$

The integration factor for this equation is $e^{-k_6 t}$ so that equation 15 integrates to

$$e^{k_6 t} s_{2,3} = k_2 \left\{ -\frac{e^{-k_2 t}}{k_2} + \frac{e^{-(k_2+k_3)t}}{k_2+k_3} \right\} + k_3 \left\{ -\frac{e^{-k_3 t}}{k_3} + \frac{e^{-(k_2+k_3)t}}{k_2+k_3} \right\}$$

$$+ \text{ Constant (say } B) \qquad (16)$$

Rearranging gives

$$s_{2,3} = -e^{-(k_2+k_6)t} - e^{-(k_3+k_6)t} + e^{-(k_2+k_3+k_6)t} + B e^{-k_6 t}$$

B is given by unity, since $s_{2,3} = 0$ when $t = 0$.
Hence

$$s_{2,3} = e^{-k_6 t} - e^{-(k_2+k_6)t} - e^{-(k_3+k_6)t} + e^{-(k_2+k_3+k_6)t} \qquad (17)$$

Similar equations arise for $s_{2,6}$ and $s_{3,6}$

$$s_{2,6} = e^{-k_3 t} - e^{-(k_3+k_6)t} - e^{-(k_2+k_3)t} + e^{-(k_2+k_3+k_6)t} \qquad (18)$$

$$s_{3,6} = e^{-k_2 t} - e^{-(k_2+k_6)t} - e^{-(k_2+k_3)t} + e^{-(k_2+k_3+k_6)t} \qquad (19)$$

The completely substituted units $s_{2,3,6}$ are produced from reaction of all the disubstituted

$$\frac{ds_{2,3,6}}{dt} = k_2 s_{3,6} + k_3 s_{2,6} + k_6 s_{2,3} \qquad (20)$$

Substituting in equation 20 for $s_{3,6}$, $s_{2,6}$ and $s_{2,3}$ gives

$$\frac{ds_{2,3,6}}{dt} = k_2 \{e^{-k_2 t} - e^{-(k_2+k_6)t} - e^{-(k_2+k_3)t} + e^{-(k_2+k_3+k_6)t}\}$$

$$+ k_3 \{e^{-k_3 t} - e^{-(k_3+k_6)t} - e^{-(k_2+k_3)t} + e^{-(k_2+k_3+k_6)t}\}$$

$$+ k_6 \{e^{-k_6 t} - e^{-(k_2+k_6)t} - e^{-(k_3+k_6)t} + e^{-(k_2+k_3+k_6)t}\} \qquad (21)$$

Integration of equation 21 gives

$$s_{2,3,6} = -(e^{-k_2 t} + e^{-k_3 t} + e^{-k_6 t}) + e^{-(k_2+k_6)t} + e^{-(k_2+k_3)t} + e^{-(k_3+k_6)t} -$$

$$- e^{-(k_2+k_3+k_6)t} + \text{Constant (say } C) \qquad (22)$$

$C = 1$, since $s_{2,3,6} = 0$ when $t = 0$.

These equations give the rate of increase of the fraction of each kind of degree of substitution. The degree of substitution will be given by

$$s = 3s_{2,3,6} + 2(s_{2,3} + s_{2,6} + s_{3,6}) + s_2 + s_3 + s_6$$

$$= 3 - e^{-k_2 t} - e^{-k_3 t} - e^{-k_6 t}$$

If $k_2 = k_3 = k_6 = k$, that is all hydroxyl groups have equal reactivity, then

$$s = 3 - 3e^{-kt}$$

$$s_6 = e^{-3kt}$$

whence

$$s_0 = \left(1 - \frac{s}{3}\right)^3 \tag{23}$$

$$s_1 = s_2 = s_3 = \frac{s}{3}\left(1 - \frac{s}{3}\right)^2 \tag{24}$$

$$s_{2,3} = s_{3,6} = s_{2,6} = \left(\frac{s}{3}\right)^2\left(1 - \frac{s}{3}\right) \tag{25}$$

$$s_{2,3,6} = \left(\frac{s}{3}\right)^3 \tag{26}$$

Equations 23–26 relate the fractions of the glucose units substituted to different degrees to the D.S.; in Fig. 46, fractions of tri-, di- and mono-substituted as well as the unsubstituted glucose units are plotted against D.S. These results, although strictly speaking applicable only to a homogeneous system, are useful in serving as a basis for further studies.

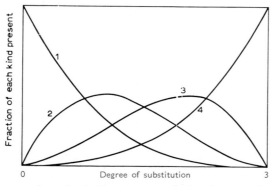

Fig. 46. Average number of substituents per anhydroglucose units *vs.* degree of substitution.

Curve 1 = unsubstituted   Curve 2 = mono-substituted
Curve 3 = disubstituted   Curve 4 = trisubstituted

References p. 220

Experimental confirmation is very difficult but may be approached in two ways. The first is to measure in partially substituted derivatives some specific type of substitution. Thus substitution at the primary alcohol groups may be determined by reaction with trityl chloride (triphenyl-methyl chloride)[58] or by tosyl chloride followed by reaction with sodium iodide[20]. The amount of hydroxyl groups left unsubstituted in the 2,3-positions can be determined by oxidation with periodate[52]. The second is to hydrolyse the partially substituted derivatives and analyse for all eight possible fragments. These methods are only really suitable for cellulose ethers. In general the results are not in disagreement with the arguments above[55,97].

(d) Reactivity of Hydroxyl Groups

It is to be anticipated that the primary alcohol groups will exhibit a greater degree of reactivity than the secondary. In sugars, however, it has been found that of the hydroxyl groups available the primary on carbon atom 6 and the secondary on carbon atom 2 are more readily esterified, and the differences in reactivity between these two are not as great as with simple alcohols. The results obtained depend on the reagents chosen as well as reaction conditions. Thus in esterification tosyl chloride reacts with the primary group[59], whereas benzoyl chloride gives the 2- and 6-derivatives of D-glucose[56]. In etherification trityl chloride prefers the primary groups; reaction with methyl iodide or dimethyl sulphate yields derivatives substituted in the 2- and 6-positions[98]. The hydroxyl group on position 3 turns out to be the least reactive.

Because cellulose is a solid, the picture is more complicated. Some reagents react mainly at the primary groups e.g. trityl chloride[58] and tosyl chloride[52,57,99]. In etherification reactions in solvents such as quaternary bases, there is a divergence of opinions; some results give greater reactivity to the primary alcohol groups[57], others find that the secondary groups are preferred[100]. Workers preparing carboxymethyl-cellulose using soda cellulose and chloroacetic acid find that, at low values of D.S., the primary hydroxyl reacts but, as D.S. increases, the other hydroxyl groups show equal reactivity[101]. This effect of greater reactivity of the primary groups at low D.S. and greater reactivity of the secondary has been shown to occur in other etherification reactions[52,99].

In esterification such as acetylation, the primary alcohol group is preferred[102] but, if cellulose acetate is allowed to hydrolyse to form the secondary acetate, acetyl groups are removed from all the 3-positions.

To make a general statement as to the different reactivities of the groups in cellulose is difficult. Although it seems that the primary group has a somewhat higher reactivity, some conditions favour conversion of secondary groups probably at the 2-rather than the 3-position. A further complication is the possibility of steric interaction between groups; substitution of one hydroxyl may affect the reactivity of another especially when bulky reagents such as trityl chloride are used.

4. Hydrolysis of Cellulose

(a) Hydrocellulose

Cellulose is sensitive to acids. Hydrolysis products with a wide range of D.P. may be obtained; progressive attack by acids causes cellulose to lose strength and ultimately its fibre structure to give a friable powder. Products formed by the acid treatment of cellulose are referred to as hydrocelluloses. Hydrolysis of cellulose will break the chain, lowering the D.P. and releasing reducing and non-reducing groups.

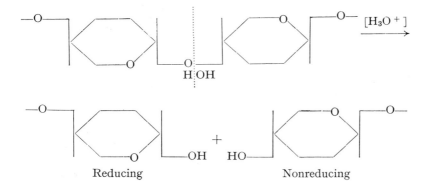

The number of reducing ends therefore increases as shown by the increase in the extent of reduction of ammoniacal silver nitrate producing a deposit of metallic silver or of formation of cuprous oxide from Fehling's solution. The latter test has been well standardised and gives a figure known as the copper number; it is used as a quantitative measure of the reducing property of hydrocelluloses.

As would be anticipated, hydrocellulose forms esters of a lower D.P. than cellulose and hence the products are more easily soluble in organic solvents. There are many methods of preparation of hydrocellulose possible, giving products which are only slightly degraded to ones where the fibrous cellulose is converted to a powder.

From the practical point of view, the extent of acid attack could be determined by the changes in the reducing properties or the viscosity of a solution of the material. There is a relation between the two parameters.

In Fig. 47 the logarithm of the viscosity of a 2% solution in cuprammonium is plotted against the copper number[60]. The figure shows that the viscosity method is more sensitive for highly degraded materials. This is

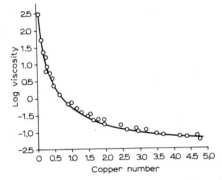

Fig. 47. Relation between the viscosity and copper number of cotton tendered by acids[60].

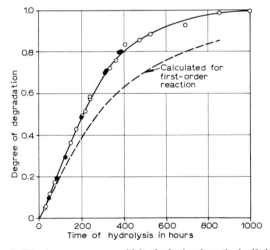

Fig. 48. The homogeneous acid hydrolysis of methylcellulose[62].
O methylcellulose in 1.81 N HCl at 50°C
● cellulose in 51% H_2SO_4 at 10°C with time scale altered by factor 0.814.

to be expected since viscosity measures chain breakage. A small number of breaks will lead to large molecular weight differences but not to large increases in the number of reducing groups with materials of high D.P. With materials of low D.P., the effect of chain scission on molecular weight will be less. The relationship between the viscosity and the copper number has been given empirically as $N_{Cu}V^2 = 2.6$ where V is the logarithm of the relative viscosity (*i.e.* log η/η_0) and N_{Cu} the copper number.

(b) Rate of Attack

The copper number has been determined for samples of cotton yarn steeped in acid solutions for varying times[60]. This gave a relation $N_{Cu} = Kt^{0.6}$ where K is a constant. However, the study of rates of hydrolysis of cellulose in terms of chemical kinetics is complicated by the heterogeneous nature of the reaction.

The rates of hydrolysis of cellulose in solution in sulphuric acid and of methylcellulose in hydrochloric acid have been measured[62]. The curves are of the same type, being super-imposable by change of scale factor only (Fig. 48). This indicates that similar factors operate for methylcellulose as for cellulose. When these experiments were done, the system appeared to follow first order kinetics. The mechanism of reaction has been shown to follow the equation below

$$-O- + H_3O^+ \underset{\text{fast}}{\overset{}{\rightleftarrows}} \overset{+}{-O-} + H_2O \overset{\text{slow}}{\longrightarrow} \text{products}$$

On this basis, the reaction of the protons with cellulose is very rapid and the rate of hydrolysis is therefore determined by the rate of breakdown of the ion. If the concentration of the ions is $[C_0^+]$, then

$$-\frac{d[C_0^+]}{dt} = k[C_0^+] \tag{27}$$

assuming each centre of reaction may be treated separately.

The concentration of the ions is then related, by the normal equilibrium equation, to the starting concentrations *i.e.*

$$K = \frac{[C] \times [H_3O^+]}{[H_2O] \times [C_0^+]}$$

where [C] is the concentration of cellulose, so that

$$[C_0^+] = \frac{[C] \times [H_3O^+]}{K[H_2O]} \tag{28}$$

This expression may be substituted into equation 27. However this treatment has neglected activity coefficients. Since the acid strengths which were used in these experiments were high, the equations must be written in terms of activities.

This gives

$$-\frac{d[C_0^+]}{dt} = \frac{k}{K} \frac{[C] \times [H_3O^+]}{[H_2O]} \times \frac{f_C \times f_{H_3O^+}}{f_{H_2O} \times f_{C_0^+}} \tag{29}$$

References p. 220

If $\{1/[C]\}d[C_0^+]/dt$ is the specific velocity constant and equal of k^1, then

$$\log k^1 = \log \frac{k}{K} \frac{[H_3O^+]}{[H_2O]} \frac{f_C f_{H_3O^+}}{f_{C_0^+} f_{H_2O}}$$

$$= \log \frac{k}{K} \frac{a_{H_3O^+}}{a_{H_2O}} \frac{f_C}{f_{C_0^+}}$$

$$= \log \frac{k}{K a_{H_2O}} + \log a_{H_3O^+} \frac{f_C}{f_{C_0^+}} \qquad (30)$$

In these equations, a and f refer to activities and activity coefficients. Thus a plot of $\log k^1$ should be linear against $\log a_{H_3O^+} f_C/f_{C_0^+}$; this has been found to be so[62].

However, if the reaction is not carried out in solution, equation 30 is not necessarily applicable. The system is now a heterogeneous one and the rate of reaction will be dependent on the ability of the reagents to reach the reactive links in the fibre. This in turn will be related to the fine structure of the cellulose and indeed has been used to throw light on the structure.

Nevertheless if all linkages are equally susceptible to attack, equation 27 relates the rate of change of the number of links to that in the system. This rate of change is equal to the rate of production of the number of broken links x, i.e. $d[C_0^+]/dt = -dx/dt$.

If there were N units in the chain and hence $N-1$ links before hydrolysis, the number remaining is $N-1-x$ and therefore

$$\frac{dx}{dt} = k(N - x - 1) \qquad (31)$$

Integration of equation 31 gives

$$\log \frac{N-1}{N-x-1} = kt$$

or

$$\log(1 - \gamma) = -kt \qquad (32)$$

where γ is the fraction of linkages broken and is equal to $x/(N-1)$. Hence $\gamma = 1 - e^{-kt}$.

This equation gives the rate of breakage. Whilst the hydrolysis of cellulose proceeds, the chain lengths of the molecules decrease and hence the viscosity of a solution of cellulose decreases. The breakdown of the linkages may be assumed to occur at random along the chain and hence no substantial quantities of single molecules of glucose appear in the early stages of the reaction. The molecule is assumed very large and has a

D.P. of N so that there are $N-1$ linkages at the commencement of reaction; at any time a number of linkages x have broken, hence the degree of degradation may be defined as

$$\frac{\text{Number of links broken}}{\text{Original number}} = \frac{x}{N-1}$$

The probability that particular bond is broken will be given by this ratio γ whereas the probability that a bond is unbroken is $1-\gamma$.

To obtain the distribution of the sizes of the fragments produced in such a random scission, the probability that n units will be separated as a single molecule must be calculated. Such a fragment would arise from scission at the mth and the $(m+n)$th bonds down the chain. The probability that these will be broken together will be the product of probabilities for breaking each $i.e.$ γ^2. The fragment of n units will have $n-1$ bonds and hence the probability of finding these unbroken will be $(1-\gamma)^{n-1}$, giving a total probability of finding fragments containing n units formed by breaking the mth and the $(m+n)$th bonds of

$$z_n = \gamma^2 (1-\gamma)^{n-1} \tag{33}$$

However, this fragment may have been formed by breaking the bonds at values of x ranging from zero to $N-1-x$. This means there are $N-x$ possible kinds of breakages to give an n-mer. If x is very small and may be neglected compared with N, then the probability of finding an n-mer independent of which bonds in the chain have actually been broken is

$$Z_n = N\gamma^2 (1-\gamma)^{n-1} \tag{34}$$

Since these fragments contain n units, the total number of units expressed as a fraction of the whole is

$$W_n = \frac{nZ_n}{N} = n\gamma^2(1-\gamma)^{n-1} \tag{35}$$

This is the fractional concentration of fragments containing n units. When α is replaced by $1-p$, the distribution is identical with the most probable one achieved in polycondensation reaction (p is the extent of reaction defined in Chapter 2). This result is not specific to cellulose but is applicable to any reaction where a chain is being split in a random fashion.

The distribution given in equation 35 will give a maximum value of W_n for any given value of the degree of degradation for the different size fractions. The equation may be shown by differentiating logarithmically

$$\ln W_n = \ln n + 2 \ln \gamma + (n - 1) \ln (1 - \gamma)$$

$$\frac{d \ln W_n}{d\gamma} = \frac{2}{\gamma} - \frac{n - 1}{1 - \gamma}$$

$$\frac{d \ln W_n}{d\gamma} = 0 \quad \text{when} \quad \frac{2}{\gamma} = \frac{n - 1}{1 - \gamma} \quad \text{or} \quad \gamma = \frac{2}{n + 1} \tag{36}$$

Substituting this value of α in equation 34 gives the maximum value of W_n for values of n, i.e.

$$W_n = n \left(\frac{2}{n + 1}\right)^2 \left(\frac{n - 1}{n + 1}\right)^{n-1} \tag{37}$$

Equation 37 shows that the maximum amount of cellobiose ($n = 2$) which occurs at one stage in the hydrolysis of cellulose is 29.6%. Further it can be shown that the total amount of cellobiose which has existed at all stages during the reaction is 66.7%. Hydrolysis based on random scission shows that, at no stage, is it possible to hydrolyse cellulose to cellobiose completely and indeed the maximum amount of cellobiose which has been isolated from the reaction was not more than 60%[64].

(c) Average Chain Lengths During Hydrolysis

The number average chain length may be calculated from the fact that the number of molecules produced when x links are broken is $x + 1$. The number average D.P. will be given by $N/(x + 1)$. The changes in D.P., $\bar{P}_n$, in terms of time may be calculated. From equation 31

$$\gamma = \frac{x}{N - 1} = 1 - e^{-kt}$$

whence

$$\bar{P}_n = \frac{N}{(N - 1)(1 - e^{-kt}) + 1}$$

or

$$\frac{\bar{P}_n - 1}{\bar{P}_n} = \frac{N - 1}{N} e^{-kt} \tag{38}$$

Hence plotting $\ln (\bar{P}_n - 1)/\bar{P}_n$ vs. t should give a slope of $-k$ and an intercept at $t = 0$ of $\ln (N - 1)/N$. This has been shown to be true for the hydrolysis of methylated cellulose with hydrochloric acid[65]. The results are given in Fig. 49. In this work the polymer is solid in the initial stages but dissolves as the reaction proceeds. To apply this theory it must be assumed that the initial reaction, even though heterogeneous, occurs in a random fashion. With this assumption the value of N has been found by extrapolation giving 400 ± 70 as the D.P. of the particular methylated cellulose used.

The molecule taken for study in the foregoing is one of "infinite" length (N is very large) with all linkages being split with the same probability. However, the results become more complex if (a) the polymer has a finite D.P., (b) if the polymer is not homogeneous at the commence-

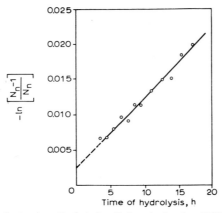

Fig. 49. Hydrolysis of methylated cellulose in fuming HCl at 0°C[65].

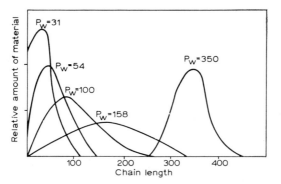

Fig. 50. Experimental distribution curves for undegraded and degraded cellulose acetate[66]. (Original chain length 350.)

ment of the reaction or (c) the probabilities of breaking of the bonds are not the same. (a) may be dealt with by an extension of the theory; (c) has been investigated and the question as to whether there are a few "weak linkages" in cellulose is not completely resolved. Some results on (b) may however be quoted.

Experiments have been carried out on cellulose acetate[66]; material of average D.P. $\bar{P}_w$ was degraded and samples, at stages corresponding to different values of $\bar{P}_w$, analysed. The distribution curves are given in

Fig. 50. From the values of $\bar{P}_w$, the theoretical distribution curves have been calculated; these are given in Fig. 51. These graphs, whilst subject to considerable error, show that the molecular weight distribution of a

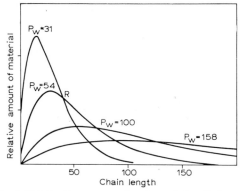

Fig. 51. Theoretical distribution curves for degraded cellulose acetate originally homogeneous of chain length 350.

material with an initially sharp distribution broadens out as hydrolysis proceeds and then becomes sharper as $\bar{P}_w$ becomes smaller. The distributions in Fig. 51 were calculated on the basis of random scission but taking into account the fact that the starting material had a finite D.P.

Hydrolysis of cotton cellulose has been studied in considerable detail by Sharples[72] who has related the rates of reaction to the structure of the fibre. In the first stages of the reaction, it is clear that the ideas of random scission may be applied provided it is assumed that reaction takes place in the amorphous regions. In the later stages, attack of the crystallites occurs; and the rate for this stage is slower than the initial one.

The completely detailed picture is made more complex by the fact that recrystallisation may occur during hydrolysis and the possibility that weak links which are more readily attacked by acid may be present[73]. If this is so, the hydrolysis will not be completely random. The position has not completely been resolved.

(d) Determination of the Degradation

The viscosity has been used to a large extent to follow degradation reactions. End group analysis is a second possibility but does not yield well defined results with cellulose.

(i) Viscosity

The rate of change with time of the intrinsic viscosity does not give a direct measure of the number of breakages. However, it is possible by using the reciprocal of the intrinsic viscosity to obtain some measure of the number of breaks in the chain.

The number of breaks is equal to the increase in the number of molecules

$$x = N_t - N \tag{39}$$

where N_t is the number of molecules in the system at any time. If at the beginning there was a weight W taken, the number of moles in the system given by W/M_n. x is then equal to the change in the value of this. To use viscosity or its reciprocal, some assumptions must be made.

In a polymer which has been degraded in a random fashion, it has been shown that the number average is approximately half the weight average molecular weight[67]. The values of the ratio $\bar{M}_w/\bar{M}_n$ have been determined experimentally at various stages during the hydrolysis of Egyptian cotton and found to be very close to 2 over wide ranges of the D.P.[68]. This result is not entirely unexpected since the simple statistical treatment leads to a distribution which is most probable and, in a polycondensation, the ratio of molecular weight averages tends to 2 as the extent of reaction tends to 1. This means that equation 39 becomes

$$x = N_t - N = \Delta\left(\frac{W}{M_n}\right) \sim \Delta\left(\frac{2W}{M_n}\right) \tag{40}$$

Further a second approximation is to replace the viscosity average

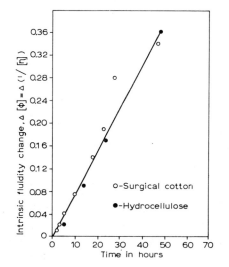

Fig. 52. Hydrolysis of cellulose in H_3PO_4 solution at 20°C[69].

molecular weight by the weight average. This is tantamount to assuming that the exponent α used in the viscosity equations is not very far from unity *i.e.*

$$M_w \sim k[\eta] \tag{41}$$

This has been shown to be a reasonable assumption for cellulose derivatives[69]. By combination of equations 40 and 41, the intrinsic fluidity may be related to time,

$$\gamma = \frac{x}{N-1} \sim \frac{1}{N-1} \Delta \left(\frac{2W}{M_w}\right) \sim \frac{2W}{N-1} \frac{1}{[\eta]} = 1 - e^{-kt} \sim kt$$

Hence a plot of $1/[\eta]$ should be linear with t. This result has been found experimentally for hydrolysis of surgical cotton and hydrocellulose; the results are shown in Fig. 52[70].

(ii) *End group analysis*

For cellulose the most used method is the determination of the copper number. Unfortunately, this valuable tool for following the changes on hydrolytic damage of cellulose in fibre form does not give a result bearing a known relation to the number of aldehyde groups. Nevertheless, these groups are the main source of reducing power of degraded celluloses but the reducing power, as far as the copper number is concerned, may be accentuated by the presence of ketone groups.

Other techniques are to oxidise the aldehyde groups to carboxyl by chlorous acid or sodium hypoiodite. In material treated with chlorous acid the copper number is decreased and the number of carboxyl groups increased. Unfortunately, the yield of carboxyl groups is not quantitative and falls short of the maximum possible in theory. The copper number of hydrocelluloses is not completely reduced to zero within a reasonable time[71] so that the method is not completely satisfactory.

Treatment of hydrocelluloses with hypoiodite produces carboxyl groups and iodide ions. The oxidising species is most likely to be the undissociated form

$$I_2 + OH \rightleftharpoons HOI + I^-$$

$$RCHO + HOI \rightarrow RCOOH + I^- + H^+$$

The solution after treatment is acidified and titrated with sodium thiosulphate. Again this method suffers from the fact that the copper number is not reduced to zero.

The use of end group analysis for following the rates of degradation must be treated with caution if more than a semi-quantitative result is required.

5. Oxidation of Cellulose

Treatment of cellulose fibres with oxidising agents in acidic, neutral or alkaline solutions leads to chemical attack and, almost invariably, to loss of tensile strength. Tendering of cellulose fibres by oxidising agents is one of the hazards of the bleaching process. Because of the commercial importance of bleaching, many data have accumulated on the treatment of cellulose with agents such as sodium hypochlorite. To obtain a fibre of satisfactory strength, control of the oxidation is important; the colouring matter must be destroyed leaving the cellulose with the minimum attack.

(a) General Formation of Oxycelluloses

Products of oxidation of cellulose are normally referred to as "oxycelluloses" even though such materials differ widely in their properties. For example, cotton treated with alkaline solutions of sodium hypobromite or hypochlorite gives products which exhibit reducing properties only to a small extent (low copper number) but which contain a large content of acid groups (as determined by the absorption of the basic dye, Methylene Blue). Reaction in acid conditions leads to the reverse of this — high copper numbers and low quantities of acidic groups. In some instances, tendering of the fibre may not be apparent until the fibre has been treated with alkali, presumably because some hydrolysis has occurred and the chain length reduced thereby giving a reduction in tensile strength. This point is exemplified by measurements of fluidity (reciprocal viscosity) by two different techniques. The determination of the viscosity of solutions of

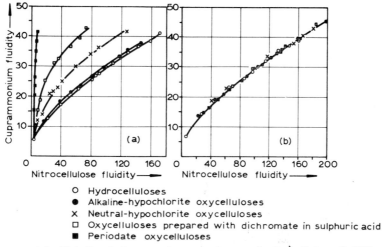

O   Hydrocelluloses
●   Alkaline-hypochlorite oxycelluloses
X   Neutral-hypochlorite oxycelluloses
□   Oxycelluloses prepared with dichromate in sulphuric acid
■   Periodate oxycelluloses

Fig. 53 a and b. Relation between cuprammonium and nitrocellulose fluidities for (a) hydrocelluloses and (b) alkali-boiled hydrocelluloses and oxycelluloses[74]

cellulose or its degradation products in cuprammonium or cupriethylene-diamine is a standard routine test for extent of degradation. Alternatively, the product may be nitrated under non-degradative conditions and the viscosity of the nitrate determined in acetone solution. The fluidities, as determined by these two methods, have been measured and one plotted against the other for a range of products including hydrocellulose (Fig. 53a). The two measurements may be taken as empirical determinations of chain length and all points should fall on the same line independent of the method by which the cellulose has been degraded. They do not so and some products e.g. periodate oxidised material shows relatively higher cuprammonium fluidities (increased degradation) than would be expected from the nitrocellulose value. However, cuprammonium is alkaline in character and causes chain breakage. Treatment of the samples with boiling alkali prior to nitration modifies the fluidity value, so that now the figures for all samples fall on the same line[74] (Fig. 53b).

Oxycellulose can thus be produced with properties which depend on the chemical nature of the oxidising agent and the conditions under which it is used. Products are degraded but the extent of degradation may not be apparent until the material has been treated with alkali. The preparation of oxycelluloses using various agents (nitric acid, bromine, water, chromic acid, potassium permanganate etc.) are described in standard works[1]. Apart from the kind of reagent, pH and temperature have considerable effects of the extent of reaction. Much of the interest in oxidative attack on cellulose is connected with the bleaching and will be discussed in the chapter dealing with that subject.

The oxidation, like the hydrolysis, of cellulose is a heterogeneous reaction; this means that attack of the reagent is not necessarily uniform throughout the fibre. In general, attack occurs most rapidly in the amorphous regions of the fibre followed by a much slower attack on the more ordered ones. The products of oxidation may retain the original fibrous form but may, depending on the reagent and the vigour of the attack, be a friable powder. This chapter is concerned only with the modes of attack.

The anhydroglucose unit in cellulose is subject to attack in at least

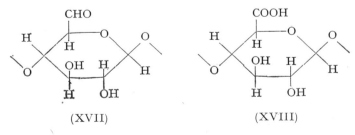

(XVII)   (XVIII)

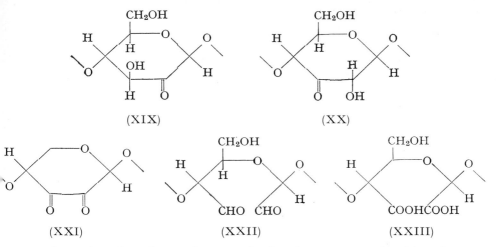

(XIX)   (XX)

(XXI)   (XXII)   (XXIII)

4 places. Attack at the 2 and 3 atoms leads to keto groups or breaking of the ring leading to two aldehyde groups which may in turn be oxidised through to carboxyl groups. Attack at the 6-position may form aldehyde or carboxyl groups. Some of the possibilities are given by formulae (XVII-XXIII).

The possible points of attack and the products are therefore numerous. Analysis of oxycellulose in the general case where the reagent does not give any one of these specific reactions is not feasible at present, since analysis of the resulting oxycellulose would require methods of measuring not only the quantity but also the position of a specific group. Most reagents would seem to attack cellulose in a non-specific manner. Some e.g. periodic acid, nitrogen dioxide and lead tetracetate are apparently more specific in their reaction.

(b) Oxycellulose from Periodates

The mechanism of reaction of periodates with α-glycols consists of a rapid reaction to form univalent anionic ester (XXIV) which can easily dehydrate to give second univalent ester (XXV)[76]. This ester decomposes slowly giving the aldehydes (XXVI) and liberating the iodate ion

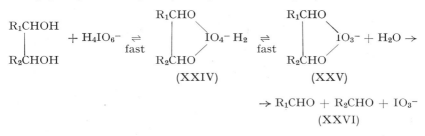

$$\rightarrow R_1CHO + R_2CHO + IO_3^-$$
$$(XXVI)$$

When iodate solutions are used, there is an equilibrium set up between the ion IO_4^- and $H_4IO_6^-$

$$IO_4^- + 2H_2O \rightleftharpoons H_4IO_6^-$$

The compound (XXIV) decomposes unimolecularly. Cellulose has a structure of the α-glycol type and has been shown to follow the same course of reaction[77] giving the dialdehyde (IX).

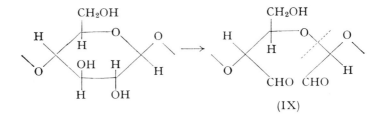

(IX)

The aldehyde may be hydrolysed across the dotted line to give glyoxal and D-erythrose (XXVII).

(XXVII)   (XXVIII)

The latter may be identified by oxidation with bromine water to give D-erythronic acid (XXVIII).

The most notable properties of oxycellulose produced by reaction with periodate were found[78] to be its high reducing power and extreme sensitivity to attack by alkali. Both are explained by the presence of aldehyde groups of the oxidised chain units.

Measurements of the rate of periodate ions consumed during reaction with cellulose have been made and, in Fig. 54, results are given at different concentrations and temperatures[76]. The curves 2 and 3 in the graphs give indications that there is an initial fast reaction which is followed by a slower one. This first reaction is identifiable with the formation of a complex (XXIV) between the periodate and the α-glycol group in the cellulose; the formation of such complexes is not accompanied by oxidation of cellulose and formation of aldehyde groups. This point is shown by the fact that the copper number does not change for cotton treated for these short periods of time. Further evidence for the initial

formation of such a complex comes from the comparison of the rates of
reaction in the presence of an inert electrolyte — sodium chloride. The
addition of electrolyte has the effect of increasing the amount of periodate ion absorbed by the solid cellulose in a fashion which might be

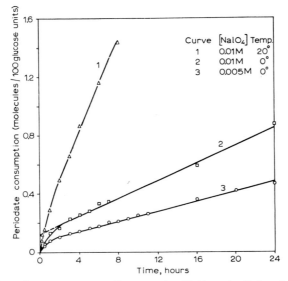

Fig. 54. Effect of temperature on the rate of oxidation of cellulose by unbuffered
sodium metaperiodate[76].

TABLE 16

EFFECT OF pH ON THE OXIDATION OF COTTON BY 0.05 M PERIODATE

(24 hours at 20°C)

pH	Periodate consumption (molecules per 100 glucose units)	Yield of carboxyl on treatment with chlorous acid (%)
0.90	5.8	90
1.64	10.9	92
2.91	11.8	91
3.91	12.4	91
4.64	13.2	89
5.03	13.8	88
5.98	14.1	86
6.80	15.7	57
7.52	11.3	40
8.26	6.2	26
9.40	3.0	10
9.84	2.1	7
10.99	1.8	4

References p. 220

predicted by the theory of membrane equilibrium of Donnan. This latter
is discussed in some detail in Volume II when the question of dye adsorption is considered. Thus the reaction of periodate with cellulose has, as its
first step in the same way as the α-glycols, the formation of a complex; the
ordinate on the axis in Fig. 54 represents the quantity of complex formed.

Changes in pH of the periodate liquor have an effect of the extent
of oxidation. This is seen from Table 16.

The quantity of oxidising agent used passes through a broad maximum
over the pH range 2–7. In strongly acid solution, an unchanged complex
(XXIX) predominates; in alkaline, the doubly charged ion (XXX).

RCHO
$$\begin{array}{c} \text{RCHO} \\ | \\ | \\ \text{RCHO} \end{array} \Big\rangle \text{IO}_4\text{H}_3$$

(XXIX)

$$\begin{array}{c} \text{RCHO} \\ | \\ | \\ \text{RCHO} \end{array} \Big\rangle \text{IO}_4\text{H}^-$$

(XXX)

Compounds with these structures do not decompose in the manner of
structure (XXIV). Also oxidation under alkaline conditions does not
produce the two aldehyde groups expected. This is shown by the figures
in the last column where the yield of carboxyl groups is given assuming
that the reaction gives two aldehyde groups which, on oxidation, give two
carboxyl (XXXI). Chlorous acid has been shown to oxidise aldehyde
groups to carboxyl. The best conditions seem to be a solution of sodium
chlorite acidified to pH 3 at 20°C[79]. The yield in no case was found to
reach the theoretical value of 2 carboxyl per atom of oxygen consumed
but was found on average to be 1.78.

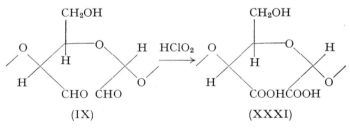

(IX)   (XXXI)

In no instance is a theoretical yield of carboxyl groups obtained, although
it is sufficiently large to show that the major reaction is the one given
above. However at high pH values, the yield falls off substantially indicating that other effects must occur.

Periodate oxycelluloses are extremely sensitive to alkali. The action
of alkali is to break the acetal linkage between the 2 and 6 carbon atoms.
The sensitivity is brought about by the presence of an electronegative
group in the α-position to the ethers β[80].

If the aldehyde groups are oxidised to carboxyl with chlorous acid thereby giving carboxyl ions in alkaline solution, the lability of the α-hydrogen atom no longer exists and hence the product is no longer alkali sensitive[79]. The reaction to form two aldehyde groups does not split the chain so that, when the oxycellulose is transformed to the carboxyl type by chlorous acid, the chains for the most part remain intact.

The acidic oxycelluloses prepared by periodate/chlorite treatment on storage show increasing fluidities and reducing properties (copper number). Hydrolysis is occurring, breaking the chain and hence giving a larger fluidity. The reaction requires the carboxyl groups for the hydrogen ions which they liberate for, when they are transformed into their sodium salts by neutralisation, the oxycellulose is stable.

A second method of rendering periodate oxycellulose resistant to alkali is by reduction of the aldehyde to primary alcohol groups. This is most simply achieved by sodium borohydride[81], a reagent which can also react with the aldehyde groups in hydrocellulose to produce a material which shows low solubility in alkali.

Chemical reactions of periodate oxycellulose can be explained by the content of aldehyde groups. Nevertheless, when the material is examined by infra-red techniques, the normal absorption band which should arise from the carbonyl group is absent[82]. To account for this, it has been suggested the cyclic hemiacetal is formed between the primary hydroxyl and either of the aldehyde groups. If the second group is hydrated as is indicated in formulae (XXXII) and (XXXIII) the carbonyl group is absent. An alternative is given below.

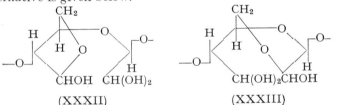

(XXXII)   (XXXIII)

Later work has shown that the C—O bonds appear when the oxycellulose is dried. This has led to the suggestion that the hemialdol form (XXX) may lose, on heating to 100°C, one molecule of water to give the free dialdehyde[104].

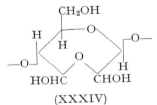

(XXXIV)

References p. 220

Another possibility is the formation of a hemiacetal between adjacent molecules to give a cross-linked structure.

(c) Oxycellulose from Nitrogen Dioxide

The reaction of cellulose with gaseous nitrogen dioxide is mainly that of attack on the primary alcohol group, thereby producing a carboxyl group (XVIII). Such acids are classified as uronic acids[83,86].

This reaction of the oxidation of the primary alcohol group as the main reaction was confirmed by treatment of the oxidised material with periodate followed by chlorous acid,

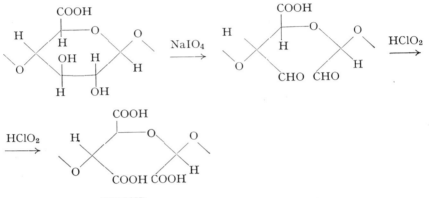

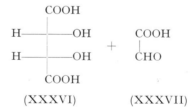

(XXXV)

Hydrolysis of (XXXV) yields mesotartaric acid (XXXVI) and glyoxylic acid[84] (XXXVII).

(XXXVI)   (XXXVII)

However the resulting oxycellulose, in addition to a high concentration of carboxyl groups, has reducing properties and is alkali sensitive. This suggests that reactions other than the one written above occur. In the reaction, the quantity of oxygen used is greater than corresponds to the number of uronic acid groups found; 2.35 atoms are used instead of 2. The high reducing power and alkali sensitivity are reminiscent of the properties of periodate oxycelluloses and it is likely that the reaction gives rise to the dialdehyde as in the periodate oxidation[85]. In addition, it has been inferred from the pale yellow colour of bone dry highly oxidised materials that the oxidation produces the diketone (XXI).

The mechanism of action of nitrogen dioxide on cellulose is not completely resolved. It seems that the 6-mononitrate is first produced and it is this derivative which decomposes.

(d) Oxycellulose from Other Agents

Two reagents which are fairly specific in their action are chlorous acid mentioned above and sodium hypoiodite. These reagents oxidise aldehyde groups to carboxyl. The production of carboxyl groups is not completely quantitative and it is not possible to bring, by treatment with chlorous acid, the copper number of hydrocelluloses, for example, to zero. This point is shown in the graph in Fig. 55[71] where, for three hydrocelluloses,

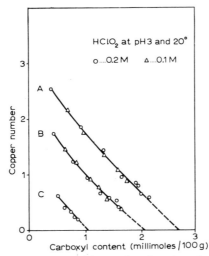

Fig. 55. Relation between copper number and carboxyl content for three hydrocelluloses treated with chlorous acid[71].

the relationship is given between the copper number and the carboxyl content produced by treatment with chlorous acid.

The action of sodium hypoiodite is considered to act through undissociated hypoiodous acid[86]

$$I_2 + OH^- \rightarrow HOI + I^-$$

$$RCHO + HOI \rightarrow RCOOH + HI$$

Unfortunately this reaction does not give completely quantitative yields.

References p. 220

6. Attack of Cellulose by Alkali

The alkaline degradation of cellulose and modified cellulose is important in the textile field *e.g.* in the ageing of soda cellulose or treatment of pulps with hot alkali[87]. Cellulose is slowly attacked by hot alkali and the loss in weight arising is dependent on the number of aldehydic groups present. This suggests that degradation occurs in a stepwise fashion from the reducing end of the cellulose chain[88]. Stability to alkali may be achieved by oxidation of the aldehyde groups to carboxyl[89], by reduction to alcohol[90] or blocking by forming the methylglucoside[91]. On the other hand, chemical attack leading to an increase in carbonyl groups (oxidation of primary or secondary alcohol groups) causes cellulose to become more susceptible to alkali[92]. The study of degradation of hydrocellulose, oxycellulose, model compounds and periodate oxidised cellulose has suggested that, out of the many complex possibilities, a reaction involving the elimination of an alkoxyl group plays a definite role. The mode of action may be demonstrated by reference to the conversion of aldol to crotonyl aldehyde (**XXXVIII**).

Aldol is a β-hydroxyaldehyde which, in the presence of alkali, is converted to crotonaldehyde. The first step involves the formation of an enediol (**XXXIX**) which presumably is in an ionised form in the presence of alkali *i.e.*

$$\underset{\text{(XXXVIII)}}{CH_3-\underset{\underset{OH}{|}}{\overset{\beta}{C}H}-\overset{\alpha}{C}H_2-CHO} \rightleftharpoons \underset{\text{(XXXIX)}}{CH_3-\underset{\underset{OH}{|}}{CH}-CH=CH} \rightarrow CH_3-CH=CH-CHO$$

The ion will cause a charge to accumulate at the β-atom as indicated by the arrows. The β-hydroxyl group is therefore labile and comes away. When this happens, the double bond shifts to the α- and β-carbon atoms giving crotonaldehyde. This mechanism may be applied to glucose. This

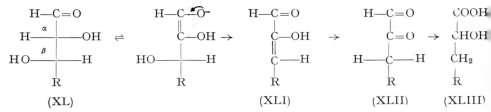

comporitteund is wn for convenience as (**XL**) the corresponding α- and β-atoms being labelled.

The compound (**XLI**) will then transpose to give the diketone (**XLII**). A diketone such as this is able to undergo a benzilic acid rearrangement to give D-metasaccharinic acid (XLIII). Metasaccharinic acid has been identified in the hydrolysis products of hydrocelluloses which have been previously treated with alkali until no further reaction takes place[93]. This reaction would lead to a cessation of the degradation through the production of an end group stable to alkali. Another major product in alkali treated hydrocellulose is isosaccharinic acid[94] (XLIV). This acid could be formed by a similar mechanism. To elucidate the mechanism of breakdown of aldoses leading to isosaccharinic acid, model compounds have been studied. 4-O-substituted aldoses have been shown to degrade after a time lag of some hours, whereas with 4-O-substituted ketoses no time lag is observed. This suggests that degradation of the aldose is via the ketose[95], a transformation

$$RCHOHCHO \rightleftharpoons RCOCH_2OH$$

which takes place during the lag. The ketose (XLV) can form an enediol (XLVI) in a manner analogous to the aldose,

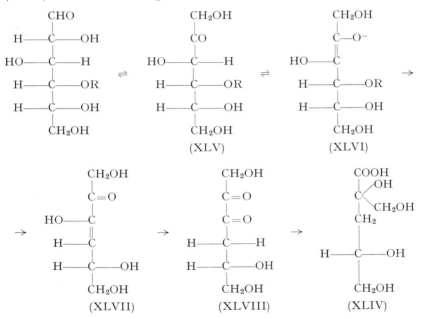

The OR group from carbon atom 4 is split off in the same way that the hydroxyl group was for the aldose. In splitting off this group, the substituent goes with it. If the glucose residue happens to be at the end of a chain, the chain after this reaction has one unit less. The process can be repeated and hence the chain gets shorter. The enediol reverts on this split back to a ketone (XLVII) and then to the diketone (XLVIII).

This compound is thus suitable to undergo, in alkaline conditions, the benzilic acid rearrangement to give isosaccharinic acid (XLIV). This work was carried out on many derivatives of glucose or fructose, *e.g.* 4-O-methyl-D-glucose, 4-O-methyl-D-fructose, maltose, cellobiose etc. In addition, cellotetrose has been investigated and shown to follow the expected course. Cellotetrose consists of 4-glucose residues joined on the 1,4-configuration; its degradation with alkali has been shown to follow the course

$$G—G—G—G \rightarrow G—G—G—Fru \rightarrow G—G—G + Isac$$
$$G + Isac \leftarrow G—Fru \leftarrow G—G + Isac \leftarrow G—G\overset{\downarrow}{—}Fru$$

where G and Fru refer to glucose and fructose units and Isac to isosaccharinic acid. The terminal reducing unit is changed to fructose which cleaves from the glucose in the 4-position and liberates a molecule of isosaccharinic acid. Stepwise degradation of this nature could be an explanation of the degradation of cellulose and hydrocellulose. This has not been proved with cellulose because of the small number of reducing ends and hence small amounts of degradation products to be estimated. Hydrocelluloses with a larger number of reducing ends give as the major product isosaccharinic acid. In addition some other acids have been identified. The degradation of cellulose and hydrocelluloses does not go to completion, but the product contains stable metasaccharinic acid end groups formed by the mechanism described above[96]. The alkali degradation reactions discussed occur about 150°C. The mechanism of these reactions given here would appear to be the most likely. Other explanations are discussed in detail elsewhere[38]. Also this is not the only reaction as is shown by the occurrence of other products. The β-alkoxyl reaction discussed here will also explain the alkali sensitivity of many oxycelluloses since oxidation will introduce carbonyl groups and hence enhance the possibilities of this kind of reaction.

REFERENCES

[1] C. Dorée, *Methods of Cellulose Chemistry*, Chapman & Hall, London, 1956.
[2] *Tappi, Standard Method*, T 203m - 44 (1944).
[3] *Swedish Standard Methods*, CCA 7 (1940); CCA 8 (1941).
[4] G. W. Monier-Williams, *J. Chem. Soc.*, 119 (1921) 803.
[5] J. C. Irvine and C. W. Soutar, *J. Chem. Soc.*, 117 (1920) 1489.
[6] J. C. Irvine and E. L. Hirst, *J. Chem. Soc.*, 121 (1922) 1585.
[7] J. Honeyman, *An Introduction to the Chemistry of Carbohydrates*, Oxford Univ. Press, 1948.
[8] C. Tauret, *Bull. soc. chim. France*, 13 [3] (1895) 728.
[9] T. M. Lowry, *J. Chem. Soc.*, 75 (1899) 211.
[10] H. Ost, *Z. Angew. Chem.*, 19 (1906) 993.
[11] W. Crum, *Ann.*, 62 (1847) 233; *Phil. Mag.*, 30 (1847) 426.
[12] K. Hess and W. Weltzien, *Ann.*, 442 (1925) 46.

13 W. S. DENHAM and H. WOODHOUSE, *J. Chem. Soc.*, 103 (1913) 1735; 105 (1914) 2357; 111 (1917) 244.
14 J. IRVINE and E. L. HIRST, *J. Chem. Soc.*, 123 (1923) 518.
   K. FREUDENBERG, E. PLANKERHORN and H. BOPPEL, *Ber.*, 71 (1938) 2435.
   H. FRIESE and K. HESS, *Ann.*, 456 (1927) 38.
15 A. P. N. FRANCHIMONT, *Ber.*, 12 (1879) 1938.
   H. FRIESE and K. HESS, *Ann.*, 456 (1927) 38.
16 E. OTT, H. M. SPURLIN and M. N. GRAFFLIN, *Cellulose and Cellulose Derivatives*, (Vol. 5 of the series *High Polymers*), Interscience, New York, 1954.
17 K. FREUDENBERG and C. BLOMQUIST, *Ber.*, 68B (1935) 2070.
   M. L. WOLFRAM and J. C. DACON, *J. Am. Chem. Soc.*, 74 (1952) 5331.
18 E. MOHR, *J. prakt. Chem.*, 98 (1918) 315; 103 (1922) 316.
19 R. E. REEVES, *J. Am. Chem. Soc.*, 71 (1949) 212.
   K. H. MEYER and L. MISCH, *Helv. Chim. Acta*, 20 (1937) 232.
20 K. FREUDENBERG and S. RASCHIG, *Ber.*, 60 (1927) 1633.
   R. S. TIPSON, M. A. CLAPP and L. H. CRETCHEN, *J. Org. Chem.*, 12 (1947) 133.
   C. J. MALM, L. J. TAUGHE and B. C. LAIRD, *J. Am. Chem. Soc.*, 70 (1948) 2740.
   F. B. CRAMER and C. B. PURVES, *J. Am. Chem. Soc.*, 61 (1939) 3458.
21 L. MALAPRADE, *Compt. rend.*, 186 (1928) 382; *Bull. soc. chim. France*, [4] 43 (1928) 683.
22 R. E. REEVES, *J. Am. Chem. Soc.*, 63 (1941) 1476.
   L. HOUGH, D. B. POWELL and B. M. WOODS, *J. Chem. Soc.*, (1956) 4799.
   L. HOUGH and B. M. WOODS, *Chem & Ind. London*, (1957) 1421.
23 J. E. WALTZ and G. B. TAYLOR, *Anal. Chem.*, 19 (1947) 448.
24 W. N. HAWORTH and H. MACHENER, *J. Chem. Soc.*, (1932) 2270.
   D. I. McGILVRAY, *J. Chem. Soc.*, (1953) 2577.
25 C. G. SCHWALBE, *Ber.*, 40 (1907) 1347.
26 K. GOTZE, *Melliand Textilber.*, 8 (1927) 624, 696.
27 M. BERGMANN and H. MACHEMER, *Ber.*, 63B (1930) 316.
28 E. GEIGER and A. WISSLER, *Helv. Chim. Acta*, 28 (1945) 1638.
   F. MULLER and S. WILLEMAN, *Helv. Chim. Acta*, 27 (1939) 208, 217, 1376.
29 M. L. WOLFROM and L. W. GEORGES, *J. Am. Chem. Soc.*, 59 (1937) 282.
   M. L. WOLFROM, J. C. SOWDEN and E. M. LASSETT, *J. Am. Chem. Soc.*, 61 (1939) 1072.
30 A. JEANES and H. S. ISBELL, *J. Research Natl. Bur. Standards*, 27 (1941) 125.
   G. F. DAVIDSON and T. P. NEVELL, *J. Textile Inst.*, 39 (1948) 102T.
31 G. JAYME and K. NEUSCHAFFER, *Naturwissenschaften*, 42 (1955) 536.
   G. JAYME and K. NEUSCHAFFER, *Papier*, 11 (1957) 47.
32 G. JAYME and W. BERGMANN, *Papier*, 11 (1957) 280.
33 H. SIHTOLA, E. KAILA and L. LAAMANEN, *J. Polymer Sci.*, 23 (1957) 809.
34 W. G. HARLAND, *J. Textile Inst.*, 45 (1954) 687T; 49 (1958) 478T.
35 R. S. E. CUMBERBIRCH and W. G. HARLAND, *Shirley Inst. Mem.*, 31 (1958) 199.
36 W. G. HARLAND, *J. Textile Inst.*, 45 (1954) 692T.
   H. A. WANNOW, *Kolloid-Z.*, 102 (1945) 29.
   C. H. LINDSLEY and M. B. FRANK, *Ind. Eng. Chem.*, 45 (1953) 2491.
   W. G. HARLAND, *J. Textile Inst.*, 46 (1955) 464T, 472T, 483T.
37 W. G. HARLAND, *J. Textile Inst.*, 46 (1955) 472T.
38 J. HONEYMAN, *Recent Advances in the Chemistry of Cellulose & Starch*, Heywood, London, 1959.
39 N. GRALÉN, Dissertation, Upsala, 1944.
   T. SVEDBERG, *J. Phys. & Colloid. Chem.*, 51 (1947) 1.
40 W. BANDEL, *Papier*, 12 (1958) 56.
41 R. J. E. CUMBERBIRCH and W. G. HARLAND, *J. Textile Inst.*, 49 (1958) 664T.
42 M. MARX, *J. Polymer Sci.*, 121 (1958) 119, 126.
43 E. BERL and G. RUEFF, *Cellulosechemie*, 12 (1931) 53; *Ber.*, 63B (1930) 3212.
44 R. DALMON, *Compt. rend.*, 201 (1935) 1123.
45 I. SAKURADA, *J. Soc. Chem. Ind. Japan*, 35 *Suppl. binding.*, 3 (1932) 283.

M. K. Sen and M. Ramaswary, *J. Textile Inst.*, 48 (1957) 75T.

[46] L. H. Greathouse, H. J. Janssen and C. H. Haydel, *Ind. Eng. Chem.*, 50 (1958) 99.

[47] C. J. Malm, L. J. Tanghe and B. C. Laird, *Ind. Eng. Chem.*, 38 (1946) 77.

[48] C. J. Malm, K. T. Markey, M. Sals and D. C. May, *Ind. Eng. Chem.*, 49 (1957) 79.

[49] S. F. Haskins and S. G. Sundewith, *J. Am. Chem. Soc.*, 79 (1957) 1492.

[50] C. F. Goldthwait, E. M. Buras and A. S. Cooper, *Textile Res. J.*, 21 (1951) 831.

[51] F. D· Farrow and S. M. Neale. *J. Textile Inst.*, 15 (1924) 157T.

[52] J. F. Mahoney and C. B. Purves. *J. Am. Chem. Soc.*, 64 (1942) 9, 15.
L. H. Bock and L. A. Honk, *U.S.P.* 2,332,049.

[53] C. K. Ingold, *Structure & Mechanism in Organic Chemistry*, Bell, London, 1953.

[54] H. Burton and P. F. G. Praill, *J. Chem. Soc.*, (1950) 1203, 2034; (1951) 522.
R. S. Gillespie, *J. Chem. Soc.*, (1950) 2997.

[55] H. M. Spurlin, *J. Am. Chem. Soc.*, 61 (1939) 2222.

[56] R. Brigl and H. Grüner, *Ann.*, 495 (1932) 60.

[57] T. Timell, *Acta Polytech.*, 63 (1950) 13.

[58] I. Sakurada and T. R. Kitabataki, *J. Soc. Chem. Ind. Japan, 37 Suppl. binding,* (1934) 604.
B. Helferich, *Advances in Carbohydrate Chem.*, 3 (1948) 79.
B. Helferich and H. Köster, *Ber.*, 57B (1924) 587.

[59] J. Compton, *J. Am. Chem. Soc.*, 60 (1938) 395, 1203.

[60] C. Birtwell, D. H. Clibbens and A. Geake, *J. Textile Inst.*, 17 (1926) 145T.

[61] F. L. Jackson and C. S. Hudson, *J. Am. Chem. Soc.*, 59 (1937) 2049; 60 (1938) 989.
F. S. H. Head, *J. Textile Inst.*, 44 (1953)209T.

[62] G. C. Gibbons, *J. Textile Inst.*, 43 (1952) 25T.

[63] L. P. Hammett and M. A. Paul, *J. Am. Chem. Soc.*, 56 (1934) 827.

[64] K. Freudenberg, *Ber.*, 54 (1924) 767.

[65] M. L. Wolfrom, J. C. Sowden and E. N. Lassette, *J. Am. Chem. Soc.*, 61 (1939) 1072.
M. L. Wolfrom, D. R. Myers and E. N. Lassette, *J. Am. Chem. Soc.*, 61 (1939) 2172.

[66] H. Mark and R. Simha, *Trans. Faraday Soc.*, 36 (1940) 611.

[67] P. J. Flory, *J. Am. Chem. Soc.*, 58 (1936) 1877.
G. V. Schulz et al., *Z. physik. Chem.*, B52 (1942) 23, 50.

[68] A. Sharples, *J. Polymer Sci.*, 13 (1954) 393.

[69] E. Ott, H. M. Spurlin and M. W. Grafflin, Vol. 5 (part I) of the series *High Polymers*, Interscience, New York, 1954, p. 110.

[70] L. A. Hiller Jr. and E. Pascu, *Textile Res. J.*, 16 (1946) 490.

[71] G. F. Davidson and T. P. Nevell, *J. Textile Inst.*, 18 (1957) 356T.

[72] A. Sharples, *Trans. Faraday Soc.*, 53 (1957) 1000.

[73] E. Husemann and E. Springler, *Makromol. Chem.*, 24 (1957) 79.

[74] G. F. Davidson, *J. Textile Inst.*, 28 (1938) 195T; 31 (1940) 81T.

[75] H. Hibbert and J. L. Parsons, *J. Soc. Chem. Ind. London*, 44 (1925) 473T.

[76] T. P. Nevell, *J. Textile Inst.*, 48 (1957) 484T.

[77] E. L. Jackson and C. S. Hudson, *J. Am. Chem. Soc.*, 59 (1937) 2049; 60 (1938) 939.

[78] G. F. Davidson, *J. Textile Inst.*, 32 (1941) 109T.

[79] G. F. Davidson and T. P. Nevell, *J. Textile Inst.*, 46 (1955)409T.

[80] B. Helferich and M. Hase, *Ann.*, 554 (1943) 261.
B. Helferich and H. Schnorr, *Ann.*, 547 (1941) 201.

[81] F. S. H. Head, *J. Textile Inst.*, 46 (1955) 400T, 584T.

[82] W. J. Rowen, F. H. Forziati and R. E. Reeves, *J. Am. Chem. Soc.*, 73 (1951) 4484.

[83] E. W. Taylor, W. F. Fowler, R. A. Mcgee and W. O. Kenyon, *J. Am. Chem. Soc.*, 69 (1947) 342.
K. Maurer and G. Reiff, *J. Makromol. Chem.*, 1 (1943) 27.

84 F. S. H. HEAD, *J. Chem. Soc.* (1948) 1135.
85 T. P. NEVELL, *J. Textile Inst.*, 42 (1951) 91T.
86 O. G. INGLES and G. C. ISRAEL, *J. Chem. Soc.*, (1948) 810.
87 D. ENTWISTLE, E. H. COLE and N. S. WOODING, *Textile Res. J.*, 19 (1949) 527.
88 G. F. DAVIDSON, *J. Textile Inst.*, 25 (1934) 174T.
89 A. MELLER, *Tappi*, 34 (1951) 171.
90 A. MELLER, *Tappi*, 36 (1953) 366.
91 R. E. REEVES, W. M. SCHWARTZ and J. E. GIDDENS, *J. Am. Chem. Soc.*, 68 (1946) 1383.
92 O. SAMUELSON, G. GRANGOID, K. JONSSON and K. SCHRAMM, *Svensk Papperstidn.*, 56 (1953) 779.
93 G. MACHELL and G. N. RICHARDS, *J. Chem. Soc.*, (1957) 4500.
94 G. N. RICHARDS and H. H. SEPHTON, *J. Chem. Soc.*, (1957) 4492.
95 W. M. CORBETT and J. KENNER, *J. Chem. Soc.*, (1955) 1431.
96 H. RICHTZENHAM and B. ABRAHAMSSON, *Svensk Papperstidn.*, 57 (1954) 538.
   O. SAMUELSON and A. WENNERBLOM, *Svensk Papperstidn.*, 57 (1954) 827.
97 K. HESS *et al.*, *Ann.*, 506 (1933) 206.
   W. TRAUBE *et al.*, *Ber.*, 69 (1936) 1483.
   T. TIMELL, *Svensk Kem. Tidskr.*, 62 (1951) 49, 129.
   T. TIMELL and H. M. SPURLIN, *Svensk Papperstidn.*, 55 (1952) 700.
98 C. C. BARKER, E. HIRST and J. K. N. JONES, *J. Chem. Soc.*, (1938) 1695.
   W. J. HEDDLE and E. G. V. PERCIVAL, *J. Chem. Soc.*, (1938) 1690; (1935) 648.
   E. G. V. PERCIVAL, *J. Chem. Soc.*, (1938) 1160.
   E. G. V. PERCIVAL and G. G. RITCHIE, *J. Chem. Soc.*, (1936) 1765.
   M. L. WOLFROM and M. A. El-TARABOULSI, *J. Am. Chem. Soc.*, 75 (1953) 5350.
99 J. HONEYMAN, *J. Chem. Soc.*, (1947) 168.
   J. W. H. OLDHAM and J. K. RUTHERFORD, *J. Am. Chem. Soc.* 54 (1932) 366.
   F. B. CRAMMER and C. B. PURVES, *J. Am. Chem. Soc.*, 61 (1939) 3458.
   C. W. TASKER and C. B. PURVES, *J. Am. Chem. Soc.*, 71 (1924) 1023.
100 L. REBENFELD and E. PASCU, *Textile Res. J.*, 24 (1954) 941.
   V. DEREVITSKAYA and Z. A. ROGOVIN, *J. Gen. Chem. U.S.S.R.*, 26 (1956) 1466.
   V. DEREVITSKAYA and Z. A. ROGOVIN, *Faserforsch. u. Textiltech.*, 8 (1957) 61.
   V. DEREVITSKAYA, YU. KOZLOVA and Z. A. ROGOVIN, *J. Gen. Chem. U.S.S.R.*, 26 (1956) 3369.
101 S. G. COHEN and H. C. HASS, *J. Am. Chem. Soc.*, 72 (1950) 3954.
   T. TIMELL, *Svensk Papperstidn.*, 52 (1949) 61; 55 (1952) 649; 56 (1953) 311, 483.
   E. DYER and H. E. ARNOLD, *J. Am. Chem. Soc.*, 74 (1952) 2677.
   S. RYDHOLM, *Svensk Papperstidn.*, 53 (1950) 561.
102 L. A. HILLER, *J. Polymer Sci.*, 10 (1933) 385.
   C. J. MALM, L. J. TANGHE, B. C. LAIRD and G. D. SMITH, *J. Am. Chem. Soc.*, 75 (1953) 80.
103 C. F. HUEBNER, S. R. AMES and E. C. BUBL, *J. Am. Chem. Soc.*, 68 (1946) 1621.
104 H. SPEDDING, *J. Chem. Soc.*, (1960) 3147.

CHAPTER 8

AMINO ACIDS AND PROTEINS

1. Introduction to Proteins

(a) Occurrence

Proteins are a class of naturally occurring compounds of high molecular weight. They are extremely widespread in nature being one of the essential constituents of the tissues of plants and animals. The function of proteins in living materials is extremely diverse; they play important roles in the animal functions such as muscular activity or enzymes used in the body for breaking down foods, as well as giving protection as in the case of hair or horns. The industrial uses of proteins are many and include plastics, adhesives and paints; in the fibre field proteins such as wool, silk, mohair etc. are of great value whilst those found in milk or in groundnuts are capable of being transformed into fibres.

Proteins usually occur in nature as mixtures, the complexity of which varies considerably according to the source. Those found in the cells of animal tissues and micro-organisms are made up of a large number of proteins, whereas others such as casein in milk or albumin in the white of an egg contain a small number with one component predominating.

Proteins must be isolated from the mixture of non-protein materials with which they are usually associated in nature. The degree of purity required will depend on the purpose to which the protein is to be put. For studies of biological activity, purity and homogeneity within defined limits are required; for industrial uses, stable and well characterised products are necessary but these may consist of a mixture of proteins. In general, proteins fall into two groups — fibrous and the globular; the former are insoluble and some of those belonging to this class of direct interest in the fibre field are discussed in Chapters 10 and 11. Remarks here are confined to the globular type.

(b) Isolation of Proteins

The difficulties of obtaining a pure protein are considerable. Changes in structure may occur through chemical or physical agencies leading to detectable modifications in the physical, chemical or biological properties

without leading to rupture of covalent bonds. These changes are described as denaturation. Thus proteins are sensitive to heat and may coagulate
on raising the temperature. The commonest example is that brought
about in the white of an egg when the latter is boiled. Other agencies will
denature proteins — extremes of pH or additions of solvents such as
ethanol. Proteins vary widely in their susceptibility to denaturation and
some solutions may even be stable at the boiling-point or to acids.

Most proteins are soluble in water, aqueous solutions of salts and certain
more polar organic solvents such as ethanol. They cannot be melted or
vapourised. Solubility is modified by changes in temperature, pH,
electrolyte concentration and dielectric constant of the solvent.

Some of the more soluble proteins such as albumin in blood plasma may
be crystallised by salting out with ammonium sulphate. Proteins known
as prolamines may be extracted from seeds with an aqueous solution of
ethanol or propanol (60–80%) and precipitated by dilution with water.
Zein from maize may be prepared this way.

The purification of proteins is usually achieved to a considerable extent
by repeated application of the above techniques; where smaller quantities are required, ultracentrifugation and electrophoresis have been used.
Chromatography is of value but care must be taken in the choice of
adsorbent in order to avoid denaturation.

Determination of the homogeneity of the protein is not easy and none
of the possible tests is adequate by itself. Tests may be based on chemical
analysis, biological activity or physico-chemical methods such as constancy of solubility, often repeated recrystallisation or reprecipitation,
electrophoresis, sedimentation in the ultracentrifuge or diffusion.
Fortunately for fibre production, proteins need to be well characterised
but not homogeneous with regard to composition.

In this chapter, four proteins which have been extracted for use in
fibre manufacture will be mentioned. These are casein from milk, zein
from maize, glycinin from soya beans and arachin from groundnuts.

(c) Chemical Constitution of Proteins

Analysis of these materials for elements shows them to be made up of C, H,
N and by inference O; some contain in addition S and P. Hydrolysis of proteins yields a mixture of α-amino acids of formula $NH_2 \cdot CHR \cdot COOH$
and at least 25 different acids have been isolated. Because of this, it
seems reasonable that proteins are composed of these acids condensed
together. Condensation can be visualised as proceeding between the
carboxyl and amino groups. Thus, formally, glycine (I) (α-aminoacetic
acid) could be condensed with itself to give a polymer

$$\text{NH}_2\text{CH}_2\text{COOH} + \text{NH}_2\text{CH}_2\text{COOH} \xrightarrow{-\text{H}_2\text{O}} \text{NH}_2\text{CH}_2\text{CONH·CH}_2\text{COOH}$$

(I)   (II)

$$+ \text{NH}_2\text{CH}_2\text{COOH} \xrightarrow{-\text{H}_2\text{O}} \text{NH}_2\text{CH}_2\text{CONH·CH}_2\text{COHN·CH}_2\text{COOH etc.}$$

(III)

Polymers so produced would be linear containing structural units joined through amide groups but, although they could be regarded as nylon 2, such compounds are not usually referred to as polyamides. They are considered because of the over-riding importance of the proteins, as special materials. The repeat unit —NHCH₂CO— (or more generally —NHCHRCO—) is referred to as the peptide group. Hence in the hypothetical reaction written down the first product glycylglycine (II), is called a dipeptide, the second (III), a tripeptide and so on; in the general case the products are referred to as polypeptides.

2. Amino Acids

(a) General

α-Amino acids of formula NH₂CHR·COOH (R ≠ H) contain an asymmetric carbon atom and hence their solutions can exhibit optical rotation. Those isolated by hydrolysis from proteins are optically active and with one or two exceptions belong to the same stereochemical series (L) independent of the sign of rotation the individual acids.

The configuration is defined in the following way. The C—H linkage is taken as defining the apex of a tetrahedron; looking along this and going around in a clockwise direction makes the other three groups appear in the order R, NH₂, COOH. Diagrammatically the L-form of alanine may be written as

The acids are all crystalline solids which vary considerably as to their solubility in water. Solutions react almost neutral. Chemically they are reactive by virtue of the amino and carboxyl groups as well as any chemical properties which may be contributed by the group R.

(b) Functional Groups

(i) Carboxyl groups

Esterification may be performed in ethanol or methanol in the presence of dry hydrogen chloride. The ester group is more reactive than the free acid and is capable of reaction with nitrogenous bases. With primary amines and ammonia, amides may be formed, hydroxylamine gives hydroxyamines (hydroxamic acids) (IV), hydrazine reacts producing hydrazides (V) which are transformed into azides (VI)[1] by reaction with nitrous acid.

$$RCOOCH_3 \xrightarrow{NH_2OH} RCONHOH$$
$$(IV)$$

$$RCOOCH_3 \xrightarrow{NH_2NH_2} RCONHNH_2 \xrightarrow{HNO_2} RCON_3$$
$$(V) \qquad\qquad (VI)$$

Hydrazine is used for the detection of those terminal amino acid residues in proteins which carry free carboxyl groups.

The protein is treated with anhydrous hydrazine when those carboxyl groups which are bound in peptide linkages are converted to hydrazides, leaving the less reactive free carboxyl groups unreacted. The free acids may be separated from the hydrazides and identified[30].

The esters can also be reduced to give the amino alcohol (VII). Agents differ with regard to their effectiveness. Hydrogen in the presence of Raney nickel has been shown to be effective[4], but the best results are obtained with the double hydrides of lithium with another metal[2] (*e.g.* LiAlH₄)

$$NH_2CHRCOOCH_3 \xrightarrow{H_2} NH_2CHRCH_2OH$$
$$(VII)$$

It is possible to reduce the amino alcohol to the amine (VIII)[3] via the *p*-toluenesulphonyl derivatives, (tosyl) (IX)

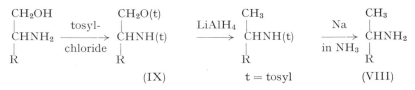

$$(IX) \qquad\qquad t = tosyl \qquad\qquad (VIII)$$

If reduction is carried out on the original protein or protein ester, the free carboxyl groups will be reduced to hydroxyl; identification of the amino alcohols produced will give a means of estimating the terminal residues carrying carboxyl groups[31].

Amino acids when carefully heated in an inert solvent can decarboxylate giving the amine with one less carbon atom.

$$NH_2CHRCOOH \rightarrow NH_2CH_2R + CO_2$$

Similar amines may be formed in acid media by enzymes known as

decarboxylases. These may be extracted from bacteria and are specific in
action. Thus, the decarboxylases from *B. Cadaveris* will change the
amino acid lysine into cadaverine(X)[5], that from *Clostridium welchie*
converts glutamic acid into aminobutyric acid (XI)[6] and so on.

$$NH_2(CH_2)_4CHCOOH \rightarrow NH_2(CH_2)_5NH_2$$
$$| \atop NH_2 \qquad\qquad (X)$$

$$HOOC(CH_2)_2CHCOOH \rightarrow HOOC(CH_2)_3NH_2$$
$$| \atop NH_2 \qquad\qquad (XI)$$

The enzyme carboxypeptidase is one which will split preferentially from
a protein those acids which have free carboxyl groups. The first acid to be
produced by the action of this enzyme on a protein may therefore be
taken as the carboxyl terminal residue[32].

(ii) *Amino groups*

The amino groups exhibit typical basic properties *e.g.* crystalline salts
may be formed with phosphotungstic, picric acid etc. They also undergo
normal condensation reactions such as alkylation, arylation and acylation.
Acylation of the amino acid may be carried out in various ways. For the
formyl derivative, heating with formic acid is sufficient, whereas the
acetyl compound requires reaction with acetic anhydride.

Acylation may also be accomplished by reaction of the amino acid with
the acid chlorides. Of particular note are the derivatives (XII) made
from *p*-iodophenylsulphonyl chloride (pipsyl)

$$I\langle\;\rangle SO_2Cl + NH_2CHRCOOH \rightarrow I\langle\;\rangle SO_2NHCHRCOOH$$
$$(XII)$$

The pipsyl compounds are used for identification of amino acids and in
particular, in the study of the N-terminal residues in proteins. In this
case the derivative of the protein is prepared, hydrolysed and the
pipsyl derivatives of the amino acids identified in the hydrolysate.

Derivatives of great value are those prepared from 1-fluoro-2,4-
dinitrobenzene.

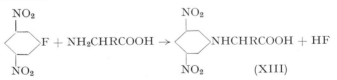

The dinitrophenyl, DNP-derivatives (XIII) are readily prepared in the
cold in a slightly alkaline medium (sodium bicarbonate)[7]; they are for the
most part soluble in ether and alkali. The bond between the nitrogen

atom and the phenyl nucleus is generally more stable than the peptide linkage. This is of enormous value in determinations of the sequence of amino acids in proteins. Thus 1-fluoro-2,4-dinitrobenzene will react with the amino group at the end of the chain; hydrolysis and analysis of the DNP-derivatives then enables the amino terminal acid to be identified.

Reaction with isocyanates and isothiocyanates can occur

$$RCH(COOH)NH_2 + R_1NCO \rightarrow RCH(COOH)NHCONHR_1$$

(XIV)

The substituted urea (XIV) so formed gives on treatment with hot mineral acids a cyclic compound, hydantoin (XV)

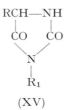

(XV)

Hydantoin itself (XV; $R_1 = R = H$) may be prepared by reaction of glycine with potassium cyanate giving hydantoic acid (XVI) which then eliminates water when boiled with hydrochloric acid

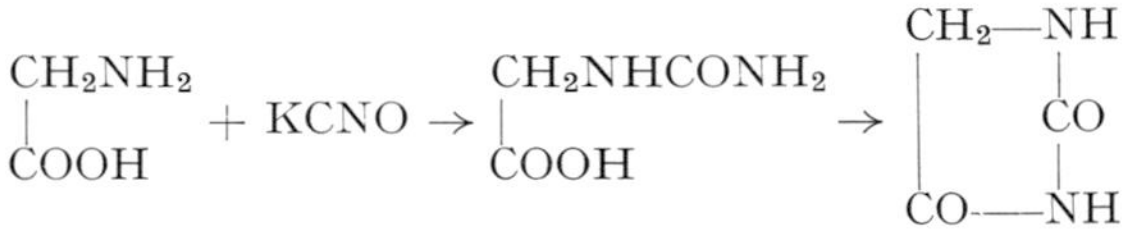

$$\begin{array}{c} CH_2NH_2 \\ | \\ COOH \end{array} + KCNO \rightarrow \begin{array}{c} CH_2NHCONH_2 \\ | \\ COOH \end{array} \rightarrow \begin{array}{c} CH_2\!-\!NH \\ | \qquad | \\ \qquad CO \\ | \qquad | \\ CO\!-\!\!-NH \end{array}$$

(XVI)

At normal temperatures and neutral pH, amino acids will react with formaldehyde. The formaldehyde presumably reacts in its hydrated form (methylene glycol) giving N-mono- and N-di-hydroxymethyl derivatives (XVII) and (XVIII)[8],

$$HOOCCHRNH_2 + CH_2(OH)_2 \rightarrow HOOCCHRNHCH_2OH$$
(XVII)

$$\overset{HCHO}{-\!\!\!-\!\!\!-\!\!\!\longrightarrow} HOOCCHRN(CH_2OH)_2$$

(XVIII)

These derivatives can be referred to as monomethylolamino and dimethylolamino acids. The introduction of the methylol group modifies the dissociation constant of the carboxyl group so that it is titratable with strong alkali. Reaction with formaldehyde may also form a methylene bridge between two amino acids. For example from glycine, tri-N-carboxymethyl-dimethylenetriamine (XIX) may be formed[9]

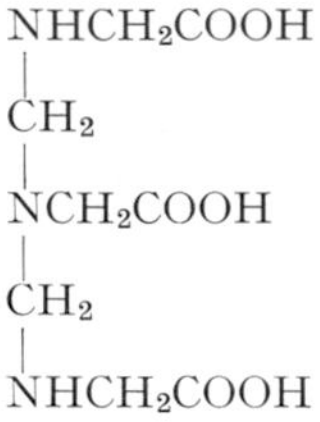

NHCH$_2$COOH

|

CH$_2$

|

NCH$_2$COOH

|

CH$_2$

|

NHCH$_2$COOH

(XIX)

The formation of such methylene bridges is of importance in the hardening of protein fibres. Reaction of formaldehyde may not, however, be as straightforward as this. The side group R may contain a labile hydrogen atom so that intramolecular reaction can occur, leading to a cyclic compound. An example of this arises if R = SH as in cysteine (XX) when 4-thiazolidinecarboxylic acid (XXI) will result[10]

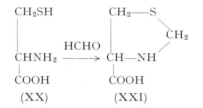

(XX)   (XXI)

Amino acids react with nitrous acid in the presence of a halogen hydracid to form hydroxyl or halogen compounds

$$\text{HOOCCHRNH}_2 \xrightarrow{\text{HNO}_2} \text{HOOCCHROH} + \text{H}_2\text{O}$$

The esters of the acids may react with nitrous acid to give the diazo compounds (XXII)

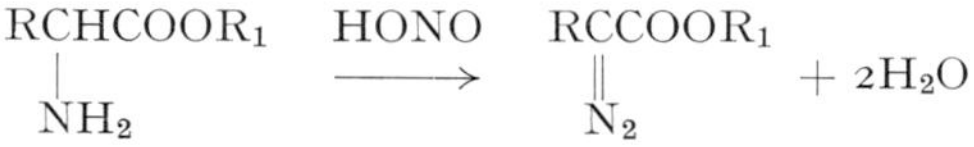

$$\underset{\underset{\text{NH}_2}{|}}{\text{RCHCOOR}_1} \xrightarrow{\text{HONO}} \underset{\underset{\text{N}_2}{\|}}{\text{RCCOOR}_1} + 2\text{H}_2\text{O}$$

(XXII)

The diazo compounds are very reactive; with water containing a trace of sulphuric acid, glycollic ester (XXIII) and nitrogen are formed

$$\text{CHN}_2\text{COOC}_2\text{H}_5 \xrightarrow{\text{H}_2\text{O}} \text{CH}_2\text{OHCOOC}_2\text{H}_5 + \text{N}_2$$

(XXIII)

(c) Properties

(i) *Properties depending on the presence of both acid and basic groups*

The presence of amino and carboxylic acid groups places amino acids in the category of amphoteric electrolytes (ampholytes). However, the acidic and basic properties are different from those expected from the formula as normally written. Evidence has accumulated to show that the amino acids exist in aqueous solution largely in a dipolar or Zwitter ion form where the hydrogen of the carboxyl group is to be found on the amino group. Reaction of such an ion with a strong acid (H_3O^+) and a strong base (OH^-) will be written as

$$^+NH_3CHRCOO^- + H_3O^+ \rightleftharpoons {}^+NH_3CHRCOOH + H_2O$$

$$^+NH_3CHRCOO^- + OH^- \rightleftharpoons NH_2CHRCOO^- + H_2O$$

Hence, it is the substituted ammonium ion which is reacting with the base and the carboxylate ion with the acid; this means that the acidic and basic functions are the reverse of that anticipated from the formula written in the normal way.

Evidence for the dipolar structure comes from the values of the measured dissociation constants. These are in line with the equations written above and not with dissociation in the normal way. Examination of the X-ray diagram of glycine crystals is in agreement with the dipolar $^+NH_3CH_2COO^-$ structure. Infra-red spectra also show bands which may be associated with groups $^+NH_3$ and COO^-.

α-Amino acids may eliminate 2 molecules of water to form diketopiperazines (XXIV) but this reaction is best carried out by heating the ester in alcoholic solution containing ammonia, 2 mols of alcohol being eliminated

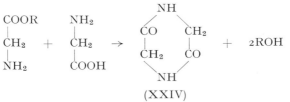

(XXIV)

Complexes with metal salts (*e.g.* silver, copper) may be formed, the most notable of these being the copper compounds. These are obtained by treatment of a solution of the acid at the neutral point with copper acetate, carbonate etc. The solution becomes deep blue. The complexes are chelate compounds, although their formula cannot in all cases be represented as simply as that below (XXV).

(XXV)

Perhaps the most important reaction of α-amino acids depending on both groups is the reaction with ninhydrin (triketohydrindene hydrate) (XXVI). Boiling in aqueous solution in the presence of this reagent liberates ammonia and carbon dioxide transforming the amino acid to an aldehyde

$$NH_2CHCOOH \rightarrow RCHO + NH_3 + CO_2$$

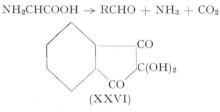

(XXVI)

This appears to be characteristic of α-amino acids. If the reaction is carried out at a pH > 4, a deep blue colour develops from the ninhydrin. The presence of this blue colour is valuable since it allows detection of very small quantities of these acids.

(ii) *Some properties depending on the nature of the substituent*

The chemical nature of the substituent R will contribute its own properties. R may be a hydrocarbon residue and therefore chemically inert; it may carry hydroxyl groups or contain the sulphur atom and so on. The structure of the individual acids is listed in Table 17. One or two features will be discussed.

(i) O-Acylation. Hydroxyl groups in α-amino acids may be acylated in acidic media; N-acylation occurs in alkaline media, and at neutral pH both O- and N-derivatives may be formed. The most important acid carrying an hydroxyl group is serine (No. 7 in Table 17).

(ii) O-Methylation. This can be carried out with the normal methylating agents.

(iii) Oxidation. The action of periodates on β-hydroxyamino acids generates the aldehyde, ammonia and glyoxylic acid (XXVII)[11]

$$
\begin{array}{c}
NH_2 \\
| \\
CHCH_2OH \\
| \\
COOH
\end{array}
\rightarrow NH_3 + HCHO +
\begin{array}{c}
COOH \\
| \\
CHO
\end{array}
$$

(XXVII)

(iv) Aromatic acids. Some of the acids carry an aromatic group (*e.g.* tyrosine No. 9 in Table 17). With iodine, this may be substituted in the nucleus or oxidised depending on the pH.

(v) Sulphur containing acids. Methionine, with $R = SCH_3$, may split off its methyl group with hydriodic acid or be oxidised with hydrogen peroxide and peracids to the sulphone, $—SO_2CH_3$.

The most important sulphur containing acid is cystine (XXVIII). This acid may be regarded as two α-amino acids joined through a disulphide linkage

$$
\begin{array}{ccc}
NH_2 & & NH_2 \\
| & & | \\
CH-CH_2-S-S-CH_2-CH & & \text{(XXVIII)} \\
| & & | \\
COOH & & COOH
\end{array}
$$

The disulphide linkage in this acid can be readily reduced to give cysteine (XX) and is also susceptible to oxidation and hydrolysis. The reactions of these sulphur acids are of considerable importance in protein chemistry.

For this reason some of the reactions of the thiol (SH) and disulphide (—S—S—) groups are discussed.

(iii) *Reactions of thiol groups*

The —SH group is capable of ionising and in cysteine derivatives such as the N-formyl and N-acetyl ethyl esters, values of the pK_{SH} about 8.5 are found. In compounds containing free amino groups the position is complicated by the fact that the tendency of the NH_3^+ and SH groups to lose a proton is similar so that several forms may be present. Thus for a compound NH_2RSH, it is possible to get

$$NH_2RS^-, \quad {}^+NH_3RSH, \quad {}^+NH_3RS^- \quad \text{and} \quad NH_2RSH$$

Thiol groups may be acylated. Thus thioacetates, $RSCOCH_3$, are prepared by reaction with acetyl chloride or acetic anhydride; sulphonyl chlorides give thiolsulphonic esters, R_1SO_2SR.

Thiourethans are prepared by reaction with isocyanates

$$C_6H_5NCO + RSH \rightarrow C_6H_5NHCOSR$$

The reactions of thiols with compounds containing active halogen compounds are bimolecular nucleophilic substitutions, the active specy being the nucleophilic mercaptide ions. The reagent 1-chloro-2,4-dinitrobenzene is a useful reagent for the identification of thiols. 1-fluoro-2,4-dinitrobenzene reacts with cysteine at both the amino and mercapto groups in bicarbonate buffer, whereas at pH 5.5 only with the mercapto group.

Thiols may undergo addition reactions with alkenes

$$
\begin{array}{ccc}
RCH{=}CH_2 + R_1SH \rightarrow RCHCH_3 & \text{or} & RCH_2CH_2SR_1 \\
& | & \\
& S & \text{(XXX)} \\
& | & \\
& R_1 & \\
& \text{(XXIX)} &
\end{array}
$$

Compounds (XXX) are to be regarded as abnormal since Markowni-koff's Rule would lead to (XXIX). The abnormal additions are catalysed by light, oxygen and peroxides and inhibited by antioxidants. Many unsaturated compounds (acids, esters, ketones etc.) will add readily the SH group being attached to the carbon atom farthest away from the other functional group. Maleic acid and its derivatives, in particular N-ethylmaleimide, react readily with cysteine at low temperatures, a reaction which has been used in wool chemistry. Reaction of cysteine with derivatives of α-aminoacrylic acid occurs to give a thioether bridge, the products being derivatives (XXXI) of lanthionine (XXXII)

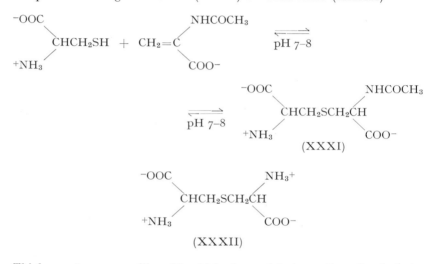

Thiols react more readily with aldehydes and ketones than do alcohols, yielding products which are more stable than the corresponding oxygen containing ones. The mechanism may be written as follows

$$RCH_2CR_1 + R_2SH \rightleftharpoons RCH_2\underset{\underset{SR_2}{|}}{\overset{\overset{OH}{|}}{C}}-R_1 \overset{H^+}{\rightleftharpoons} RCH_2\underset{\underset{SR_2}{|}}{\overset{\overset{\overset{+}{O}H_2}{|}}{C}}-R_1$$

$$\Downarrow -H_2O$$

$$RCH_2\underset{\underset{SR_2}{|}}{\overset{\overset{SR_2}{|}}{S}}-R_1 \overset{H^+}{\rightleftharpoons} RCH_2-\underset{\underset{SR_2}{|}}{\overset{\overset{\overset{+}{HSR_2}}{|}}{C}}-R_1 \quad \overset{R_2SH}{\rightleftharpoons} \quad \left[RCH_2\overset{+}{\underset{\underset{SR_2}{|}}{C}}-R_1 \right]$$

When cysteine adds to carbonyl compounds, the hydroxyl group formed will react with the amino group to form a thiozolidine (XXXIII)

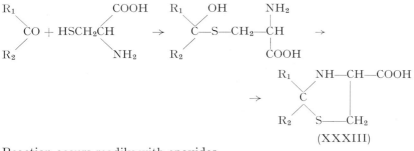

(XXXIII)

Reaction occurs readily with epoxides

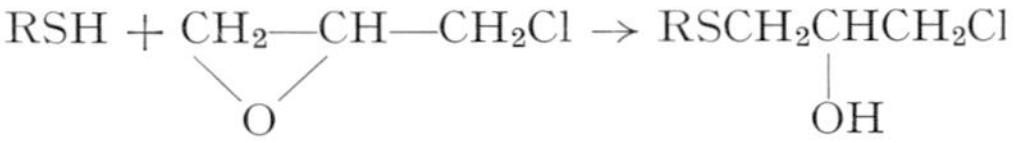

$$RSH + CH_2\text{—}CH\text{—}CH_2Cl \rightarrow RSCH_2CHCH_2Cl$$
$$\underset{O}{\diagdown\diagup} \qquad\qquad \underset{OH}{|}$$

Thiols may be oxidised by molecular oxygen and oxidising agents. With the former, disulphides are formed but the reaction is a complex one and one very susceptible to traces of heavy metal ions. With other oxidising agents, it is possible by careful choice to obtain the disulphide in quantitative yield; thus phosphotungstic acid at pH 5 gives cystine quantitatively from cysteine. Some agents will oxidise through a sulphinic acid to the sulphonic acid.

$$RSH \rightarrow RSOH \rightarrow RSO_2H \rightarrow RSO_3H$$

(iv) *Reactions of disulphides*

These compounds react with alkyl halides in the presence of catalysts such as mercuric iodide or ferric chloride

$$RSSR + 4RI + HgI_2 \rightarrow 2R_3\overset{+-}{SI}HgI_2 + I_2$$

Oxidation with peroxide or perchloric acid gives thiosulphonic esters

$$RSSR + 2O \rightarrow RSO_2SR$$

These esters readily decompose to a sulphinic acid and a disulphide. More usually disulphides are oxidised to sulphonic acids

$$RSSR + 6O \xrightarrow{H_2O} 2RSO_3H$$

Reaction with salts of heavy metals yields complex compounds; with mercuric chloride the reaction may be written as

$$2RSSR + 3HgCl_2 + 2H_2O \rightarrow 3RSHgCl + RSO_2H + 3HCl$$

With silver under mild conditions, an analogous equation may be written

$$2RSSR + 3Ag^+ + 2OH^- \rightarrow 3RSAg + RSO_2H + H^+$$

References p. 243

The reaction may not always follow this course and may give rise to more extensive degradation of the disulphide molecule. The speed with which these disulphides react with the metal ions is dependent on the electron density in the neighbourhood of the disulphide group. Thus the rate of reaction of the negatively charged dithiodipropionic acid is greater than that of cystine with zero net charge. Alternatively, the formation of the acetyl or formyl derivatives of cystine reduces the rate, since these groups reduce the electron density at the disulphide bonds.

The reactions of disulphides with two reagents in particular, sulphite and cyanide ions, are important. The reaction with SO_3^{--} may be written as

$$RSSR + SO_3^{--} \rightleftharpoons RSSO_3^- + RS^-$$

This is a nucleophillic attack of the SO_3^{--} ion on the disulphide bond. At pH values above 9, the reaction is a reversible bimolecular one but below this pH the mechanism is more complex. The main factor however, governing the rate of reaction is the charge in the vicinity of the disulphide bond, the more negative this is the slower the reaction. The reaction in the presence of air, particularly in the presence of traces of metal ions will be modified by oxidation of the thiol so that the thiosulphate is obtained quantitatively.

Reaction with cyanide may be written in a similar way to that with sulphite ions

$$RSSR + CN^- \rightarrow RSCN + RS^-$$

However, cyanide solutions are alkaline so that alkaline degradation may occur simultaneously. The reaction may go further to yield a thioether, an important point in the formation of lanthionine in wool. The reaction is considered in the case of cystine to occur via a β-elimination mechanism

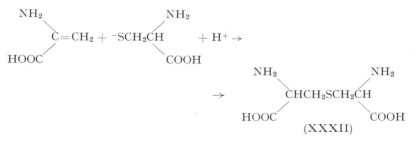

The double bond is capable of adding on to a molecule of the thiol to form a thioether

This is not the only possible mechanism and it may be that SCN^- is displaced without the intermediate formation of the unsaturated compound.

Disulphides are attacked by alkali and many products may result. The initial reaction however has been suggested to be one of hydrolysis

$$RSSR + H_2O \rightleftharpoons RSOH + RSH$$

Another mechanism however seems more likely in which the hydroxyl ions split the carbon sulphur bond by causing the ionisation of a hydrogen atom attached to a carbon atom in a position β to the sulphur atom. Thus for cystine the reaction would be

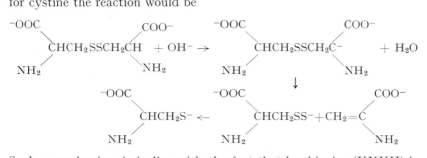

Such a mechanism is in line with the fact that lanthionine (XXXII) is decomposed at a rate comparable to cystine (XXVIII), since the reaction could go in exactly the same way.

Unsaturated groups attached to the carbon atom in a position β to the sulphur are known to render the C—S bond in disulphides labile to alkali, *e.g.* β-keto sulphides (XXXV). If an extra methylene group is introduced, the carboxyl and amino groups are now on the carbon atom in a position γ from the sulphur. This mechanism will not be applicable. Hence homocystine (XXXIV)

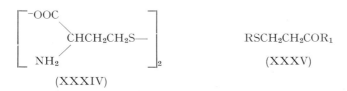

(XXXIV)

degrades only slowly. Disulphides may be reduced to the thiol but it is difficult to obtain a quantitative yield. Of particular interest is the reaction when excess thiol is used as a reducing agent, when an oxidation/reduction system might be set up

$$RSSR + 2R_1SH \rightleftharpoons 2RSH + R_1SSR_1$$

However, mixed disulphides have been characterised in such a reaction

References p. 243

and the first stage of the reduction may be written as

$$RSSR + R_1SH \rightleftharpoons RSSR_1 + RSH$$

The reaction occurs via the mercaptide ion *i.e.*

$$RSSR + R_1S^- \rightleftharpoons RSSR_1 + RS^-$$
$$RSSR_1 + R_1S^- \rightleftharpoons R_1SSR_1 + RS^-$$

Mixtures of disulphides may in neutral or alkaline solution interchange if thiols are present

$$RSSR + R_1SSR_1 \rightleftharpoons 2R_1SSR$$

The reaction can be visualised as identical to the previous one.

(d) Characterisation of Amino Acids in Proteins

The identification of the acids tryptophan and tyrosine may be carried out on the intact protein because they show characteristic absorption bands in the ultraviolet region of the spectrum at 277 and 295 mμ. The other amino acids have to be identified and determined in the hydrolysate. Hydrolysis is usually carried out in an acid medium but can also be achieved by alkali or enzymes. The individual acids can be isolated by methylation and fractionation by distillation of the methyl esters, or by partition between water and butanol. Separations can however, be more readily achieved chromatographically using alumina, silica, anion exchange resins, activated charcoal[12] etc.

Paper chromatography[12] is perhaps the most useful tool. The hydrolysate from the protein is evaporated to remove most of the hydrochloric acid, taken up in a suitable solvent (phenol, benzyl alcohol, picoline, collidine etc.) and the mixture of amino acids eluted down a piece of filter paper. The most used solvents are water saturated phenol and collidine and mixtures of butanol and acetic acid. The identity of the amino acid is determined by its position on the paper which may be readily seen by treatment with ninhydrin. Improved separation can be obtained by eluting in one direction followed by a second elution in a direction at right angles to the former[13] using a different eluent.

It has been shown possible to separate some groups of acids by means of paper electrophoresis[14]. This requires a knowledge of the isoelectric points of the acids; thus at pH 7.5, histidine is isoelectric whereas lysine moves towards the cathode or at pH 3.7 glutamic acid is isoelectric and aspartic travels towards the anode. In general at any particular pH, some of the amino acids in a mixture will travel towards the anode and others towards the cathode, whereas those which are isoelectric will remain stationary. Those acids which move will do so at rates dependent on their degree of dissociation and molecular size. In this way they may be separated into bands on the paper.

3. Proteins

(a) *Structure*

The quantities of the amino acids composing the four proteins mentioned above are given in Table 17.

TABLE 17

AMINO ACID COMPOSITION

(Residues of amino acid per 10^5 g protein)[2]

No.	Amino acid	Side group R	Casein	Arachin	Glycinin	Zein
1.	Glycine	H	26.7	—	—	—
2.	Alanine	$CH_3—$	36.0	—	—	118
3.	Valine	$(CH_3)_2CH—$	61.4	42	39	34
4.	Leucine	$(CH_3)_2CHCH_2—$	116.9	58	62	161
5.	Isoleucine	$CH_3(C_2H_5)CH—$		34	44	38
6.	Phenylalanine	$C_6H_5CH_2—$	30.3	42	35	44
7.	Serine	$HOCH_2—$	60.0	21	25	67
8.	Threonine	$CH_3CHOH—$	41.1	24	—	29
9.	Tyrosine	$HOC_6H_4CH_2$	34.8	31	20	29
10.	Histidine	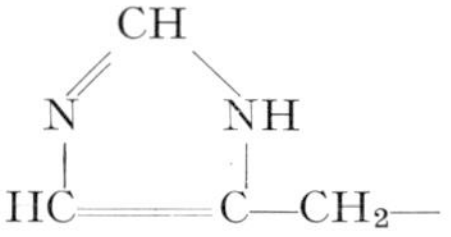	20.0	14	13	

$$\underset{\underset{HC=\!=\!=\!=C-CH_2-}{}}{\overset{CH}{N\diagup\quad\diagdown NH}}$$

No.	Amino acid	Side group R	Casein	Arachin	Glycinin	Zein
11.	Tryptophan	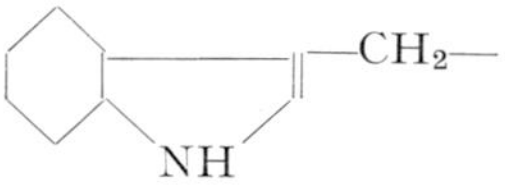 $—CH_2—$ (indole ring with NH)	5.9	3	—	—
12.	Arginine	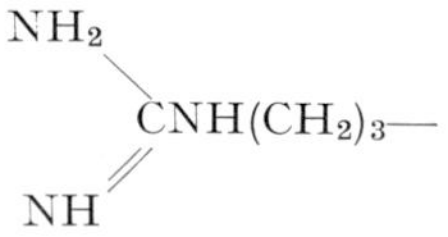 $\underset{NH}{\overset{NH_2}{\diagdown}}CNH(CH_2)_3—$	23.6	78	46	10
13.	Lysine	$NH_2CH_2(CH_2)_3—$	56.1	19	47	—
14.	Glutamic Acid	$HOOC(CH_2)_2—$	152.4	—	—	183
15.	Aspartic Acid	$HOOCCH_2—$	53.4	—	—	35
16.	Methionine	$CH_3S(CH_2)_2—$	18.8	4	17	2.4
17.	Cystine/2	$—CH_2—S—S—CH_2—$	2.8	11	10	0.8
18.	Proline*	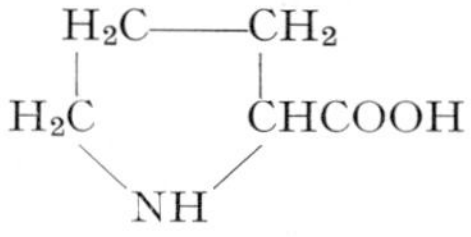 $\underset{\underset{NH}{H_2C\diagdown\quad\diagup CHCOOH}}{H_2C—\!\!—CH_2}$	92.2	—	—	91
19.	Amide nitrogen		(114.3)	—	—	(216)

* This is the complete formula of Proline.

Joining these α-amino acids to form a polypeptide produces a molecule which carries side groups R and an amino and carboxyl group at the end of the chain.

(b) *Classification of Proteins*

Although many proteins have been examined as possible sources of raw materials for fibre preparation, only four need at present be considered, *viz*. casein, zein, glycinin and arachin. They are found in nature in a globular form and the protein or a derivative must be transformed to a dispersed form suitable for making fibres. The manufacture of fibres from proteins is discussed in a later chapter.

The structure of a protein molecule is not an invariable thing. Even when great care is taken as far as preparation and purification are concerned, some variations of composition occur as shown by amino acid analysis. Indeed it would not be surprising that protein composition can be altered by varying climatic conditions (*e.g.* for zein found in maize) or diet (for animal proteins). The proteins may not be chemically homogeneous, but generally the protein material extracted from one particular source is regarded as a single substance.

Only broad classifications are possible, one of these is the distinction between simple and conjugated proteins. This is a chemical distinction, the simple proteins consisting of polypeptide chains only whereas, in a conjugated protein, the polypeptide chain is combined with some other chemical species. For example, haemoglobin consists of four iron-containing porphyrin residues combined with polypeptide molecules. Silk fibroin, on the other hand, is entirely a polypeptide.

The second broad classification is based on differences in the shape and orientation of the polypeptide molecules, resulting in fibrous and globular proteins. In a fibrous protein, the polypeptide chains are more or less extended but only very seldom to their full length, more often they are coiled into a long helix. With molecules in this form, the chances of molecular association and entanglement taking place are very great and as a result, fibrous proteins are insoluble, simply because solvent molecules cannot penetrate completely between the protein molecules. With globular proteins, the polypeptide chains are more tightly coiled so that the degree of interchain entanglement is much lower. Because of this, the polypeptide molecules exist as relatively small aggregates which can readily be completely surrounded by solvent molecules and hence globular proteins are soluble.

It is important to note that the fibrous and globular forms are not distinctive to any particular protein but are interchangeable. The process of denaturation is essentially the transformation of globular molecules into the fibrous form. This occurs readily with most proteins and is often reversible.

(c) Properties of Proteins

Protein molecules are large and reactive. They are able to form complexes with anions, cations, carbohydrates, and with each other. Some proteins may be well defined e.g. insulin, others may have a special affinity for molecules with certain configurations and may have a capacity to react with substrates. Examples of the latter are the enzymes, the numbers of which are legion. In the field of proteins the term molecule is in general too restricted. There is evidence that the fundamental sub-units in the protein are held together by hydrogen bonds. Comparison of proteins with synthetic polymers shows that, whereas the latter are made from repeat units joined together by covalent bonds leaving free characteristic terminal groups at the end, the protein molecule may be composed of sub-groups joined through hydrogen bonds. For example, arachin, the principal globulin of groundnuts, has been found to associate reversibly according to the equation $2A \rightleftharpoons A_2$, so that the molecular weight as found by sedimentation or diffusion is about 330,000 whereas the associated product has a value around 180,000[15].

(d) Proteins Used in Fibre Manufacture

(i) Casein

Skimmed milk contains casein, albumin type proteins, lactose, soluble salts etc. Casein forms some 80% of the total protein and is readily isolated by treatment with acid. It is one of the proteins containing phosphoric acid possibly united with the hydroxyl group of serine[16]; its solubility is not greatly affected by salts. Commercially, this protein is obtained from skimmed milk by the natural souring process, addition of acids such as hydrochloric or by the action of the enzyme rennet found in the inner lining of the fourth stomach of the cow. Although precipitation of casein gives a product of almost consistent composition, separation into fractions known as α and β is possible since the α has a lower solubility at pH 4.2 and 2 °C than the β and the β a lower solubility at pH 4.9 and 20 °C[17].

More recently by the use of electrophoresis, three fractions α, β and γ in the proportion 75, 22 and 3% have been detected[18,19,20]. The α- and β-fractions have been studied more than the γ and have been shown to differ in several ways. The amino acid compositions are different: the amounts of combined phosphate are 31.6 and 19.7, the number of anionic groups 91.9 and 80.4 and cationic groups 104.4 and 84.1 groups per 10^5 g respectively. The isoelectric points are at pH 4.7 and 4.9[20].

References p. 243

Evidence is accumulating for the idea of an interaction between these two fractions [17,21]. This shows in the electrophoretic results, even though the two fractions may carry like charges.

The molecular weight of casein has been given as 75,000–375,000[23], but osmotic pressure determination in the presence of urea gives a value of 33,000[23]. This is again suggestive of the components of casein being split apart by the action of a substance such as urea which is capable of breaking hydrogen bonds.

Little is known as yet of the sequence of the amino acids in casein; information is confined to the end groups, where it has been shown (by the dinitrofluorobenzene method) that there are present in α-casein 1.7 equivalents and 1.5 equivalents of terminal arginyl groups and lysyl groups respectively per 10^5 g. The figures for the β-casein are 5.3 and 2.4.

(ii) Arachin

The globulins from groundnuts (*Arachis hypogrea* L) are obtained from the meal after prior extraction with solvent to remove the oils. The nuts contain 24–26% of protein.

Meal from groundnuts is first treated with an organic solvent to remove the oil and then with dilute caustic soda solution[24]; the extract is filtered or treated with acid until the isoelectric point is reached (*ca.* pH 5), when the proteins precipitate leaving the carbohydrate material behind. The extracted protein has been found to consist of two globulins — arachin (73%) and conarachin (27%). Amino acid analysis show them to be rich in lysine and arginine residues and hence they are expected to react readily with formaldehyde used in the hardening of protein fibres.

(iii) Glycinin

The soya bean (*Soya Lispode* L) contains 35% of protein. For extraction, the beans are first pressed and extracted with hexane to remove the oil. The flakes which remain from this are treated with 0.1% solution of sodium sulphite when the protein is dissolved. After clarification the solution is filtered and the protein precipitated by bringing the pH to 4.5. The globulin, making up 80–90% of the protein in the bean, is called glycinin[25] as indeed is the commercial product. Soya beans have been shown to contain two main globulins[26] but electrophoretic studies of water extracts show at least seven [27].

(iv) Zein

Zein is the main vegetable protein from maize and is soluble in 50–90% alcohol but insoluble in water or absolute alcohol. Zein is a member of a group of proteins known as prolamines and is probably not really to be regarded as a globulin since it is insoluble in water. The molecular weight of zein is found to be about 40,000–50,000[28]. This protein is notable for its solubility in non aqueous solvents. It is soluble in methanol and other alcohols provided a small amount of water is present, in anhydrous ethylene glycol etc. Acid groups are in excess of basic.

Commercially, zein may be prepared from corn (maize) from the meal obtained by removal of the starchy part (cornflour). The meal can be treated with aqueous alcohol followed by precipitation by water, or by extraction with caustic soda solution and precipitation with acid.

The grain is steeped in warm liquor containing a small amount of sulphur dioxide; the husks and germ can be removed by crushing and washing. The residue is ground and allowed to flow over long "tables" when the heavier cornflour settles. The lighter cellulosic and protein fractions remain in suspension and are drawn off as a yellow slurry after removal of the supernatant liquor. On drying, the slurry gives maize gluten meal. The meal so made contains about 50% of protein together with some cellulosic and other carbohydrates and oil. Zein composes about 70% of the protein, the remainder being maize glutelin or zeinin. The dried meal may then be extracted with 92% ethanol (v/v) or 85% isopropyl alcohol; after filtration, the extract is mixed with hexane giving two layers[29]. The protein is found in the alcohol layer which is sprayed into ice-cold water to precipitate the zein. The product is a fine, near white powder. Zeinin, the globulin representing nearly 30% of the total protein in maize, is insoluble in the aqueous alcohol used for the extraction and remains behind in the gluten meal.

REFERENCES

[1] M. BERMANN, L. ZERVAS and J. P. GREENSTEIN, Ber., 65 (1932) 1692.
M. BERMANN and L. ZERVAS, J. Biol. Chem. 113 (1936) 341.
[2] H. NEURATH and K. BAILEY, The Proteins, Academic Press, New York, Vol. 1, Part A, 1953.
[3] P. KARRER and E. EHRHARDT, Helv. Chim. Acta, 34 (1951) 2204.
[4] H. ADKINS and H. R. BELLICA, J. Am. Chem. Soc., 70 (1948) 3121.
[5] E. F. GALE and H. M. R. EPPS, Biochem. J., 38 (1944) 232.
[6] E. F. GALE, Biochem. J., 39 (1945) 46.
[7] K. BAILEY, Biochem. J., 49 (1951) 23.
F. SANGA, Biochem. J., 45 (1949) 563.
[8] M. LEVY and D. E. SILBERMAN, J. Biol. Chem., 118 (1937) 723.
[9] D. FRENCH and J. T. EDSALL, Advances in Protein Chem., 2 (1945) 277.
[10] S. RATNER and H. T. CLARK, J. Am. Chem. Soc., 59 (1937) 200.
[11] B. H. NICOLET and L. A. SHIMM, J. Am. Chem. Soc., 61 (1939) 1615.
[12] F. CRAMER, Paper Chromatography, Macmillan, London, 1955.
[13] R. CONSDEN, H. GORDON and A. S. P. MARTIN, Biochem. J., 38 (1944) 224.
[14] M. LEDERER, Introduction to Paper Electrophoresis, Elsevier, Amsterdam, 1957.
[15] P. JOHNSON and E. M. SHOOTER, Biochim. et Biophys. Acta, 5 (1950) 361.
[16] S. PASTERNAK, Compt. rend., 184 (1927) 306.
P. A. LEVENE and D. W. HILL, J. Biol. Chem., 101 (1933) 711.
[17] R. C. WARNER, J. Am. Chem. Soc., 66 (1944) 1725.

[18] W. G. GORDON, W. F. SENNETT, R. S. CABLE and M. MORRIS, *J. Am. Chem. Soc.*, 71 (1949) 3293.
W. G. GORDON, W. F. SENNETT and M. BENDER, *J. Am. Chem. Soc.*, 72 (1950) 4282.

[19] N. J. HIPP, M. C. GROVES, J. H. CUSTER and T. L. McMEEKIN, *J. Am. Chem Soc.*, 72 (1950) 4928.

[20] O. MELLANDER, *Biochem. Z.*, 300 (1939) 240.

[21] H. NITSCHMANN and H. ZURCHER, *Helv. Chim. Acta*, 33 (1950) 1698.

[22] T. SVEDBERG, L. M. CARPENTER and D. C. CARPENTER, *J. Am. Chem. Soc.*, 52 (1930) 241.

[23] N. F. BURK and D. M. GREENBERG, *J. Biol. Chem.*, 87 (1930) 197.

[24] D. TRAIL, *Chem. and Ind. London*, (1945) 58.
D. TRAIL and A. MCLEAN, *J. Soc. Chem. Ind. London*, 64 (1945) 221.

[25] T. B. OSBORNE and G. F. CAMPBELL, *J. Am. Chem. Soc.*, 20 (1898) 419.

[26] N. S. HIPP, M. L. GROVES and T. L. McMEEKIN, *J. Am. Chem. Soc.*, 74 (1952) 4822.

[27] C. E. DANIELSSON, *Biochem. J.*, 47 (1949) 387.

[28] J. F. FOSTER and J. T. EDSALL, *J. Am. Chem. Soc.*, 67 (1945) 617.

[29] L. C. SWALLOW, *Ind. Eng. Chem.*, 33 (1941) 394.

[30] S. AKABORI, K. OHNO and K. NARITA, *Bull. Chem. Soc. Japan*, 25 (1952) 214.

[31] A. C. CHIBNALL and U. W. REES, *The Chemical Structure of Proteins*, Ciba Foundation Symposium, 1954.
C. FROMAGEOT and M. JUTISZ, *ibid.*

[32] F. SANGER, *Symposium on Fibrous Proteins*, Cambridge, 1935.

CHAPTER 9

SYNTHETIC POLYPEPTIDES

These compounds are of interest not only as high polymers with potential fibre forming properties but also because of their relation to proteins. Fibres prepared from synthetic polypeptides have been mentioned in patents but so far none have been developed on a large scale.

Synthetic polypeptides or poly-α-amino acids are of major interest as synthetic prototypes for the proteins. Thus poly-γ-methyl-L-glutamate has been shown to have a structure similar to fibrous proteins e.g. wool. Those polypeptides which are water soluble polymers allow not only study of the basic or backbone structure but also the behaviour of side chains. Further, they have also been shown to be good substrates for proteolytic enzymes and some resemble natural materials in their interaction with viruses and bacteria.

1. Preparation

It is not possible to prepare polypeptides of a high molecular weight by polycondensation of α-amino acids, since under the conditions normally employed in polycondensation reactions cyclic dimers — diketopiperazines — are formed and the reaction at the high temperatures used may be accompanied by decomposition. Condensation of the esters of amino acids has been studied but the yields of polymer are very small. Recourse must be made to other reactions, if polymers of high molecular weight are required. As a class, synthetic polypeptides are not easy to prepare and have the disadvantage that a large number of them are infusible and insoluble in common solvents, although fibres have been spun from polypeptides using solvents such as phenols, trichloroacetic acid etc. The following methods of preparation have been used.

(1) Fischer's Method. Polypeptides were first obtained by Fischer who prepared up to the octadecapeptide, a compound which contained 3 leucine and 15 glycine residues. His products were of low D.P. and were prepared to show that polypeptide chains formed the backbone of protein molecules.

The syntheses were carried out in a stepwise fashion. The amino group was first blocked by reaction with chloroformic ester (I)

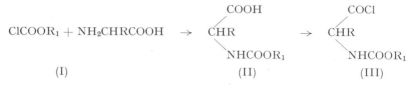

$$\text{ClCOOR}_1 + \text{NH}_2\text{CHRCOOH} \quad \rightarrow \quad \begin{matrix} \text{COOH} \\ \diagup \\ \text{CHR} \\ \diagdown \\ \text{NHCOOR}_1 \end{matrix} \quad \rightarrow \quad \begin{matrix} \text{COCl} \\ \diagup \\ \text{CHR} \\ \diagdown \\ \text{NHCOOR}_1 \end{matrix}$$

$$\text{(I)} \qquad\qquad\qquad\qquad \text{(II)} \qquad\qquad \text{(III)}$$

The acid (II) so produced can be converted to the acid chloride (III) and thence reacted with a second molecule of amino acid.

$$\text{R}_1\text{OOCNHCHRCOCl} + \text{NH}_2\text{CHRCOOH} \rightarrow$$

$$\rightarrow \text{R}_1\text{OOCNHCHRCONHCHRCOOH}$$

(III)

Removal of the protective group by hydrolysis yields a dipeptide. A second example of masking the amino group is by formation of the α-bromoisocaproyl derivative. This can then be transformed to the acid chloride (IV) which will react with a molecule of acid to give (V)

$$\text{C}_4\text{H}_9\text{CHBrCONHCH}_2\text{COCl} + \text{NH}_2\text{CH}_2\text{COOH} \rightarrow$$

(IV)

$$\rightarrow \text{C}_4\text{H}_9\text{CHBrCONHCH}_2\text{CONHCH}_2\text{COOH} \rightarrow$$

(V)

$$\xrightarrow{\text{NH}_3} \quad \begin{matrix} \text{C}_4\text{H}_9\text{CHCONHCH}_2\text{CONHCH}_2\text{COOH} \\ | \\ \text{NH}_2 \end{matrix}$$

(VI)

The removal of the bromine atom by treatment with ammonia gives a tripeptide, leucylglycylglycine (VI). It should be noted that in this method the identity of the N-terminal residue is determined by the protecting agent.

(2) From diketopiperazine[1]. Heating this compound with water gives yields of products which depend on the amount of water and reaction conditions. The suggested reaction mechanism is

$$\begin{matrix} \text{CH}_2 \\ \diagup \quad \diagdown \\ \text{NH} \quad\; \text{CO} \\ | \qquad | \\ \text{CO} \quad\; \text{NH} \\ \diagdown \quad \diagup \\ \text{CH}_2 \end{matrix} \xrightarrow{\text{H}_2\text{O}} \text{NH}_2\text{CH}_2\text{CONHCH}_2\text{COOH} + \begin{matrix} \text{CH}_2 \\ \diagup \quad \diagdown \\ \text{NH} \quad\; \text{CO} \\ | \qquad | \\ \text{CO} \quad\; \text{NH} \\ \diagdown \quad \diagup \\ \text{CH}_2 \end{matrix} \rightarrow$$

(VII)

$$\rightarrow \text{GlyGlyGlyGly etc.}$$

Partial hydrolysis by water gives the dipeptide glycylglycine (VII) which then reacts with further molecules of diketopiperazine to build up higher peptides. In such a system, it is possible for the glycylglycine to hydrolyse further to glycine which in turn may decompose. In writing polypeptide formulae, it is common to abbreviate as for example above where glycine is given as Gly. Yields of polymer by this method are small.

(3) From the chloroacetyl derivatives (VIII) by reaction with ammonia

$$ClCH_2CONHCH_2COOH \xrightarrow{NH_3} NH_2CH_2CONHCH_2CONHCH_2COOH$$
$$(VIII)$$

The peptide so made can then be chloroacetylated and reacted with amino acids to give a tripeptide; repetition of this process enables higher peptides to be prepared.

(4) The hydrochlorides of the α-amino acyl chlorides (IX) will polymerise when heated in the presence of a strong base

$$NH_2CHRCOCl \rightarrow H(NHCHRCO)_nOH$$
$$(IX)$$

In this way leucine, alanine etc. have been polymerised[2].

(5) From tripeptide azides. Polyglycyl[3] has been obtained from triglycyl acid azide (X). This is prepared from the tripeptide ester (XI) by reaction with hydrazine; the resulting hydrazide (XII) on treatment with nitrous acid yields the acid azide.

$$H(NHCH_2CO)_2NHCH_2COOR \xrightarrow{NH_2NH_2} H(NHCH_2CO)_2NHCH_2CONHNH_2$$
$$(XI) \qquad\qquad\qquad\qquad (XII)$$

$$\xrightarrow{HNO_2} H(NHCH_2CO)_2NHCH_2CON_3 \rightarrow H(NHCH_2CO)_nN_3 + NH_3$$
$$(X)$$

Addition of alkali to the acid azide (X) removes hydrazoic acid and the azide polymerises.

(6) N-carbothiophenol (XIII) derivatives of α-amino acids decompose when heated in inert solvents to give polymeric materials[4]

$$C_6H_5SCONHCHCOOH \rightarrow C_6H_5SH + OCNCHCOOH$$
$$\qquad\quad | \qquad\qquad\qquad\qquad\qquad\qquad | $$
$$\qquad\quad R \qquad\qquad\qquad\qquad\qquad\qquad R$$
$$(XIII)$$

$$nOCNCHCOOH \xrightarrow{H_2O} H(NHCHRCO)_nOH + nCO_2$$
$$\quad\; | $$
$$\quad\; R$$

(7) From N-carboxy-α-amino acid anhydrides (4-substituted oxazolidine-2,5-diones). These compounds, usually abbreviated to N.C.A.'s, are the most convenient and the most important ones for the synthesis of poly-peptides, and were first made by Leuchs[5]. They may be prepared in several ways:

(α) Reaction of methyl chloroformate with the amino acid in cold aqueous alkali is followed by treatment with thionyl chloride at 40°C. On raising the temperature to 60°C the anhydride (XIV) is formed.

$$NH_2CHRCOOH + CH_3OCOCl \rightarrow CH_3OOCNHRCOOH$$

$$\xrightarrow{SOCl_2} CH_3OOCNHCHRCOCl \rightarrow$$

RCH—CO
| O + CH₃Cl
NH—CO
(XIV)

Other derivatives have been used. The N-carbobenzoxy- and N-carbo-allyloxy-α-amino acid chlorides (XV) and (XVI) split off benzyl and allyl chloride

$C_6H_5CH_2OCONHCHRCOCl$ $+ C_6H_5CH_2Cl$
(XV)

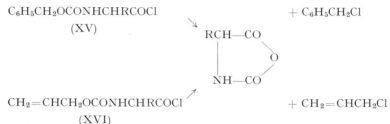

RCH—CO
| O
NH—CO

$CH_2=CHCH_2OCONHCHRCOCl$ $+ CH_2=CHCH_2Cl$
(XVI)

The mechanism of this reaction would appear to be via an intermediate intramolecular oxonium salt (XVII) formed by reaction of the carbon atom bearing the electrophilic halogen and the nucleophilic oxygen of the N-carboalkoxy (urethan group). The oxonium salt splits off the alkyl halide to give the N.C.A.

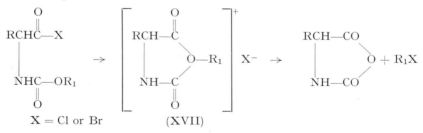

X = Cl or Br   (XVII)

(β) From malonic esters[6]. The diester (XVIII) is hydrolysed to the monoester (XIX) which is reacted with hydrazine to form hydrazide (XX)

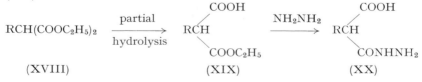

(XVIII)   (XIX)   (XX)

The hydrazide will react with nitrous acid in ether to give an azide (XXI) which on heating liberates nitrogen and gives the required anhydride

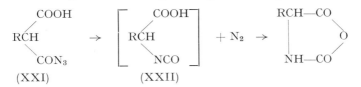

(XXI)   (XXII)

The reaction probably takes place intramolecularly via the intermediate formation of an isocyanate (XXII).

(γ) From the amino acid and phosgene[7,8]

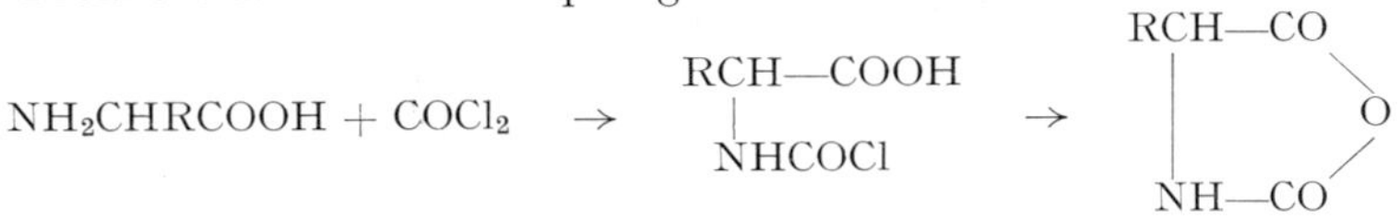

$$NH_2CHRCOOH + COCl_2 \rightarrow \begin{matrix} RCH—COOH \\ | \\ NHCOCl \end{matrix} \rightarrow \begin{matrix} RCH—CO \\ | \quad \diagdown \\ \quad \quad O \\ | \quad \diagup \\ NH—CO \end{matrix}$$

This method is a convenient one since the product is obtained in one operation by suspending finely ground amino acid in a suitable liquid and passing in phosgene with warming.

(δ) From the disodium salts of N-carboxy-α-amino acids (XXIII)[8]. The amino acid is treated with carbon dioxide in a solution of sodium methoxide or sodium carbonate. The disodium salt (XXIII), precipitated by the addition of methanol, is suspended in dioxane or sodium carbonate and treated with thionyl chloride or phosgene

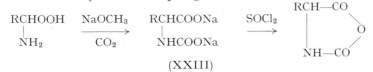

(XXIII)

2. Properties of N-Carboxyanhydrides

The anhydrides are colourless crystalline solids when pure. They are extremely reactive and above their melting points readily loose carbon dioxide giving a polymeric product. Only in one or two special cases can they be sublimed. They react with water or amines under certain conditions to give α-amino acids or amides (XXIV)

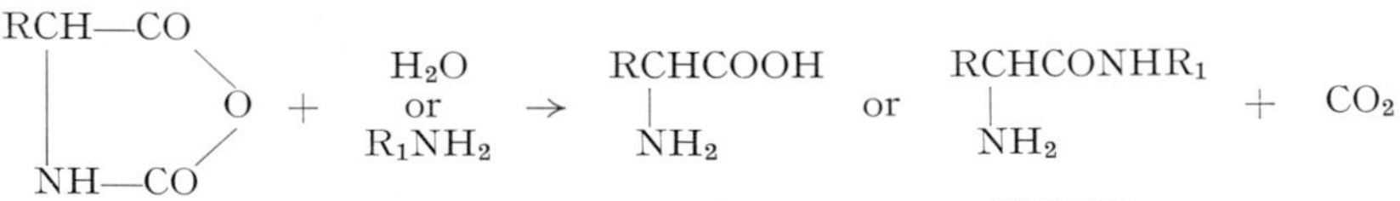

$$\begin{matrix} RCH—CO \\ | \quad \diagdown \\ \quad \quad O \\ | \quad \diagup \\ NH—CO \end{matrix} + \begin{matrix} H_2O \\ or \\ R_1NH_2 \end{matrix} \rightarrow \begin{matrix} RCHCOOH \\ | \\ NH_2 \end{matrix} \quad or \quad \begin{matrix} RCHCONHR_1 \\ | \\ NH_2 \end{matrix} + CO_2$$

(XXIV)

Alcoholic solutions in the presence of hydrochloric acid evolve carbon dioxide to give the ester hydrochloride (XXV)

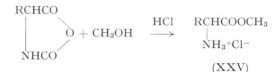

$$(\text{XXV})$$

Reaction of the N-carboxyanhydrides in an inert solvent in the presence of hydrochloric acid gives the acid chloride (XXVI)

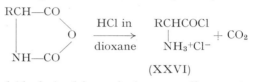

$$(\text{XXVI})$$

With the anhydride derived from glycine, a small amount of water at 0°C will give the dicarboxylic or substituted carbamic acid (XXVII) which may be precipitated on addition of baryta

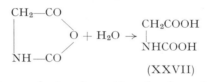

$$(\text{XXVII})$$

The nature of the products of reaction do depend on conditions of reaction and, more generally, may be entirely glycine or an insoluble polymeric product.

   The amino acid formed by reaction with water (or amide from reaction with an amine) contains an amine group which is itself capable of reacting with a second molecule of the anhydride

$$\begin{array}{c} \text{RCH—CO} \\ | \qquad\qquad \diagdown \\ | \qquad\qquad\quad \text{O} + NH_2CHRCOOH \rightarrow NH_2CHRCONHCHRCOOH + CO_2 \\ | \qquad\qquad \diagup \\ \text{NH—CO} \end{array}$$

The dipeptide so formed can react with a further molecule and so on thereby building up a polymer. To obtain glycine, a large excess of water is required suggestive of the idea that the amino groups in glycine react more readily than does water. The products of reaction with primary and secondary amines depend on the character of the amine as well as that of the parent amino acid. A strong aliphatic amine when used in excess gives a substituted amine[9] (XXVIII)

$$\begin{array}{c} \text{C}_6\text{H}_5\text{CH}_2\text{CH—CO} \\ | \qquad\qquad\qquad \diagdown \\ | \qquad\qquad\qquad\quad \text{O} + (CH_3)_2NH \rightarrow C_6H_5CH_2CHCON(CH_3)_2 + CO_2 \\ | \qquad\qquad\qquad \diagup \qquad\qquad\qquad\qquad\quad | \\ \text{NH—CO} \qquad\qquad\qquad\qquad\qquad\qquad NH_2 \end{array}$$

$$(\text{XXVIII})$$

With aniline, the di- and higher peptides are produced[10] and, in this case, it would seem that the anhydride prefers to react with the primary amine in the anilide rather than the rather weakly basic amino group of aniline.

If the nitrogen atom of the N.C.A. is made more weakly basic by substitution with a phenyl group, e.g. N-phenylglycine carboxy-anhydride (XXIX), reaction with amines gives only the monosubstituted product, (XXX)

$$\begin{array}{c} CH_2\text{---}CO \\ | \qquad\qquad\quad O + RNH_2 \rightarrow C_6H_5NHCH_2CONHR + CO_2 \\ C_6H_5N\text{----}CO \\ \quad\text{(XXIX)} \qquad\qquad\qquad\qquad \text{(XXX)} \end{array}$$

The absence of further reaction is attributed to the weakly basic character of the N-substituted amide.

In general, the initial reaction between N.C.A.'s and primary or secondary bases is more rapid the stronger the bases. The propagation steps involved in forming higher peptides are dependent on the strength of the base produced by the initiation, i.e. on the basic strength of the amino group arising from the N.C.A. itself.

3. Polymerisation of N-Carboxyanhydrides

(a) The Polymerisation Process

The reactions which occur when water and amines are added to N.C.A.'s can be regarded as the initiation and propagation steps in a polymerisation. Assuming the reaction followed the simple route suggested above, each molecule of initiator starts one chain which only stops growing when the N.C.A. is used up. If to M_0 molecules of the anhydride is added I_0 of water or amine, a polymer would be produced which had a number average D.P. of M_0/I_0. This has as a consequence that, if a polymer of high D.P. is prepared, only a small quantity of initiator is required and the reaction must go to completion. Moreover, the molecular weight distribution would be very sharp in exactly the same manner as the reaction of caprolactam discussed in Chapter 2 with the difference that, in the case of the polypeptides, the reaction conditions are such that transamidation does not occur. This picture however, is one which applies to initiation with strong bases but breaks down, as may be expected, when weak bases are used.

The mechanism of reaction, by analogy with the mechanism suggested for the reaction between acid anhydrides and amines, may proceed through the intermediate species (XXXI) and (XXXII) given below

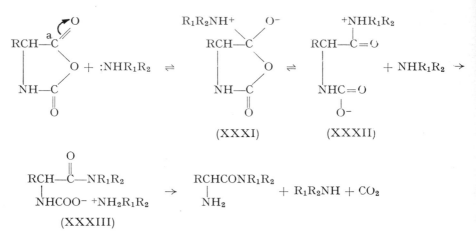

$$\text{(XXXI)} \qquad \text{(XXXII)}$$

$$\text{(XXXIII)}$$

The intermediate is first formed by reaction between the nucleophilic amine and the electrophilic carbon atom (a) of the N.C.A. This rearranges to a dipolar ion (XXXII) which gives the ammonium carbamate derivative (XXXIII) in the presence of excess amine; the carbamate, by analogy with the ammonium salts of carbamates of α-amino esters, splits of carbon dioxide.

Polymerisation of N.C.A.'s is best carried out in solution in solvents such as chloroform, nitrobenzene, benzene etc. Polymerisation in bulk gives usually polymers of low D.P. Reactions in solution may be performed at low temperatures, and can lead to high molecular weight products. Ideally, the solvent should dissolve the N.C.A. as well as the polypeptide. To the solution of the N.C.A. in a dry solvent is added an initiator such as a primary or secondary base. The polypeptide is isolated by titrating the reaction mixture with ether and filtering. If the polypeptide comes out of solution during the reaction, the reaction could cease when only a small extent of polymerisation has occurred. More often however, the polymer, if precipitated, will come down as a swollen gel into which the small monomer molecules can diffuse thereby allowing the chains to grow. Thus, although it is preferable for the polypeptide to be soluble in the solvent, products of high molecular weight can be obtained if the solvent swells the polymer. So far the discussion has assumed that the side chain of the parent amino acid is not reactive. If this is not so, then in order to prepare the N-carboxyanhydride it is necessary to block the reactive group. Thus the amino group in lysine (XXXV) may be protected by reaction with carbobenzoxy chloride (XXXIV) and the anhydride produced by reaction with phosphorous pentachloride,

NH₂CHCOOH
$|$
(CH₂)₄   + C₆H₅CH₂OCOCl   →
$|$
NH₂

(XXXV)   (XXXIV)

C₆H₅CH₂OCONHCHCOOH
$|$
(CH₂)₄
$|$
NHCOOCH₂C₆H₅

$\xrightarrow{PCl_5}$ N.C.A.

Side chain carboxyl groups, as in aspartic acid, may be transformed to the methyl or benzyl esters. The β-methyl ester of aspartic acid (XXXVI) may be obtained by esterification in methanol and hydrochloric acid[11]. The anhydride is then produced by reaction with phosgene.

Hydroxyl groups as in serine (XXXVII) may be masked by acetylation or carbobenzoxylation[12] prior to reaction with phosgene.

H₂NCHCOOH   CH₂OH   CH₂OCOCH₃   COCl₂   CH₂OOCCH₃
$|$ $|$ → $|$ $\longrightarrow$ $|$
CH₂   NH₂CHCOOH   NH₂CHCOOH   CH—CO
$|$ (XXXVII) $|$ \
COOCH₃ $|$ O
                                                         NH—CO   /
(XXXVI)

The masking groups vary in the difficulty of subsequent removal from the polypeptide. The acetyl group will come off in concentrated ammonia at room temperature[12], ester groups may be removed by alkaline hydrolysis in aqueous alcohol[11] and the carbobenzoxy group by hydrobromic acid in glacial acetic acid[13].

(b) Kinetics

The polymerisation scheme may be described in terms of (i) initiation, (ii) propagation and (iii) termination reactions. Reactions (i) and (ii) have been discussed earlier: the existence of (i) is confirmed by the disappearance of initiator from the reaction mixture with the simultaneous appearance of the corresponding amino acid amide when an amine is used; (ii) is confirmed by the fact that peptides or preformed poly-α-amino acids will also initiate polymerisation. An important feature of base initiated polymerisation is the retention of the optical configurations of asymmetric carbon atoms. Polymers consisting wholly of L- or D-residues or mixtures of the two may be prepared.

Copolymers are formed when two or more N.C.A.'s are polymerised together; the arrangement of the α-amino acid residues in such materials may not necessarily be at random since the reactivities of the various N.C.A.'s will vary.

If the initiator is a polymer or other material containing a terminal basic group, say a polypeptide, block copolymers are possible[9]. If a

References p. 261

protein is used carrying ε-amino acids, a graft polymer may be formed; indeed, multi-chain polypeptides have been formed using initiators containing lysine residues[15].

(i) *Initiation*

For the initiation reaction may be written

$$\text{M} + \text{I} \rightarrow \text{M}_1$$

so that formally the rate of loss of monomer (N.C.A.) by reaction with the base will be given by

$$-\left(\frac{d\,[M]}{dt}\right)_{\text{Initiation}} = k_i\,[M][I] \qquad (\text{I})$$

i.e. first order in both reactants.

(ii) *Propagation*

This reaction may be written as

$$\text{M}_1 + \text{M} \rightarrow \text{M}_2$$
$$\text{M}_2 + \text{M} \rightarrow \text{M}_3$$
$$\text{M}_3 + \text{M} \rightarrow \text{M}_4$$
$$\begin{matrix} \cdot & & \cdot & & \cdot \\ \cdot & & \cdot & & \cdot \\ \cdot & & \cdot & & \cdot \end{matrix}$$
$$\text{M}_{n-1} + \text{M} \rightarrow \text{M}_n$$

It has been shown that these reactions may be taken to have the same rate constants since, when the reaction is initiated with preformed polymer, the initial rate of polymerisation is independent of the average D.P. of the initiator[16,17]. For such a system, the total rate of loss of monomer (measured by the carbon dioxide evolved) will be the sum of the rate of loss of monomer from each reaction step including that of initiation. Hence

$$-\frac{d\,[M]}{dt} = [M]\,\{k_i\,[I] + k_p\,([M_1] + [M_2] + [M_3]\ldots)\,\}$$

If $k_i = k_p$, then

$$-\frac{d\,[M]}{dt} = k_p\,[M]\,\{[I] + [M_1] + [M_2] + [M_3]\ldots\} = k_p\,[M][I_0] \quad (2)$$

Since each initiator molecule commences one chain, the second term on the right-hand side is equal to $[I_0]$, the concentration of initiator molecules at the commencement of the reaction. This is a constant for any one experiment and hence a plot of $(1/[M])(d[M]/dt)$ against $[I_0]$ is linear[16,18]. This is shown in Fig. 56a and 56b.

However the kinetics are not always as simple as this. The polymerisation is catalysed by carbon dioxide so that, if the reaction is carried out at constant volume, the pressure of CO_2 will build up and the effective concentration will change. The kinetics are no longer first order. In Fig. 57 the variation of the polymerisation rate of the N.C.A. from sarcosine is plotted as a function of carbon dioxide concentration[16]. The effect of

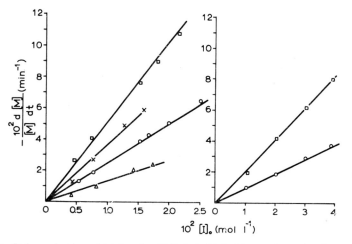

Fig. 56a. Polymerisation of DL-leucine-N.C.A. initiated by preformed polymer I_0[16]. □ Solvent nitrobenzene 45°; × = o-nitroanisole 45°; O = nitrobenzene 25.2° △ = o-nitroanisole 25°.

Fig. 56b. Polymerisation of DL-phenylalanine-N.C.A. in nitrobenzene initiated by preformed polymer. □ 45° O 22°

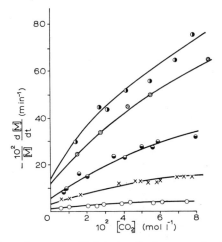

Fig. 57. Polymerisation of sarcosine-N.C.A. in nitrobenzene at 25 °C under constant pressures of CO_2. Initiated by preformed polymer[16].

References p. 261

carbon dioxide has been attributed to the formation of a substituted carbamic acid (XXXVIII) by reaction with the amine.

$$2RNHCH_3 + CO_2 \rightleftharpoons RNCOO^{-+}NH_2CH_3R \rightleftharpoons RNCOO^- + {}^+NH_2CH_3R$$
$$\qquad\qquad\qquad\qquad |\qquad\qquad\qquad\qquad\qquad\quad |$$
$$\qquad\qquad\qquad\qquad CH_3\qquad\qquad\qquad\qquad\qquad CH_3$$

(XXXVIII)

$$\Updownarrow$$
$$RNCOOH + RCH_3NH$$
$$\qquad |$$
$$\qquad CH_3$$

If the reaction is carried out at constant pressure, the carbon dioxide concentration remains constant and the kinetics revert to first order.

(iii) *Termination*

The termination step may occur if the amino group responsible for propagation reacts in an alternative way with the N.C.A. to give a ureido acid (IXL)

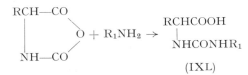

(IXL)

In this reaction, the ureido acid is produced without evolution of carbon dioxide[14] and without the formation of a further amino group to continue propagation. Any other side reaction capable of diminishing the number of free amino groups will act as a termination reaction. If no such reactions occur, the polymerisation will carry on until all the N.C.A. is exhausted.

4. Distribution of Molecular Weights

For simplicity a system in which the polymerisation is initiated with a substance such as the preformed polymer will be considered. In these circumstances, the initiation and propagation constants may be considered the same *i.e.* $k_i = k_p = k$. In addition, the concentration of carbon dioxide is assumed constant so that first order kinetics may be applied. Termination reactions are ignored. The rate of consumption of monomer is given by equation 2.

If $[M_n]$ is the concentration of polymer molecules with n residues, then its rate of formation is

$$\frac{d[M_n]}{dt} = k[M][M_{n-1}] - k[M][M_n] \qquad (3)$$

Equations 3 are a set of equations which can be solved.

For this purpose, the contribution of the initiator to the size of the polymer molecule is ignored as its size does not affect the kinetic analysis.

The equation for loss of monomer may be written as

$$-\frac{\mathrm{d}[M]}{\mathrm{d}t} = k[M][I_0] \tag{4}$$

which on integration gives

$$[M] = [M_0]\,\mathrm{e}^{-kI_0t} \tag{5}$$

Initiator is lost through reaction with the monomer

$$\mathrm{M} + \mathrm{I} \rightarrow \mathrm{M}_1$$

so the rate of loss of initiator is given by

$$-\frac{\mathrm{d}[I]}{\mathrm{d}t} = k[M][I] \tag{6}$$

Integration of equation 6 gives

$$\log[I] = -k\int_0^t [M]\,\mathrm{d}t + \text{Constant} \tag{7}$$

The constant is given by log $[I_0]$, since $[I] = [I_0]$ when the integral is zero *i.e.* at time $t = 0$. The formation of the species M_1 is determined by the rate of reaction of I with M and the loss of M_1 by reaction *i.e.*

$$\mathrm{I} + \mathrm{M} \rightarrow \mathrm{M}_1$$

$$\mathrm{M}_1 + \mathrm{M} \rightarrow \mathrm{M}_2$$

Hence, the rate of change of the concentration of M_1 (*i.e.* rate of accumulation of M_1) may be written as

$$\begin{aligned}\frac{\mathrm{d}[M_1]}{\mathrm{d}t} &= k[I][M] - k[M][M_1] \\ &= k[M]\{[I] - [M_1]\}\end{aligned} \tag{8}$$

Now in all the equations to be discussed, $[M]$ appears on the right-hand side and is a function of time. To make the situation simpler for solution equation 8 may be rewritten as

$$\frac{1}{[M]}\frac{\mathrm{d}[M_1]}{\mathrm{d}t} = k\{[I] - [M_1]\} \tag{9}$$

If $[M]\mathrm{d}t$ be chosen as a new variable, say $\mathrm{d}\nu$, equation 9 simplified to

$$\frac{\mathrm{d}[M_1]}{\mathrm{d}\nu} = k\{[I] - [M_1]\} \tag{10}$$

References p. 261

The new variable v is then given by

$$\mathrm{d}v = [M]\,\mathrm{d}t$$

or

$$v = \int_0^t [M]\,\mathrm{d}t = [M_0] \int_0^t \mathrm{e}^{-kI_0 t}\,\mathrm{d}t = \frac{[M_0] - [M]}{k[I_0]} \tag{11}$$

In terms of the new variable, equation 7 becomes

$$\log \frac{[I]}{[I_0]} = -kv \qquad \text{or} \qquad [I] = [I_0]\,\mathrm{e}^{-kv} \tag{12}$$

The value for $[I]$ may be substituted in equation 10 giving

$$\frac{\mathrm{d}[M_1]}{\mathrm{d}v} = k\{[I_0]\,\mathrm{e}^{-kv} - [M_1]\} \tag{13}$$

Equation 13 may be integrated by multiplying both sides by the integrating factor

$$\mathrm{e}^{\int k\,\mathrm{d}v} = \mathrm{e}^{kv}.$$

Hence

$$\mathrm{e}^{kv}\frac{\mathrm{d}[M_1]}{\mathrm{d}v} + k\,\mathrm{e}^{kv}[M_1] = k[I_0] \tag{14}$$

Equation 14 becomes on integration

$$[M_1]\,\mathrm{e}^{kv} = [I_0]\,kv + \text{Constant} \tag{15}$$

The value of the constant may be obtained by considering the conditions at the commencement of the reaction. Both v and $[M_1]$ are then zero so that the constant is also zero.
Hence

$$[M_1] = [I_0]\,kv\,\mathrm{e}^{-kv} \tag{16}$$

The equation for the rate of accumulation of the dimer M_2 will be

$$\frac{\mathrm{d}[M_2]}{\mathrm{d}t} = k[M][M_1] - k[M][M_2] \tag{17}$$

Changing the variable to v gives

$$\frac{\mathrm{d}[M_2]}{\mathrm{d}v} = k\{[M_1] - [M_2]\}$$

or

$$\frac{\mathrm{d}[M_2]}{\mathrm{d}v} + k[M_2] = k[M_1] = k^2[I_0]\,v\,\mathrm{e}^{-kv} \tag{18}$$

The integration of equation 18 is carried out in the same way as in equation 14, by multiplying by the integrating factor e^{kv} thereby making the left-hand side a perfect differential. Hence equation 18 becomes

$$[M_2]\,\mathrm{e}^{-kv} = \frac{k^2[I_0]\,v^2}{2} + \text{Constant}$$

Again the constant is zero.

Hence

$$[M_2] = \frac{[I_0](kv)^2 e^{-kv}}{2} \tag{19}$$

This process may be repeated for M_3, M_4 ... M_n and gives for M_n

$$[M_n] = I_0 \frac{(kv)^n}{n!} e^{-kv} \tag{20}$$

The variable v is given by equation 11 and, since a molecule of carbon dioxide is evolved for each monomer reacted, the value of $[M_0] - [M]$ is equal to the quantity of carbon dioxide evolved thus

$$v = \frac{1}{k} \frac{[M_0] - [M]}{[I_0]} = \frac{1}{k} \frac{[CO_2]}{[I_0]} \tag{21}$$

The ratio $[CO_2]/[I_0]$ is the number of moles of monomer used to the quantity of initiator introduced.

In terms of this quantity, equation 20 gives the number distribution of the various species of D.P. $= n$. This is a "Poisson" type and is very sharp as indicated in Chapter 2. The same kinetics and resulting molecular weight distribution applies to all systems of polymerisation of the type where an initiator sets off a chain reaction without the chains being stopped by a termination step. The number average D.P. will be given by

$$\overline{(\text{D.P.})}_n = \frac{\sum n M_n}{\sum M_n} = \frac{\sum n [I_0] \dfrac{(kv)^n}{n!} e^{-kv}}{\sum [I_0] \dfrac{(kv)^n}{n!} e^{-kv}} = \frac{\sum n \dfrac{(kv)^n}{n!}}{\sum \dfrac{(kv)^n}{n!}} \tag{22}$$

The numerator may be written as

$$kv \left(1 + kv + \frac{(kv)^2}{2!} \cdots \frac{(kv)^n}{n!} \cdots \right) = kv\, e^{kv}$$

The denominator is simply e^{kv} and hence

$$\overline{(\text{D.P.})}_n = kv = k \frac{[M_0] - [M]}{k[I_0]} = \frac{[M_0] - [M]}{[I_0]} \tag{23}$$

At the end of the polymerisation $[M] = 0$ and hence

$$\overline{(\text{D.P.})}_n = \frac{[M_0]}{[I_0]} \tag{24}$$

The weight average D.P. will be given by

$$\overline{(\text{D.P.})}_w = \frac{\sum n^2 M_n}{\sum n M_n} = \frac{\sum n^2 [I_0] \dfrac{(kv)^n}{n!} e^{-kv}}{\sum n [I_0] \dfrac{(kv)^n}{n!} e^{-kv}} = \frac{\sum n^2 \dfrac{(kv)^n}{n!}}{\sum n \dfrac{(kv)^n}{n!}} \tag{25}$$

References p. 261

The numerator of equation 25 may be written as

$$kv + 2^2 \frac{(kv)^2}{2!} + 3^2 \frac{(kv)^3}{3!} \ldots n^2 \frac{(kv)^n}{n!} \ldots \tag{26}$$

Taking kv out leaves

$$kv \left(1 + 2kv + 3 \frac{(kv)^2}{2!} \ldots n \frac{(kv)^{n-1}}{(n-1)!} \ldots \right) \tag{27}$$

The terms inside the bracket in equation 27 may be integrated with respect to kv to give

$$kv + (kv)^2 + \frac{(kv)^3}{2!} + \ldots \frac{(kv)^n}{(n-1)!} \ldots \tag{28}$$

which sums to $kv\, e^{kv}$.

The numerator thus becomes

$$kv \frac{d}{d(kv)} kv\, e^{kv} = kv \{e^{kv} + kv\, e^{kv}\}$$
$$= kv(1 + kv)\, e^{kv}$$

The denominator in equation 25 sums to $kv\, e^{kv}$.

Hence

$$\overline{(\text{D.P.})}_w = \frac{kv(1+kv)\, e^{kv}}{kv\, e^{kv}} = 1 + kv \tag{29}$$

Since $1 + kv \sim kv$, it follows that the weight average D.P. approximately equals the number average and hence confirms the fact that the distribution is very sharp. The difference between the weight and number averages gives an idea of the breadth of the distribution. Determination of molecular weight distributions are difficult to carry out in practice, but in one or two cases (polysarcosine[19], poly-γ-benzyl-L-glutamate) the polymers have been shown to have sharp distributions. This picture may be complicated in various ways. The initiation constant may not be equal to the propagation constant, or there may be a termination reaction. These features of the reaction modify the kinetic scheme and the latter in particular will have a broadening on the distribution curve.

Some authors have found that the propagation may occur at two rates, the first rate being slower than the second. This has been associated with the steric configuration which the polymer may take up[18,20]. Other workers have not observed this effect[21] — a fact which stresses the difficulties encountered in the study of such systems.

1 A. B. MEGGY, *J. Chem. Soc.*, (1953) 851.
2 M. FRAUKEL, Y. LEWISCHITZ and A. ZILKHA, *Experimenta*, 9 (1953) 161.
3 M. Z. MAGEE and K. HOFMANN, *J. Am. Chem. Soc.*, 71 (1949) 1515.
4 Y. GO, J. NOGUCHI, M. ASAI and T. HYAKAWA, *Chem. High Polymers (Tokyo)*, 13 (1956) 171; *J. Polymer Sci.*, 21 (1956) 147.
5 H. LEUCHS, *Ber.*, 39 (1906) 857.
  H. LEUCHS and W. MANASSE, *Ber.*, 40 (1907) 3235.
6 H. LEUCHS and W. GEIGER, *Ber.*, 41 (1908) 1721.
7 A. L. LEVY, *Nature*, 165 (1950) 152.
  J. L. BAILEY, *J. Chem. Soc.*, (1950) 3261.
  F. FUCHS, *Ber.*, 55 (1922) 2943.
  A. C. FARTHING and R. J. W. REYNOLDS, *Nature*, 165 (1950) 647.
8 A. C. FARTHING, *J. Chem. Soc.*, (1950) 3213.
9 W. E. HANBY, S. G. WALEY and J. WATSON, *J. Chem. Soc.*, (1950) 3009.
10 F. SIGMUND and F. WESSELY, *Z. physiol. Chem.*, 151 (1926) 91.
11 W. E. HANBY, S. G. WALEY and J. WATSON, *Nature*, 161 (1948) 132.
   I. COLEMAN, *J. Chem. Soc.*, (1957) 2294.
12 M. FRANKEL and M. HALMANN, *J. Chem. Soc.*, (1952) 2735.
13 D. BEN-ISHAI and A. BERGER, *J. Org. Chem.*, 17 (1952) 1564.
14 M. SELA and A. BERGER, *J. Am. Chem. Soc.*, 77 (1955) 1893.
15 E. KATCHALSKI and M. SELA, *Advances in Protein Chem.*, 13 (1958) 243.
16 D. G. H. BALLARD and C. H. BAMFORD, *Proc. Roy. Soc. (London)*, 223A (1954) 495.
17 S. G. WALEY and J. WATSON, *Rec. trav. chim.*, 69 (1950) 27.
18 R. D. LUNDBERG and P. DOTY, *J. Am. Chem. Soc.*, 79 (1957) 3961.
19 J. H. FESSLER and A. G. OGSTON, *Trans. Faraday Soc.*, 47 (1951) 667.
20 P. DOTY and R. D. LUNDBERG, *J. Am. Chem. Soc.*, 78 (1956) 4810.
21 D. G. H. BALLARD and C. H. BAMFORD, *J. Am. Chem. Soc.*, 79 (1957) 2336.

CHAPTER 10

WOOL

1. Occurrence

Substantial quantities of textile fibres come from the hairlike covering of animals, wool from the sheep being by far the most important. Other hair fibres, in general, come from goats, camels and llamas as indicated in Table 18.

TABLE 18

SOURCES OF ANIMAL FIBRES (HAIR)

Fibre	Animal	Location
Wool	Sheep	Widely spread
Mohair	Angora goat	Asia Minor, South Africa, U.S.A.
Cashmere wool	Cashmere goat	China
Camel hair	Bactrian camel	Mongolia, China
Alpaca	Llama glama pasas	Peru
Vicuña	Llama vicuña	Peru

Of these, wool only will be discussed.

Very little is known of the ancestry of the original breeds of sheep; in the earlier stages of civilisation, sheep formed a substantial part of wealth and were exchanged by nomads for other commodities. In more recent times, three main types of wool out of many may be distinguished *viz.*, fine wool from Spanish merino, medium from English Down breeds and long wool from Cotswolds, Cheviots and Carpet wool breeds. Outstanding among these breeds are the merino sheep which give a wool noted for its fineness. In the times around 1500–1700, Spanish merino were strictly guarded but in later years were exported. This breed has now been adapted to live in many countries as well as crossbred with the sheep which give the coarser types of wool; the wool from crossbred sheep has some of the characteristics of both. Wool quality such as fineness, length, colour, lustre, crimp etc. is determined in a large measure by the breed, the number of which is large. The breeds may be classified broadly according to the kind of wool they yield as fine, medium, long, crossbred and carpet[1]. Commercially, wool is primarily graded according to its fineness which is designated by the count of the finest yarn that can be spun (count for worsted yarn is the number of hanks of 560 yards which can be obtained from a pound of material). Raw wool from the sheep contains wax, perspiration (suint), dirt and burrs, and, hence prior to use, wool must be scoured and bleached, a subject which is discussed in Volume II. Wool fibres differ in length as well as in mechanical properties and crimp. Some indication of wool characteristics is given in Table 19 which shows the great variability in length and breadth which is possible.

TABLE 19

Type	Breed	Average length (in.)	Average diameter (μ)	Count ('s)
Fine	Merino	1.5– 4	10–30	58–90
Medium	Cheviot Suffolk etc.	2 – 4	20–40	46–60
Long	Cotswold Leicester	5 –14	25–50	36–50
Crossbred	Corriedale	3 – 6	20–40	50–60

The skin of the higher animals is made up of two layers — an inner dermis and an outer epidermis. Animal fibres grow from small pits known as follicles in the epidermis (Fig. 58a). The first stage in the formation of the follicle is a growth down from the epidermis into the dermis and, before long, outgrowths of the sebaceous and sweat glands develop. The lower end

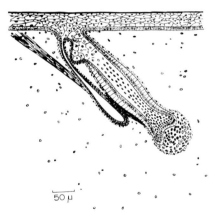

50 μ

Fig. 58a. Diagram showing an early stage in the development of a single fibre. (Courtesy W.I.R.A.)

of the follicle becomes shaped like a bulb but the base is turned in to form a dome called the papilla. After a time, the fibre begins to form by multiplication of the epidermal cells around the papilla. A sheath — the inner — forms round the fibre and the fibre and the sheath grow up through the follicle; the young fibre originally cone shaped is pushed upwards by the pressure of the dividing cells of the root. The cells of the original follicle which grew down now form the outer sheath (Fig. 58b).

The growing fibre is fed by blood vessels both in the papilla and the lower third of the fibre. At the lower levels of the follicle, the fibre is soft

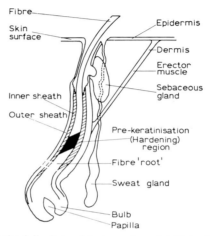

Fig. 58b. Diagram of the fully formed (primary) wool follicle. (Courtesy W.I.R.A.)

but the inner sheath hardens so as to form a rigid tube which helps to mould the plastic fibre. The fibre hardens or keratinises about one third of the way up the follicle, a process which occurs at a lower level on one side of the fibre than on the other; this uneven keratinisation is one of the factors which go to account for the crimp and the bilateral structure of wool fibres[2].

The complete fibre has a root found in the follicle and a main shaft which, in an animal not previously shorn, tapers to the tip. Further, before the fibre reaches the surface of the epidermis it is coated with a greasy secretion from the sebaceous gland and a watery secretion from the sweat gland. Shorn fibres naturally do not possess the root system, but those which are pulled from the hide after treatment with lime (fellmongering) will have a degraded one.

2. Histology

(a) Cuticle

The picture of a wool fibre under the microscope is characteristic (Fig. 59); the fibre is covered with flat scale-like cells of irregular shape known as the cuticle. The scale pattern is best revealed by a replica prepared by impressing the fibre on to a film of a transparent thermoplastic medium. The cuticle cells overlap one another like the tiles on a roof (Fig. 60) both around the fibre as well as longitudinally[3]. Many wool fibres have a

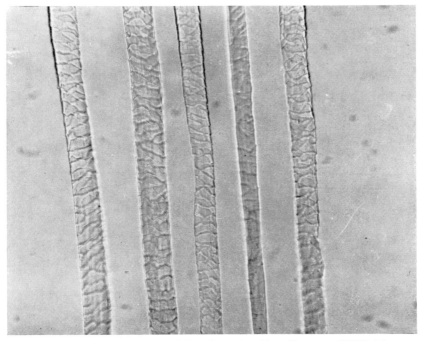

Fig. 59. Micrograph of wool fibre from 64 s Top. (Courtesy W.I.R.A.)

cuticle only one scale thick with only a small degree of overlap whereas many animal fibres, alpaca, hog bristles etc. have cuticles many scales thick and a high degree of overlap. The cuticle cells make up the outer layer of the fibre; their width is around $36\,\mu$, their thickness $0.5-1\,\mu$ and their visible length about $16\,\mu$. The size and density of the scales vary along the fibre and from fibre to fibre. They can be removed by ultra-sonics, scraping over a glass edge, grinding the fibre whilst frozen in liquid air or, in a degraded state, by enzymatic treatment[4,5,24]. The scales would seem to be distinct cells and their purpose may be to help to hold the fibre in the follicle.

(b) Cortex

Cross sections of the fibre may be circular but more often they are elliptical. The main bulk (*ca.* 90%) of the fibre inside the cuticle is the cortex and consists of spindle shaped cells approximately 80–100 μ long and 2.5 μ and 1.2–2.6 μ for the major and minor diameters respectively. The cortex may be divided into its cells by treatment with enzymes (*e.g.* trypsin) or by degradation with acid (sulphuric, formic etc.)[7]. The

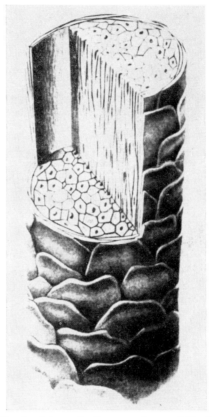

Fig. 60. Schematic diagram of a wool fibre[6].

corticle cells are composed of fibrils which may be exposed when the fibre is broken down by mechanical means (Fig. 61). These fibrils can be further separated into sub-fibrils which can be seen under the electron microscope. A model section of a wool fibre is given in Fig. 60.

It is, in general, considered that the morphological components which make up the fibre are held together by a cement which may bind the microfibrils as well as the fibrils[100,101].

(c) Medulla

In some of the medium or coarser wools and in particular the so-called kemp wool which forms an undercoat for the sheep, there is a central core

Fig. 61. Spindle-shaped corticle cells showing subfibrils (250 ×)[6].

(medulla). The medulla arises from the growing root and is made up of many superimposed cells of various shapes, often polygonal. Channels pass through the medulla which is normally filled with air. In some cases, the medulla cells break down completely giving a hollow tube in the centre of the fibre. Many variations occur in the shape and size of this part of the fibre.

(d) Epicuticle

The presence of other structural features has been detected. Treatment of wool by chlorine or bromine water produces sacs (Fig. 62)[9]. These sacs contain liquid and are presumably formed by expansion under osmotic forces of a thin membrane situated on the surface of the scales. They can be burst by a needle. The membrane called the epicuticle[10] appears to be semi-permeable and has been detected by the electron microscope in the residue left after digestion of wool with sodium sulphide (Fig. 63). It is likely to be made of material which is chemically inert to this reagent and

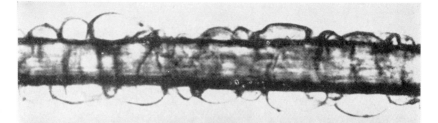

Fig. 62. Wool fibre showing Allwörden sacs after treatment with chlorine[6].

Fig. 63. Electron micrograph of the epicuticle from wool (7000 ×). Obtained as a residue when treating the fibres for several months with dilute Na$_2$S at room temperature[6].

which may well be a polysaccharide, since hydrolysis of wool extract containing 30% of epicuticle yields sugars as well as the amino acids[11] expected from the wool portion. The epicuticle reduces the rate of penetration of dyes [12] and acid[13] into the fibre. More detailed examination reveals that the membrane surrounding the sacs may vary in thickness according to the fibre and the reagent used[14]; it seems that the wall of the sac may be epicuticle together with some of the cuticle itself.

3. Bilateral Structure

The cell boundaries in the cortex can be made visible by treatment with trypsin and a transverse cross section reveals them to be many sided

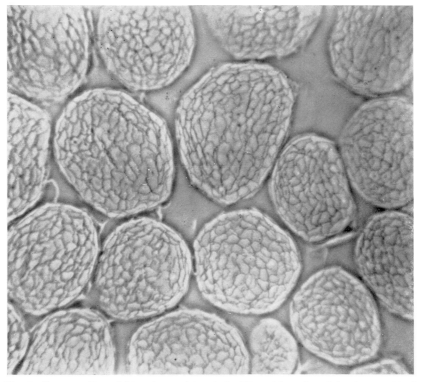

Fig. 64. Cross section of Lincoln wool treated with *o*-chlorophenol to show cortical cells. (Courtesy W.I.R.A.)

(Fig. 64). Staining techniques with basic dyes (*e.g.* Janus Green) have shown that in fine merino wool one half of the cortex absorbs dye more intensely than the other; this half lies on the convex side of the curve of the crimp. Thus there is a difference in structure across the fibre which

References p. 298

is usually referred to as bilateral. The side with the greater reactivity is called the ortho and that with the lesser the para cortex[15,16]. The bilateral structure of wool will also show up after chemical pre-treatment under the microscope using polarised light. After treatment of wool with a reagent such as urea/sodium bisulphite at 65°C for 2–4 min, the bilateral structure appears due to the decreasing birefringence of the ortho cortex. After 4–8 min the birefringence of the ortho cortex disappears and after 16–24 min the birefringence of the para disappears and the fibre becomes isotropic[44].

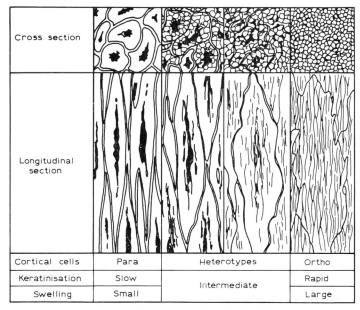

Cross section				
Longitudinal section				
Cortical cells	Para	Heterotypes		Ortho
Keratinisation	Slow	Intermediate		Rapid
Swelling	Small			Large

Fig. 65. Comparison of cortical cells.
(Courtesy l'Institut Textile de France)

The bilateral structure is associated with the asymmetrical keratinisation which occurs in the follicle, the para side being the one which keratinises first[17]. Evidence for this has been found by injecting a lamb with the amino acid cystine containing radioactive sulphur, when the presence of radioactivity appeared at a higher level in the ortho than on the para side[18]. A bilateral structure exists in the unkeratinised fibre down in the follicle since the fibre roots show differential swelling[19] and differential reactions for thiol groups between the two sides[20].

The ortho side of the fibre is more readily attacked by enzymes[16] and this gives a method of obtaining extracts of the two sides for analysis.

Other methods of effecting a separation between the cells of the ortho and para cortices have been devised. For example, wool may be treated with hydrochloric acid and macerated with water. The resulting material may be suspended and filtered through a wire gauze and macerated again; the residue retained by a sintered glass filter is made up of ortho corticular cells containing less than 6% of the para[21]. Electron microscopists have further shown a difference in appearance between the cells in the two parts[22].

As far as wool is concerned, the bilateral structure is well defined in the fine crimped fibres but some of the coarser wools (*e.g.* Masham wool) show an irregular distribution throughout the cortex.

Longitudinal and transverse sections are given diagrammatically in Fig. 65. The ortho and para structures might be regarded as extremes;

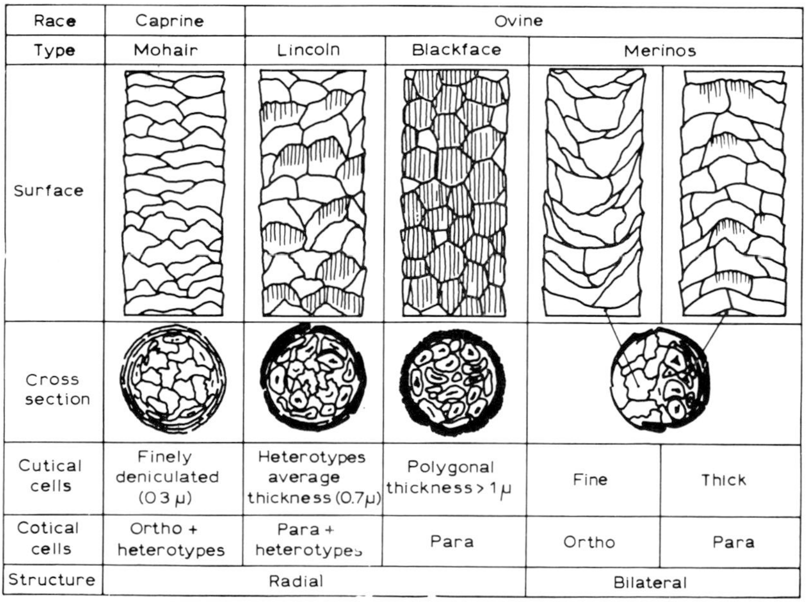

Race	Caprine	Ovine			
Type	Mohair	Lincoln	Blackface	Merinos	
Surface					
Cross section					
Cutical cells	Finely deniculated (0 3 μ)	Heterotypes average thickness (0.7μ)	Polygonal thickness > 1 μ	Fine	Thick
Cotical cells	Ortho + heterotypes	Para + heterotypes	Para	Ortho	Para
Structure	Radial			Bilateral	

Fig. 66. Comparison of scale structure of different fibres.
(Courtesy l'Institut Textile de France)

the other cell structures known as heterotypes appear to be intermediate in character. When a wide range of animal fibres are examined, it is observed that the quantities and arrangements of the different kind of cell vary considerably. Thus, mohair will have an axial distribution of ortho and para cells with the ortho ones in the centre[2] whereas human hair has only ortho cells[24].

References p. 298

An analogous differentiation exists with regard to the cuticle cells; the shape of these varies with the source of the fibre. This is shown schematically in Fig. 66. An attempt has been made to divide the cells into two extreme patterns — polygonal and denticulate with intermediate types (heterotypes) lying between these extremes. In the figure too, is some indication that the shape of the scale structure is related to the structure of the corticle cells; cuticle cells of the polygonal type are associated with corticle cells of the para type, whereas the denticulated ones go with a fibre with ortho character. When the fibre has a bilateral structure, the cortical cells on the ortho side are denticulate and thin; those on the para side are polygonal and thick[23].

4. Chemical Constitution

Elementary analysis shows that scoured wool contains C, H, N, S and by inference O; it is closely allied chemically to hair, horn, feathers etc. Hydrolysis of wool with acid or alkali yields a mixture of α-amino acids of general formula $NH_2CHRCOOH$. In all, eighteen different acids have been identified; the proportions of the various acids have been tabulated[6, 25, 26] but the agreement between results is not very good. In Table 20 are given the analytic values of Simmonds[109] and Corfield and Robson[110]. Differences in the quantities of amino acids occur to some extent from worker to worker, partly because of the improvements which have occurred in techniques of analysis, but possibly due to the fact that wool prior to analysis must be purified. Purification is often carried out by treatment with ether, water and alcohol to remove the non-protein material. Degradation to small extents may occur because of this, but also from the fact that different wools will have been subject to different weathering conditions.

The simplest picture of the wool fibre is one of a polypeptide composed of α-amino acid residues. Attached to the α-carbon atom are two hydrogen atoms or one hydrogen and a side group R. These side groups vary markedly in size and chemical nature; some may be hydrophobic, some hydrophilic, some acidic and some basic. In the special case of cystine, the groups R form a cross link joining two chains.

The side chains carried by the polypeptide backbone of wool vary in size and may be grouped according to their chemical nature:

(1) Hydrocarbon (acids 2, 3, 4, 5, 6 in Table 20). These are non-polar and may to some extent be responsible for the difficulties encountered in the wetting out of wool.

(2) Hydroxyl containing (acids 8, 9, 10 in Table 20)

(3) Acidic (acids 17, 18 in Table 20)

(4) Sulphur containing (acids 11, 12 in Table 20). Methionine (11) is

present in small amounts and plays a small part. Cystine (12), on the other hand, is distinctive in that it can be pictured as two amino acids joined via a disulphide linkage. The two halves of the molecule can therefore be

TABLE 20

No.	Amino acid	Structure of side chain (R)	N, % of total N (109)	(110)
1	Glycine	$H-$	5.37-6.21	6.29
2	Alanine*	CH_3-	4.07	4.12
3	Phenylalanine	$C_6H_5 \cdot CH_2-$	1.54-1.75	2.12
4	Valine*	$(CH_3)_2 : CH-$	3.77	4.16
5	Leucine*	$(CH_3)_2 : CH \cdot CH_2-$	4.95	5.85
6	Isoleucine*	$CH_3 \cdot CH_2 \cdot (CH_3)CH-$	2.06	2.44
7	Proline*	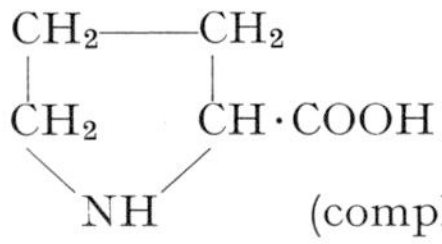 CH_2——CH_2 $\quad$ $CH_2 \quad CH \cdot COOH$ $\quad$ NH $\quad$ (complete formula)	4.80	5.05
8	Serine*	$HO \cdot CH_2-$	7.37	8.66
9	Threonine	$CH_3 \cdot CH(OH)-$	4.28-4.72	5.12
10	Tyrosine	$HO \cdot C_6H_4 \cdot CH_2-$	2.37-2.80	2.62
11	Methionine*	$CH_3 \cdot S \cdot CH_2 \cdot CH_2-$	0.34	0.32
12	Cystine	$-CH_2 \cdot S \cdot S \cdot CH_2-$	8.35-9.35	7.30
13	Arginine*	$NH_2 \cdot C(:NH) \cdot NH \cdot (CH_2)_3-$	17.82	19.10
14	Lysine*	$NH_2 \cdot (CH_2)_4-$	3.37	3.92
15	Tryptophan*	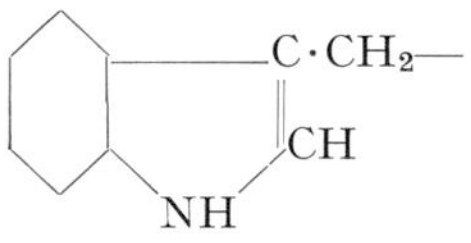 (ring structure) $C \cdot CH_2-$ CH NH	1.92	0.82
16	Histidine*	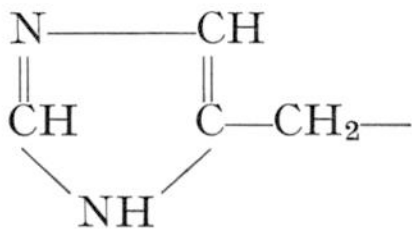 N——CH $CH \quad C-CH_2-$ NH	1.35	1.91
17	Aspartic acid	$HOOC \cdot CH_2-$	4.08-4.60	4.38
18	Glutamic acid* Amide N*	$HOOC \cdot (CH_2)_2-$	8.83 6.95	8.48 6.73

* No variation between samples (109)

References p. 298

members of two chains with the disulphide linkage forming a bridge across (I).

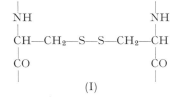

(I)

The presence of these cross links allows a three dimensional structure to be formed, thereby conferring insolubility in common solvents capable of breaking hydrogen bonds.

(5) Proline (acid 7 in Table 20) does not have the normal side chain R which projects from the main backbone. In this acid, the nitrogen and α-carbon atoms form part of a saturated 5-membered ring system; the disposition of the imino and carboxyl groups is such that, when this acid is joined in the polypeptide chain, the linkages are oriented at right angles. This is best shown by means of a model but an attempt to demonstrate this effect is shown in formula (II) where the plane of the ring

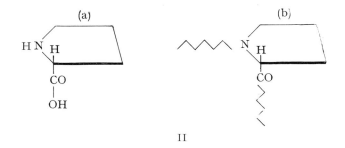

II

is considered to be at right angles to the plane of the paper. This acid therefore must have a considerable influence on the shape of the polypeptide chain.

(6) Ammonia. The ammonia produced in the hydrolysis of wool is presumed to arise from amide groups ($-CONH_2$) and gives a measure of the number of these groups originally present. These amide groups are associated with the dicarboxylic acids; it seems that the aspartic acid is present largely in the form of its amide (asparagine) but only a part of the glutamic acid content.

5. Chemical Composition of the Different Parts of Wool

The chemical constitution of wool has been dealt with as though this fibre were homogeneous material; the morphological structure indicates that this is not so, and hence the composition discussed above must be regarded as belonging to the cortex since this forms the bulk of the wool fibre.

Attempts have been made to analyse the composition of the scales produced by enzymic degradation of fibre which has been treated with thioglycollic acid[27]. These results indicate a marked difference in chemical make up (Table 21).

TABLE 21

COMPOSITION OF UNTREATED WOOL AND OF WOOL SCALES[27]

| Constituent | Untreated wool | Wool scales | |
		Found	Corrected value
Sulphur	3.50	4.83	5.42
Cystine	12.20	18.10	20.30
Nitrogen	16.69	13.53	15.17
Arginine	8.60	4.30	4.80
Tyrosine	6.10	3.00	3.30
Serine	9.50	9.90	11.20
Others (ash, lipid etc.)	0.20	9.80	—

On the other hand, only slight differences were observed between the two portions when the scales were detached by treatment with sulphuric acid[29]. In another investigation, the scales were removed mechanically and the sulphur content of the normal and descaled wool found to be identical[28]. However, although the position may not be regarded as satisfactory it must be borne in mind that the scales make up only 2–3% of the fibre and are normally removed from the cortex after attack of some reagent (enzyme or sulphuric acid) liable to cause a certain amount of degradation.

The epicuticle constitutes *ca.* 0.1% of the fibre but is very resistant to chemical attack. It may not even be composed of protein. The composition of the medulla is also obscure. Indications are that medulla cells behave differently from cortical *e.g.* they are digested by the enzyme pancreatin[30] and take up basic dyes more readily suggesting a larger content of the dicarboxylic acids but no complete analysis has as yet been achieved[31].

6. Chemical Properties of the Ortho and Para Cortices

Because of the bilateral structure of wool, interest has naturally arisen in the question as to whether chemical composition is different in the two parts of the cortex. Attempts have been made to determine the amino acid content of the two fractions, ortho and para[32,33,34]. The agreement between the results of different workers is not satisfactory. Difficulties arise in this work because treatments effecting the separation of the ortho from the para cells use processes causing degradation *e.g.* hydrolysis with acid. During such treatments, some destruction of the amino acids may occur, some protein fractions in the wool may be extracted or the peptide bonds of certain amino acids may be preferentially hydrolysed. Destruction of the acids themselves is only likely to be important with tryptophan but, since the quantities of this acid are small, this is not an important difficulty. Extraction of low molecular weight proteins is more serious; these in particular may be found in the intercellular cement[35] and undoubtedly modify the subsequent analyses. An additional difficulty lies in the fact that the speed of hydrolysis of the peptide bonds to different amino acids varies considerably as has been shown by studies of the hydrolysis of egg albumin[36]. A detailed analysis of the amino acid composition combined with a study of the factors discussed above has led Leveau[37] to the conclusion that there is no difference in chemical composition of these two parts of the wool fibre. This has received some confirmation from the analysis of wool from lambs which had been injected with radioactive sulphur, when the radioactivity of the fibre was found to be the same in the two halves[17,38]. The differences between the two parts of the cortex are briefly:

(1) Difference in dye uptake. Ortho is more intensely stained. This is not due to a differential rate of entry of the dye[39].

(2) Ortho swells more easily and presumably is more readily accessible to reagents such as dye or enzymes[32,40].

(3) Differences in loss in weight on treatment with various reagents. Wool because of the cross linkages, is insoluble in reagents which are not capable of breaking disulphide bonds. However, any damage arising from chemical treatments for example may break some of these links as well as peptide bonds; this will modify the ability of wool to dissolve so that loss in weight of wool on treatment with different reagents may be used as a parameter of degradation of the fibre[41,42]. If a difference exists in the number of cross linkages in the two fractions of the cortex, a difference between the solubilities might be observed. Wool was treated with boiling water, with 4 N hydrochloric acid at 65°C for one hour and then with $N/10$ sodium hydroxide at 65°C for one hour, when the loss in weight was found to be greater for the ortho than the para part of the wool.

Again, a solvent such as formamide which is capable of breaking hydrogen bonds dissolves considerably more of the ortho cortex than the para. Such a result suggests that some of the chains may be dissolved without the breaking of disulphide cross links. This position is possible if some of the cystine is used not to form cross linkages but is incorporated in the polypeptide chain in the manner indicated in formulae (I) or (XVI)[43,52]. Such intrachain linkages have been detected in insulin, a protein whose structure has been worked out; a high proportion of intrachain linkages would result in a structure which is more readily penetrated than a highly cross-linked one. If the ortho cortex has a substantial quantity of cystine incorporated in an intrachain fashion, it will swell more readily and be more receptive to dye than the more highly cross-linked structure suggested for the para cortex.

7. Arrangement of Amino Acids

The arrangement of the amino acids in the wool chain remains unsolved. It is possible, however, to determine the terminal amino groups by reaction with fluorodinitrobenzene followed by hydrolysis and identification of the amino acids containing this group. This technique has yielded seven acids which are responsible for N-terminal amino groups in wool (Table 22).

TABLE 22

TERMINAL AMINO ACID RESIDUES IN WOOL[45,46]

Terminal amino acid	Number of moles in 10^6 g of protein
Aspartic	0.63
Glutamic	1.25
Serine	1.25
Threonine	4.80
Glycine	5.20
Alanine	1.25
Valine	2.40

These values may not be the final word on the matter, since it is possible that some of the terminal groups may not be accessible for steric reasons[46,47] or may have formed ring compounds with neighbouring carboxyl groups.

Techniques for obtaining evidence of the order in which the amino acid residues occur in a protein are based on partial hydrolysis[48]. The protein is partially hydrolysed and fragments identified. With wool, the possible combination of the eighteen amino acids in the chain is legion but some facts have emerged.

(1) A large proportion of the glutamic acid is joined to other glutamic acid residues (shown by a large quantity of the dipeptide, glutamyl glutamate, in the hydrolysate of wool)[49].

(2) Polar residues are frequently joined to others.

(3) Non-polar groups occur together.

(4) Basic amino acids are not linked together.

(5) The acidic acids often occur with the non polar acids.

However DNP-cystine is not stable to hydrolysis and is therefore difficult to detect in the hydrolysate; more recently oxidation of the DNP-cystine residues gives DNP-cysteic acid residues, a product which is stable to hydrolysis. Detection of cystine by this method indicates that this acid supplies a substantial number of N-terminal residues[143]. Furthermore there appear to be at least seven polypeptides in wool. Real progress is not possible until these can be separated.

8. Size of Molecule

If the cystine molecule joins the polypeptide chains together via the disulphide cross linkages, the protein forms a three dimensional network and hence its molecular weight is rather indefinite. However, if attention is confined to the chains themselves, a molecular weight for these may be considered. The number of terminal amino ends as assessed from analysis of the N-terminal acids is 1.68 mol per 10^5 g of wool.

The assumption that there is one amino group per chain enables an average molecular weight of 59×10^3 for the primary chains to be estimated. This value may not be correct because not each chain may necessarily have a terminal amino group and not all the end amino groups are accessible or some amino acids fail to react. Estimation of carboxyl end groups may be possible[50]. In this, the carboxyl groups are reduced to the alcohol. Such a technique has as yet been applied to the protein insulin. A better method for detection of C-terminal residues is to react the protein with anhydrous hydrazine when those acids combined in peptide linkages are converted to the hydrazides. The free carboxyl groups do not react and hence C-terminal groups are liberated as amino acids and may be separated from the hydrazides.

To obtain more information of the detailed composition and arrangement of the amino acids in wool, it should be possible to break the fibre into polypeptides which are soluble and analyse these. About 40% of wool substance may be extracted by treatment with formamide[142] at 120°C and isolated by subsequent precipitation with water. The product, called formamide keratose, gives an analysis similar to the undissolved material. Other methods of obtaining peptides from wool involve rupture of the disulphide linkage either by reduction with sodium thioglycollate or oxidation with peracids. The products obtained by these methods have been shown to be complex; for details the reader is referred to other works[6].

9. Chemical Reactions of Wool

(a) Reaction with Acids

The acid most commonly used for the hydrolysis of wool is hydrochloric acid. With concentrated acid, the amide groups ($CONH_2$) are first to be attacked followed by the peptide groups in the chain[62].

It is not feasible to stop the hydrolysis reaction at a stage which would correspond to the formation of peptides of a given size; even when mild conditions are used, some free amino acids and lower peptides are formed. The ability of the different peptide groups to hydrolyse varies considerably and aspartic and glutamic acids as well as serine may be extracted by partial hydrolysis whilst most of the protein remains in the polypeptide form[36,51]. Degradation of wool by hydrolysis of peptide groups is shown by loss of tensile strength and may occur to some extent in processes involving the use of acids[52,53]. The sensitivity of wool to acid hydrolysis is increased if the cystine is transformed by oxidation to cysteic acid (XXII), the peptide bond adjacent to a cysteic acid group being very sensitive[54]. Treatment of wool with sulphuric acid (80%) gives a fibre containing increased amounts of sulphur[55]. The mode of reaction is a little obscure, but the number of amino groups is reduced[56] and it is therefore possible that a sulphamic acid (III) may be formed by lysine

$$RNH_2 + H_2SO_4 \rightarrow RNHSO_3H + H_2O$$
$$(III)$$

On the other hand, tyrosine[57] can be sulphonated and sulphonation of the serine[58] and threonine (IV) may occur

$$RCH_2OH + H_2SO_4 \rightarrow RCH_2OSO_3H + H_2O$$
$$(IV)$$

Hydrolysis of the peptide linkages produces free carboxyl and amino groups, a fact which is reflected in the increased capacity of the wool to combine with acids. The extent of hydrolysis is increased in the presence of anions which are attracted to the fibre (anions of high affinity)[59]. It has been suggested that the adsorption of anions will be accompanied by a corresponding adsorption of hydrogen ions and hence the hydrogen ion concentration in the fibre is increased.

(b) Reaction with Alkali

Alkalis will also hydrolyse wool but less selectively than with acids; in fact, a 5% solution of caustic soda will completely dissolve wool at the boil. In acid hydrolysis, only the amino acid tryptophan is destroyed. With alkali, cystine is readily attacked and possibly arginine, histidine and serine[60]. The products of hydrolysis are usually smaller peptides but complete hydrolysis with alkali has not received a great deal of attention[61]. The extent of reaction of wool with alkali depends on the conditions (temperature, concentration etc.). From the practical point of view, solubility of wool in alkali has been used as a parameter for assessing damage which may have occurred during wet processing. Treatment for one hour with 0.1 N caustic soda at 65°C has been standardised as suitable[41]. The alkali solubility increases when wool has been degraded by hydrolysis of peptide bonds or rupture of the disulphide bonds. The manner in which the solubility changes with loss of cystine is shown in Fig. 67. The true chemical basis of this test is at present uncertain so that deductions based on it must be treated with reserve.

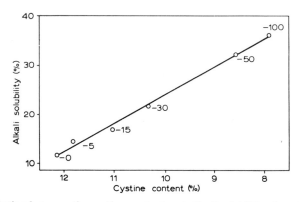

Fig. 67. Relation between the cystine content and alkali solubility of wool exposed to irradiation with ultraviolet light. Figures on the curves represent the duration of exposure (hours)[41].

Wool may be treated with enzymes (pancreatin, trypsin) when it is split into its morphological elements *i.e.* cortical cells and scales[63]. With pepsin, the fibre is more resistant but partial reduction of the disulphide bonds assists[64]. The ability of the enzyme to attack and eventually digest wool does not seem to be determined by the cystine groups[65] but by treatments which change the structure to a disoriented β-configuration (Chapter 14).

Reaction of wool with dilute caustic soda attacks 50% of the cystine[69,70] but only a little of the remaining 50% reacts even after prolonged treatments[71]. In this reaction, sodium sulphide is first produced which is capable of reducing the disulphide linkage. It has been suggested that[70] alkali disrupts the bonds and that new cross linkages are formed.

Alkali treated wool contains residues of lanthionine (V)[72,73], an amino acid similar to cystine with a sulphur atom joined to two carbon atoms

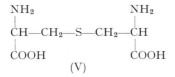

$$\text{(V)}$$

The mechanism of lanthionine formation is not known, but it has been suggested[69,70] that α-aminoacrylic acid (VI) is first formed from decomposition of sulphenic acid produced by hydrolysis of the disulphide linkage $-S-S-+H_2O\rightarrow-S\cdot OH+HS-$

$$
\begin{array}{ccc}
| & | & | \\
NH & NH & NH \\
| & | & | \\
CH-CH_2SOH \rightarrow & C=CH_2 + H_2O + S + & HSCH_2-CH \rightarrow \\
| & | & | \\
CO & CO & CO \\
| & | & | \\
 & (VI) &
\end{array}
$$

$$
\begin{array}{cc}
| & | \\
NH & NH \\
| & | \\
\rightarrow CHCH_2-S-CH_2-CH \\
| & | \\
CO & CO \\
| & |
\end{array}
$$

which then reacts further with the thiol group. Unfortunately, no intermediate thiol groups have been detected to support this hypothesis[70] but pyruvic acid arising from the α-aminoacrylic acid has been detected in hydrolysates. The formation of aminoacrylic acid is supported by the detection of this acid in cystine containing peptides after they has been treated with alkali[74]. Nevertheless, attempts to form lanthionine from the free acid cystine have failed.

Other workers have suggested[75] there is an intermediate aldehyde group formed in lanthionine formation. The loss in weight of wool on heating in 50% urea-sodium bisulphite solution[76] at pH 7 for 60 min at 65°C has been put forward as a test for detection of the pretreatment of wool by alkalis. The lanthionine bridges are claimed to be more stable than disulphide linkages thereby accounting for lower reactivity to reducing agents and lessened solubility in the above reagent[77]. Some doubt on this conclusion has been suggested. Experiments on the stability of lanthionine[78] indicate that this acid is nearly as unstable as the disulphide linkage. An alternative suggestion has been made to account for the decreased solubility; namely the possibility of an interchange between the intra- and inter-chain disulphide bonds. This exchange can be brought about through the help of the negative ion S⁻ which arises from the presence fo a small amount of cysteine[79]. The reaction is represented diagrammatically below

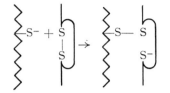

This reaction would effectively increase the number of cross linkages and hence decrease the solubility.

(c) Treatment with Water

On treatment of wool with water, some water soluble proteins are formed. These are known as wool gelatin[66].

The sulphur content of wool can be markedly reduced by treatment with boiling water over prolonged periods[67]. It has been suggested that the disulphide linkage is hydrolysed to give a thiol group (VIII) as well as a sulphenic acid (V) which can break down to give an aldehyde (VII) and liberate hydrogen sulphide.

$$
\left[\begin{array}{c} | \\ NH \\ | \\ CHCH_2S- \\ | \\ CO \\ | \end{array} \right]_2 \rightarrow \begin{array}{c} | \\ NH \\ | \\ CHCH_2SOH \\ | \\ CO \\ | \end{array} + \begin{array}{c} | \\ HSCH_2CH \\ | \\ CO \\ | \\ (VIII) \end{array} \rightarrow \begin{array}{c} | \\ NH \\ | \\ CHCHO \\ | \\ CO \\ | \\ (VII) \end{array} + H_2S + \begin{array}{c} | \\ NH \\ | \\ HSCH_2CH \\ | \\ CO \\ | \end{array}
$$

Some evidence for the presence of thiol[68] and aldehyde[67] groups has been obtained by the increased reaction with sodium hydroxide[144] at pH 9.5 and p-bromophenylhydrazine[145] respectively but it has so far not been found possible to demonstrate the initial step of hydrolysis to give the sulphenic acid.

(d) Properties Resulting from Acid and Basic Groups

(i) The amphoteric character of wool

Wool protein, since it contains a high proportion of acidic and basic side chains in addition to end groups is amphoteric in nature and will therefore adsorb both acids and alkalis. The numbers of free amino and carboxyl groups in wool are approximately equal[80] (82–90 residues/10^5 g).

Studies of the behaviour of wool towards acid and alkali indicate that the groups behave as though they were in an ionised state. Wool, therefore, adsorbs acids through back titration of the carboxyl groups; for alkali adsorption a proton is removed from the charged amine group. This process is discussed in more detail in connection with dyeing. The juxtaposition of the carboxyl and amino groups is commonly regarded as forming an extra cross linkage between two chains. The force between these groups is electrostatic in character and will naturally depend on the distance between the groups; if the force is to be sufficiently large to be regarded as a bond the groups will be very closely positioned. However, it seems possible that the groups may be distributed randomly down the chain and in this case such "salt" linkages may not exist. The salt link has been regarded as a hydrogen bond between two ionisable groups and it will be broken by the addition of acid or alkali. When treated with acid, the fibre becomes weaker as shown by the changes in the amount of work required to stretch the fibre 30% (a figure chosen because if the extension does not exceed this value the load/extension curve is reproducible) (Fig. 68). It was the good relation

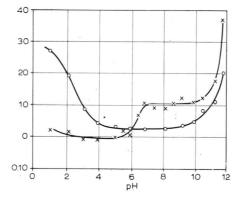

Fig. 68. The effect of pH on the reduction in work to stretch a fibre by 30% for normal O and deaminated hair × [146].

between acid uptake and changes in mechanical properties which gave the basis for the idea of the amino and carboxyl groups being sufficiently close together to form a "link"[80],[81]. If the amino groups be almost re-. moved by deamination, the salt linkages are destroyed (curve × in Fig.68). Additions of acid do not change the tensile properties but reductions in strength at the higher pH values occur. It has been suggested that, in this pH region, titration of carboxyl groups occurs. The reduction in strength can no longer be attributed to the breakdown of salt linkages but is due to the increased number of carboxyl groups giving an increase in osmotic pressure and hence swelling of the fibre. This latter evidence based on deaminated material is not however conclusive in view of the degradation which takes place on the deamination reaction.

References p. 298

Other workers[82] have suggested that the salt linkages do not exist, and the fact that swelling of the fibre occurs is sufficient reason for reduction in the tensile strength. It was shown that a plot of loss in tensile strength against swelling showed a close relation[83] (Fig. 69). However the relation-

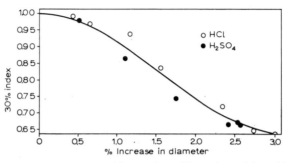

Fig. 69. Relation between extensibility and swelling of wool in acid solutions of different concentrations[144].

ships between the bonds in a fibre, its swelling behaviour and its mechanical properties are very complex. The position as to whether salt linkages exist has not been unequivocably resolved and it is possible that the explanation of the mechanical properties would combine both salt linkages and swelling.

(ii) *Amino groups*

The amino groups will undergo the normal reactions. They can be acetylated for example or treated with nitrous acid

$$-CH_2NH_2 + (CH_3CO)_2O \rightarrow -CH_2NHCOCH_3$$
$$-CH_2NH_2 + HNO_2 \rightarrow -CH_2OH + N_2$$

The latter reaction has been used frequently by workers for preparing deaminated wool. The reagent used in this field is made up to the recipe of Van Slyke[84] who showed that the nitrous acid reacted rapidly with terminal amino groups and those of lysine but the arginine reacted very slowly[85]. Treatment of wool with nitrous acid has however been shown to remove most of the basic groups only after a prolonged treatment (*ca.* 6 days)[86]. Treatments for times as long as this are liable to cause degradation *e.g.* oxidation of cystine and, as a method for amino group removal, it can not be regarded as particularly satisfactory. Nevertheless, the method is still widely used as an analytical procedure for determining the free amino content of proteins, including wool. One mol. of N_2 liberated is equivalent to one amino group. In acetylation, care must be taken to avoid the introduction of sulphonic acid groups arising from the use of sulphuric acid as a catalyst[87] in a normal acetylating mixture. Acetic anhydride alone reacts with the terminal amino groups as well as with lysine and arginine[88]. To obtain acetylation to the extent of 90%, the experiments must be carried out under very carefully controlled conditions using acetic anhydride with sulphuric acid as catalyst[89].

Fluorodinitrobenzene[90] may react with amino groups to give the corresponding dinitrophenyl derivatives

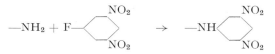

These derivatives of the amino acids are not decomposed in subsequent hydrolysis of the protein with the exception of that of cystine and hence may be recovered and identified.

Other important reactants for amino groups are phenylisothiocyanate (IX)[91] and p-iodophenylsulphonyl chloride[92] (pipsylchloride). The latter gives pipsylamino acid derivative in the usual way. With the former it is possible to split off the N-terminal acid as a phenylthiohydantoin (X) leaving the rest of the chain intact

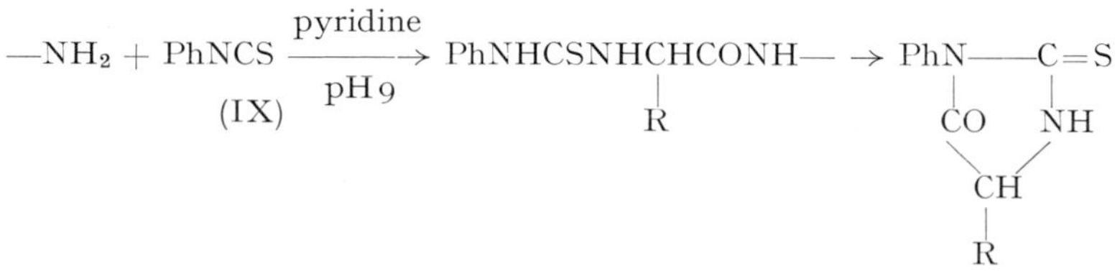

$$-NH_2 + PhNCS \xrightarrow[\text{pH 9}]{\text{pyridine}} PhNHCSNHCHCONH- \rightarrow$$

(IX)

$$\begin{array}{c} | \\ R \end{array}$$

$$PhN\underbrace{\begin{array}{cc} | & | \\ CO & NH \\ \diagdown & \diagup \\ CH \\ | \\ R \end{array}}C=S$$

(X)

The arginine side chains are naturally different in character from the simpler amino groups of lysine. The guanidine residue acting as the basic side chain in arginine reacts, as mentioned above, slowly with nitrous acid and will combine with glyoxal bis-sodium bisulphite (XI) to give a ring compound (XII)

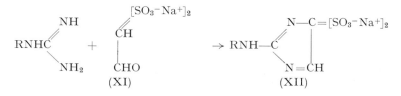

(iii) Carboxyl groups

Apart from terminal groups, the carboxyl groups in wool are provided by the side chains of aspartic and glutamic acids, although it has been suggested that the aspartic acid is mainly in the form of the amide[93].

Esterification of carboxyl groups may be carried out by the usual reagents as well as many others e.g. alkyl halides, dimethyl sulphate etc.[94]. Diazomethane will esterify not only the carboxyl groups but will react with the phenolic hydroxy groups of tyrosine[61]. The reaction with dimethyl sulphate, methyl iodide and methyl bromide introduces methyl groups into wool but the carboxyl content is not reduced to the expected degree[94]. Treatment of wool even for 30 hours with dimethyl sulphate only esterifies 25% of the carboxyl groups[6]. Unfortunately, the range of pH used in esterification of wool with this kind of reagent (3–7) is not suitable for esterification of the carboxyl groups of organic acids. Conditions are to some extent restricted by the necessity to avoid degradation of the wool and those used are more likely to cause methylation of the amino groups or even the hydrogen atoms in the peptide chain[94]. A better reagent for esterification is anhydrous methanol containing a small amount of mineral acid as catalyst[95]; esterification with this reagent gives up to 69% reaction with the carboxyl groups. Little main chain degradation occurs under these conditions.

When reaction is carried out with a range of alcohols, the degree of esterification has been shown to be less with those of higher molecular weight (Table 23).

TABLE 23

REACTION OF WOOL WITH ALCOHOLS[97]

Alcohol (containing 0.1 N hydrochloric acid*)	Percentage of carboxyl groups available
Methanol	69
Ethanol	56
n-Propanol	54
n-Butanol	39
n-Amylalcohol	21
Isopropanol	15
Isobutanol	21
sec.-Butanol	15
Benzyl alcohol	12

* Reacted for 6 hours at 100°C or at b.p. of alcohol if this is lower.

These results may be regarded as a measure of accessibility of the fibre to molecules of different sizes. The degree of esterification of the higher alcohols is increased when the fibre is swollen, for example with water. Alternatively, cetyl or benzyl iodide will react up to 40% if a solvent capable of swelling wool is used. Although small amounts of water will increase the number of carboxyl groups esterified, if too much is used ($> 5\%$) it will assist hydrolysis and the yield will decrease.

The esterified wool is fairly stable to acid but is very sensitive to even the mildest alkali; slow hydrolysis may even occur at pH 7.5–8. Reagents of the ethylene oxide type (XIII) are capable of reacting with carboxyl, amino or hydroxyl groups[96] in water soluble proteins.

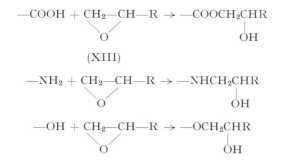

(XIII)

With wool, epichlorohydrin (XIII, $R = CH_2Cl$) has been found to esterify the carboxyl groups to a maximum of 50% but other epoxides only react to an extent of 10% of the carboxyl groups[97].

(e) Reactions of Tyrosine Residues

The fraction of tyrosine in wool is small but nevertheless the acid carries a p-phenol group which will undergo reaction. This group can be methylated with diazomethane[61] and nuclear nitration can also be brought about[98] but the latter reaction may not be complete.

Reaction of wool with iodine gives the mono- and di-iodo derivatives of tyrosine[103]. The reaction with iodine has been used to give additional information on the accessibility. Thus iodine reacts with wool completely in methanol and ethanol solution but only about half in propanol and hardly any in butanol or pentanol[99].

Tyrosine itself may be oxidised with alkaline potassium permanganate to give a mixture of oxalic, acetic and p-hydroxybenzoic acids; when combined in wool or other proteins, the reaction may be modified since indirect evidence suggests that an indole may be formed when proteins are oxidised.

More recently, the formation of a quinone has been suggested when permanganate or chlorine water are used[106]. The tyrosine in wool is not all equally accessible or reactive to some reagents — sodium hypochlorite and potassium permanganate will react with only 30%[107] whereas others are more reactive e.g. chlorine and chlorine dioxide will oxidise this acid completely.

References p. 298

(f) Reactions of Serine and Threonine Residues

These acids each contain a pendant hydroxyl group capable of reaction. Of particular interest is the so-called N—O peptidyl shift. This is an interchange between the amide (XIV) and the hydroxyl group of serine or threonine in proteins to give an ester (XV)

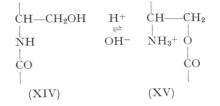

(XIV)   (XV)

Such a reaction has been investigated in protein chemistry and is one likely to occur when wool is treated with acids such as sulphuric used in the carbonising process[108]. This latter is a treatment used to degrade and hence remove cellulosic impurities from wool. Carbonised wool was shown to contain an increased number of free amino groups arising from serine and threonine, a result which is to be anticipated from the shift of the amide group to the ester. This reaction is partly reversible, as when the wool is neutralised after treatment with acid the number of free serine and threonine amino groups is reduced, indeed the quantities of these acids in each form are dependent on the pH of the neutralisation liquor. Complete recovery, however, is not attained since some of the O-peptidyl (*i.e.* ester) bonds are hydrolysed.

(g) Reactions of Cystine

The proteins of the keratin group have a high sulphur content, most of which arises from the presence of cystine residues. Cystine may be incorporated, into the polypeptide chains in at least two ways

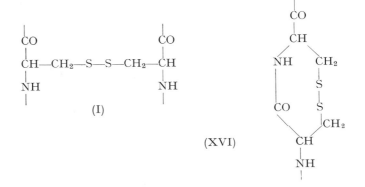

(I)

(XVI)

These arrangements are (1) the formation of cross linkages between two chains (I) and (2) incorporation in the chain itself (XVI). The arrangement (2) is not necessarily as simple as given in formula (XVI) but the ring may be formed so that additional amino acid residues may be joined between the NH and CO groups.

In insulin, both arrangements are adopted[102],

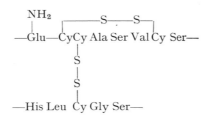

The disulphide group is however very reactive chemically and disruption occurs in most reactions, a change which is reflected in the mechanical properties of the fibre. All the cystine residues do not react with the same speed but apparently depend on the degree of availability.

(i) *Reduction*

The disulphide groups can be broken to give thiol groups. This may be exemplified by the reaction with thioglycollic acid[111].

$$\overset{|}{\underset{|}{CH}}-CH_2-S-S-CH_2-\overset{|}{CH} + 2HSCH_2COOH \rightleftharpoons$$

$$\rightleftharpoons 2\overset{|}{\underset{|}{CH}}CH_2SH + (-SCH_2COOH)_2$$

Reduction in acid or neutral solution goes only to a certain equilibrium extent and hence, if the cystine content is to be reduced to a value greater than 60%, repeated treatments are necessary. The extent of reduction which occurs depends on the electrode potential of the reducing agent used[112].

The extent of reaction as shown by the cystine content of wool is dependent on pH[109]. The amount of cystine reduced is almost constant over the pH range 2–6 and increases considerably as the pH is further increased.

The breaking of these cross linkages has the effect of diminishing the strength of the fibre; in fact, the wet strength of the fibre can be reduced to one tenth[113] (Fig. 70). The thiol groups produced are very reactive and can be reoxidised back to the disulphide; in fact, the original strength could be almost restored by reforming the cross linkages by oxidation[114].

Cross linkages (XVII) between the two thiol[109,113] groups may also be formed by reaction with a difunctional reagent such as ethylene dibromide

$$2\overset{|}{\underset{|}{C}}HCH_2SH + BrCH_2CH_2Br \rightarrow \overset{|}{\underset{|}{C}}HCH_2SCH_2CH_2SCH_2\overset{|}{\underset{|}{C}}H$$

(XXVII)

This kind of reaction has been shown to apply to many bifunctional alkylating agents[113,115]. Monofunctional alkylating agents (e.g. RBr)

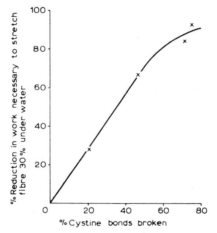

Fig. 70. Relation between wet strength of wool fibres and number of disulphide bonds[129].

leave the cross link broken. Of other agents capable of reacting with reduced wool, benzoquinone has been known for some time. The reaction may be written diagrammatically as follows

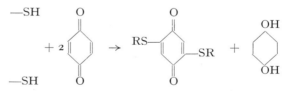

but it is likely that reaction with amino groups and the formation of resins may occur[116].

Many reducing agents will attack the disulphide linkage but sodium bisulphite and formaldehyde have been most extensively studied. Dilute solutions of sodium bisulphite do not react but more stringent conditions cause 50% of the cystine to be reduced[77,117]

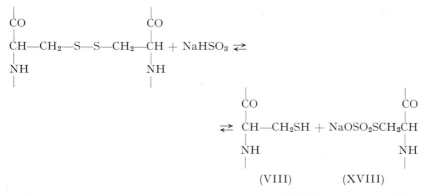

(VIII)   (XVIII)

giving the thiol compound and a sulphonate (XVIII) of cysteine. This reaction is reversible. If the reduced wool is hydrolysed, the cysteine sulphonate is changed to cysteine.

Prolonged reaction at a high temperature causes sulphur containing residues of (XVIII) to split off as thiosulphate leaving an aminoacrylic acid residue (VI)

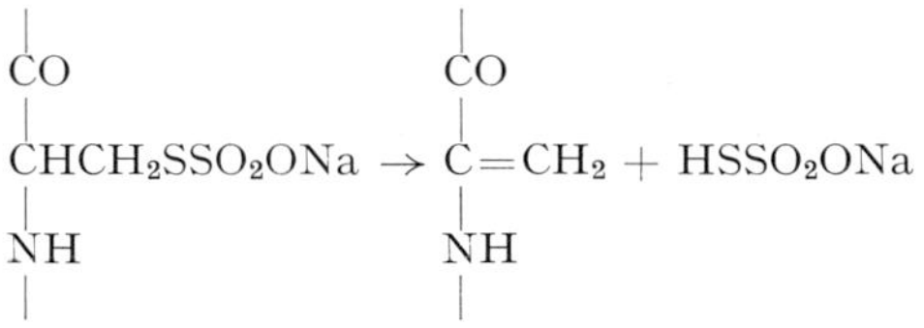

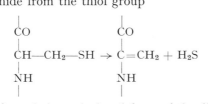

(XVIII)   (VI)

The formation of aminoacrylic acid may also occur through elimination of hydrogen sulphide from the thiol group

$$\overset{|}{\underset{|}{\overset{CO}{\underset{NH}{CH}}}}\text{—}CH_2\text{—}SH \rightarrow \overset{|}{\underset{|}{\overset{CO}{\underset{NH}{C}}}}{=}CH_2 + H_2S$$

In the presence of cupric ions, the breakdown of the disulphide groups is symmetrical and, indeed, wool treated at room temperature with a solution of 0.02 M cuprammonium hydroxide, 0.05 M sodium sulphite and 8 M urea at pH 9.8–10.5 will dissolve up to 90% in a few days. The reaction is

$$R\text{—}S\text{—}S\text{—}R + 2Cu^{++} + 2SO_3^{--} \rightarrow 2RSSO_3^- + 2Cu^+$$

Reaction of wool with hydros (sodium hydrosulphite or dithionite) has been studied but few details are given[118]. Other reagents (e.g. sodium sulphide) are capable of reacting with wool fibres; again it is presumed to produce thiol groups. If ethylene sulphide (XIX) is used to reduce the disulphide bond[119], the thiol groups can react with further molecules of ethylene sulphide

(XIX)

to form a chain in a manner similar to the reaction of ethylene oxide with hydroxyl groups.

With formaldehyde, reaction occurs in warm solution and it is possible to form a cyclic thiazolidine-4-carboxylic acid (XX)[120]

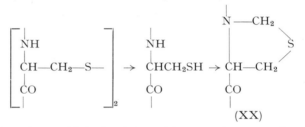

(XX)

The reaction of formaldehyde with wool is a complex one and not confined to cystine.

Formaldehyde will react with thiol groups and form a methylene bridge producing djenkolic acid (XXI)[120]

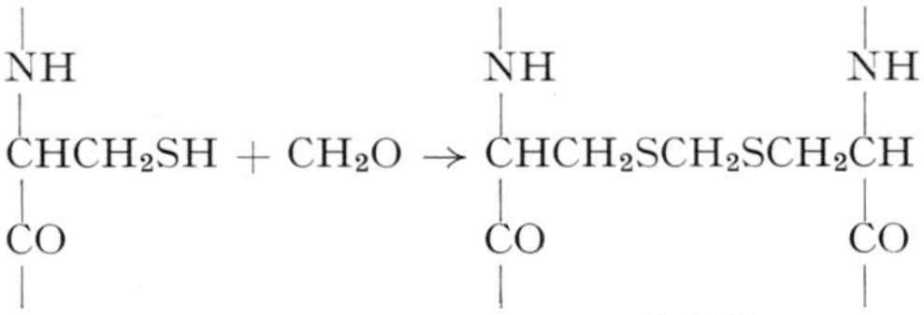

$$\begin{matrix} \mid & & \mid & & \mid \\ NH & & NH & & NH \\ \mid & & \mid & & \mid \\ CHCH_2SH + CH_2O \rightarrow & CHCH_2SCH_2SCH_2CH \\ \mid & & \mid & & \mid \\ CO & & CO & & CO \\ \mid & & \mid & & \mid \end{matrix}$$

(XXI)

(ii) *Oxidation*

In bleaching of wool, hydrogen peroxide may be used. The reaction of this reagent with the proteins is relatively slow except in alkaline solution. When wool is immersed in hydrogen peroxide solutions, some of the reagent is initially adsorbed on the amino and imino groups[121]. The adsorbed peroxide seems to be remarkably stable and may be removed by washing. Oxidation of all the cystine can occur[41,122] but there is some doubt as to the products of oxidation since attack of the peptide bonds themselves occurs. The presence of a certain amount of the disulphoxide has been shown[122]; decomposition of this gives some cysteic acid. Other workers have shown that in the oxidation, besides the sulphoxide, cysteic acid was formed[124] and some of the sulphur split off as sulphate.

Heavy metal ions catalyse the reaction with hydrogen peroxide; whether the reaction is identified with that in the absence of these ions is uncertain, although the disulphide bond is readily oxidised[125].

With performic acid, reaction with tryptophan, methionine and cystine occurs, the latter giving cysteic acid quantitatively (XXII)[126]. Oxidation of proteins with this acid gives polypeptide chains which can be analysed separately; this has been done for insulin where oxidation produces two chains[127]. Other organic peracids (*e.g.* peracetic) can be used to oxidise wool without attack at the peptide bond and hence without main chain degradation[128], provided care is taken. Hydrolysis of such oxidised wool yielded cysteic acid[129] (XXII)

$$
\begin{bmatrix} \overset{|}{C}O \\ | \\ \overset{|}{C}HCH_2S- \\ | \\ \underset{|}{N}H \end{bmatrix}_2 \xrightarrow{O} 2\ \begin{matrix} \overset{|}{C}O \\ | \\ \overset{|}{C}HCH_2SO_3H \\ | \\ \underset{|}{N}H \end{matrix} \xrightarrow{\text{hydrolysis}} \begin{matrix} NH_2 \\ | \\ \overset{|}{C}HCH_2SO_3H \\ | \\ \underset{|}{C}OOH \end{matrix}
$$

$$\text{(XXII)}$$

However attempts to detect sulphonic acid groups in wool were not successful; for example sulphonic acid groups should exhibit typical ion exchange properties. Thus, the group is obscured in the oxidised protein itself but is released on hydrolysis with acid. Reaction of the oxidised protein with mild alkali apparently removes no sulphur but the product on hydrolysis for 5 hours with hydrochloric acid yields no cysteic acid. Thus, the action of alkali could produce a grouping such as the sulphonamide which is resistant to acid. Indeed, it is possible to suggest an intramolecular cyclisation which may on treatment with alkali give a sulphonamide group[29].

The reaction scheme could be as follows:

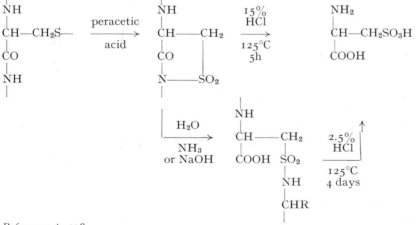

However against this scheme, other workers claim by infra-red measurements to have detected cysteic acid residues in wool treated with peracetic acid[122], so that more work is required to elucidate these reactions.

Oxidation reactions are important in wool processing since they are applied in some processes to confer anti-shrink properties.

(iii) *Action of light*

The disulphide bond in dry wool may be disrupted by the action of ultraviolet radiation[130] and eventually all the cysteine may be oxidised. Weathering of wool may therefore lead to loss of cystine; the tips of wool have in fact been shown to be lower in cystine content and to contain some cysteic acid[131]. Weathering involves the action of light and oxygen so that it is likely that either the disulphide bond is activated by light, hydrolysed and oxidised, or that light produces the hydroxyl radical which is then able to attack the disulphide linkage.

(iv) *Halogens*

Chlorine is used in anti-shrink processes for wool. The reactions of chlorine or hypochlorous acid with the disulphide linkage are not as specific as those of the peracids; treatment reduces the cystine content but not all the sulphur turns up in the form of cysteic acid[129]. After chlorination, wool behaves as an oxidising agent presumably due to the possible formation of a labile sulphoxide or a chloramine; further, although treatment with the peracids to an extent to break all disulphide linkages enables wool to dissolve in dilute alkali, complete oxidation with chlorine renders only 70% of the wool soluble in dilute ammonia. It seems that, in the chlorinated wool, some new cross linkages may be formed.

Reaction with bromine has not been studied in detail but the course of reaction would seem to be similar to that of chlorine[131]. Iodine being the least reactive halogen does not oxidise the disulphide bond[132], although reaction with wool occurs presumably with the tyrosine or the amino groups[133].

(v) *Other chlorinating reagents*

In order to regulate the speed of chlorination of wool, chloramines have been used — chloramine T, dichloroacetamide, chlorophthalimide and chlorosulphamic acid[134]. In general characteristics, the reaction is similar to that with chlorine and the disulphide bond is found to have been attacked. In the case of oxidation with chlorosulphamic acid, cysteic acid was found in the hydrolysate.

Chlorine peroxide is a reagent which will attack cystine; oxidation does not go exclusively to cysteic acid as some sulphate is formed[106].

(vi) *Reaction with potassium cyanide*

Potassium cyanide reacts with free cystine[135]

$$
\begin{bmatrix}
\text{NH}_2 \\
| \\
\text{CHCH}_2\text{S}- \\
| \\
\text{COOH}
\end{bmatrix}_2
\xrightarrow{\text{KCN}}
\begin{array}{c}
\text{NH}_2 \\
| \\
\text{CHCH}_2\text{SCN} \\
| \\
\text{COOH}
\end{array}
+
\begin{array}{c}
\text{NH}_2 \\
| \\
\text{CHCH}_2\text{SK} \\
| \\
\text{COOH}
\end{array}
$$

(XXIII)

to give cysteine and α-aminorhodaninepropionic acid (XXIII). By repeated oxidation of the cysteine back to cystine and further reacting with cyanide all the sulphur can be transformed into the acid (XXIII)[136]. In wool however, lanthionine is formed almost quantitatively and potassium thiocyanate eliminated.

$$
\begin{array}{c}
| \\
\text{NH} \\
| \\
\text{CHCH}_2\text{SCN} \\
| \\
\text{CO} \\
|
\end{array}
+
\begin{array}{c}
| \\
\text{NH} \\
| \\
\text{CHCH}_2\text{SK} \\
| \\
\text{CO} \\
|
\end{array}
\rightarrow
\begin{array}{c}
| \\
\text{NH} \\
| \\
\text{C}{=}\text{CH}_2 \\
| \\
\text{CO} \\
|
\end{array}
+
\begin{array}{c}
| \\
\text{NH} \\
| \\
\text{CHCH}_2\text{SH} \\
| \\
\text{CO} \\
|
\end{array}
\rightarrow
\begin{array}{c}
| \\
\text{NH} \\
| \\
\text{CHCH}_2\text{SCH}_2\text{CH} \\
| \\
\text{CO} \\
|
\end{array}
\begin{array}{c}
| \\
\text{NH} \\
| \\
 \\
| \\
\text{CO} \\
|
\end{array}
$$

The aminorhodaninepropionic acid residues decompose to give α-amino-acrylic acid which reacts with cysteine to give the lanthionine. This reaction differs from the reaction with alkali, as the sulphur is all converted to lanthionine or thiocyanate and none is eliminated as sulphide.

However, studies of the synthetic material N-mercaptomethyl-poly-hexamethyleneadipamide disulphide (XXIV) have led to the postulation of a different mechanism[137].

This compound is nylon 66 in which some of the hydrogen atoms of the amide nitrogen atom have been replaced by the —CH$_2$—S—S—CH$_2$— group, thereby producing a cross linked polymer which can be studied as a model for wool. Reaction of this material with potassium cyanide reduced the sulphur content by half but still gave a cross linked (insoluble) material, half the sulphur being eliminated as thiocyanate. This indicates that the disulphide bond has been replaced by a sulphide in an analogous manner to lanthionine formation in wool. In this case, the CH$_2$-group is joined to a nitrogen atom so that the postulated intermediate amino-acrylic acid cannot be formed. The following mechanism has been put forward:

References p. 298

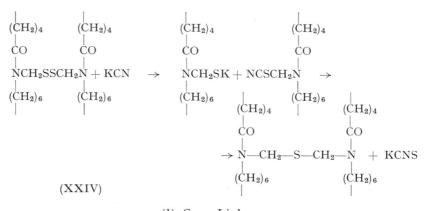

(XXIV)

(h) Cross Linkages

With few exceptions wool differs from other textile fibres in that it contains covalent cross linkages holding the chains together. The cross linkages are responsible for the insolubility in polar solvents, its limited lateral swelling and relatively high wet strength. These properties may be modified by breaking the disulphide bonds e.g. the wet strength of wool is reduced as the number of linkages is broken. The cross links thus make an important contribution to the properties of wool; interest has, in consequence, been aroused in the possibility of introducing cross linkages which are more stable than the disulphide ones.

Cross linking has been attempted with many agents some of which are discussed below.

(i) By formaldehyde

This reagent is used to cross link a variety of materials both proteins and cellulose.

On introduction of wool into formaldehyde solution, methylol groups are formed with lysine

$$RNH_2 + HCHO \rightarrow RNHCH_2OH$$

The basicity of the lysine is reduced by this reaction. This reaction may be reversed by washing the wool[138]. Stable cross linkages can be formed by reaction of the methylol groups with the acid amide groups of glutamine

$$RNHCH_2OH + H_2NCOR_1 \rightarrow RNHCH_2NHCOR_1$$

Cross linking between two amine groups does not occur, but two guanidyl groups may be linked through a methylene bridge[139]. Another worker in this field, by reacting wool with formaldehyde at 100°C in acid solution, has concluded that cross linking can occur between the acid groups of glutamic acid and the guanidyl residue in arginine[93]. New cross linkages of this kind are stable to alkali but broken by acid.

(ii) By polyfunctional alkylating agents

Chloromethyl ethers (XXV) will react with wool when applied from organic solvents, giving a product with increased tensile strength and reduced alkali solubility[115,140]. The course of the reaction is not clear but may be as follows

$$RNH_2 + ClCH_2OCH_2Cl \rightarrow RNHCH_2OCH_2Cl + R_1COOH \rightarrow$$

(XXV)

$$\rightarrow RNHCH_2OCH_2OOCR_1$$

Other bifunctional reagents have been tried e.g. ethylene imines (XXVI), 1,3-difluoro-4,6-dinitrobenzene, bisepoxides (XXVII) etc.[141]

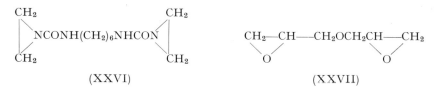

(XXVI)   (XXVII)

It has been shown that acetylated wool could not be cross linked whereas esterified wool could; this stresses the importance of the amino group in these reactions.

(iii) By rebuilding of reduced disulphide bonds

Reduction of disulphide bonds to thiol groups can be followed by reaction with a compound such as an alkyl dibromide (XXVIII) to form a cross linkage[109]

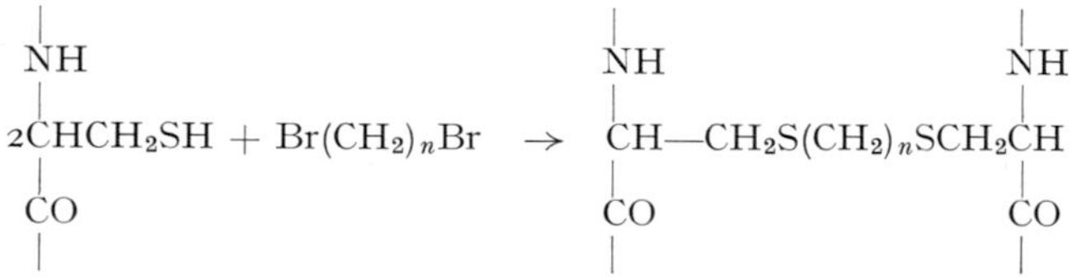

$$
\begin{array}{ccc}
| & | & | \\
NH & NH & NH \\
| & | & | \\
2CHCH_2SH + Br(CH_2)_nBr \rightarrow CH{-\!\!-}CH_2S(CH_2)_nSCH_2CH \\
| & | & | \\
CO & CO & CO \\
| & | & |
\end{array}
$$

(XXVIII)

Wool modified in this way was found to be more resistant towards reagents such as alkali, acids, oxidizing and reducing.

References p. 298

REFERENCES

[1] J. M. Mathews, *Textile Fibres*, H. R. Mauersberger, (Editor), Chapman & Hall, London, 1954.

[2] M. Ryder, *Fibre Structure*, J. W. Hearle and R. H. Peters, (Editors), Butterworth, London.

[3] H. M. Appleyard and C. M. Grenville, *Nature*, 166 (1950) 1031.

[4] C. W. Hock, R. C. Ramsey and M. Harris, *J. Research Natl. Bur. Standards*, 27 (1941) 181.

[5] E. Elod and H. Zahn, *Melliand Textilber.*, 24 (1943) 157.

[6] P. Alexander and R. F. Hudson, *Wool—its Chemistry and Physics*, Chapman & Hall, London, 1954.

[7] H. M. Appleyard and C. M. Dymoke, *J. Textile Inst.*, 45 (1954) 480T.

[8] J. Woods, *Proc. Roy. Soc.* (*London*), 166A (1938) 76.

[9] K. von Allwörden, *Z. angew. Chem.*, 29 (1916) 77.

[10] J. Lindberg, B. Phillip and N. Gralen, *Nature*, 162 (1948) 458.
P. Alexander, *J. Soc. Dyers Colourists*, 66 (1950) 349.
R. D. B. Fraser and G. E. Rogers, *Biochim. et Biophys. Acta*, 16 (1955) 307.

[11] G. Lagermalm and N. Gralen, *Acta Chem. Scand.*, 5 (1951) 1209.

[12] C. S. Whewell and H. J. Woods, *J. Soc. Dyers Colourists*, 60 (1944) 148.
H. E. Millson and L. H. Turl, *Am. Dyestuff Reptr., Proc. Am. Assoc. Textile Chemists Colorists*, 39, No. 20 (1950).

[13] J. Lindberg, *Textile Research J.*, 20 (1950) 381.

[14] A. Parisot and M. Leveau, *Textile Research J.*, 23 (1953) 441.

[15] M. Horio and T. Kondo, *Textile Research J.*, 23 (1953) 373.

[16] E. H. Mercer, *Textile Research J.*, 23 (1953) 338.

[17] L. Auber and M. L. Ryder, *Proc. Intern. Wool Textile Research Conf., Australia* F 36 (1956).

[18] M. L. Ryder, *Proc. Roy. Soc. Edinburgh*, 67 (1958) 65.

[19] R. O. B. Frazer and G. E. Rogers, *Proc. Intern. Wool Textile Research Conf. Australia*, F 151 (1956).

[20] M. L. Ryder, *Quart. J. Microscop. Sci.*, 99 (1958) 221.

[21] P. Kassenbeck and M. Leveau, *Bull. inst. textile France*, 67 (1957) 7.

[22] M. Leveau, *Bull. inst. textile France*, 61 (1956) 61; 63 (1958) 91.

[23] P. Kasssenbeck, *Bull. inst. textile France*, 83 (1959) 25.

[24] J. H. Bradbury, *Nature*, 183 (1959) 305.

[25] T. Vickerstaff, *Physical Chemistry of Dyeing*, Oliver & Boyd, London, 1954.

[26] J. T. Edsall and J. Wyman, *Biophysical Chemistry*, Vol. 1, Academic Press, New York, 1958.

[27] W. B. Geiger, *J. Research Natl. Bur. Standards*, 32 (1944) 127.

[28] N. H. Chamberlain, *J. Textile Inst.*, 23 (1932) 13T.

[29] B. Lustic and A. A. Kondritzer, *Arch. Biochem.*, 8 (1945) 51.

[30] E. Elod and H. Zahn, *Melliand Textilber.*, 25 (1944) 361.

[31] L. A. Hausmann, *Am. J. Anat.*, 27 (1920) 463.

[32] D. H. Simmonds and J. S. Bartulovich, *Textile Research J.*, 28 (1955) 378.

[33] W. H. Ward, C. H. Binkley and N. N. Snell, *Textile Research J.*, 25 (1955) 314.

[34] R. L. Golden, J. C. Whitwelland and E. H. Mercer, *Textile Research J.*, 25 (1955) 334.
M. Leveau, *Bull. inst. textile France*, 74 (1958) 75.
J. Derminot and M. Leveau, *Text. France*, 64 (1956) 7.
J. Derminot, *Text. France*, 72 (1958) 69.
H. Lindley, *Nature*, 160 (1947) 190.

[35] E. D. Stakheeva-Kaverzneva and N. I. Gavrilov, *Bull. soc. chim. France*, [5], 4 (1937) 647.
J. B. Speakman and P. R. Macmahon, *Nature*, 141 (1938) 118.

[36] H. B. Bull, *Cold Spring Harbor Symposia Quant. Biol.*, 14 (1950) 1.

[37] M. Leveau, *Bull. inst. textile France*, 85 (1959) 57.

[38] M. L. Ryder, *Nature*, 178 (1956) 1409.

[39] J. MENKART and A. B. COE, *Textile Research J.*, 28 (1958) 218.
[40] H. P. LUNDGREN, *Proc. Intern. Wool Textile Research Conf. Australia*, F 200 (1956).
[41] M. HARRIS and A. L. SMITH, *J. Research Natl. Bur. Standards*, 17 (1936) 557.
M. HARRIS, *Am. Dyestuff Reptr.*, 24 (1935) 306.
[42] H. ZAHN, *Textil-Praxis*, 2 (1949) 70.
[43] L. LINDLEY, *Proc. Intern. Wool Textile Research Conf. Australia*, B 193, 1955.
E. ELOD and H. ZAHN, *Koll.-Z.*, 108 (1944) 94.
[44] G. SATLOW and H. KISSLER, *Textile Research J.*, 28 (1958) 359.
[45] W. R. MIDDLEBROOK, *Biochim. et Biophys. Acta*, 7 (1951) 547.
[46] S. BLACKBURN, *Biochem. J.*, 47 (1950) 443.
[47] P. ALEXANDER, *Kolloid-Z.*, 122 (1951) 8.
R. R. PORTER, *Biochim. et Biophys. Acta*, 2 (1948) 105.
[48] F. SANGER, *Symposium Fibrous Proteins and their Biological Significance*, Cambridge, University Press, 1955.
[49] A. J. P. MARTIN, *Symposium on Fibrous Proteins, Soc. Dyers Colourists*, 1946.
R. CONSDEN, A. H. GORDON and A. J. P. MARTIN, *Biochem. J.*, 44 (1949) 548.
[50] CL. FROMAGEOT, D. MEYER and L. PENASSE, *Biochim. et Biophys. Acta*, 6 (1950) 283.
[51] S. M. PARTRIDGE and H. F. DAVIS, *Nature*, 165 (1950) 62.
[52] E. ELOD, H. NOWOTNY and H. ZAHN, *Koll.-Z.*, 92 (1940) 50.
[53] E. ELOD, H. NOWOTNY and H. ZAHN, *Koll.-Z.*, 100 (1942) 297.
[54] F. SANGER, *Biochem. J.*, 45 (1949) 563.
[55] M. HARRIS, R. MEASE and H. RUTHERFORD, *J. Research Natl. Bur. Standards*, 18 (1937) 343.
[56] D. LEMIN and T. VICKERSTAFF, *Symposium on Fibrous Proteins, Soc. Dyers Colourists*, 1946.
[57] J. B. SPEAKMAN, *J. Textile Inst.*, 32 (1941) 83T.
[58] H. C. REITZ, R. E. FERREL, H. FRAENKEL-CONRAT and H. S. OLCOTT, *J. Am. Chem. Soc.*, 68 (1946) 1026.
[59] J. STEINHARDT and C. H. FUGITT, *J. Research Natl. Bur. Standards*, 29 (1942) 315.
[60] R. C. WARNER and R. K. CANNAN, *J. Biol. Chem.* 142 (1942) 725.
[61] H. A. RUTHERFORD, W. I. PATTERSON and M. HARRIS, *J. Research Natl. Bur. Standards*, 25 (1940) 451.
[62] J. STEINHARDT, *J. Biol. Chem.*, 141 (1941) 995.
[63] L. MEUNIER, P. CHAMBARD and H. COMTE, *Compt. rend.*, 184 (1927) 1208.
CL. FROMAGEOT and A. PORCHEREL, *Compt. rend.*, 193 (1931) 738.
E. ELOD and H. ZAHN, *Melliand Textilber.*, 24 (1943) 157, 245.
[64] W. B. GEIGER, W. R. PATTERSON, L. W. MIZELL and M. HARRIS, *J. Research Natl. Bur. Standards*, 27 (1941) 459.
[65] E. ELOD and H. ZAHN, *Melliand Textilber.*, 27 (1946) 68.
[66] H. ZAHN, *Meuinhofer Textile Research J.*, 25 (1955) 738.
[67] A. STRÖBERL, *Collegium*, 412 (1936); *Angew. Chem.*, 53 (1940) 227.
[68] J. A. CROWDER and M. HARRIS, *J. Research Natl. Bur. Standards*, 30 (1943) 47.
[69] M. HARRIS, *J. Research Natl. Bur. Standards*, 15 (1935) 63.
[70] W. R. CUTHBERTSON and H. PHILLIPS, *Biochem. J.*, 39 (1945) 7.
[71] J. B. SPEAKMAN and C. WHEWELL, *J. Soc. Dyers Colourists*, 52 (1936) 380.
[72] M. J. HORN, D. B. JONES and S. J. RUNGEL, *J. Biol. Chem.*, 138 (1941) 141.
[73] H. LINDLEY and H. PHILLIPS, *Biochem. J.*, 39 (1945) 17.
[74] M. BERGMANN, F. STATHER, *Z. physiol. Chem. Hoppe-Seyler's*, 152 (1926) 189.
[75] A. SCHOBERL and T. HORNUNG, *Ann. Chemie Liebigs*, 534 (1938) 210.
[76] L. LES and F. F. ELSWORTH, *Proc. Intern. Wool Textile Research Conf. Australia*, C 363 (1955); *J. Soc. Dyers Colourists*, 68 (1952) 204.
[77] F. F. ELSWORTH and H. PHILLIPS, *Biochem. J.*, 35 (1941) 135.
[78] H. ZAHN, G. BASCHANG, H. J. KESSLER and H. STEUERLE, *Angew. Chem.*, 69 (1957) 101.
[79] H. KESSLER and H. ZAHN, *Textile Research J.*, 28 (1958) 357.

[80] J. B. SPEAKMAN and M. C. HIRST, *Nature*, 127 (1931) 665; *Trans. Faraday Soc.*, 29 (1933) 148.

[81] J. B. SPEAKMAN, *J. Textile Inst.*, (1941) 32.
H. EYRING and E. STEARN, *Chem. Revs.*, 29 (1939) 253.

[82] M. HARRIS and A. M. SOOKNE, *J. Research Natl. Bur. Standards*, 19 (1937) 535.

[83] M. HARRIS, *J. Research Natl. Bur. Standards*, 8 (1932) 779.

[84] D. D. VAN SLYKE, *J. Biol. Chem.*, 9 (1911) 185.

[85] J. R. KANAGY and M. HARRIS, *J. Research Natl. Bur. Standards*, 14 (1935) 563.

[86] J. B. SPEAKMAN, *J. Soc. Dyers Colourists*, 52 (1936) 335.
H. A. RUTHERFORD, M. HARRIS and A. L. SMITH, *J. Research Natl. Bur. Standards* 19 (1937) 467.

[87] J. H. ELLIOT and J. B. SPEAKMAN, *J. Soc. Dyers Colourists*, 59 (1943) 185.

[88] H. LINDLEY and H. PHILLIPS, *Biochem. J.*, 41 (1947) 34.

[89] P. ALEXANDER, R. F. HUDSON and M. FOX, *Biochem. J.*, 46 (1950) 27.

[90] F. SANGER, *Biochem. J.*, 39 (1945) 507.

[91] P. EDMAN, *Acta Chem. Scand.*, 4 (1950) 283; 7 (1953) 700.

[92] S. UDENFRIEND and S. F. VALIAK, *J. Biol. Chem.*, 190 (1951) 733; 191 (1951) 233.

[93] W. B. MIDDLEBROOK, *Biochem. J.*, 44 (1949) 17.

[94] S. BLACKBURN, D. CARTER and H. PHILLIPS, *Biochem. J.*, 35 (1941) 627.

[95] H. L. FRAENKEL-CONRAT and H. S. OLCOTT, *J. Biol. Chem.*, 161 (1945) 259.
S. BLACKBURN and H. LINDLEY, *J. Soc. Dyers Colourists*, 64 (1948) 505.

[96] H. L. FRAENKEL-CONRAT, *J. Biol. Chem.*, 154 (1944) 227.

[97] P. ALEXANDER, D. CARTER, C. EARLAND and O. E. FORD, *Biochem. J.*, 48 (1951) 629.
P. ALEXANDER, *Melliand Textilber.*, 34 (1953) 756.

[98] H. ZAHN and K. KOHLER, *Z. Naturf.*, 56 (1950) 137.

[99] J. B. SPEAKMAN and D. HARRISON, *Textile Research J.*, 28 (1958) 1005.

[100] W. G. CREWTHER and L. M. DOWLING, *J. Textile Inst.*, 51 (1960) 775 T.

[101] M. FEUGHELMAN, *J. Textile Inst.*, 51 (1960) 589.

[102] F. SANGER, *Symposium Fibrous Proteins*.

[103] S. BLACKBURN and H. PHILLIPS, *J. Soc. Dyers Colourists*, 61 (1945) 100.

[104] B. B. DRAKE and C. V. SMYTHE, *Arch. Biochem.*, 4 (1944) 255.

[105] P. ALEXANDER, D. CARTER and R. F. HUDSON, *J. Soc. Dyers Colourists*, 65 (1949) 152.

[106] D. B. DAS and J. B. SPEAKMAN, *J. Soc. Dyers Colourists*, 66 (1950) 583.

[107] P. ALEXANDER and D. GOUGH, *Biochem. J.*, 48 (1951) 504.

[108] H. ZAHN, *Intern. Federation Assoc. Textile Chemists and Colourists*, 1959.
E. HILLE and H. ZAHN, *2nd Intern. Wool Textile Research Conf.*, (1960) 576.

[109] D. H. SIMMOND, *Proc.Intern. Wool Textile Research Conf. Australia*, C 65 (1955).

[110] M. L. CORFIELD and A. ROBSON, *ibid.*, C 79 (1955).

[111] D. R. GODDARD and L. MICHAELIS, *J. Biol. Chem.*, 106 (1934) 605; 112 (1935) 361.

[112] H. E. JASS and L. S. FOSBICK, *Textile Research J.*, 25 (1955) 343.

[113] W. B. GEIGER, F. F. KOBAYASHI and M. HARRIS, *J. Research Natl. Bur. Standards*, 29 (1942) 381.

[114] M. HARRIS, L. R. MIZELLE and L. FOENT, *Ind. Eng. Chem.*, 34 (1942) 833.

[115] W. KIRST, *Melliand Textilber.*, 28 (1947) 169, 314; 29 (1948) 236.

[116] W. B. SPEAKMAN and P. L. D. PEILL, *J. Textile Inst.*, 34 (1943) 70T.
J. L. STOVES, *Trans. Faraday Soc.*, 39 (1943) 301.

[117] F. F. ELSWORTH and H. PHILLIPS, *Biochem. J.*, 32 (1938) 837.

[118] E. ELÖD and H. ZAHN, *Textil-Praxis*, 27 (1949).

[119] S. BLACKBURN and H. PHILLIPS, *J. Soc. Dyers Colourists*, 61 (1945) 203.

[120] W. R. MIDDLEBROOK and H. PHILLIPS, *Biochem. J.*, 36 (1942) 294; 41 (1947) 218.

[121] P. ALEXANDER, D. CARTER and C. EARLAND, *Biochem. J.*, 52 (1950) 159.

[122] M. HARRIS and A. SMITH, *J. Research Natl. Bur. Standards*, 16 (1936) 301, 309; 18 (1937) 623.

[123] E. ELÖD, H. NOWOTNY and H. ZAHN, *Melliand Textilber.*, 23 (1942) 313.

[124] R. Consden and A. H. Gordon, *Biochem. J.*, 42 (1950) 8.
[125] J. C. Andrews and K. C. Andrews, *J. Biol. Chem.*, 102 (1933) 253.
[126] G. Toennis and R. P. Hommiller, *J. Am. Chem. Soc.*, 64 (1942) 3004.
[127] F. Sanger, *Cold Spring Harbor Symposia Quant. Biol.*, 12 (1947) 237.
[128] P. Alexander, R. F. Hudson and M. Fox, *Biochem. J.*, 46 (1950) 27.
P. Alexander, D. Carter and C. Earland, *J. Soc. Dyers Colourists*, 67 (1951) 23.
[129] P. Alexander, M. Fox and R. F. Hudson, *Biochem. J.*, 49 (1951) 129.
[130] G. J. Watson, *Biochim. et Biophys. Acta*, 17 (1955) 462.
[131] R. Consden, A. H. Gordon and A. F. P. Martin, *Biochem. J.*, 40 (1946) 580.
[132] S. Blackburn and H. Phillips, *J. Soc. Dyers Colourists*, 61 (1945) 100.
[133] R. Haller, *Helv. Chim. Acta*, 13 (1930) 620.
H. vom Hove, *Angew. Chem.*, 47 (1934) 786.
[134] *D.P.* 647,566.
U.S.P. 2,427,097.
P. Alexander, D. Carter and C. Earland, *J. Soc. Dyers Colourists*, 67 (1951) 17.
[135] J. Mauthna, *Z. physiol. Chem. Hoppe-Seyler's*, 78 (1912) 32.
[136] A. Schöberl and R. Hamm, *Biochem. Z.*, 318 (1948) 331.
[137] C. Earland and D. J. Raven, *2nd Intern. Wool Research Conf.* (1960) 161.
[138] J. Steinhardt, C. H. Fuggitt and M. Harris, *J. Biol. Chem.*, 165 (1946) 285.
[139] H. L. Fraenkel-Conrat and H. S. Olcott, *J. Am. Chem. Soc.*, 68 (1946) 34; *J. Biol. Chem.*, 174 (1948) 827.
[140] E. Elöd and H. Zahn, *Melliand Textilber.*, 29 (1948) 17, 269.
[141] P. Alexander, M. Fox, A. Smith and K. A. Stacey, *Biochem. J.*, 52 (1952) 174.
[142] E. Elöd and H. Zahn, *Kolloid-Z.*, 108 (1944) 6.
[143] E. O. P. Thompson, *Australian J. Biol. Sci.*, 12 (1959) 303.
[144] J. B. Speakman and E. Stott, *Trans. Faraday Soc.*, 30 (1934) 539.
P. R. McMahon and J. B. Speakman, *Trans. Faraday Soc.*, 33 (1937) 844.
[145] E. Race, F. M. Rowe, T. B. Speakman and T. Vickerstaff, *J. Soc. Dyers Colourists*, 54 (1938) 141.
[146] J. B. Speakman and E. Stott, *Nature*, 141 (1938) 414.

CHAPTER 11

SILK

1. Occurrence

This fibre is produced in continuous filament form by the larvae of caterpillars when the cocoons are formed. Silkworms belong to the order Lepidoptera (scale winged insects) and hence are really caterpillars. Most silk is produced from the species *Bombyx mori* an insect which feeds on mulberry leaves[1]. The moth itself is of medium size and creamy white in colour with indistinct darker markings; the larvae are black and hairy when hatched, later becoming whitish green or grey. The silk moths lay eggs which stick by virtue of a gummy substance to a sheet; these sheets of eggs may be kept in cold storage for several months until supplies of food are available, when the eggs may be taken out of hibernation and placed in an incubator at 80°F where they hatch after 10 days (1 oz. eggs gives 40–60,000 larvae). The caterpillars, originally 3 mm long, eat and grow rapidly but at the end of 20–30 days they cease to eat, being now 5–9 cm long. The worms are removed to straw mountings where

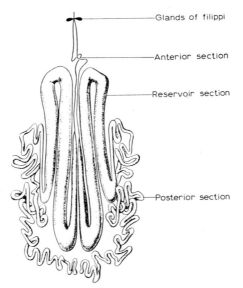

Glands of filippi

Anterior section

Reservoir section

Posterior section

Fig. 71. Silk glands of the larva of *Bombyx mori* $(2\frac{1}{2} \times)$[41].

they find an anchorage for their silk filament. Each worm builds an oval casing by extruding a viscous fluid from two large glands through two channels to a common exit tube in the head of the insect. The fibre, as it is produced by the insect, is composed of two filaments of a protein known as fibroin, coated and cemented together by another protein — sericin. The two glands exist side by side in the larvae and increase in size during the later stages of development until they make up about half its weight. The glands of the *Bombyx mori* are shown in Fig. 71 and may be seen to consist of (1) posterior, (2) reservoir and (3) anterior sections. (1) is a long thin tube (*ca.* 30 cm long), (2) is short with a diameter of 2–3 mm whereas (3) is very thin and leads to the orifice or spinneret in the head of the larvae. Through this orifice, the silk is excreted. Immediately before the orifice, the two glands join together into a single duct and, at this point, the secretions of the glands of Filippi are discharged. The fibroin is secreted in the posterior portion and transferred by peristalsis into the reservoir where it is stored as a viscous aqueous solution until required for spinning. In the walls of this reservoir, the bulk of the sericin is produced and it is possible to show in some insects a sharp latitudinal line of demarcation between the fibroin and the sericin; by taking cross sections at points along the reservoir and carrying out differential staining, it can be shown that the gelatinous sericin forms a layer around a fibroin core. In the reservoir then, the two proteins in viscous solutions exist side by side without any indication of one diffusing into the other. The fibroin core is expressed with a layer of sericin and the secretions from the two glands join at the junction when the sericin is fused into one layer. The glands of Filipi discharge a liquid whose function remains obscure. The worm extrudes this thread and working from the inside adds layer after layer to complete its protective covering — the cocoon. This takes 24–72 hours. At the end of this activity, the caterpillar transforms to a pupa or chrysalis then later to the moth.

The thread or bave which the worm extrudes from its "spinnerets" thus is composed of two filaments, each known as brin, and as it comes from the cocoon ranges in fineness from 1.75–4.0 denier. When the cocoon is complete most of the pupa are killed, only sufficient being allowed to become moths in order to supply eggs for the next generation. The cocoons are boiled to soften the gum and brushed to find the outside ends of the filament which is reeled off. In unwinding the cocoon, not all the silk comes away as continuous filament (grege); some is in short lengths and used in stable fibre (schappe). In silk processing, there is some waste produced; this may arise in the rearing of the worms *e.g.* cocoons that have been pierced, or in the reeling or twisting. This fibre is used for schappe spinning.

References p. 313

In the class insecta, many species produce long silken filaments to form substantial cocoons in which they pupate. There are thousands of silk spinning insects and spiders but apart from the *Bombyx mori* only the larvae of the Tussah and Anaphe moths have been exploited commercially. Tussah silk is produced by the tussah silkworm, the four principal members of the genus being *Antheraea*. The worm *Antheraea perrigi* feeds on an oak tree of a shrub type. Its habitat is China.

The raw silk as reeled is soaked in oil or soap emulsion to soften the thread without removing the gum. Several threads can be twisted together or "doubled" to give yarns of the desired fineness.

2. Histology

Raw silk, when examined under the microscope, shows an irregular surface structure consisting of transverse tissues, creases, folds etc. When degummed (*i.e.* the outer coating of sericin is removed), the fibre appears to be smooth and translucent. The cross section of the filament from the cocoon is approximately elliptical in shape but that of the two filaments or brins are triangular in shape (Fig. 4, Chapter 1).

3. Chemical Structure

The silk thread from its mode of formation contains two filaments or brins enclosed by the coating of gum. These substances known as fibroin and sericin respectively are chemically proteins.

Sericin is an insoluble protein which, on hydrolysis, yields α-amino acids, of which glycine, alanine, leucine and tyrosine are the most abundant. Sericin is now considered to contain two proteins — sericin A and B[2]; A is the more soluble and plastic whereas B is stiff and hornlike. In quantity, raw silk contains from 15–25% of sericin. Sericin, although giving raw silk rather a harsh handle, is useful to the manufacturer as it acts as a protective layer during processing. The removal of the sericin brings out the soft and glossy properties of the silk and is usually carried out by means of a soap solution; this scouring process is normally referred to as degumming. Fibroin may be prepared for chemical studies from reeled raw silk and isolated by extracting the sericin with water, dilute alkalis, soaps or proteolytic enzymes. In this work, it is necessary to ensure removal of the sericin but, at the same time, reduce attack of the fibroin to a minimum. Fibroin from the degumming bath should be washed thoroughly with distilled water, dried and extracted with organic solvents to remove any residual traces of soap and wax.

Fibroin on hydrolysis yields about 15 amino acids. Analyses by workers in this field agree fairly well but there are small differences which may arise from the different locations from which the silk was taken[3]. In

Table 24 are given the results by Schroeder and Kay[4] for *Bombyx mori* fibroin. Silk differs from wool in that it contains no cystine and hence no disulphide cross linkages. The most notable features are the large quantities of the simple amino acids glycine, alanine and serine, and the fact

TABLE 24

Amino acid	Moles of acid/10^5 g	Substituent R in acid of formula $NH_2CHRCOOH$
1. Glycine	567.2	H—
2. Alanine	385.7	CH_3—
3. Leucine	6.2	$(CH_3)_2CHCH_2$—
4. Isoleucine	6.9	$CH_3CH_2CH(CH_3)$—
5. Valine	26.7	$(CH_3)_2CH$—
6. Phenylalanine	8.0	$C_6H_5CH_2$—
7. Serine	152.0	CH_2OH—
8. Threonine	12.5	$CH_3CH(OH)$—
9. Tyrosine	62.3	$HOC_6H_5CH_2$—
10. Aspartic acid	17.6	$HOOCCH_2$—
11. Glutamic acid	11.8	$HOOCCH_2CH_2$—
12. Arginine	5.6	$NH_2C(NH)NH(CH_2)_3$—
13. Lysine	3.8	$NH_2(CH_2)_4$—
14. Histidine	1.9	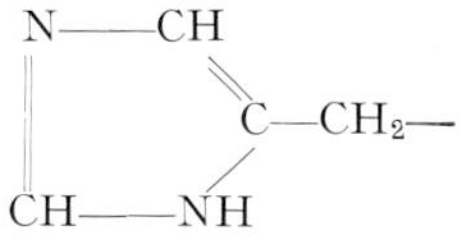 N——CH, C—CH₂— , CH——NH
15. Proline	5.1	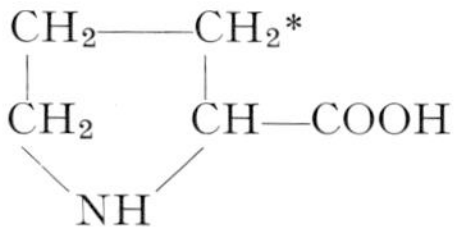 CH₂——CH₂*, CH₂ CH—COOH, NH
16. Tryptophan	2.5	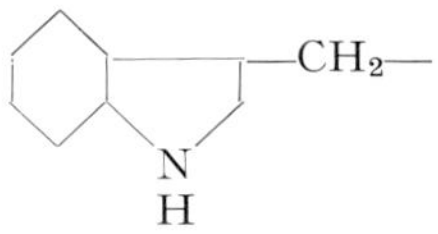 —CH₂—, N, H

* This is the complete formula of the acid.

References p. 313

that no ammonia is liberated on hydrolysis so that none of the free carboxyl groups are in the amide form. In Table 25, the number of the kinds of side group, R, are given in moles per 10^5 g.

TABLE 25

Polar groups		Non-polar groups	
Basic	11.3	Hydrocarbons (aliphatic)	425.5
Acidic	29.4	Glycine	567.2
Phenolic	62.3		
Hydroxyl	164.5		

Thus, the numbers of basic and acid side chains in silk are comparatively small compared with wool. The quantity of acid or alkali absorbed by silk will therefore be less than wool. The absorption of acid by the basic groups of silk is around 0.15 equivalents per kg compared with wool at about 0.82 equivalents[5]. Most of the polar side chains in silk are supplied by the serine and threonine residues. However, this is still a small quantity compared with the fact that the bulk of the polypeptide is made up from glycine or amino acids containing hydrocarbon side chains. Because of the relatively few bulky side chains, it is possible for the main chains to approach each other closely and form hydrogen bridges from one chain to another via the polar amide groups. Thus a solvent such as cupriethylenediamine, with a strong capacity for breaking hydrogen bonds, will be able to dissolve silk; in this respect, there is a marked contrast with wool where dissolution is only effected by breaking of disulphide cross linkages.

4. Molecular Weight of Silk

Data on the molecular weights of fibroin are not conclusive. A value of 33,000 has been obtained from osmotic pressure measurements of solutions of fibroin prepared by dissolving the protein in cupriethylenediamine followed by neutralisation with acetic acid and dialysis[6]. Using the ultracentrifuge, the higher value of 84,000 was obtained[7]. From viscosity and streaming birefringence techniques of solutions in lithium thiocyanate, a value of 55,000 has been deduced[8]. Light scattering measurements have yielded values of a million, a result which is suspect because of possible aggregation of the molecules in these rather difficult solvents[9]. Other workers, by end group analysis using a solution of fibroin in lithium iodide, obtained values[10] of 200,000–300,000 whereas fibroin dissolved in cupriethylenediamine gave a considerably lower value — 60,000.

Attempts have been made to separate undegraded fibroin into fractions. By treatment of a solution in cupriethylenediamine with acid until a pH of 3 was reached, some of the protein came out as a swollen gel; the proportions of each (gel and soluble matter) varied according to the concentrations and the time the fibroin was left in the solvent prior to neutralisation. Amino acid analyses gave no difference between the two fractions[11]. Other separations have been achieved by stepwise precipitations by additions of water to solutions in lithium thiocyanate; viscosity measurements on solutions of the fractions varied and hence indicated polydispersity of the protein[12]. Two components were obtained by treatment of a solution in cupriethylenediamine with Rivanol (2-ethoxy-6,9-diaminoacridine lactate) when part of the fibroin came down as a yellow precipitate. The complex (about 10–15%) was treated with dilute acid and then precipitated with acetone to remove the reagent. This fraction has been described as silk plastin[13]. The remainder was precipitated by acetone and called silk fibrin. Thus, evidence has accumulated to show that fibroin is polydisperse but a lot more work remains to be done to clarify the picture.

5. Arrangement of Amino Acids in the Polypeptide Chain

The terminal groups of fibroin have been estimated. The N-terminal groups have been found to be mainly glycine, alanine and serine[10,13,14]. The qualitative agreement between the workers in this field has not been good; this may be due to the difficulties of removing sericin without degradation of the fibroin. For C-terminal acids, glycine, valine and serine have been obtained[13] as well as tyrosine, valine and proline[15].

When fibroin is submitted to random hydrolysis, a mixture of lower peptides is obtained. The dipeptides GlyAla, AlaGly, GlyTyr were detected (in this formulation Gly, Ala, Tyr refers to the amino acids glycine, alanine and tyrosine respectively)[16]; later larger peptides e.g. GlySerPro-Tyr were found[17] (Pro=proline, Ser=serine). These tetrapeptides contain no glycine showing that there are sequences of amino acids in silk which do not contain this acid. Glycine turns up to a large extent in the dipeptides AlaGly and GlyAla but very little GlyGly is found. At first sight, this result suggests that the large quantities of these two amino acids present in fibroin might be in a long sequence, in which the residues alternate in the molecule. However, analyses[18] of silk hydrolysates show that the yield of AlaGly is very much larger than GlyAla instead of being equal as would be expected from such an alternating chain. The residues of glycine and alanine are also not joined in a random fashion since hydrolysis of such a molecule would lead to substantial yields of GlyGly in the hydrolysate. Only small quantities of this dipeptide have been found ($< 1.8\%$). Again, large yields of the tripeptide GlyAlaGly have been found[19]. This, together with the greater yield of AlaGly (about 2.5–3 times) as compared with GlyAla and the fact that no evidence for long sequences of these two acids is available, suggests that, in fibroin, the amino acid residues are in the form —XAlaGlyAlaGlyY— (where X and Y are residues other than alanine or glycine). Such a sequence would be expected to yield, on partial hydrolysis, about twice as much AlaGly as GlyAla. In addition, the tripeptide GlyAlaGly has been identified in the partial hydrolysate[20]. Against this evidence, some workers[21] have isolated the dipeptide AlaAla and suggest that, in an hydrolysis experiment, the ease of hydrolysis of the groups —XAla— and —GlyY— will be determined by the acids X and Y and this, in turn, will have its effect on the yield of the dipeptide —AlaGly—.

Further evidence for the structure of the fibroin chain comes from work using enzymes[22,23]. Hydrolysis of fibroin solution with the proteolytic enzyme chymotrypsin breaks the chains at the tyrosine residues, and yields a granular precipitate amounting to 60% of the fibroin. This product has been called both protofibrin and CTP and has been assigned the empirical formulae

$$Gly_{21}Ala_{14}Ser_7Tyr \text{ and } Gly_{29}Ala_{20}Ser_9Tyr$$

The N- and C-terminal groups have been identified and this has lead to the formula [GlyAlaSerGlyAlaGly]$_7$Tyr being postulated[22]. Other workers[23] in addition have carried out specific fission at the peptide bonds concerned with serine. The N-peptide to O-peptide shift occurs in anhydrous phosphoric acid at 40°C

$$
\begin{array}{ccc}
\overset{|}{CO} & & \\
| & & \\
NH & NH_2 & \overset{|}{CO} \\
| & | & | \\
CH—CH_2OH & \rightarrow \quad CH—CH_2—O & \\
| & | & \\
CO & CO & \\
| & | & \\
NH & NH & \\
| & | &
\end{array}
$$

After removal of the phosphoric acid, the material was treated with FDNB and the pH raised gradually to that of sodium carbonate in order to dinitrophenylate the amino groups. It was also hoped that the O-peptide groups were hydrolysed before substantial reversion took place. By analysis of the partial hydrolysis products after dinitrophenylation, it was possible to obtain an idea of the amino acid residues adjacent to the serine. A large yield of the DNP-peptides, DNP-Ser(Gly$_3$Ala$_2$) (36.2%), was obtained.

As a result of their analyses, the formula GlyAlaGlyAlaGly[SerGly(Ala-Gly)$_n$]$_8$SerGlyAlaAlaGlyTyr was postulated for CTP where n has a mean value of 2.

The precipitate formed from fibroin by chymotrypsin hydrolysis has a higher degree of crystallinity than the original protein[24]. The X-ray pattern of the CTP is in general structure identical to that of the silk itself; the conclusion is therefore reached that silk is composed of the crystalline segments of the CTP joined by irregular chains which carry those amino acids with large bulky side chains. These segments form the amorphous regions of the silk fibre but, unfortunately, little is known about their structure except that they must have those sequences of amino acid residues which have been identified and are not found in CTP[11,24] *e.g.* GlyTyrGly; GlyValGly; GlySerProTyrPro; TyrSerProTyr.

Some confirmation of the sequence SerGlyAlaGlyAlaGly comes from similarity of the infrared spectrum of this peptide to that of CTP[25].

6. Solution of Fibroin

Dissolution is possible in concentrated aqueous solutions of inorganic salts, notably the thiocyanates of lithium, sodium and calcium[26]. Little or no degradation of the fibroin occurs; the inorganic ions may be dialysed leaving a solution in water from which films may be cast[27]. These films can be redissolved in water. Other workers[6] have used cupriethylene-diamine as solvent and obtained, after dialysis, solutions which gave films of similar characteristics, apart from a certain amount of degradation which occurred in this rather alkaline solvent. Solutions of fibroin are of interest because of the production of a fibre carried out in nature from a solution. The transformation of the molecules of the protein coiled or folded in solution to the insoluble and more or less extended form may be defined as denaturation. The protein molecule in its extended form has the property of adhering to adjacent chains and becomes incapable of developing the high degree of hydration possible in the coiled or folded state. Thus a mass of bundles are produced, the chains being held together by hydrogen bonds and randomly distributed throughout the coagulated mass. When a protein solution is transformed into a fibre, the bundles are oriented to a considerable extent in a direction parallel to the fibre axis.

Silk fibroin when in the gland is present in the coiled form and is straightened out probably due to the mechanical forces which operate in the passage through the narrow aperture. The molecules are oriented in the direction of the spinning and an insoluble fibre results.

The changes which occur in silk are an example of the denaturation in proteins. In general, the globular proteins are readily soluble in water or dilute aqueous solutions of inorganic salts. Loss of solubility and crystallisability and the appearance of fibrous characteristics *i.e.* denaturation may occur by treatment with heat, mechanical shaking, organic solvents etc. The structure of the globular protein may be pictured to be one in which the long polypeptide chains are folded in definite planes, which themselves are arranged in a laminated structure[28]. An example is given in Fig. 72 where the four laminae are given. The laminae are

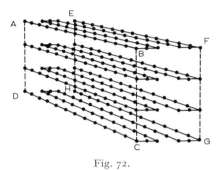

Fig. 72.

formed by the folding of single peptide chains and the linking together by some kind of cross linkages (disulphide bonds, non-proteinous material). Those links between the chains in the laminae are the weaker hydrogen bond type, as for example may be formed between CO and NH in the peptide groups. The ends of such molecules could be drawn out and the chains unfolded to form sheets. These sheets could form fibrous aggregates, a state which could be reached more readily if the linkages across the laminae were broken, when the chains themselves would be unfolded and allowed to adlineate. Thus it is possible to visualise how a protein such as casein may be transformed into a fibre; in this process, the protein is matured in an alkaline solution when the cross linkages are broken leaving the chain capable of adlineating on extrusion and coagulation. Denaturation is responsible for the change which occurs when blood clots; the fibrinogen in blood is acted on by the enzyme system (thrombose) and is transformed into the insoluble fibrin which is present in the blood clot as a tangled mass of fine filaments. The enzyme system contains a component capable of rupturing and presumably of reuniting disulphide linkages.

The formation of the silk fibre occurs when the protein solution is denatured presumably by mechanical forces. In the laboratory, solutions of fibroin may be used to form films. The film produced is soluble in water and has little tensile strength until remoistened and stretched.

This stretching causes the protein chains to elongate and form a fibrous material. With the protein insulin, it has been possible to convert to the fibrous form which was shown to contain fibrils, and reconvert back to the globular to obtain a crystalline material with identical physiological activity to the original[29]. The factors connected with the conversion appear to be similar for all proteins.

Aqueous solutions of fibroin can not with certainty be claimed to be identical to the native protein in the gland of the silk worm. The solutions however have much in common. Both are sensitive to shear, as for example shearing of a solution between glass plates or vigorous stirring will separate the protein. Surface forces are adequate to produce insoluble membranes or threads (*e.g.* bubbling). The normal denaturing agents (alcohol, aqueous trichloroacetic acid etc.) also produce insoluble fibroin. When the silk from the gland comes into contact with air it deposits fine fibrils. Physical techniques, as infra-red spectra, X-rays, birefringence etc. show that fibroin can exist in two configurations. One of these is found in the fibre and in stretched or rolled films; in this form, there is extensive interchain hydrogen bonding and the chains are oriented in the direction of the fibre axis or stretching. The N—H and C=O bonds are perpendicular to the axis of rolling. The second form is found in films freshly cast from aqueous solution when the hydrogen bonding is intramolecular; this form is readily converted to the more stable β-form.

7. Chemical Reactions of Silk

(a) Degradation by Acids, Alkalis, etc.

Treatment of silk fibres with acid or alkali causes hydrolysis of the peptide linkages; the degree of hydrolysis is dependent on the pH and is least between 4 and 8. Degradation of the fibre is shown by loss in tensile strength or changes in the viscosity of a solution. Hydrolysis by acid is more effective than alkali[6,30], and it has been suggested that acid hydrolysis occurs at linkages widely distributed along the chain whereas, in the early stages at least of alkaline treatment, attack is at the end of the protein chain.

Hydrochloric acid, especially when hot, readily dissolves fibroin and is used mainly in studies of hydrolysis. Hot concentrated sulphuric acid, whilst rapidly dissolving and hydrolysing fibroin, causes sulphation of the tyrosine and, when fibroin is left in concentrated acid for 3 days at $21\,°C$, 60% of the serine residues have undergone the $N \rightarrow O$ peptidyl shift. Nitric acid readily attacks fibroin, due partly to its powerful oxidising properties but, at the same time, nitration of the benzene nuclei can occur. Organic acids have little effect at room temperature when dilute but when concentrated fibroin may be dissolved, possibly with a certain amount of decomposition.

The effect most clearly shown as far as alkalis are concerned is the reaction of the hydroxyamino acids. Boiling with 0.1 N alkali, results in a loss of about $\frac{1}{3}$ of the serine and threonine residues and an increase in amide nitrogen. It seems that the acids serine and threonine show an increased sensitivity to alkali when combined in a polypeptide.

Proteolytic enzymes do not readily attack fibroins in fibrous form presumably because the chains in silk, due to the lack of bulky side chains, are packed very close to each other. Significant degradation may also be caused by water or steam at 100°C.

(b) Oxidation

Work on the oxidation of proteins is rather meagre since the reactions are very complex. Oxidising agents may attack proteins in three possible points (a) at the side chains, (b) at the N-terminal residues and (c) at the peptide bonds of adjacent amino groups.

Hydrogen peroxide is absorbed by silk and it is thought to form complexes with amino groups and peptide bonds[31]. Other workers[32] have shown hydrogen peroxide to diminish the tyrosine content and have suggested that peptide bonds are broken at the tyrosine residues. Peracetic acid causes more rapid scission and produces more acid groups than peroxide, as determined by the methylene blue uptake[33].

Unfortunately, the products of oxidation are not certain. Silk coloured yellow, pinkish yellow or brown may be produced by the action of oxidising agents. It is because of this colour that the formation of quinones[34] has been suggested but, as yet, the presence of o-quinones has not been detected in silk oxidised by peracetic acid nor by oxidation of tyrosine[33]. Another possibility is that the yellow colour produced when silk is exposed to oxygen and water arises from oxidation of the amino groups first formed by hydrolysis. Workers[35] using potassium permanganate have concluded that with this reagent attack also occurs at the phenolic group of the tyrosine.

(c) Other Agents

Chlorine attacks fibroin more vigorously than does sodium hypochlorite. Attack appears to be mainly at the tyrosine residues but the overall reaction is one of oxidation. Iodine and bromine also cause oxidative degradation but considerable combination occurs giving, for example, the 3,5-diiodo derivative of tyrosine.

Acetylation using acetic anhydride gives some degradation and acetylation of the free reactive groups e.g. hydroxyls in tyrosine and serine. If the reaction is carried out in methanol, both O- and N-acetylation can occur as well as methylation of the free carboxyl groups.

Reaction with methylating agents such as methyl iodide and methyl sulphate gives the methyl derivative of the tyrosine residues and the O-methyl derivatives of the serine residues.

The hydroxyl groups of serine and tyrosine in silk also react with chlorosulphonic acid in pyridine solution[37]. The reactivity and accessibility of these groups varies with the reagent used[38]. Thus although practically all the tyrosine can be methylated and acetylated, only about half of the serine reacts in this way. Similar results are obtained with tosyl chloride[39]. On the other hand, treatment with p-chlorobenzene diazonium chloride brings about coupling with about 84% of the tyrosine[40].

(d) Cross Linking

Fibroin will react with FDNB and FFDNB (1,3-difluoro-4,6-dinitrobenzene) to give products with enhanced resistance to hydrochloric acid and a reduced solubility.

Reaction of fibroin with FDNB occurs with the tyrosine hydroxyl groups to the extent of 96–99%, but with only 79% of the free amino groups of lysine. Other reagents carrying bifunctional groups have been used and it has been shown possible to obtain cross linkages provided that the fluorine groups are about 10 Å apart. Of those investigated, the most suitable reagent for bifunctional reaction was found to be 4,4'-difluoro-3,3'-dinitrodiphenyl sulphone (I)

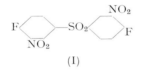

(I)

Fibroin treated with this reagent gives, on hydrolysis, large amounts of 3,3'-dinitrodiphenyl sulphone-4,4'-o,o'-bistyrosine and smaller amounts of the corresponding lysine derivative[36].

REFERENCES

1 J. M. Mathews, *Textile Fibres*, H. R. Mauersberger, (Editor), Chapman & Hall, London, 1954.
2 E. M. Shelton and T. B. Johnson, *J. Am. Chem. Soc.*, 47 (1925) 412.
3 C. H. Bamford, A. Elliot and W. E. Hanby, *Synthetic Polypeptides*, Academic Press, New York, 1956.
4 W. A. Schroeder and L. M. Kay, *J. Am. Chem. Soc.*, 77 (1955) 3908.
5 D. J. Lloyd and P. B. Bidder, *Trans. Faraday Soc.*, 31 (1953) 864.
  L. F. Gleysteen and M. Harris, *Am. Dyestuff Reptr.*, 30 (1941) 25.
6 D. Coleman and F. O. Howitt, *Symposium on Fibrous Proteins*, Soc. Dyers Colourists, 1946, p. 144; *Proc. Roy. Soc. London*, 109A (1947) 145.

[7] F. H. Holmes and D. I. Smith, *Nature*, 169 (1952) 193.

[8] R. Signer and R. Straessle, *Helv. Chim. Acta*, 30 (1947) 155.

[9] E. H. Mercer, *Textile Research J.*, 24 (1954) 135.

[10] G. Braunitzer and D. Wolff, *Z. Naturforsch.*, 10b (1955) 404.

[11] B. Drucker and S. G. Smith, *Nature*, 165 (1950) 196.

[12] R. Signer and R. Glanzmann, *Makromol. Chem.*, 5 (1951) 257.

[13] K. Narita, *J. Chem. Soc. Japan*, 75 (1954) 1005.

[14] H. Zahn and A. Würz, *Biochem. Z.*, 322 (1952) 327.

[15] J. T. B. Shaw and S. G. Smith, *J. Textile Inst.*, 45 (1954) 934T.

[16] E. Fischer and E. Abderhalden, *Ber.*, 40 (1907) 3544.

[17] E. Abderhalden and A. Bahm, *Z. physiol. Chem.*, 215 (1933) 246; 219 (1933) 72.

[18] M. Levy and E. Slobodian, *Cold Spring Harbor Symposia Quant. Biol.*, 14 (1949) 113; *J. Biol. Chem.*, 199 (1952) 563.

[19] E. Slobodian and M. Levy, *Federation Proc.*, 11 (1952) 288.

[20] H. G. Ioffe, *Biokhimiya*, 19 (1954) 495.

[21] L. M. Kay and W. A. Schroeder, *J. Am. Chem. Soc.*, 76 (1957) 3564.

[22] E. Waldschmidt-Leitz and O. Zeiss, *Z. physiol. Chem.*, 300 (1955) 49.

[23] F. Lucas, J. T. B. Shaw and S. G. Smith, *Nature*, 178 (1956) 861; *Biochem. J.*, 66 (1957) 468.

[24] B. Drucker, R. Hainsworth and S. G. Smith, *J. Textile Institute*, 44 (1953) 420T.

[25] H. Zahn and E. Schnabel, *Ann.*, 604 (1957) 62.

[26] P. P. von Veimarn, *Can. Chem. Met.*, 10 (1926) 227.

[27] E. J. Ambrose, C. H. Bamford, A. Elliot and W. E. Hanby, *Nature*, 167 (1951) 264.

[28] J. M. Preston (Editor), *Fibre Science*, The Textile Institute, 1955.

[29] D. F. Waugh, *J. Am. Chem. Soc.*, 66 (1944) 663.
D. F. Waugh, J. Smith and D. F. Fearing, *Proc. Soc. Exptl. Biol. Med.*, 7 (1948) 131.

[30] A. S. Tweedie, *Can. J. Research*, 16 (1938) 134.

[31] P. Alexander, D. Carter and C. Earland, *Biochem. J.*, 47 (1950) 251.

[32] M. Nakanishi and K. Kobayashi, *J. Soc. Textile and Cellulose Ind., Japan*, 10 (1954) 128, 131.

[33] D. A. Sitch and S. G. Smith, *J. Textile Institute*, 48 (1957) 341T.

[34] D. B. Das and J. B. Speakman, *J. Soc. Dyers Colourists*, 66 (1950) 583.
C. Schrile and J. Meybeck, *Compt. rend.*, 232 (1951) 732.

[35] S. Abune, *Bull. Fac. Agr. Kagoshima Univ.*, 2 (1953) 91, 97.
S. Abune and K. Koga, *Bull. Fac. Agr. Kagoshima Univ.*, 2 (1953) 103.

[36] H. Zahn and H. Zuber, *Textil-Rundschau*, 9 (1954) 119.

[37] H. C. Reitz, R. E. Ferrel, H. L. Fraenkel-Conrat and H. S. Olcott, *J. Am. Chem. Soc.*, 68 (1946) 1031.

[38] T. Kuramura, *J. Chem. Soc. Japan*, 56 (1953) 699.

[39] A. H. Gordon, A. J. P. Martin and R. L. M. Synge, *Biochem. J.*, 37 (1943) 538.

[40] I. Sakurada and K. Noina, *J. Soc. Textile and Cellulose Ind. Japan*, 6 (1950) 251.

[41] C. B. Anfinsen, M. L. Anson, K. Bailey and J. T. Edsall (Ed.), *Advances in Protein Chemistry*, Academic Press, New York, 1958.

CHAPTER 12

CRYSTALLINE STRUCTURES OF POLYMERS

1. General

Interaction of electromagnetic radiation with structures, whose size is comparable with the wavelength of the radiation, gives diffraction effects. If the structure is an orderly array or lattice, the diffraction becomes sharp so that the radiation is only scattered or diffracted in certain directions. Knowledge of the directions of scattered radiation in the pattern gives information on the geometry of the structure causing the scattering. Since the wavelengths of X-rays are of comparable order to the distances between atoms or molecules found in crystals, this kind of radiation is capable of yielding information on the crystal structure. The diffraction patterns obtained when a large crystal is interposed in a beam of X-rays are very sharp but, to obtain all the information required for analysis, the crystal must be oriented in all possible directions. This may be done by rotating the crystal around its axes. An alternative is to use a powder made up of small crystals arranged in a random fashion, when all configurations are encompassed by the sample. For details of the analysis of the X-ray pattern, the reader is referred elsewhere[1].

Examinations of polymers by X-rays gives more complex diagrams than wholly crystalline materials. A material such as polyvinyl acetate gives an X-ray photograph which shows rather diffuse haloes (Fig. 73). The position of these haloes corresponds to a distance in the polymer of 4–5 Å. This value is similar to that obtained with organic liquids and corresponds to the distance of closest approach of two molecules in liquid n-paraffins and alcohols[40,41]. Further, the main halo in the X-ray pattern is similar to that produced from examination of the monomer. Such comparisons lead to the conclusion that the chains in polyvinyl acetate are not arranged in an ordered fashion and that the structure of this polymer is amorphous.

A filament of nylon 66 when freshly extruded shows an X-ray pattern (Fig. 74a) consisting of a series of well defined rings. This is to be anticipated from crystalline material when the crystal axes are disoriented. However, the pattern changes when the filament is stretched or drawn. Sharply defined reflections develop (Fig. 74b and c), indicating that the crystalline material has been oriented. Diffuse haloes analogous to those of polyvinyl acetate are present so that the polymer now exhibits the characteristics of both crystalline and amorphous materials.

More detailed analysis has shown that the crystalline regions vary in size but will range up to 600 Å in length; this value is considerably less than the length of a polymer molecule. Hence the polymer chains must

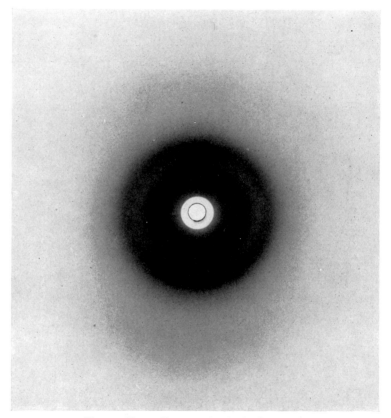

Fig. 73. X-ray diagram of polyvinyl acetate.
(Courtesy Cotton, Silk and Man Made Fibres R.A.)

run through more than one crystalline region. A picture of the structure has been built up in which crystalline regions are interspersed with amorphous ones as is represented diagrammatically in Fig. 75a and b.

For a polymer which contains crystalline regions after extrusion, the drawing process will have the effect of orientation of the crystallites as indicated in Fig. 75b. Whether the freshly extruded materials contain crystalline regions depends on the polymer; some will tend to be formed

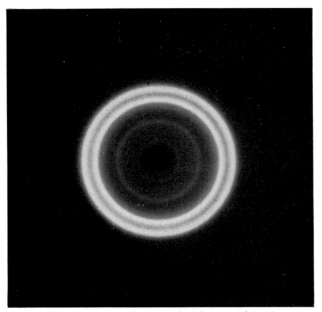

Fig. 74a. X-ray diagram of undrawn nylon 66.
(Courtesy British Nylon Spinners)

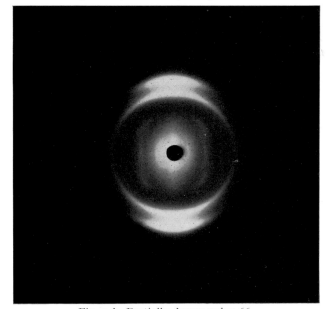

Fig. 74b. Partially drawn nylon 66.
(Courtesy British Nylon Spinners)

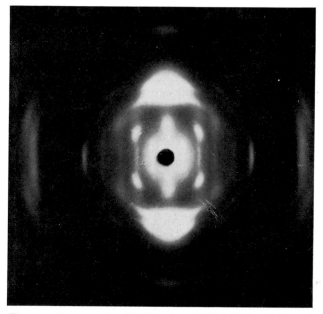

Fig. 74c. Drawn nylon 66. (Courtesy British Nylon Spinners)
N.B. Diagrams 74 are negatives.

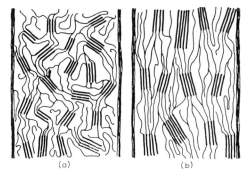

(a)　　　　　　　　　　(b)

Fig. 75. Model of micellar structure of polymers (a) unoriented, (b) oriented[59].

in an amorphous state and crystallise on stretching (see Chapter 15). The
true structure is more complex[52] than this but nevertheless pictures
such as Fig. 75 serve as a useful guide.

Polymers range in properties from almost completely amorphous to
highly crystalline. Only in some instances a macrocrystalline material
has been obtained. In the field of globular proteins, crystals may
sometimes be obtained as, for example, of necrosis virus protein[47] (Fig.

Fig. 76a. Monocrystal of necrosis virus protein spilling its unit cells at bottom corner[47]. Each small sphere contains four protein molecules.

76a). Single crystals of polyethylene and isotactic polyolefins[31] (Fig 76b) and of nylon 66[44] have been prepared. Normally the polymer is not completely crystalline.

Reference to Fig. 74c shows that the X-ray diagram is not composed of spots as expected from a perfectly crystalline material but of arcs. This spreading of the reflections arises to a large extent from the fact that the crystallites, as indicated diagrammatically in Fig. 75b, are not oriented perfectly along the axis of the fibre. Further, the crystallites in the fibre will be oriented at random in a plane at right angles to the fibre axis. The pattern obtained from a fibre (often known as a fibre diagram) thus resembles that obtained when a single crystal is rotated about one of its axes. The differences of the fibre diagram from that given by rotation of the single crystal are however characteristic, and arise not only from the

Fig. 76b. Electron micrograph of a single crystal of polyethylene[3].

imperfect orientation of the crystallites along the fibre axis but also from the fact that the crystallites will be of different sizes. Small crystallites give a certain amount of diffuseness since there is a lower limit below which a sharp diffraction pattern is not obtained. In addition the

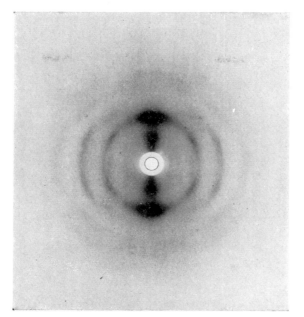

Fig. 77. X-ray patterns of fibers.
Fig. 77a. An oriented viscose monofil.
(Courtesy Cotton, Silk and Man Made Fibres R.A.)

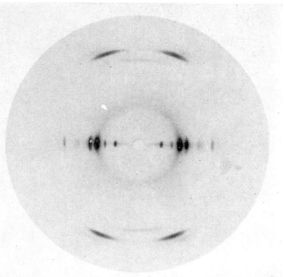

Fig. 77b. Ramie.
(Courtesy Cotton, Silk and Man Made Fibres R.A.)

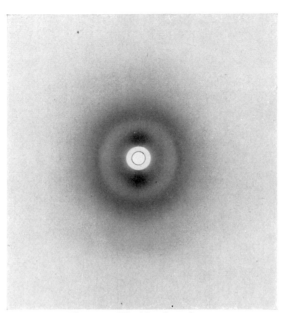

Fig. 77c. Wool in the α-form.
(Courtesy Cotton, Silk and Man Made Fibres R.A.)

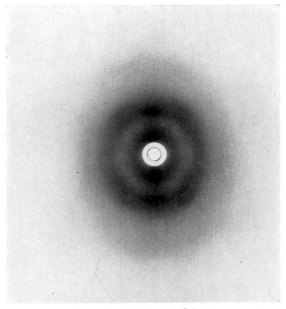

Fig. 77d. Wool in the β-form.
(Courtesy Cotton, Silk and Man Made Fibres R.A.)

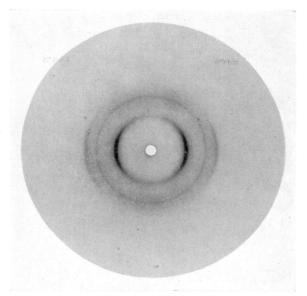

Fig. 77e. Vinylon.
(Courtesy Messrs. Courtaulds Ltd.)

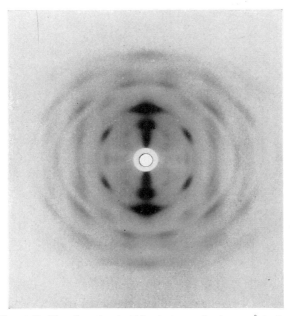

Fig. 77f. Courtelle (the sharping in this photograph at 3.51 Å is due to TiO₂).
(Courtesy Messrs. Courtaulds Ltd.)

fibre diagrams show diffuse haloes arising from the scattering of the amorphous regions.

The degree of sharpness of the diffraction pattern varies from fibre to fibre. In Fig. 77 are given examples of patterns obtained with some typical fibres.

2. Conditions for Crystallinity

The ability of polymers to crystallise depends among other things on the regularity of the structure and the chemical nature of the chains. Since the crystalline state is essentially one where the chains are arranged in an orderly and regular fashion, any factors which decrease the regularity will reduce the ability to crystallise. Considerable advantage is gained if the chains are linear; thus polyethylene terephthalate is a highly crystalline polymer whereas the corresponding isophthalate and phthalates have never been obtained crystalline[19]. The chains in an amorphous polymer such as polyvinyl acetate are composed of the random arrangement of the D- and L-enantiomorphs of the units (—CH$_2$CHR—).

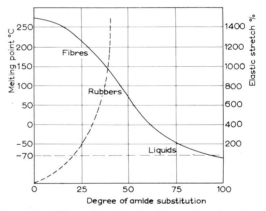

Fig. 78. Elasticity and melting point of nylon 66 as a function of the degree of substitution of the amide hydrogen by methoxyl[48].

Crystalline addition polymers of the vinyl type are formed when only one of the enantiomorphs is present as in isotactic materials, or when both are arranged in a regular fashion as in syndiotactic polymers.

By the same token, bulky side groups which do not pack well and hence force the chains apart will also have the effect of hindering the development of crystallinity. Occasional irregularities such as chain branching in polyethylene, or copolymerisation with a minor amount of a comonomer, may limit the crystallisation to regions between the comonomer units.

The chemical nature of the groups in the chain will modify the tendency of the polymer to crystallise. Groups which are strongly polar or capable of forming hydrogen bonds will act as points of attraction for forming crystallites. The tendency to crystallise is markedly reduced when such groups are not regularly disposed.

The effect of introducing side chains on the crystallinity of the polymer is demonstrated very clearly in work[48] carried out on nylon 66. In this polymer, the hydrogen bonding amide groups may be methylated or methoxylated. This results in a progressive decrease in elastic modulus (or an increase in elasticity) and melting point as substitution increases; there is a steady transition from the crystalline fibre to an amorphous rubber-like state until, when substitution reaches completion, the polyamide has become a viscous liquid (Fig. 78).

3. Principles of Packing of Polymer Chains

Geometric analysis shows that there are 232 different arrangements of the elements of symmetry in a three dimensional crystal lattice. These arrangements, normally referred to as space groups, possess different combinations of the symmetry elements. An element of symmetry is an operation such as reflection or rotation which would bring a crystal (pictured as having an infinite extension) back into coincidence with its original structure. The space elements occurring most frequently in crystals are those containing screw axes and glide planes.

A screw axis is perhaps best demonstrated by the structure of polythene (Fig. 79). The carbon atoms are disposed in a zig-zag arrangement with a distance between repeat methylene groups of 2.54 Å. If the chain be rotated through $180°$ and moved along by a distance of $\frac{1}{2}$ (2.54) Å (*i.e.* half the repeats), the new arrangement will coincide exactly with the old. Thus a screw axis is an ordinary axis of symmetry but, superimposed on the rotation through an angle ($60°$, $90°$, $120°$ or $180°$), there is a displacement along the axis. The structure of rubber hydrochloride (Fig. 80) possesses a glide plane; the plane may be put at right angles to the plane of the paper to coincide with the dotted line. If the structure be imagined to be reflected in this plane and translated half the repeat distance ($\frac{1}{2} \times 8.8$ Å), the new disposition of the chain becomes coincident with the old. Thus, a glide plane is a mirror plane in the structure coupled with a displacement. It has been shown that these two symmetry elements are of particular significance, since their occurrence enables savings in space to be made when packing the molecules in a crystal. The importance of these elements compared with normal axes and planes of symmetry lies in the fact that polymer molecules possess protuberances which, if reflected, would coincide with protuberances in a neighbouring chain.

It is the addition of the translation that allows the protuberances of one chain to lie in the hollows of another.

There exist a large number of polymers whose backbones consist of carbon atoms. Such materials may be regarded as substituted polyethyl-

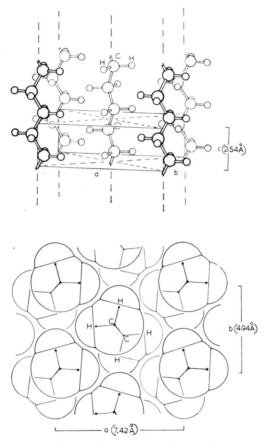

Fig. 79. Structure of polythene[53].

enes. The substituents, however, exert a considerable influence on the configurations adopted by each chain as well as the manner in which the chains are packed laterally.

The types of structure occurring in fibres may broadly be classified as follows:

(a) linear configurations which may be fully extended or moderately perturbed from full extension;
(b) helical configurations, the long axes of the helices lying parallel to one another;

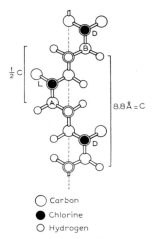

Fig. 80. Chain structure of rubber hydrochloride[8].

(c) sheet-like aggregates of molecules bonded perpendicularly to the long axes of the molecules by hydrogen bonds, the sheets themselves being parallel and possibly puckered or pleated.

4. Details of Polymer Structure

Where possible the size of the unit cell in the crystalline regions is given below. It should be noted that these are defined by three axes a, b and c, one of which corresponds to the axis of the fibre together with three angles.

(a) Polyethylene

In the zig-zag structure of polyethylene, the hydrogen atoms occur at the repeat spacing of 2.54 Å; they are so to speak stacked vertically above each other. A model giving the correct size to the atoms (ca. 2.3 Å for hydrogen) shows that this vertical stacking leaves little waste space between them. Substituents other than hydrogen are, in general, too large to allow, except in special circumstances, this kind of packing (Fig. 79). The chains are packed side by side to give an orthorhombic (i.e. rectangular) unit cell with $a = 7.42$ Å, $b = 4.94$ Å, and c (fibre axis) $= 2.54$ Å. The fibre axis dimension corresponds to the plane zig-zag chain and the dimensions are almost the same as those for a hydrocarbon of a shorter chain[4]. The packing resembles that in simple crystalline paraffins.

(b) Polyvinyl Chloride

The atactic material is very poorly crystalline but it gives a chain repeat of 5.1 Å, twice that for polyethylene. Even when stretched into a fibre, the crystallisation is poor[1,2,5]. For this polymer it is possible to have both D- and L-forms of the units in the chains; a random distribution of these units would not be expected to allow the compact packing required to form a crystallite. If, however, the D- and L-units were to alternate, every second monomer unit would be equivalent and a planar configuration would lead to a repeat distance between the chlorine atoms[32] of 5.1 Å. The possible structure for such an arrangement is given in Fig. 81. Thus

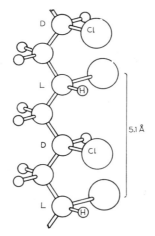

Fig. 81. Structure of syndiotactic polyvinyl chloride[8]. The lettering indicates the alternation of hydrogen (H) and chlorine atoms (Cl) in the vertical stacking.

the development of crystallinity even to a small extent might be taken to show that, in some measure, polyvinyl chloride has a syndiotactic structure; if this had been the overall structure, the polymer could have been highly crystalline, as in syndiotactic polybutadiene where the pendant groups are vinyl[6]. Syndiotactic polyvinyl chloride itself takes up a planar form[44].

(c) Polyvinylidene Chloride

This material has a repeat distance of 4.68 Å in the direction of the chain. Some shortening of the expected 5.1 Å repeat for the zig-zag structure is indicated, and a *cis* arrangement of the chain has been suggested[7,32]. The cell dimensions[38] are $a = 22.54$ Å, b (fibre axis) $= 4.68$ Å, $c = 12.35$ Å and $\beta = 84°10'$.

The planar zig-zag does not seem to be possible because of the size of the chlorine atoms, and a spiral form may be adopted with 5 turns for 8 monomer units[45].

It may be noted that, in this substance, the units are symmetric and enantiomorphs do not exist.

(d) Polyvinyl Acetate and Alcohol

Polyvinyl acetate is an amorphous material prevented from crystallising by the random arrangement of the asymmetric carbon centres.

Polyvinyl alcohol is prepared from amorphous polyvinyl acetate by hydrolysis[8] but may be obtained highly crystalline. The unit cell turns out to be monoclinic[9,10] with $a = 7.81$ Å, b (fibre axis) $= 2.52$ Å and $c = 5.51$ Å and the angle $\beta = 91°42'$. The fibre axis distance corresponds to a carbon skeleton in the extended zig-zag form as found in polyethylene: the hydroxyl groups must therefore occupy the sites of the hydrogen atoms in the polyethylene structure. Earlier workers, because of the high crystallinity of polyvinyl alcohol suggested that all the hydroxyl groups were situated on one side of the chain[10], but this has been shown to be untenable since analysis shows that the hydroxyl groups are positioned indiscriminately[11]. The crystallinity arises from the ability of the hydroxyl to replace the hydrogen atoms in polyethylene without seriously disrupting the structure.

(e) Polyesters

Polyethylene terephthalate, although differing in composition from polyethylene, nevertheless possesses a not dissimilar crystal structure[12].

The repeat unit in polyethylene terephthalate along the chain is 10.75 Å, a value only slightly less than that expected for a fully extended chain with one chemical unit to the geometric repeating unit, and successive ester groups in the *trans* configuration to each other (10.9 Å). The chains are therefore nearly planar (Fig. 82). The unit cell is triclinic[12] with dimensions $a = 4.56$ Å, $b = 5.94$ Å, c (fibre axis) $= 10.75$ Å, $\alpha = 98.5°$, $\beta = 118°$ and $\gamma = 112°$. It is noteworthy that the atomic positions in the crystallite indicate that no special forces of attraction exist between the molecules. The spacings between atoms of neighbouring molecules is of the order expected if van der Waals forces operate.

The structures of aliphatic polyesters have not yet been determined in great detail. In the simplest structures — those from ethylene and decamethylene glycols and dicarboxylic acids with an even number of atoms — there is one chemical unit per repeat. The chains are packed side by side in monoclinic cells of angle 65° and the carbonyl groups lie in planes inclined with respect to the chain axis. This structure also holds for polyesters of ω-hydroxy acids with an even number of carbon atoms (Fig. 83a). Polyesters with an odd number of carbon atoms require two chemical units before geometric repetition is found, and a unit cell is suggested which is rectangular with the carbonyl groups lying in

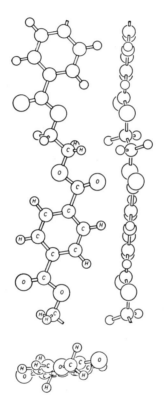

Fig. 82. Structure of polyethylene terephthalate[54].

planes normal to the chain axis[32] (Fig. 83b). The structures of other polyesters *e.g.* those from trimethylene glycol are more complex. In this series, the zig-zag configuration leads to an unstable arrangement of dipoles, and there is a uniform folding of the chains along the fibre axis with the main twisting at the ester bonds[34].

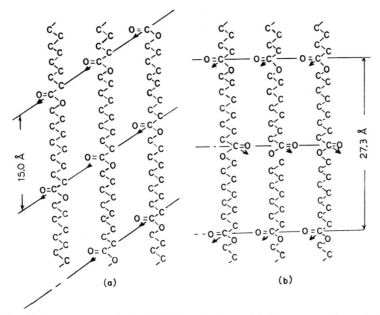

Fig. 83. Chain arrangements in aliphatic polyesters with (a) even numbers of chain atoms, (b) odd numbers of chain atoms[32].

(f) Polyamides

In the crystalline regions of polyamides, the molecules are fully extended and hence the chains have a planar zig-zag configuration[14]. However with nylon 66 and 610, the position is complicated by the existence of two crystal forms designated α and β. The α-form is found alone in annealed or phenol treated specimens; it is the predominating form in ordinary samples as well as being the more stable. The two forms differ in the side by side arrangements of molecules. In the α-form, the cell is triclinic with the following dimensions.

TABLE 26

	a	b	c (fibre axis)	α	β	γ
Nylon 66	4.9	5.4	17.2	48.5°	77°	63.5°
610	4.95	5.4	22.4	49°	76.5°	63.5°

The molecules are linked together by hydrogen bonds to form sheets and a simple packing of these sheets gives rise to the triclinic cell. Hydrogen bonds are favoured, since the oxygen atoms of an amide group in one chain lie opposite the NH group of a neighbouring one. The distance between oxygen and nitrogen atoms is 2.8 Å, a value suitable for hydrogen bond formation and shorter than the expected distance (*ca.* 3.21 Å) for van der Waals forces to be operative (Fig. 84).

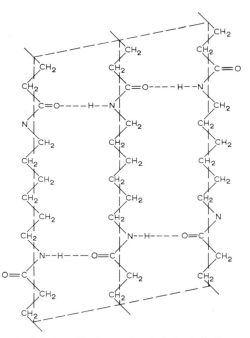

Fig. 84. Arrangement of chains of hydrogen bonded sheets in the crystal structure of nylon 66[56].

The β-form has not been as well investigated as the α but it appears that hydrogen bonded sheets are the same as in α-crystals but stacked in a different way.

Structures of polyamides made from ω-amino acids are of two kinds depending on whether there is an even or odd number of carbon atoms. The two structures differ in the directions in which the chains are laid down *i.e.* whether they are parallel or antiparallel. This is to be expected since reversal of the chain alters the sequence of atoms encountered in going along the chain. This situation does not apply to polymer chains made from diamines/dicarboxylic acids, where the sequence is independent of the chain direction[49].

The two possible arrangements, parallel and anti-parallel, are shown schematically in Fig. 85 for nylon 7. In this example, all the amide groups

nylon 8 but in which successive layers are displaced with respect to the chain direction, so that the polar groups are in planes tilted with respect to the plane of the page. It may be that there exist in nylon 6 both parallel and anti-parallel forms.

(g) Polytetrafluoroethylene

The chains in this compound deviate from the planar form. In polyethylene the hydrogen atoms can be stacked, when the carbon chain assumes a planar zig-zag configuration. When these are replaced by fluorine with a diameter of 2.7 Å, a planar arrangement is not possible but the congestion of the fluorine atoms, which would arise if the planar form were adopted, is relieved by a slight regular twist introduced in the chain. A spiral form is taken up[20]. The spiral is a gentle one with a repeat unit of 13 carbon atoms or 26 in a full turn of the spiral (Fig. 87). Such packing gives rise

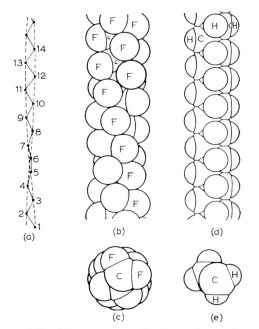

Fig. 87. Comparison of the chain structures of polytetrafluoroethylene[8] (a, b, c) and polyethylene (d, e)[8].

to a stiffness in the chain and is a deterrent to melting whereas the interchain forces are small, as shown by the low polarity and low heat of evaporation.

(h) Tactic Polymers

X-ray examination of isotactic materials shows that their crystalline structures are consistent with the hypothesis that each repeating unit has the same steric configurations, at least over long intervals of the chain. Isotactic 1,2-polybutadiene and polypropylene, if considered as a zig-zag, show considerable steric interference between successive substituents;

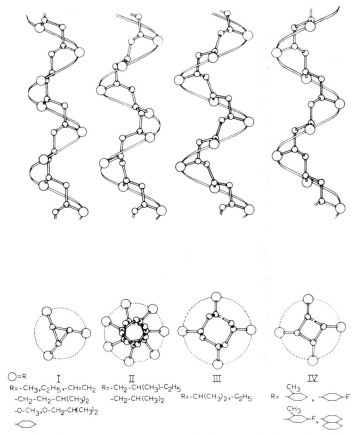

Fig. 88. Helicoidal forms assumed in crystalline state by isotactic chains with different symmetries[55].

the molecular backbones become folded around the C—C bonds to give a helix with the substituents projecting radially at an angle to the long axis. The helical pitch and cross section are sensitive to the dimensions and nature of the pendant groups (Fig. 88).

Some characteristics of polymers which adopt the helical form are given in Table 28.

TABLE 28

Polymer	Chain characteristics		
	Crystallographic repeat distance (Å)	Turns of helix per repeat	Number of monomer units per repeat
Polytetrafluoroethylene (below 20 °C)	16.8	0.5	13
Isotactic polypropylene	6.5	1	3
Isotactic poly-*p*-fluorostyrene	8.3	1	4
α-Poly-L-alanine	70.4	13	47

The situation is complicated by left and right hand helices[36] and, in isotactic crystallites, it is to be expected that the spirals are subdivided according to the handedness of the carbon centres studded along them. They may be classified into 4 groups.

TABLE 29

SUBDIVISION OF CHAIN CONFORMATIONS IN ISOTACTIC CRYSTALS

	Handedness		
	of spiral	of all carbon centres along spiral	
(1)	Right	Right	(D)
(2)	Left	Left	(L)
(3)	Right	Left	(L)
(4)	Left	Right	(D)

All four conformations have the same free energy since definite symmetry operations bring them into mutual coincidence. The basic operations are (1) reflection reverses the handedness of the spiral and of the carbon centres; (2) inverting the chain changes the handedness of the carbon centres but not the direction of the spiral. By suitable combinations of these operations, any of the four conformations may be transferred into any of the other. When an isotactic crystallite forms, the chains can take up more than one conformation and the crystal accommodates the various conformations rather than disentangling the available chains and making a more restricted choice. Thus in a crystallite, equivalent lattice positions can accept a spiral of definite handedness with equal ease, irrespective of whether it contains only left- or right-handed centres; in other words, the properties of the spirals will be randomised. By randomising, the crystallite loses to some extent its efficiency of close packing. The degree of randomness, leads to a lower closeness of packing; polypropylene may be obtained (in a highly randomised form) by rapid chilling of the melt, when it seems that the crystallites do not have time to sort out right-handed and left-handed spirals. This kind of randomised polymer has a lower density (0.88 g/ml) than the usual form (0.92 g/ml). Evidence for the randomised nature of the left-handed and right-handed spirals is indicated from the X-ray diffraction pattern coupled with the identity of the I.R. spectrum of the two forms[46]. It seems that lateral dovetailing is not essential in tactic polymer crystals, since the densities of these polymers are low and not much greater than that of the amorphous polymer. This is because the lack of lateral dovetailing of the spiral chain polymers and detailed study of the structure reveals large empty channels.

(i) Cellulose

Four crystal structures have been recognised in this material; these are designated as cellulose I, II, III and IV. Only the more important cellulose I and II will be discussed.

(i) Cellulose I is found in the native cellulose of plants. The cellulose chain is made up of glucopyranose residues in strainless puckered chair form[16]. The most favoured structure[17] for the cellobiose unit is the "symmetrical" configuration (Fig. 89). The cell dimensions are $a = 8.35$,Å

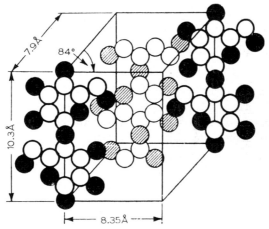

Fig. 89. The unit cell of cellulose I[17].

b (fibre axis) $= 10.3$ Å, $c = 7.9$ Å, $\beta = 84°$. β is the angle between the a and c axes which are both perpendicular to the axis b. The length of the cell is that of the length of a cellobiose unit.

(ii) Cellulose II. This modification is the one which occurs in regenerated cellulose or when cellulose esters are hydrolysed; it may be derived from cellulose I by vigorous swelling treatments, *e.g.* mercerisation. The dimensions of the unit cell are $a = 8.1$ Å, $b = 10.3$ Å (fibre axis), $c = 9.1$ Å and $\beta = 62°18$. The volume of this unit cell is very nearly that of cellulose I. The pyranose rings are rotated as indicated in Fig. 90 where cellulose I and II are compared. The cellobiose units are hydrogen bonded.

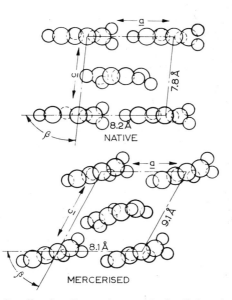

Fig. 90. The unit cells of native and mercerised cellulose in projection[8].

As a result of caustic soda penetration into the lattice of cellulose I to form cellulose II, many hydrogen bonds are broken and it is estimated that the number of available hydroxyl groups is increased by 25%.

(j) Cellulose Derivatives

In certain cellulose derivatives such as the triacetate, substitution of the hydroxyl groups affects only the lateral spacing.

Cellulose triacetate has two possible arrangements. Triacetate I is obtained from acetylation of cellulose I under conditions which retain the fibre form; triacetate II is the arrangement which occurs if the polymer has been dispersed. The dimensions of the unit cells have been given[39] in Table 30.

TABLE 30

	a	b	c	β
Triacetate I	22.6 Å	10.5	11.8	79°
Triacetate II	25.8	10.5	11.45	66.4°

(k) Silk

Only fibroin from the caterpillar of *Bombyx mori* will be discussed here.

The detailed analysis of the X-ray photographs is formidable due, amongst other things, to the fact that fibroin is made up of a series of different amino acids and the difficulties of assessing the order in which the different residues occur in the crystalline regions. However, in spite of these complications a structure has been proposed[22]. In formulating the most probable configurations of the chains, two principles have been employed *viz.* that the atoms of the amide group should be coplanar and the formation of hydrogen bonds between NH and CO groups should be near to the maximum possible.

This protein gives an X-ray diagram which is considered to arise from an extended form of the chain and is classified as a β-form as distinct from α-structures found in synthetic polypeptides and wool.

The designation α and β to polypeptide structures arose from work on wool. Normal wool gives a fibre diagram which is characteristic and for convenience the structure giving rise to this was called the "α-form" (Fig. 77c). Subsequent work, however, showed that wool fibres could be stretched by a factor of about 2 and, in this condition, the fibre gave a different X-ray pattern. The modified structure was then designated as

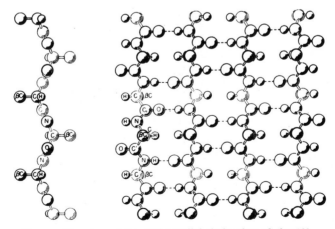

Fig. 91. Drawing of the anti-parallel chain pleated sheet[22].

the "β-form" (Fig. 77d). The α-structure is an extended helical form of
the chain in which the CO and NH groups of the successive residues protrude from opposite sides and are perpendicular to the axis of the helix.
Hydrogen bonds may be formed between the CO and NH groups of
adjacent chains. The arrangement of the chains can be described as
a pleated sheet. In such a sheet, the chains may run in parallel or anti-
parallel directions. The former gives a fibre axis identity period of 6.50 Å
whereas the latter gives 7.00 Å, a value found in fibroin[21]. A diagram of
the anti-parallel pleated sheet is given in Fig. 91. Further in the crystalline regions of fibroin, there is evidence for suggesting that the sequence
GlyYGlyYGly occurs, where Y is alanine or serine. This restricts the
number of residues to be considered and hence a structure may be built
up in which anti-parallel chains are linked together to form sheets, the
hydrogen atoms from the glycine residues protruding from one side of
the sheet whereas the hydroxymethyl and methyl protrude from the
other. These sheets are packed so that the distance between corresponding
(alternating sheets) is 9.50 Å with the distances between individual
sheets being approximately 3.5 and 5.7 Å occurring alternately (Fig. 92)[22].

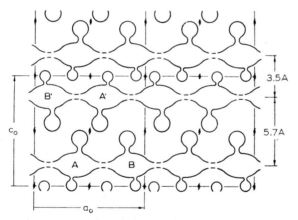

Fig. 92. Schematic representation of the pseudo unit of structure of *Bombyx mori*
fibroin, viewed along fibre axis[22].

The only cell compatible with the X-ray data is an orthogonal one with
$a = 9.40$ Å, b (fibre axis) $= 6.97$ Å and $c = 9.20$ Å. The a axis is parallel
to the hydrogen bonds in the same sheet and refers to the distance
between alternate chains. The b is parallel to the main chains with an
identity distance which corresponds to two residues along the chain. The
distribution of pleated sheets along the c axis has shown that they are

separated by 3.5 Å and 5.7 Å. It is a feature of these pleated sheets that the side chains of the amino acid residues project perpendicularly and that, within a given chain, the side chains of adjacent residues protrude on opposite sides. The packing distance of the sheets depends on the size of the side chains which, for hydrogen atoms, leads to a distance of 3.5 Å and, for methyl or hydroxymethyl, to 5.7 Å. This structure which has been described does not explain the X-ray data completely as there are indications of repeat spacings at 35 Å and 15 Å. Such variations in which the sheets are packed could arise from acids containing side chains larger than glycine, alanine and serine being present in the crystalline regions and hence increasing the spacing. It is also interesting to note that the structure of fibroin is similar to those of synthetic polypeptides in the extended or β-form.

(l) Synthetic Polypeptides and Wool

Only an indication can be given of the structures of these complex materials. Polypeptides may exist in two forms the α and β. Fibroin just discussed is an example of the β. This is essentially a stretched polypeptide chain with intermolecular hydrogen bonds. It has a 2-fold screw axis and a repeat distance of around 7.23 Å[23]. The α-form takes up the shape of a helix in which the CO and NH groups are hydrogen bonded intramolecularly. Thus polymers in the β-form are cross linked and will not be as soluble as the α, e.g. polymethylglutamate in the α-configuration is soluble in chloroform but, when films of this polymer are made and stretched, a substantial quantity of the molecules are transformed into the β-form and hence the material loses its solubility in this solvent.

(i) Polyglycine occurs in two forms; I and II. Form I may be obtained by casting films from dichloroacetic acid. It has an extended β-configuration. Form II may be precipitated from a solution of the polymer in aqueous lithium bromide; it differs from polypeptides in both the α- or β-configuration. The X-ray data have been interpreted by giving the chains a 3-fold screw axis (Fig. 93a) and a residue translation of 3.1 Å[57]. The chains can then be packed in a hexagonal lattice and held by intermolecular hydrogen bonds (Fig. 93b).

(ii) Polyalanines from the D-, L- and DL-forms have been prepared. Two forms of the poly-DL-alanine and poly-L-alanine have been made. Films made from these materials gave products which possessed an α-configuration but was transformable to the β on stretching[24,25].

The β-forms of these materials have structures similar to that of fibroin. The α-forms take up a helical structure in which the polypeptide chains are not fully extended. Studies of the possible sizes and number of turns of helices has led most workers in this field to the conclusion that

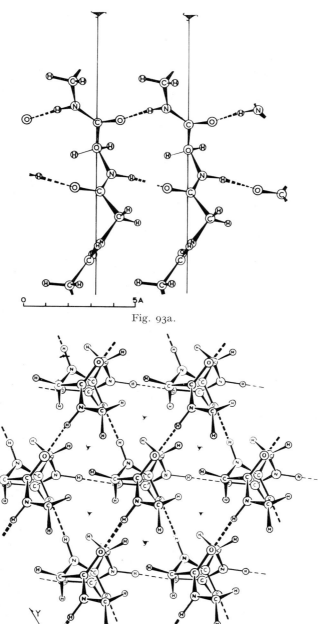

Fig. 93a.

Fig. 93b.
Fig. 93a and b. The structure of polyglycine II[5].

References p. 347

the so-called α-helix is the most likely[26]. This is given diagrammatically in Fig. 94. With a helix it is possible to form intramolecular hydrogen bonds which, in fact, hold the spiral together. This helix has 3.6 residues per turn and hence will have an integral number in a finite number of

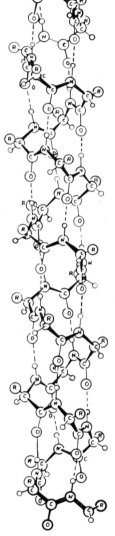

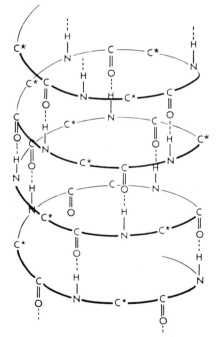

Fig. 94. Diagram of the α-helix[58].

Fig. 95. The α-helix made up of D-residues[13].

turns, and so can have a fundamental repeat distance. In the α-helix, the consecutive residues have an axial translation of 1.5 Å, the ratio of these figures is the number of residues per turn. The exact details of this helix will vary within fairly narrow limits according to the bond angle at the α-carbon atoms. An actual helix made up of D-residues and a left-handed spiral is shown in Fig. 95. The decision as to the sense of the α-helix is rather difficult but recent studies of poly-L-alanine are in favour of the right-handed spiral rather than the left[35] although it has been suggested that the sense of the helix may change at the cystine residues[42].

Although transformation of synthetic polypeptides from the α- to the β-form can be carried out by stretching, the reverse transformation is not so simple and must be carried out by, for example, dissolving the β-

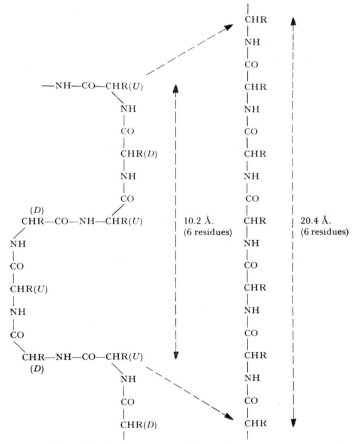

Fig. 96. Astbury's structure for wool[28,29].

form in a solvent. This usually happens slowly with a solvent such as chloroform, but more strongly interacting solvents such as *m*-cresol may be used. The polymer is regenerated in the α-form by evaporation or precipitation by a non-solvent[27].

In general, polypeptides with bulky side chains (*e.g.* polyphenylalanine) are readily obtained in the α-form. By contrast, polyglycine is normally β; as the side chain increases in size, the α-form becomes progressively more stable. Wool gives an X-ray diffraction pattern indicative of the α-form but, when extended under suitable conditions, this fibre changes the molecular arrangement to the β-configuration. This change is reflected in the considerable difference between the X-ray diagrams of the two forms (Fig. 77).

On stretching by more than 20–30%, the X-ray diagram of wool or hair changes from the α and is replaced by the β photograph[28]. The change can be reversed by the release of tension and may be carried out repeatedly by slow extension and relaxation of the fibre. In addition, wool when treated in water with 1% aqueous sodium hydroxide could be reversibly extended 100% and it was suggested this extension was numerically proportional to the molecular orientation which accompanies stretching; in other words, the stretched β-form was twice that of the folded α-chain. This was explained by the structure given in Fig. 96[28,29].

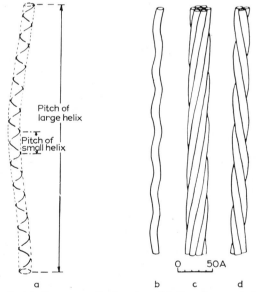

Fig. 97. Coiled coils (a) diagrammatic drawing of helix whose axis is deformed into a helix of larger pitch; (b) a single coiled helix; (c) seven-strand rope of coiled helices; (d) three-strand rope of coiled helices[30].

In this figure, the side chains were considered to project alternately above (U) and below (D) the plane of the folded chain. This structure unfortunately does not explain all the X-ray data.

The single α-helical structure found in the polypeptides appears not to occur in wool since the reflections expected from such a structure do not coincide sufficiently with those found in the X-ray diffraction pattern. A structure based on the α-helix has been proposed in which the helices are coiled together (Fig. 97). The pitch of the single helix is very much smaller than the compound ones[30] and there are seven helices coiled together and packed hexagonally. In the simple helix, the amino acid translation is 1.50 Å and hence seven residues take up 10.5 Å measured along the axis of a simple helix. The inclination of the simple helix to the axis of the cable is 9°, so that the component in the direction of the cable axis is 10.36 Å and the translation of the amino acid residues becomes 1.48 Å. This structure agrees reasonably well with the X-ray data and gives an expected elongation (assuming this is only due to chain unfolding) of 120%.

However, the situation may not necessarily be completely resolved as it is not completely clear what role the disulphide linkages are playing.

REFERENCES

[1] C. W. Bunn, *Chemical Crystallography*, Oxford University Press, London, 1945.
[2] E. M. Frith and R. F. Tuckett, *Linear Polymers*, Longmans, Green & Co., London, 1951.
[3] A. Keller, in *Growth and Perfection of Crystals*, R. H. Doremus, B. W. Roberts and D. Turnbull, (Eds.), Chapman and Hall, London, 1959.
[4] C. W. Bunn, *Trans. Faraday Soc.*, 35 (1939) 482.
[5] L. D. Caspar, *Nature*, 177 (1956) 476.
    L. Pauling and R. B. Corey, *J. Am. Chem. Soc.*, 72 (1950) 5394.
[6] G. Natta and P. Corradini, *Atti. accad. nazl. Lincei, Rend. Mem. Classe sci. fis., mat. e nat.*, 18 (1955) 19; 4 Sez. II (1955) 62, 73.
    G. Natta and P. Corradini, *J. Polymer. Sci.*, 20 (1956) 251.
[7] R. C. Reinhardt, *Ind. Eng. Chem.*, 35 (1943) 422.
[8] M. Gordon, *The Structure and Physical Properties of High Polymers*, Plastics Inst., London, 1957.
[9] C. W. Bunn, *Nature*, 161 (1948) 929.
[10] R. C. L. Mooney, *J. Am. Chem. Soc.*, 63 (1941) 2828.
[11] C. W. Bunn, *Advances in Colloid Science*, Vol. II, Interscience, New York, 1946.
[12] R. de P. Daubeny, C. W. Bunn and C. J. Brown, *Proc. Roy. Soc. London*, 226A (1954) 531.
[13] L. Pauling and R. B. Corey, *Proc. Natl. Acad. Sci. U.S.*, 37 (1951) 235.
[14] C. W. Bunn and E. V. Garner, *Proc. Roy. Soc. London*, 189A (1947) 39.
[15] R. Bull, *Z. phys. Chem. Leipzig*, B53 (1943) 61.
    L. G. Wallner, *Monatsh. Chem.*, 79 (1948) 279.
[16] W. T. Astbury and M. M. Davies, *Nature*, 154 (1944) 84.
[17] K. H. Meyer and L. Misch, *Helv. Chim. Acta*, 20 (1937) 232.
    D. W. Jones, *J. Polymer Sci.*, 32 (1958) 371.
[18] K. R. Andress, *Z. phys. Chem.*, B4 (1929) 190.
[19] C. W. Bunn, *J. Appl. Phys.*, 25 (1954) 820.
[20] C. W. Bunn and E. R. Howells, *Nature*, 174 (1954) 549.

[21] H. S. McNicholas, *Textile Research J.*, 11 (1940) 39.
R. Bull, *Z. physik. Chem.*, B53 (1943) 61.
C. H. Bamford, L. Brown, A. Elliott, W. E. Hanby and I. F. Trotter, *Nature*, 171 (1953) 1149.
[22] R. E. Marsh, R. B. Corey and L. Pauling, *Acta Cryst.*, 8 (1955) 62; *Biochim. et Biophys. Acta*, 16 (1955) 1.
[23] R. B. Corey and L. Pauling, *Proc. Roy. Soc. London*, 141B (1953) 21.
[24] A. Elliott, *Nature*, 170 (1952) 1066.
[25] C. H. Bamford, L. Brown, A. Elliott, W. E. Hanby and I. F. Trotter, *Nature*, 173 (1954) 27.
[26] L. Pauling, R. B. Corey and H. R. Branson, *Proc. Natl. Acad. Sci. U.S.*, 37 (1951) 205.
[27] C. H. Bamford, W. E. Hanby and F. Happey, *Nature*, 164 (1949) 751.
C. H. Bamford, W. E. Hanby and F. Happey, *Proc. Roy. Soc. London*, 205A (1951) 30.
[28] W. T. Astbury and A. Street, *Phil. Trans. Roy. Soc. London*, 230A (1935) 75.
[29] W. T. Astbury and F. O. Bell, *Nature*, 147 (1941) 696.
[30] F. C. H. Crick, *Nature*, 170 (1952) 882.
L. Pauling and R. B. Corey, *Nature*, 171 (1953) 59.
[31] P. H. Till, *J. Polymer Sci.*, 17 (1957) 447.
A. Keller, *Phil. Mag.*, 2 (1957) 1171.
E. W. Fischer, *Z. Naturforsch*, 12a (1957) 753.
F. C. Frank, A. Keller and A. O'Connor, *Phil. Mag.*, 4 (1959) 200.
[32] C. S. Fuller, *Chem. Revs.*, 26 (1946) 143.
[33] A. Keller and I. Sandemann, *J. Polymer Sci.*, 15 (1955) 133.
[34] C. S. Fuller, C. J. Frosch and N. R. Pape, *J. Am. Chem. Soc.*, 64 (1942) 154.
[35] A. Elliott, W. E. Hanby and B. R. Malcolm, *Nature*, 178 (1956) 1170.
A. Elliott and B. R. Malcolm, *Proc. Roy. Soc. London*, 249A (1959) 30.
A. Elliott and B. R. Malcolm, *Nature*, 178 (1956) 912.
[36] G. Natta and P. Corradini, *J. Polymer Sci.*, 39 (1959) 29.
[37] W. P. Slichter, *J. Polymer Sci.*, 36 (1959) 259.
[38] S. Narita and K. Obidu, *J. Polymer Sci.*, 38 (1959) 270.
V. L. Erlich, *Textile Research J.*, 29 (1959) 679.
[39] B. S. Sprague, J. L. Riley and H. D. Noether, *Textile Research J.*, 28 (1958) 275.
W. J. Dulmage, *J. Polymer Sci.*, 26 (1957) 277.
[40] G. W. Stewart, *Revs. Modern Phys.*, 2 (1930) 116.
[41] J. R. Katz, *Trans. Faraday Soc.*, 32 (1936) 77.
[42] H. Lindley, *Proc. Intern. Wool Research Conf.*, B193 (1955).
[43] D. R. Holmes, C. W. Bunn and D. J. Smith, *J. Polymer Sci.*, 17 (1955) 159.
[44] D. V. Badami and P. H. Harris, *J. Polymer Sci.*, 41 (1959) 540.
[45] C. W. Bunn and D. R. Holmes, *Discussions Faraday Soc.*, 25 (1958) 95.
[46] G. Natta, *Lecture to I.U.P.A.C. Symposium on Macromolecules in Wiesbaden*, 1959.
[47] L. W. Labaw and R. G. W. Wyskoff, *Proc. Acad. Sci. Amsterdam*, B59 (1956) 171.
[48] R. Hill, *J. Soc. Dyers Colourists*, 68 (1952) 158.
[49] R. Hill and E. E. Walker, *J. Polymer Sci.*, 3 (1948) 609.
[50] W. O. Baker and C. S. Fuller, *J. Am. Chem. Soc.*, 64 (1942) 2399.
[51] W. P. Slichter, *J. Polymer Sci.*, 35 (1959) 77.
[52] J. W. S. Hearle, *J. Polymer Sci.*, 28 (1958) 432.
[53] A. Renfrew and P. Morgan (Eds.), *Polythene*, Iliffe & Sons, London (1957).
[54] R. Hill, (Ed.), *Fibres from Synthetic Polymers*, Elsevier, Amsterdam, 1953.
[55] N. G. Gaylord and H. F. Mark, *Linear & Stereoregular Addition Polymers*, *Polymer Reviews*, Vol. 2, Interscience, New York, 1959.
[56] D. R. Holmes, C. W. Bunn and D. J. Smith, *J. Polymer Sci.*, 17 (1955) 159.
[57] F. H. C. Crick and A. Rich, *Nature*, 176 (1955) 780.
[58] C. H. Bamford, A. Elliott and W. E. Hanby, *Synthetic Polypeptides*, Academic Press, New York, 1956.
[59] T. Alfrey, J. J. Bohrer and H. Mark, *Copolymerisation*, Vol. VIII, in *High Polymers*, Interscience, New York, 1952.

CHAPTER 13

MELTING AND CRYSTALLISATION

1. Introduction

The physical examination of polymers has led to a picture of the structure as one containing regions where the chain molecules are adlineated and packed sufficiently well to be regarded as crystalline. These are interspersed with regions which are amorphous where the chains can be visualised as tangled. In the latter, it is possible for segments to be roughly parallel but any arrangements found in the amorphous regions are not precise.

Little can be said about the arrangement of the chains in the amorphous regions since the degree of order varies over wide limits. In fibres and films, the two phase structure is maintained but, when the material is stretched, the molecules in these phases are drawn in the direction of stretch and become preferentially oriented; thus, although the crystallites are highly oriented regions, a second orientation effect must be considered *i.e.* to what extent the micelles themselves are oriented. The degree of orientation in the amorphous phase will be changed, and may help to produce further crystalline regions. The complete specification of the arrangement of molecules in the polymer is obviously extremely complex; even more so when it is realised that the crystallites may not be perfect and the transition between the crystalline and amorphous regions not sharp, regions of intermediate order existing between the two phases. The range of structures will vary from one specimen to another and from polymer to polymer. Nevertheless, in spite of these difficulties, polymers have been regarded as being in two distinct phases and techniques have been used to estimate the quantities of each present. If this simplification is borne in mind, a parameter of this property — fraction of crystalline or amorphous material — can be useful to characterise polymers.

2. Crystallisation of Polymers

When a simple compound is crystallised[1,2], nuclei are formed sporadically and crystallisation proceeds from them. The process of nuclei formation in polymers is not essentially different from that in monomeric materials. The probability of formation of nuclei in simple materials increases as the temperature is lowered on cooling the liquid from the melting point, attains a maximum and then decreases again[4]. The probability may become extremely small at low temperatures so that, if the substance is taken rapidly through the temperature range of easy nucleus formation, the structure will remain amorphous and, since the viscosity increases as the temperature is lowered, will eventually become glass-like.

A nucleus must arise in a polymer from the random or thermal motion of chain segments which are temporarily placed in the structure of the crystallite. The region of adlineation must, however, reach a certain size after which it becomes stable by crystal growth. The formation of nuclei in polymers appears at first sight to be difficult due to the high viscosity and tangling of chains but, since only relatively short sections of the chains are found in any one crystallite, it is only necessary for segments of the chains to rotate or move in order to form a nucleus. A diagrammatic representation of the way rotation might occur is given in Fig. 98.

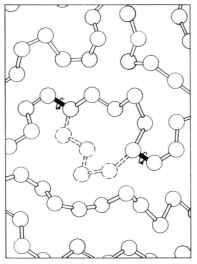

Fig. 98. Segmental jump by rotation about two carbon to carbon bonds in a chain molecule (schematic)[3].

The mechanism of growth of the crystallites has been considered as arising from sideways accretion[5]. More recently however, growth along the length of the crystallite has been regarded as important, since the chain segments near the ends of the crystallite are in a restrained position and possibly more likely to come together to increase the crystallite size[55]. Further, because of the increase of viscosity as the temperature is reduced, the difficulties in forming crystallites increases and the rate of growth decreases as discussed above. The fact that the crystallites are more difficult to form means also that the perfection is lower. This will be reflected in the melting point since the less perfect crystals will melt at a lower temperature.

Measurement of the rate of crystallisation is not very easy. Because of the difference between the specific volumes of the amorphous and crystalline states, the changes in the density of the polymer may be used as a measure of the rate of crystallisation. It is often usual to define the rate as the inverse of the time needed to reach one half the total volume change. Where crystallisation is accompanied by birefringence, the rate of change of depolarisation of polarised light may be followed after passage through the specimen. This has been used to follow crystalline changes in a melt of nylon 66 when under no external stress. Other workers have followed changes in infra-red spectra[62].

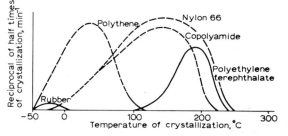

Fig. 99. Temperature ranges of polymer crystallisation[55].

In Fig. 99[38,55] are given curves of the rate of crystallisation of some polymers. Unfortunately some of the data are not very accurate and are put in as dotted lines; nevertheless the differences in the properties of polymers are clearly brought out. These differences are associated with the different chemical constitutions and structures of the polymers.

Investigation of the kinetics of polymer crystallisation by density measurements has shown that the course of crystallisation follows the equation,

$$\text{fraction of amorphous material} = \exp\left(-Kt^n\right)$$

where n is a constant and may take on values 2, 3 or 4 depending on the polymer and conditions of crystallisation[56].

The rate of growth of crystalline material in polymers is of great importance; for some e.g. isotactic polystyrene or polyethylene terephthalate chilling the melt quickly can bring the polymer into the meta-stable glass-like state where the rate of crystallisation is low without developing crystallinity. With others e.g. polymethylene it has been found impossible, presumably because of the high rate of crystallisation to obtain the polymer in a completely amorphous condition. Polyethylene terephthalate, when melt spun and quenched at room temperature in the conventional manner, gives a fibre which is amorphous whereas, in the same circumstances, nylon 66 will have undergone some crystallisation. In general, polymers crystallise over a range of temperatures extending from about 10° below the melting point to a temperature somewhat higher than the glass temperature (this is the temperature at which movement of chain segments in the amorphous regions ceases).

Since the individual crystalline regions in polymers are small, no evidence of their presence would show up under the optical microscope, their size being less than the wavelength of light. Nevertheless under the microscope, crystallised sheets show evidence of an organised structure on a scale greater than the estimated crystallite size ($<$ 600 Å). Indeed, crystallised undrawn specimens may be semi-opaque. Polyethylene, a material which crystallises readily shows in the polarising microscope well defined circular regions which are illuminated except for a dark Maltese Cross[5] (Fig. 100). The presence of such a cross can arise from an assemblage of crystals radiating from a point with their crystallographic axes radiating outwards; the arms of the cross are parallel to the vibration directions of the polariser and analyser and hence arise from crystals

Fig. 100. Thin film of polyethylene in optical microscope between crossed polarisers (1000 $\times$)[5].

in their extinction directions, crystals of intermediate orientation being illuminated. Similar results have been obtained for polyamides[6], polyesters, etc. so that it is reasonable to conclude that this is the usual mode of crystallisation. These structural features are referred to as spherulites.

Growth radiates from a nucleus. The problem of the mechanism of the formation of such structures is difficult to resolve. The nuclei grow by lateral aggregation of chain segments and by growth in the direction of the chain axis where the units of the polymer are pulled into line. Because of the size of the crystallites relative to the length of the chain, the latter will be involved in the formation of more than one crystallite; hence between the two nuclei must lie parts of chains which, because they are by thermal motions originally tangled, cannot be accommodated in the crystallite. Because there is a contraction of about 10%, growth of the crystallite will produce stresses which tend to pull the chains out of their randomly coiled state; this process will be resisted by virtue of the random thermal motions. Thus, a balance is set up between the tendency of crystallites to grow and the stresses produced in the amorphous regions.

The optical character of the spherulites varies from polymer to polymer. Polyethylene and polyurethan give optically negative spherulites *i.e.* the refractive index of light vibrating along the radius is lower than that along the tangential direction[5,7]. In polyethylene from the properties of the drawn fibres in which the molecules are parallel to the fibre axis, the refractive index turns out to be greater along the fibre axis (and hence the chain) than at right angles to it, thus indicating that the molecules lie tangentially to the radial directions. However, if the refractive index is large in one of the two directions perpendicular to the chain, the chain can lie tangentially but give rise to positive spherulites. This situation may happen when a strongly polarisable group is present as in polyamides and polyesters. In some materials, positive and negative spherulites can be present. This may arise from different chain orientation or by different orientation of the crystallites around the chain direction.

With nylon 66, formation of negative or positive spherulites depends on the thermal history of the melt. Negative spherulites are formed at high temperatures after fusion just above the melting point; fusion above 258° but below 265° and crystallisation between 250 and 258°C gives negative spherulites. It is interesting to note that these have a higher melting point than the more usual positive ones[57]. In general, the optical melting points (determined by loss of birefringence) differ according to the samples crystallisation history[8,9,58].

Orientation in spherulites has been made more definite by examination by micro X-ray methods[10]. Examination of the peripheral positions indicated that the molecules lay tangentially in polyamides. It was further found that the planes with hydrogen bonds were parallel to the radius of the positive but perpendicular to the radius of the negative spherulites. Such micro X-ray studies confirmed the tangential disposition of the molecules in polyethylene terephthalate and polyethylene.

Further examination of the spherulites showed that a radiating fibrous structure exists within the spherulite even if the definite structural units could not be clearly distinguished[5,11,12]. In polyethylene (Fig. 101)[39], the

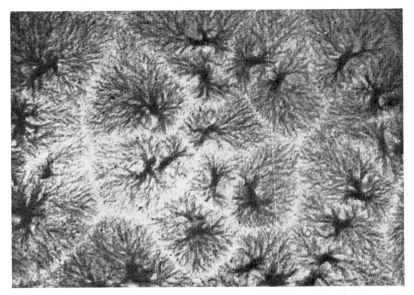

Fig. 101. Very thin film of polyethylene in electron microscope (9000 ×)[38].

fibrils radiate but there is much meandering and branching so that radial orientation is not perfect. Individual fibrous units may be identified using dark ground illumination and the fibrous nature could be enhanced by solvents or swelling agents or by etching[13,59]. It is possible that the observable fibrous appearance may correspond to genuine structural discontinuities parallel to spherulite radii, an idea in agreement with the fact that dyes do not enter crystallites but can be deposited along radial lines[12]. Discontinuities parallel to the radius could also be responsible for mechanical weaknesses in polymers containing spherulites[14]. These spherulitic fibrils seem to be important structural elements but, although the size is indicated in Table 31, very little information is at present available.

TABLE 31

Unit	Molecule	Crystallite	Single crystal	Spherulitic fibril	Spherulite
Shortest dimension	$2-5$ Å	$20-50$ Å	order of 100 Å	$10^3 - 5 \times 10^4$ Å	–
Longest dimension	10^3-10^5 Å	$50-1000$ Å	10^4-10^5 Å	10^5-10^6 Å	10^5-10^6 Å or larger

Spherulite size in polyethylene has been shown to decrease by rapid cooling[40]; those specimens with smaller spherulites are more flexible than slowly cooled or annealed specimens. In nylon 66, this yields a higher flexural modulus and yield point but a lower elongation[41]. The effects arising from spherulite size are difficult to assess since the size and perfection of the crystalline regions is affected by the manner of cooling as well as the size of the spherulites.

A crystalline polymer thus consists of entities ordered to lesser or greater extents which have different sizes and belong to different dimensional levels. This stratification is shown in Table 31 but it must be remembered that there is a considerable overlap between the sizes of the entities adjacent in the sequence.

3. Melting of Polymers

With an increase in temperature, the physical properties change markedly until eventually the material becomes a viscous liquid. The changes which occur are similar in kind to those which occur when a substance of low molecular weight is heated and may be followed by the increases in specific volume[15] (Fig. 102). The changes on melting of a polymer are, in

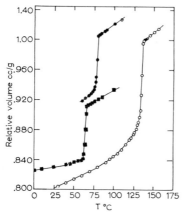

Fig. 102. Plot[16] of relative volume *vs.* temperature: o, polymethylene[33]; ■, polyethylene oxide[65]; ●, polydecamethylene adipate[66].

References p. 373

contrast to low molecular weight materials, not very sharp and occur over a range of temperature. In the case of compounds of low molecular weight, poorly defined melting points arise from the presence of molecules of different size; for polymers, even though they be composed of molecules of different chain lengths, the overriding cause of the melting range lies in the "two phase" nature of the polymer. In polymers, the crystallites contain only short lengths of the total length of the molecules so that the results are not dependent on chain length above some critical length. Heating will effect the motion of the segments in the molecular chain, and those segments which possess adequate energy will break away from the crystallites and become part of the amorphous regions. The smaller crystals will melt before the larger. It is likely that some of the crystals are being reduced in size whereas the others may be increasing even though the overall amount of crystalline material is decreasing as the temperature rises (Fig. 103). The term m.p. when polymers are discussed

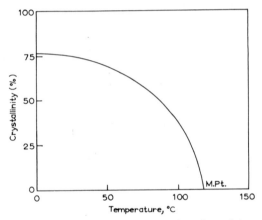

Fig. 103. Crystallinity of polyethylene as a function of temperature[63].

refers to the temperature at which all crystallinity disappears. It is probably best determined by observation of the point when the material becomes transparent and birefringence disappears. This may be determined by viewing (between crossed nicols) the sample mounted on the hot stage of a microscope[42]. With reference to chain length, the curve of m.p. vs. chain length for normal paraffins is of the form given in the diagram (Fig. 104). The lower m.p. chains give sharp points and mobile liquids on melting. The higher molecular weight compounds give higher m.p.'s and viscous liquids. The m.p. reaches a maximum and becomes constant at the larger values of chain length. For very long chains, the liquids become more and more viscous and eventually become rubbery in character.

A detailed examination of crystallisation and melting has been carried out by Wood on rubber[43]. When this polymer is crystallised at temperatures below 10°C and the temperature raised, the melting range is a function of the temperature at which crystallisation occurred (Fig. 105). Melting takes place over a range 10–40°C above the crystallisation temperature. If crystallisation is allowed to occur slowly at around 14°C and the temperature raised very slowly, crystallinity disappears at about 28°C, a temperature at which the most perfect crystallites are in equilib-

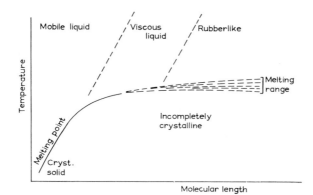

Fig. 104. Relation between melting point and molecular length[67].

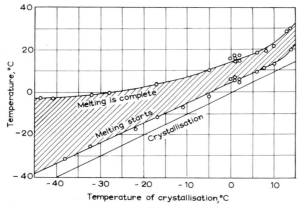

Fig. 105. Melting range of rubber crystallites as a function of crystallisation temperature[64].

rium with the amorphous phase. Crystallites form more rapidly when lower crystallisation temperatures are used, are less perfect and melt at lower temperatures. The presence of a melting range implies a continuous redistribution of polymer chains between the amorphous and crystalline regions.

Most of the melting in a polymer, as shown by the abnormal increase in volume, occurs in a range of 10 °C and terminates abruptly at a temperature which may be defined to within ± 0.50 °C. To obtain satisfactory dilatometric data, the temperature is raised by small increments and held at that temperature until the volume remains constant. When the m.p. is approached, this may require about 24 h; as the less perfect and therefore less stable crystallites melt, more stable ones are formed during the time required to reach constant volume. Melting points obtained using a rate of heating higher than that required to achieve constancy of volume at each temperature will be lower.

4. Structure and Melting Point

(a) General

It has been suggested that melting will occur when the thermal energy or vibration amplitude of a molecule reaches a critical value so that it can break away from the range of influence of the neighbouring molecules but, since melting is an equilibrium phenomenon, crystallisation must be considered as well as melting. However, although there is not a satisfactory theory of melting, it is to be expected that, as the intermolecular forces increase, the melting point would rise. The intermolecular forces may be indicated by the molar cohesive energy density, a quantity which is deduced from the latent heat of vapourisation, and which is a measure of the energy required to separate molecules. This parameter should be a measure of the forces holding molecules together in a crystal and seems to be satisfactory for a series of similar substances e.g. benzene, naphthalene etc. when the m.p. is proportional to the molar cohesive density.

The situation in a polymer is not so simple since the crystal only contains segments of the whole chains. The cohesion energy would have to be calculated for polymers on the basis of segments and cannot easily be measured as is indicated later. However, such figures can be estimated but do not fall in line with the experimentally determined m.p.'s. This would indicate that chain forces are not alone in influencing m.p.

For a rigid molecule (benzene, anthracene etc.), the m.p. rises rapidly with the size; on the other hand, straight chain paraffin compounds increase their m.p.'s fairly rapidly as the number of carbon atoms is increased but the rate of increase rapidly decreases until a constant value is obtained (Fig. 104). One of the striking differences between these two groups of compounds lies in the possibility which the paraffins possess of rotation around the C—C bonds and, if a model is constructed, it can be seen that groups of segments can rotate independently of the other sections of the chain (Fig. 98). On melting, the molecule will be able to assume a coiled arrangement and hence it is anticipated that there will be an entropy change which is much larger than for a rigid molecule. In terms of thermodynamics, the melting point T_m is related to the latent heat ΔH and entropy of melting ΔS by

$$T_m = \frac{\Delta H}{\Delta S}$$

so that, provided ΔH remains substantially constant, T_m will be determined by the entropy change which occurs on melting. If the molecule is able to coil itself easily, the entropy change in going from the organised structure to a random one in the melt will be high and hence T_m will be low; the converse also holds that if the chain is rigid and, on melting, does not coil easily, the entropy change is low and the melting point high.

The growing crystallites restrict the motion of the amorphous segments so that each successive linkage is more difficult to get into place. ΔS for crystallisation is therefore greater for the later segments and this blurs the m.p. since ΔS varies whilst ΔH remains constant[44]. This also means

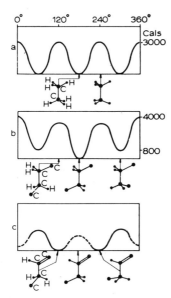

Fig. 106. Potential energy curves for rotation around bonds (a) ethane, (b) n-butane, (c) single bond adjacent to a double bond[67].

that the breadth of the melting range increases with the number of nuclei. The energies required for rotation round single bonds range between 1000–5000 cal/mol and are similar in order to the cohesion energies so that this factor will rank equal in importance to interchain forces[17]. In rotating around a bond, there are maxima and minima according to the disposition of the bonds. For example, in ethane there are 3 maxima and minima and the ability of the atoms to rotate around these bonds depends on the interaction between the atoms and the disposition of the bonds. The rates at which the configuration can change is determined by the heights of the maxima and minima whereas the average configuration is determined by the differences between the minima. Some examples of the maxima and minima are given in Fig. 106 (see also Table 33). The positions of the maxima control the difficulty of changing configurations whereas the minima represent stable configurations. There are other factors which may be of some considerable importance in melting point studies. These are the symmetry of the molecules and the density of packing. Unfortunately, the relation with these factors is complex.

(b) Homologous Series

In Fig. 107 are given the melting points of a series of aliphatic polyesters in which the number of ester groups is increased[18,23]. The esters all melt at temperatures lower than the parent polymethylene and the greater the number, the lower the m.p. This is surprising from one point of view since the ester groups are expected to give a higher cohesive energy than methylene groups, but the increased flexibility in

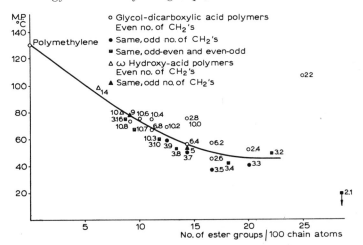

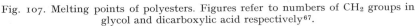

Fig. 107. Melting points of polyesters. Figures refer to numbers of CH₂ groups in glycol and dicarboxylic acid respectively[67].

the compounds containing ester groups counteracts this. The increased cohesive energy is shown by monomeric compounds which have higher melting points. Chain polymers with keto groups as part of the main chain have higher m.p.'s so that in polyesters the increased cohesive energy of the CO group is offset by increased flexibility of the chains. The results with the esters and anhydrides suggest that rotation round the COO- and CH_2O-bonds may be easy. A chain oxygen atom, as it bears no substituent, allows easy rotation and leads to chain flexibility. The melting behaviour is considered, therefore, to be mainly determined by a balance of the forces binding the molecules together and their ability to be released and take up other configurations.

The polyamides by contrast have higher m.p.'s than polymethylene and in Fig. 108, where the m.p. is plotted against number of amide groups per 1000 chain atoms, there is a general increase[19,20]. The increase can be explained on the basis that hydrogen bonds can be formed between the amide groups. The formation of these means a high cohesive energy. In addition, it seems likely that the amide groups have less flexibility than the ester. The position in detail is made a little more complex by the fact that those structures containing an even number of carbon atoms have higher melting points than those with an odd number. It is likely that the melting points of the polyamides are connected with the ability to form the maximum number of hydrogen bonds; models of these

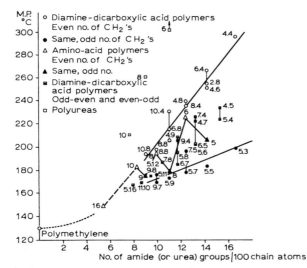

Fig. 108. Melting points of polyamides and polyureas. Figures refer to numbers of CH_2-groups in the diamine and dicarboxylic acid respectively[67].

References p. 373

polyamides would suggest that to bring the CO and NH groups of neighbouring chains into juxtaposition is more difficult when there is an odd number of methylene groups between the amide groups in the individual chains[19,21]. However, this suggestion may apply to the polyamides but it is one which can not be applied in general to the variation of melting points found in homologous series of organic compounds.

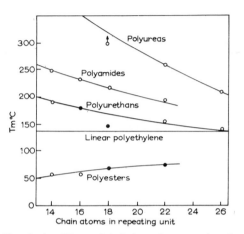

Fig. 109. Trend of melting points in homologous series of polymers[45].

A more general picture is shown in Fig. 109 where T_m is plotted against the number of chain atoms in the repeating unit (the reverse of Figs. 107 and 108); this figure shows that, as the number of methylene groups between the polar groups increases, the melting points tend to converge to that of linear polyethylene[45].

(c) Replacement of Methylene Groups

If six methylene groups are replaced by a phenyl, there is a marked increase in melting point which, since the cohesive energies of six methylenes are similar to one phenyl, must be explained on the rigidity of the aromatic ring. Larger rigid groups such as p,p'-diphenyl and 2,6- or 1,5-naphthyl also produce large increases. Some values are compared in the Table 32[19,22,23].

This effect is of particular importance when it is realised that polyethylene terephthalate is a valuable commercial fibre whereas the corresponding aliphatic compound is not. The reverse, a lowering of melting point, occurs when a methylene group is replaced by an oxygen atom as has been discussed above.

TABLE 32

Polymer unit	m.p. (°C)
$-O(CH_2)_2OCO(CH_2)_6CO-$	45
$-O(CH_2)_2OCO\langle ring \rangle CO-$ 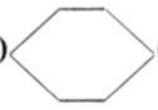	264
$-NH(CH_2)_6NHCO(CH_2)_6CO-$	235
$-NH(CH_2)_6NHCO\langle ring \rangle CO-$ 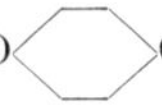	350 decomp.
$-O(CH_2)_5OCO\langle ring \rangle CO-$ 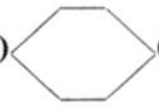	116
$-O(CH_2)_2O(CH_2)_2OCO\langle ring \rangle CO-$ 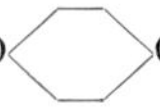	20
$-NH(CH_2)_5NHCO(CH_2)_2CO-$	198
$-NH(CH_2)_5NHCOCH_2OCH_2CO-$	130

(d) Side Groups

Replacement of hydrogen for methyl in polymers such as that from 10-aminoundecanoic acid, $(-NHCH(CH_3)(CH_2)_8CO-)_n$ will reduce the melting point (125–130°C from 175° for the unsubstituted polymer)[24] but, in spite of the presence of the asymmetric carbon atom, the material still gives X-ray evidence of crystallinity presumably because of the strength of hydrogen bonds. Replacement of the hydrogen atom in the amide group removes the possibility of hydrogen bond formation and causes a large reduction in melting point e.g. N-methylundecanoic acid, $-NCH_3(CH_2)_{10}CO-$ melts at 60°C[24] as against 182°C for the unsubstituted material (cf. methoxylated nylon, Chapter 12).

5. Glass Transitions

The phenomenon of melting is normally described as being a first order transition because a change of state occurs. In the field of polymers, changes of less than this magnitude may occur. Non-crystalline polymers at low temperatures are relatively hard glass-like solids; at high temperatures, they become soft, flexible and rubber-like. Much of the change which occurs in properties such as coefficient of expansion, dielectric constant, elastic modulus does so at a fairly well defined temperature. With amorphous polymers, the term melting point should not be used as there is no discontinuous change in properties such as volume or latent

References p. 373

heat as happens when a crystalline material melts. Only a change in shape of the line relating properties such as specific volume to temperature[25] takes place (Fig. 110). The change in hardness which occurs resembles that on melting a crystalline material although it is less marked. The

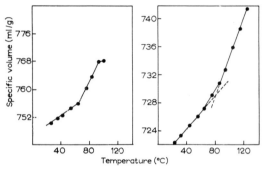

Fig. 110. Relation between specific volume and temperature for polyethylene terephthalate[25]. Left amorphous. Right crystalline.

temperature at which these changes take place is called the second order transition or glass or brittle temperature. As the temperature is raised further, the rubbery material is converted to a liquid, a change which is gradual and reversible; the rubber goes gradually through the states of a viscoelastic liquid which shows both slow liquid flow and weak rubbery elasticity to a liquid which is highly viscous but shows no rubbery elasticity, until finally the viscosity will come into the range of ordinary liquids. At lower temperatures, the material with the characteristics of a rubber is transformed into a glassy material. The temperature at which this occurs is one where the motion of the segments constituting the polymer chains become frozen.

The chain molecules in the amorphous regions can be pictured as

TABLE 33

ENERGY BARRIERS FOR METHYL GROUP ROTATION

	kcal/mol
CH_3—CH_3	2.75
$CH_3CH_2CH_3$	3.30
CH_3—$CH(CH_3)_2$	3.87
CH_3—$C(CH_3)_3$	4.80
CH_3—OCH_3	2.70
CH_3—$CH{=}CH_2$	1.95
CH_3—$CH{=}O$	1.00

similar in structure to the contents of a bowl of cooked spaghetti. At a sufficiently high temperature the spaghetti undergoes a wriggling motion. This movement arises from the thermal motion of the segments in the chains and from the existence of free volume in the polymer. At a sufficiently low temperature, the free volume becomes small and the thermal energy RT becomes low compared with the energy barriers for rotational jumps at low temperatures the wriggling motion of the segments ceases. The magnitudes of the energy barriers to rotation vary considerably as may be seen from Table 33.

The magnitudes of the energies are comparable to direct forces of interchain association so that configurational stability in fibre molecules is maintained by

(1) cohesion

(2) existence of preferred conformation

(3) internal resistance to change of geometrical forms.

In an amorphous polymer, T_g will be modified by changes in molecular weight. This may be imagined to occur by considering a chain of infinite length in the rubbery state and progressively cutting the chains. Each cut brings new end groups and amounts to a removal of a restraint; the end groups so produced may undergo more vigorous thermal motions.

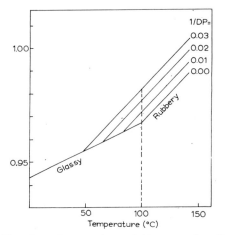

Fig. 111. Specific volume/temperature relations as a function of D.P.[27].

Hence, the polymer expands. In the glassy state where movements are frozen, the increase in volume will not happen so that, if the specific volume is plotted against temperature, there will be one line for the glassy state but several for the rubbery. The results for such studies of polystyrene of different D.P. are given in the Fig. 111[27] where the "glass" line intersects a family of "rubber" lines. For an amorphous polymer whose chains contain N links or segments, the value of T_g varies with chain length according to the equation

$$T_g = T_g{}° - \frac{C'}{N}$$

where $T_g{}°$ is the transition temperature for a polymer of infinite D.P. and C' is a constant for each polymer[46].

The deformations of a polymer in the rubbery state thus depend on the rotatory segmental motions; these occur at a natural relaxation rate at any temperature. If forces causing deformation are applied to a polymer faster than the natural relaxation rate of the polymer, it is to be expected that the elastic modulus will increase as the speed of deformation increases (*i.e.* dynamic modulus exceeds the static). This effect may be investigated by imposing a sinusoidal vibration on the polymer specimen: there will exist, as the frequency range is covered, a point at which the segmental motions are matched by the period of the applied vibration. This is a resonant point and one at which the maximum energy can be transferred to the polymer. As an alternative, the frequency of the applied force may be maintained constant and the temperature varied. Under these conditions when the segmental frequency matches the external, resonance will occur. An elegant and simple way

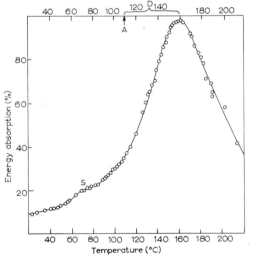

Fig. 112. Mechanical-energy absorption for ball impact on methyl methacrylate[3]. The main peak at 160°C is due to the dynamic glass transition displaced by the amount D from the static transition A. The shoulder S is attributed to the mobilisation of CO_2CH_3 side chains.

to show this is to measure the energy losses by the rebound which occurs when a steel ball is dropped on to a polymer disc. For maximum energy loss the segmental jump must match the time taken by the impact of the ball. In Fig. 112, the energy loss in such an experiment is plotted against temperature; it shows that the energy absorbed increases to the resonance point and then decreases. Deformation occurs at a rate determined in this experiment by the rate of penetration of the ball. It is not surprising that the transition as measured by this technique differs from those under static conditions. The transition may be taken as the temperature at the maximum of the curve.

Polymers which are crystalline also show transitions but to a considerably smaller degree than amorphous materials. In general for polymers which can be obtained in both forms, T_g for the crystalline is higher than the amorphous form (Fig. 110); in the case of polyethylene terephthalate, the T_g has been shown to increase continuously with increasing crystalinity[60].

T_g varies with chemical constitution. What the melting point is to a crystalline material, the second order transition is for the amorphous material. The ability of the chain segments to jump must depend on molecular cohesion and rigidity of chains so that some qualitative relation between m.p. and T_g may be expected.

Another way of modifying the T_g is by the addition of monomolecular compounds. Absorption of substances such as monomer or dioctyl phthalate produces small regions in the polymer where rotation of the chain segments becomes easier and hence T_g occurs at a lower temperature. This is tantamount to an internal lubrication and such compounds are called plasticisers.

On the face of it, there would seem to be a frequency characteristic of the segmental motions of the different groups in the molecules. An energy loss curve would then show up as a "spectrum", the bands of which correspond to the points at which certain groups become unfrozen. However, detailed analysis of the polymers using magnetic resonance techniques has shown the curves to be more complex and the main transitions may arise from the motions of more than one group.

The energetics of interaction between molecules may perhaps be best described by the cohesive energy density or its square root, the solubility parameter. For a liquid the former is defined as the energy of vapourisation, E_v, divided by the molar volume V; this measures the cohesion per unit volume of liquid[47]. The solubility parameter δ is taken as the square root of this, *i.e.*

$$\delta = \left(\frac{E_v}{V}\right)^{\frac{1}{2}}$$

References p. 373

These parameters cannot be measured directly for polymers but are found by placing a slightly cross-linked polymer in a series of liquids of known values of δ[48]. The polymer is swollen in these liquids to different extents but not dissolved because of the cross linkage; a plot of swelling *versus* δ gives a Gaussian shaped curve with a maximum at a certain value of δ which is taken to be the value of δ_p, the solubility parameter for the polymer. The glass transition will be dependent on the value of δ_p, the barriers hindering rotation around the bonds, the free volume, the stiffness of the chain and the number of links in the chain. Polymers of high δ_p tend to have low transition temperatures T_g and *vice versa*. Thus, polybutadiene with a value of δ_p of 8.1 has a low T_g whereas polyacrylonitrile with a δ_p of 15.4 has a high T_g.

Polymers with small rotational barriers tend to have low T_g. Thus, polyethylene $(T_g < -100\,°C)$[26] has a low solubility parameter and a barrier to rotation of 3.3 kcal/mol whereas polytetrafluoroethylene $(T_g > 20\,°C)$ has also a low δ_p but a larger rotational barrier of 4.7 kcal[50]. Examples of the effects of stiffness are difficult to assess, since polymers which are geometrically stiff also tend to have large barriers to rotation.

In the fibre field, glass transition phenomena are important. The drawing process to which fibres are subjected in order to develop strength is really only practical above the T_g. The changes in properties which occur at T_g affect the properties of yarns and cloths such as stiffness,

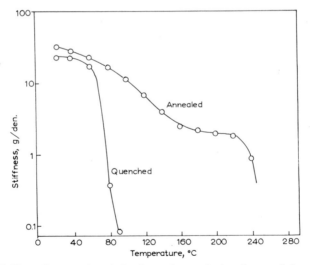

Fig. 113. Stiffness/temperature behaviour of quenched and annealed polyethylene terephthalate[61].

resilience, extensibility etc. and must be considered when yarns or fabrics are to be dyed, printed or finished. An as example the change of stiffness has been studied[61]. This has been measured as a function of temperature (Fig. 113). Little change takes place until the temperature of the glass transition is reached. At this point the stiffness drops sharply to a lower level when it remains constant until the crystallites melt and the material becomes soft. When this happens, the stiffness decreases rapidly. In Fig. 113 a comparison is made between crystalline and amorphous

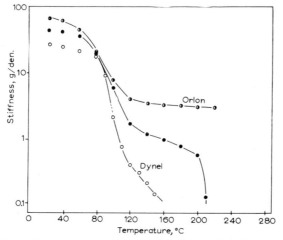

Fig. 114. Stiffness/temperature behaviour of Orlon, Dynel and experimental acrylic fibre[61].

polyethylene terephthalate. The amorphous material does not have a point at which the crystallites melt and hence has only one transition. For the amorphous material, the stiffness drops rapidly once T_g is reached. In Fig. 114, the results for fibres of different crystallinity are given where it can be seen that going from the more highly crystalline Orlon to amorphous Dynel the curves become steeper.

6. Copolymers

If a copolymer is prepared in comparable proportions from two units geometrically very different, it is not surprising that the material will have difficulty in crystallising but, if the proportion of one constituent is low, there will be present uninterrupted sequences of one kind of unit and hence crystallisation to some extent is possible. It follows that the proportion of crystalline material is less and the size of the crystallites is lower than the homopolymers; and the melting point is also reduced. The following relation between the melting point T_m of the copolymer and that of the pure polymer $T_m{}^\circ$ and the mole fraction of the crystallising constituent has been deduced by Flory to be

$$\frac{1}{T_m} - \frac{1}{T_m{}^\circ} = -\frac{R}{h} \ln X$$

where h is the heat of fusion of the repeating unit. In this equation, it is assumed that the copolymer consists of A units which crystallise and B which do not; the units are assumed to occur at random along the chain. X then refers to the mole fraction of A units[51].

The predictions of this equation have been confirmed and show that the melting point will be reduced. In Fig. 115 are given melting point data for polyethylene terephthalate–adipate and terephthalate–sebacate copolymers[22]. The melting points of the homopolymers are reduced as the second component is added, leading to a minimum point rather akin to a eutectic found in melting point curves of mixtures of compounds of low molecular weight. When the copolymer constituents are able to form mixed crystals as may occur in some aliphatic polyamides[28,29], the reduction of melting point is less and the copolymers may remain partly

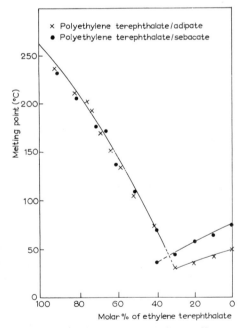

Fig. 115. Melting points of polyethylene terephthalate–adipate and terephthalate–sebacate copolymers[22].

crystalline over the whole composition range. Indeed, additions of terephthalic acid to hexamethyleneadipamide increases the melting point (Fig. 116). The reason for this seems to be that the adipamide, —NHCO(CH₂)₄CONH— and terephthalamide units are about the same length and this allows isomorphous replacement whereas, if hexamethyl-

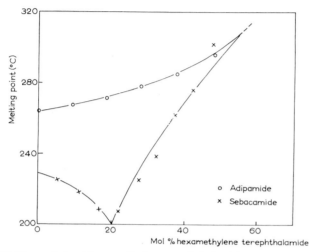

Fig. 116. Melting points of hexamethyleneterephthalamide–adipamide and terephthalamide–sebacamide copolymers[22].

ene-sebacamide is used, the melting point drops, the sebacamide units —NHCO(CH₂)₆CONH— being longer than the terephthalamide ones.

In addition to these two cases, a third must be added. When the structural disturbances are large the centre part of the curve in Fig. 115 does not exist since crystallisation is prevented in the central part of the composition range. When this occurs, an amorphous copolymer is produced which, depending on whether it has its T_g above or below room temperature, will be rubbery or resinous.

Analogous effects are found in the addition copolymers where regularity will be disrupted in a random copolymer. Thus, polyvinylidene fluoride (CH₂=CF₂) and polytrifluorochloroethylene (CF₂=CClF) are both highly crystalline; the monomers copolymerise over the whole range of compositions. When one of the other comonomers dominates, the material is crystalline although the extent of crystallinity and the melting point is lowered. In the region of composition of 50/50, the copolymers are amorphous and are rubbery at room temperature.

How the physical properties change in response to the presence of copolymeric units depends on the degree to which the lattice may tolerate minor deviations from symmetry. The changes will be determined by the extent to which the intruding species resembles the parent polymer. However, the second component may be of a different shape or size or have different cohesion; the random occurrence of the units will interfere with the ability of the polymer to form a regularly repeating lattice.

Judging from X-ray patterns, the effect of building up the copolymer is to increase the amorphous material and to distort slightly the molecular geometry of the main phase[30,34]. This behaviour implies that the copolymeric constituent lies in the amorphous phase. If this constituent is related to the amorphous homopolymer, as its concentration increases the crystallisability of the copolymer is decreased, being extinguished at some composition. For example, copolymers of vinylidene and vinyl chlorides containing more than 30% of vinyl chloride are amorphous[31]. When the second component yields a crystalline homopolymer then, as its concentration increases, the characteristic crystallinity of the first homopolymer disappears and that of the second homopolymer predominates. The concentration range over which this occurs is one of minimum crystallinity and maximum deviation of the properties of the copolymer from the homopolymers. Thus, copolymers of nylon 66 and 610 show single X-ray patterns corresponding to one or other of the homopolymers except when the concentrations were almost equal[28]. In general through the randomising of the structure, the crystallinity may be reduced so that the imperfections and reduced size of the crystallites will lower their reinforcing actions; copolymers are often softer, more elastic and of lower tenacity than the homopolymers[32].

Changes occur as a result of copolymerisation in the T_g which is often lowered[34,35,36], and solubility in organic solvents is increased. For the copolyamides, the solubility is greatest in the eutectic region where the melting point and crystallinity are the lowest[37]. Perhaps the simplest approach to show how T_g may change is based on the following argument[52]. Consider a copolymer whose volume/temperature relation is already known. The polymer is glassy or rubbery according to which state has the higher specific volume. As a first approximation, it may be assumed that the volume of the units in the copolymer are the same as in the homopolymer; this means that the units mix ideally without volume change. For such a copolymer the specific volume V_{co} will be

$$V_{co} = xV_1 + (1 - x)V_2$$

where V_1 and V_2 are the specific volumes in either the glassy or rubbery states. Thus, the specific volume of the copolymer may be determined in terms of the weight fraction x. This equation has been shown to be satisfactory for the important pair of comonomers butadiene and styrene in the ratio 75/25.

In general, the value of T_g for an amorphous copolymer can be predicted approximately if the transition temperatures $T_g(1)$ and $T_g(2)$ of the homo-polymers are known. An empirical formula[53] which works fairly well for many copolymers is

$$\frac{1}{T_g} = \frac{x_1}{T_g(1)} + \frac{x_2}{T_g(2)}$$

where x_1 and x_2 are the weight fractions of the components.

This equation has been used in the converse way. Values of T_g for copolymers of different composition may be determined and values of $T_g(1)$ and $T_g(2)$ calculated. In this way, the T_g of crystalline polymers may be determined when no clearly defined change of slope in the volume *versus* temperature curves is detectable; the equation has been applied to studies of the copolymers of trifluorochloroethylene and vinylidene fluoride when the T_g of the homopolymers has been calculated[54].

REFERENCES

[1] H. E. BUCKLEY, *Crystal Growth*, Chapman & Hall, London, 1950.

[2] P. J. FLORY and A. D. McINTYRE, *J. Polymer Sci.*, 18 (1955) 593.

[3] M. GORDON, *The Structure & Physical Properties of High Polymers*, Plastics Monograph No. C 10, Plastics Institute, London, 1957.

[4] G. TAMMANN, *The States of Aggregation*, translated by Mehl Constable, London, 1926.

[5] C. W. BUNN and T. C. ALCOCK, *Trans. Faraday Soc.*, 41 (1945) 317.

[6] C. M. LANGKAMMERER and W. E. CARLIN, *J. Polymer Sci.*, 3 (1948) 300.
G. L. CLARK, M. H. MUELLAR and L. L. STOTT, *Ind. Eng. Chem.*, 42 (1950) 831.

[7] W. M. D. BRYANT, *J. Polymer Sci.*, 2 (1947) 547.

[8] W. BRENSCHEDE, *Z. Electrochem.*, 54 (1950) 191.

[9] A. KELLER, *J. Polymer Sci.*, 17 (1955) 291; *Nature*, 169 (1952) 913.
E. H. BOASSON and J. M. WOESTENENK, *J. Polymer Sci.*, 21 (1956) 151.
E. H. BOASSON and J. M. WOESTENENK, *J. Polymer Sci.*, 24 (1957) 57.
W. BRENSCHEDE, *Kolloid Z.*, 114 (1949) 35.

[10] M. HERBST, *Z. Elektrochem.*, 54 (1950) 318.
A. KELLER, *J. Polymer Sci.*, 17 (1955) 351.
R. J. BARRIAULT and L. F. GRONHOLZ, *J. Polymer Sci.*, 18 (1955) 393.
A. KELLER, *Nature*, 171 (1953) 170.

[11] R. B. RICHARDS, *J. Appl. Chem.*, 1 (1951) 370.
R. GABLER, *Naturwiss.*, 35 (1948) 284.
E. JENCKEL and H. WILSING, *Z. Elektrochem.*, 53 (1949) 4.

[12] E. JENCKEL and E. KLEIN, *Kolloid Z.*, 118 (1950) 86.

[13] A. KELLER and J. R. S. WARING, *J. Polymer Sci.*, 17 (1955) 447.

[14] F. P. REDING and A. BROWN, *Ind. Eng. Chem.*, 46 (1954) 1962.
H. W. STARKWEATHER, G. E. MOORE, J. E. HANSEN, TH. M. RODER and R. E. BROOKS, *J. Polymer Sci.*, 21 (1956) 189.

[15] R. D. EVANS, H. R. MIGHTON and P. J. FLORY, *J. Am. Chem. Soc.*, 72 (1950) 2018.

[16] L. MANDELKERN, *Chem. Revs.*, 56 (1956) 911.

[17] W. NOWACKI, *Mitt. naturforsch. Ges. Bern*, 2 (1945) 43.

[18] W. H. CAROTHERS and J. A. ARVIN, *J. Am. Chem. Soc.*, 51 (1929) 2560.

C. S. FULLER and C. J. FROSCH, *J. Am. Chem. Soc.*, 61 (1939) 2575; 64 (1942) 15, 154.

F. J. VAN NATTA, J. W. HILL and W. H. CAROTHERS, *J. Am. Chem. Soc.*, 56 (1934) 455.

[19] R. HILL and E. E. WALKER, *J. Polymer Sci.*, 3 (1948) 609.

[20] D. D. COFFMAN, N. L. COX, E. L. MARTIN, W. E. MOCHEL and F. J. VAN NATTA, *J. Polymer Sci.*, 3 (1948) 85.

[21] G. CHAMPETIER and R. AELION, *Bull.Soc. Chim. France*, (1948) 683.

[22] O. B. EDGAR and R. HILL, *J. Polymer Sci.*, 8 (1952) 1.

[23] C. S. FULLER and C. L. ERICKSON, *J. Am. Chem. Soc.*, 59 (1937) 344.

[24] R. AELION, *Ann. chim. Paris*, [12], 3 (1948) 5.

[25] J. J. KOLB and E. F. IZARD, *J. Appl. Phys.*, 15 (1944) 398.

[26] P. J. FLORY, *Simposio Internazionale di Chimica Macromolecolare*, 25 (1955).

[27] T. G. FOX and P. J. FLORY, *J. Appl. Phys.*, 21 (1950) 581.

[28] W. O. BAKER and C. S. FULLER, *J. Am. Chem. Soc.*, 64 (1942) 2399.

[29] W. E. CATLIN, E. P. CZERWIN and R. H. WILEY, *J. Polymer Sci.*, 2 (1947) 412.

[30] O. D. EDGAR and E. E. ELLERY, *J. Chem. Soc.* (1952) 2633.

J. R. CALDWELL and R. GILKEY, *Abstract of Papers, Am. Chem. Soc., 134th Meeting*, 1958.

[31] J. JACK and R. A. HORSLEY, *J. Appl. Chem.*, 4 (1954) 178.

[32] M. D. SYNDER, *U.S.P.* 2,623,033.

[33] L. MANDELKERN, M. HELLMAN, D. BROWN, D. E. ROBERTS and F. A. QUINN, *J. Am. Chem. Soc.*, 75 (1953) 4093.

[34] H. C. HAAS, S. G. COHEN, A. C. OGLESBY and E. R. KARLIN, *J. Polymer Sci.*, 15 (1955) 427.

[35] D. COLEMAN, *J. Polymer Sci.*, 14 (1954) 15.

[36] O. B. EDGAR, *J. Chem. Soc.*, (1952) 2638.

B. FULKAI and G. BODOR, *Faserforsch. u. Textiltech.*, 8 (1957) 114.

[37] H. LUDEWIG, *Faserforsch. u. Textiltech.*, 6 (1955) 277.

[38] A. S. BROWN, *J. Appl. Phys.*, 20 (1949) 552.

[39] W. M. D. BRYANT, *J. Polymer Sci.*, 2 (1947) 547.

[40] E. GRAMS and E. GAUBE, *Angew. Chem.*, 67 (1955) 548.

[41] H. W. STARKWEATHER and R. E. BROOKS, *J. Appl. Polymer Sci.*, 1 (1959) 236.

[42] C. A. SPERATI, W. A. FRANTA and H. W. STARKWEATHER JR., *J. Am. Chem. Soc.*, 75 (1953) 6127.

[43] D. F. ROBERTS and L. MANDELKERN, *J. Am. Chem. Soc.*, 77 (1955) 781.

[44] T. ALFREY and H. MARK, *J. Phys. Chem.*, 64 (1942) 112.

E. M. FRITH and R. F. TUCKETT, *Trans. Faraday Soc.*, 40 (1944) 251.

R. B. RICHARDS, *Trans. Faraday Soc.*, 41 (1945) 127.

[45] R. HILL and E. E. WALKER, *J. Polymer Sci.*, 3 (1948) 609.

[46] A. V. TOBOLSKY, *Properties & Structure of Polymers*, Wiley, New York, 1960.

[47] J. H. HILDEBRAND and R. L. SCOTT, *Solubility of Non-Electrolytes*, Rheinhold, New York, 1950.

[48] G. GEE, *Thermodynamics of Rubber Solutions & Gels, Advances in Colloid Science*, Vol. II, Interscience, New York, 1956.

[49] G. M. BRISTOW and W. F. WATSON, *Trans. Faraday Soc.*, 54 (1958) 1567, 1731.

[50] G. J. JANZ, *Estimation of Thermodynamic Properties of Organic Compounds*, Academic Press, New York, 1958.

[51] P. J. FLORY, *J. Chem. Phys.*, 17 (1949) 223; 15 (1947) 684.

[52] M. GORDON and J. S. TAYLOR, *J. Appl. Chem.*, 2 (1952) 493.

[53] T. G. FOX, *Bull. Am. Phys. Soc.*, 1, No. 3 (1956) 123.

[54] L. MANDELKERN, G. M. MARTIN and F. A. QUINN JR., *J. Research Natl. Bur. Standards*, 58 (1957) 137.

[55] C. B. MORGAN, *J. Appl. Chem.*, 4 (1954) 160.

[56] F. D. HARTLEY, F. W. LORD and L. B. MORGAN, *Simposio Internazionale di Chimica Macromolecolare*, 25 (1955) 3.

[57] E. H. BOASSON and J. M. WOESTENENK, *J. Polymer Sci.*, 24 (1957) 57.

[58] F. KHOURY, *J. Polymer Sci.*, 33 (1958) 289.

[59] F. Khoury, *J. Polymer Sci.*, 26 (1957) 375.
[60] A. B. Thompson and D. W. Woods, *Trans. Faraday Soc.*, 52 (1956) 1383.
[61] A. Brown, *Textile Research J.*, 25 (1955) 891.
[62] W. H. Cobbs and R. L. Burton, *J. Polymer Sci.*, 10 (1953) 275.
[63] H. Raine, R. B. Richards and H. Ryder, *Trans. Faraday Soc.*, 41 (1950) 56.
[64] N. Bekkedahl and L. A. Wood, *J. Appl. Phys.*, 17 (1946) 362.
[65] L. Mandelkern, *J. Appl. Phys.*, 26 (1955) 443.
[66] L. Mandelkern, R. R. Garrett and P. J. Flory, *J. Am. Chem. Soc.*, 74 (1952) 3949.
[67] R. Hill, *Fibres from Synthetic Polymers*, Elsevier, Amsterdam, 1953.

CHAPTER 14

FINE STRUCTURE

1. Introduction

The production of a fibre from a high polymer begins with the extrusion of a melt or solution of that polymer. However, in thread-like specimens of polymers immediately after extrusion, the molecules do not show any preferred orientation and, in general, such material is not suitable for a fibre. To obtain a suitable fibre, the threads are stretched or drawn when in most instances, the crystallites are oriented or, if crystallites are not already present, crystallisation may occur. The number and size of the crystallites as well as their orientation affects the properties of the fibre *e.g.* crimp, stiffness, resistance to abrasion etc.; indeed, most of the properties which go to make a successful fibre are connected with the fine structure of the fibres. Thus with unoriented nylon 66 or 610, increases in the degree of crystallinity improve the hardness, tensile strength, yield point and stiffness[3].

The detailed picture of the two phase structure of fibrous polymers is still a matter for discussion[12]. The picture which has developed has been described as the fringe micellar theory. In this, the micelles are regions of high order statistically distributed in regions of lower order. No clear boundary between these phases can be defined and the change from the regions of high order to low order are gradual. The structure is thus reticular in nature with the chains anchored at various points.

The crystalline regions vary in size and perfection. Information on the size may be obtained from X-ray diffraction experiments, since the breadths of the lines in the pattern depend on crystal size. If the crystallites are oriented, the lines arising from planes perpendicular to the fibre axis are narrower than those from planes parallel. This means that the crystallites are rod shaped. Crystallite sizes are also found from scattering of X-rays at low angles and some of the results for cellulosic materials are given in Table 34.

Many properties of fibres are dependent on the degree of crystallinity. Relationships are complex and must therefore be qualitative. In Table 35, the effect of crystallinity on some of the properties of cellulose is indicated. Similar relations apply to other fibres.

The relationships are modified by the size and orientation of the crystallites. Most native cellulosic fibres with crystallinities of the order of 80%

TABLE 34

Material	Length(Å)	Breadth(Å)	Method
Ramie	500–600	50–100	Line Broadening[13]
Viscose rayon	300	40	Line Broadening[13]
Ramie	—	70	Low angle scatter[14]
Regenerated cellulose filaments	—	40	Low angle scatter[14]
Jute	—	22–27	Low angle scatter[15]

TABLE 35

PROPERTIES OF CELLULOSE FIBRES MODIFIED BY INCREASING THE DEGREE OF CRYSTALLINITY

Increases	Decreases
Tensile strength	Extensibility
Initial modulus	Flexibility
Hardness	Toughness
Dimensional stability	Dye absorption
Density	Moisture sorption
	Chemical reactivity towards certain reagents

have higher dynamic moduli than regenerated cellulosic fibres with crystallinities of the order of 40–60%.

Changes in crystallinity alone do not tell the whole story. It appears that a high density is essential to increase the modulus; this can be achieved by increasing the orientation without necessarily increasing the crystallinity. For viscose monofilaments of a low degree of crystallinity, it has been found that the moduli increase with increase in orientation[17] (Fig. 117). Furthermore, the initial modulus of cotton appears to vary

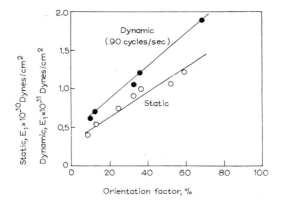

Fig. 117. Static and dynamic Young's moduli as a function of orientation factor for viscose monofilaments[17].

with the orientation[18]. That the properties depend on structural arrangements is indicated by the results in Table 36.

TABLE 36[19]

Fibre	Dynamic modulus (dynes/cm² × 10⁻¹⁰)	Orientation angle	Crystallinity
Ramie	32	8	88–90
Cotton	7–13	25–35	88
Viscose rayon	7–18.4	25–30	57
High tenacity viscose rayon	15.2–19.7	12–20	46

Thus, cotton with the same crystallinity as ramie but with a lower
orientation has a much lower modulus. High tenacity viscose with a low
crystallinity but a more complete orientation tends to have a larger
dynamic modulus than normal viscose.

Some properties depend almost entirely on the existence of the rather
open amorphous regions; examples are dyeing, moisture sorption, creasing, etc. Naturally, they are influenced by the amount of each region but
again orientation plays a part. Orientation of the fibre will tend to straight-
en the chains and reduce the accessibility. Increase in orientation decreases the ease with which large dye molecules or chemical reagents can
penetrate; lateral swelling increases but longitudinal swelling decreases,
elongation decreases and so on. Absorption of a molecule as small as water
is almost unaffected by orientation alone.

2. Properties Depending on the Amorphous Regions

Some of the properties depending on the amorphous regions will be briefly
considered.

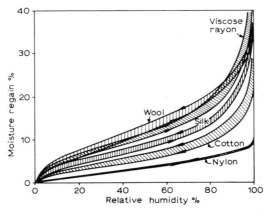

Fig. 118. Absorption and desorption moisture regain isotherms for textile fibres[16].

(a) Moisture Regain

The relation between regain and relative humidity of the atmosphere is sigmoid in shape (Fig. 118). Analysis of these curves is complicated by the hysteresis effect; by this is meant that the amounts of vapour absorbed are different, according to whether the fibre is going from a lower to a higher regain (absorption) or *vise versa* (desorption). For details, the reader is referred elsewhere[4].

(b) Heat Absorption

When textile fibres absorb water, they evolve heat. The heat evolved is important in practice since it has a thermostatic action tending to keep the wearer warm when moisture is absorbed and cool when desorbed. The quantity of heat evolved on sorption is significant — a woollen jacket in going from a room at 18°C and 45% r.h. to one at 5°C and 95% r.h. will give out 100 kcal[20]. The differential heat of absorption of water at zero moisture (which can be deduced from the slope of the curve obtained by plotting heat of wetting against moisture regain[4]) is almost constant for all fibres being between 200–300 cal/g, a value roughly the same as

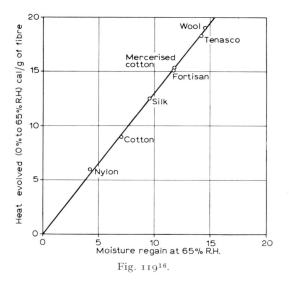

Fig. 119[16].

the heat of hydration of hydroxyl groups or carboxyl ions[21]. It is therefore to be expected that the integral heat of absorption and moisture regain of all fibres under standard conditions will be linearly related. This has been shown in Fig. 119. The definitions of the two heats of absorption are (1) differential heat — heat evolved by an infinite mass of material at

regain *a* on absorbing unit mass of water, (2) integral heat — heat evolved
by dry material in absorbing sufficient water vapour to raise its moisture
content from zero to *a*. For more details the reader is referred elsewhere[4].

(c) *Swelling*

Water can penetrate quite readily the amorphous regions and, since the
chain molecules are oriented along the fibre axis, this water will swell the
fibre mainly in the lateral direction. Thus nylon, cotton and wool, in
going from the dry to the wet state, increase in length by only 1.2% but
in diameter by 5, 14 and 16% respectively; the figures for viscose are
3–5% and 26%[22]. The swelling properties are dependent on the orientation of the fibres and with viscose rayon for example the ratio of lateral
to longitudinal swelling can vary over quite a wide range. Volume
swelling, on the other hand, is not affected by orientation.

The amount of swelling which occurs depends on the amount of amorphous material, the size of the crystallites and the presence of polar
groups. For example, silk and nylon have the same amount of amorphous
material but there is a larger number of polar groups in silk than nylon
so its swelling is much greater.

When water is absorbed, the total volume of the fibre and water taken
together decreases. The plot of density as measured in a non-swelling
medium such as toluene has been plotted against regain[16] (full line in
Fig. 120); there is an initial rise of density followed by a fall at higher

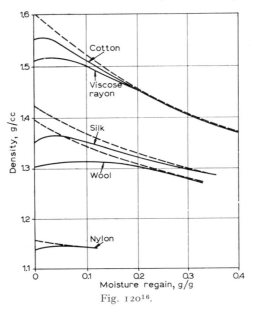

Fig. 120[16].

regains. This is explained by the idea that there is some free volume in the fibre[23]. If the density is measured in water, this increase is not apparent and the curves follow the dotted line.

(d) Dyeing

Dyes are absorbed exclusively in the amorphous regions of fibres. Usually the fraction of amorphous material present is adequate for a dyer to obtain all the shades required. Dye uptake is a subject discussed in detail in Volume 3.

3. Crystallinity and Accessibility

One of the parameters defining the fibre is its degree of crystallinity. Techniques for determining this are of two types (a) physical and (b) chemical. Although some of the methods yield absolute values, none is absolute in defining the polymer structure. Methods under (a) depend on the fact that regions are packed and oriented differently and include X-rays, infra red analysis etc. Methods under (b) have been employed particularly for cellulose, probably on account of the greater reactivity of this polymer compared with most others. In these methods, it is the amorphous regions and possibly the crystallite surfaces which are reactive. For this reason the term accessibility, A, has been used; this is related to the fraction of material, γ, in the crystalline form by

$$A = \sigma\gamma + (1 - \gamma)$$

where σ is the fraction of the crystallites accessible to the reagent. For cellulose, kinetic studies in which some reaction proceeds initially at a rapid rate followed by a slower one have been used. If the fast reaction is considered to be confined to the amorphous regions and the slow one to the crystalline portions, a suitable extrapolation of the slow rate will give a measure of the non-crystalline material originally present[24].

(a) Chemical Methods for Determining the Degree of Crystallinity

(i) Reactivity of phases

The difference in reactivity between the amorphous and crystalline phases was brought out in the experiments of Davidson who treated cotton with hydrochloric acid and found that, long after the cotton had fallen to a powder and though it was still being eroded with acid, the X-ray diffraction photograph remained the same as the original cotton[25].

When these chemical studies are made, disagreement on an absolute scale is not surprising because each determination brings its own definition of crystallinity. Different reagents for example will have molecules of different sizes and will be able to penetrate the amorphous regions to different extents. Differences in accessibility have been shown by immersing fibres in different alcohols and other liquids when, as the size of the molecules increased, the penetration decreased[26]. Such experiments give an idea of the accessibility in terms of size of reagent. An ingeneous method was to react cellulose with thallous alkoxide in a series of ethers of different molecular volumes, and extrapolate the results to obtain the degree of reactivity at zero molecular volume of solvent[27]. These methods give results which depend on the state of swelling of the material.

(ii) *Hydrolysis*

Hydrolytic reactions have been studied. Reaction is initially rapid but slows down to a more or less constant rate arising from hydrolysis of the crystalline regions.

Extrapolation of the rate of hydrolysis curves has been used as a measure of the quantity of amorphous material present. This is given[24,28]

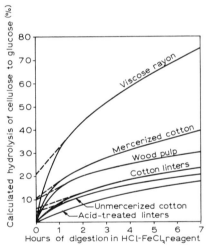

Fig. 121. Percentage of cellulose hydrolysed *vs.* time for various cellulosic materials boiling 2.4 N hydrochloric acid and 0.6 M ferric chloride[24].

by the ordinate in Fig. 121. However, this extrapolation is not satisfactory and a more detailed analysis is desirable[32]. On the assumption that there is one specific rate for amorphous and one for crystalline regions, it is possible to write the rate of reaction for hydrolysis of cellulose to glucose as

$$\text{rate} = \gamma\,e^{-k_c t} + (1 - \gamma)\,e^{-k_a t} \tag{1}$$

This assumes that the reaction may be represented by first order kinetics with rate constants k_c and k_a for the crystalline and amorphous regions respectively. Further since the hydrolysis of the amorphous regions is rapid, the second term becomes negligible at the longer times of hydrolysis. If the unhydrolysed residue is determined and its logarithm plotted against time, a straight line should result when practically all the amorphous cellulose has disappeared. The straight line can therefore be easily extrapolated to zero time to give an ordinate which represents the logarithm of the concentration of crystalline cellulose initially present. Some data are given in Fig. 122.

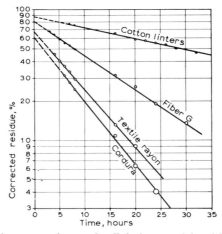

Fig. 122. Hydrolysis curves of several cellulosic materials with 4 N hydrochloric acid at 100°C yielding different degrees of crystallinity[32].

Unfortunately under the rather drastic conditions required to achieve extensive hydrolysis, increases in crystallinity have been shown to occur. The method has been criticised on this count. Less drastic conditions can be used if the reaction is taken to a smaller extent, and a study made of the initial position of the rate curve. The technique of measuring either the production of glucose or the loss in weight of the material as used in the above experiments is unsuitable, since the changes in the earlier stages of the reaction are small. The property in this region which does change markedly is the D.P. and this has been employed as follows[31].

Essentially this method measures the fraction of bonds α available for hydrolysis. The value of α is a measure of the accessibility A. The reaction is again taken as first order. If N_t and N_0 are the number of bonds present at time t, the number of bonds not available for breaking is given by $N_0(1-\alpha)$ and the number capable of being broken at time t is given by

N_t—$N_0(1$—$\alpha)$. For a first order reaction, the rate of change of this quantity will be given by

$$\frac{-\mathrm{d}\,[N_t - N_0(1 - \alpha)]}{\mathrm{d}t} = k[N_t - N_0(1 - \alpha)] \tag{2}$$

Integration of equation 2 gives

$$\ln\,[N_t - N_0(1 - \alpha)] = kt + \text{Constant} \tag{3}$$

Since $N_t = N_0$ when $t = 0$, equation 3 may be written as

$$\ln\,\frac{N_0\alpha}{N_t - N_0(1 - \alpha)} = kt \tag{4}$$

Equation 4 may be put into terms of degree of polymerisation. If there are N_0 links at the commencement of the reaction, the average D.P. at this stage P_0 is $N_0 + 1$; at time t, the number of broken links is N_0—N_t and hence the number of molecules is $N_0 - N_t + 1$, giving for the D.P., P_t, $(N_0 + 1)/(N_0$—$N_t + 1)$.

Substituting these values in equation 4 gives

$$\ln\left(1 - \frac{1}{P_0}\right) - \ln\left(1 - \frac{1}{P_0} + \frac{1}{\alpha P_0} - \frac{1}{\alpha P_t}\right) = kt \tag{5}$$

or since $1/P_0$ and $1/P_t$ are $\ll 1$, this equation may, on expansion of the logarithms, be approximated to

$$\frac{1}{P_t} - \frac{1}{P_0} = \alpha kt \tag{6}$$

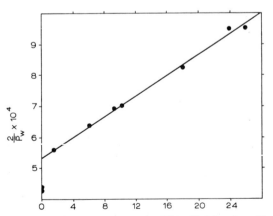

Fig. 123. Hydrolysis of Egyptian cotton in $N/10$ H_2SO_4 at $50\,°C$ — first stage abscissa time $\times 10^{-4} \sec$[31].

Equation 6 renders possible, from a knowledge of the changes in the degrees of polymerisation and the rate constant, the determination of α. Experimentally however, it is easier to measure the weight average D.P. instead of the number average given above and, as discussed in Chapter 7, the number averages may be replaced by half the weight average D.P. Results for this method are given in Fig. 123, where an accessibility of 10% was found for Egyptian cotton.

(iii) *Reaction with deuterium oxide and formic acid*

Accessibility can also be measured by studying the exchange reaction of the hydroxyl groups with deuterium oxide[34,35]. The degree of exchange may be found from the change in density of the heavy water in which the cellulose is immersed. The reaction proceeds very rapidly in the initial stages, slows suddenly at a certain point and proceeds thereafter at a slow rate. The extent of reaction in the initial rapid stages is taken as indicative of the amount of the accessible material. Formic acid esterification has also been used but, with this technique, different values are obtained according to the reaction conditions; this method has the advantage that crystallisation does not occur during the reaction, presumably due to the fact that the cellulose will be partially substituted[36]. Some results are given in Table 37.

TABLE 37
PERCENTAGE ACCESSIBILITY OF CELLULOSE

Source	By D_2O exchange[37]	By formylation[38] (a)	(b)	By acid hydrolysis	By infra-red[29]
Cotton	41	28	16	5–13	—
Mercerised cotton	—	52	28	11–32	—
Viscose rayon	68	—	54	22–32	78
Viscose treated with 18% sodium hydroxide solution	—	—	—	—	70

(a) 98% formic acid 15 h at 55°C
(b) 90% formic acid 12 h at 30°C

With wool, deuterium interchange has been used[30]; wool was exposed to D_2O vapour and the increase in weight determined. The amount of interchange which would occur if all the wool was accessible was calculated from exchange experiments using amino acids, and from a knowledge of the amino acid analysis of wool. From the measured and calculated total exchange, the accessibility was found to be around 80%.

(b) *Physical Methods for Determining the Degree of Crystallinity*

(i) *Density*

If the densities of the amorphous and crystalline regions are known, a knowledge of the density of the fibre can be used to calculate the degree of crystallinity. This of course assumes that the different regions in the fibre are discrete and of uniform density. If d, d_c and d_a are the densities of the fibre, crystalline and amorphous regions respectively, the fraction γ of crystalline material will be obtained by assuming that the masses of the two parts are additive. Thus for 1 g of fibre,

$$\frac{1}{d} = \frac{\gamma}{d_c} + \frac{(1-\gamma)}{d_a}$$

or

$$\gamma = \frac{d_c(d-d_a)}{d(d_c-d_a)}$$

The density of the crystalline region may be found from the crystal structure but that of the amorphous must be estimated from the density of the melt, from the density of a quenched amorphous sample or derived from that of a solution of the polymer. Where the crystalline and amorphous regions give characteristic absorption bands in the infra-red region of the spectrum, it is possible using samples of different degrees of crystallinity to plot the intensity of the two bands against the sample density and extrapolate to zero intensity (Fig. 124[33]).

The density method has been used for cellulose[2] but, although the crystalline density may be calculated with reasonable accuracy from the

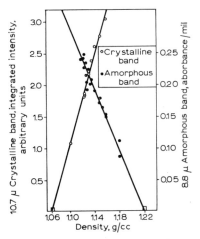

Fig. 124. Determination of the densities of the amorphous and crystalline regions in nylon[33].

dimensions of the unit cell, no direct method exists for the measurement of the density of the amorphous regions. Nevertheless, the method is capable of giving comparative values for different cellulosic materials.

(ii) *X-ray methods*

If the contributions to the X-ray diagram of the crystalline and amorphous parts of the fibre can be resolved, it is possible to obtain some idea of the degree of crystallinity. The percentage crystallinity may be obtained by comparison of the integrated intensities of the maxima with that which arises from the polymer molecules in the disordered regions. In Fig. 125, the X-ray diagrams of viscose and bacterial cellulose are treated

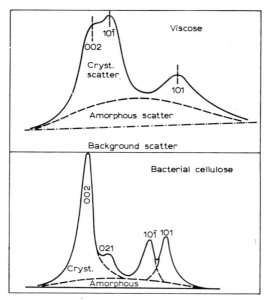

Fig. 125. Determination of proportions of crystalline and amorphous material by X-ray methods[40].

in this way. The method suffers from the disadvantage that only crystallites of a certain size will contribute to the maxima and hence the value for the fraction of each phase must be regarded as approximate. Experimentally, it is not always easy to apportion the composite diffraction curve between that arising from the amorphous regions, crystalline regions and background scatter. In some instances *e.g.* polyethylene, in order to obtain the amorphous scattering, a melt has been used[9,39].

The relative intensities of the X-rays diffracted by the two phases provide a measure of the proportions. Most polymers studied have been unoriented specimens since more computation is required for the oriented ones.

(iii) *Infra-red measurements*

In the infra-red region of the electromagnetic spectrum, absorption bands arise from molecular vibrations and rotations. The frequencies corresponding to wavelengths of $1-50\,\mu$ ($1\,\mu = 10^{-4}$ cm) are usually given in wave numbers (reciprocal wavelength $1\,\mu = 10,000$ cm^{-1}). With more complex molecules, the vibrations and rotations and hence the absorption bands tend to be characteristic of small groups of atoms which go to make up the whole molecules. Infra-red absorption spectra are very valuable for identifying groups such as methyl, hydroxyl, carbonyl etc.; the possible number of groups capable of identification is quite large but nevertheless, some groups do not give characteristic absorption bands. This latter arises because any transition which occurs must be accompanied by a change in dipole moment. In Fig. 126, some of the absorption

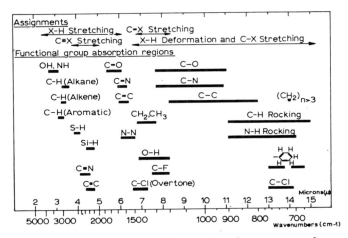

Fig. 126. Infra-red absorption bands of interest in polymers arranged according to wavelength and frequency[46].

bands arising in infra-red spectra are plotted; most of these bands are to be found in the spectra of one polymer or another but, with these compounds, additional bands arise from the skeleton of the molecule.

The number of bands in the spectra is very large and considerable care is necessary when they are analysed as may be seen from the spectra reproduced in Fig. 127[44].

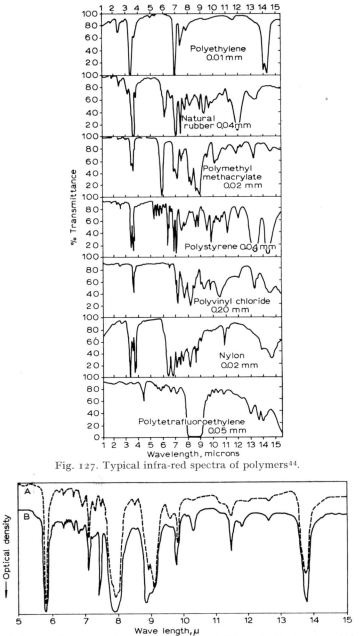

Fig. 127. Typical infra-red spectra of polymers[44].

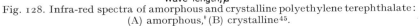

Fig. 128. Infra-red spectra of amorphous and crystalline polyethylene terephthalate:
(A) amorphous, (B) crystalline[45].

The absorption spectra of polymers may undergo characteristic changes with changes in crystallinity. With some polymers such as polyethylene terephthalate[45] (Fig. 128), nylon 66 etc., all the bands are sensitive; with others, the changes are more specific *e.g.* polyethylene has an absorption band at 13.9 μ from the rocking vibration of the CH_2-group; this develops a second peak *i.e.* splits into a doublet in crystalline material. Thus, the bands are characteristic of the amorphous and crystalline regions, and the degree of crystallinity may be obtained from the intensities[6] when the bands have been calibrated by the intensity of a purely amorphous specimen.

The shape of the absorption band of cellulose due to the hydroxyl group in the crystalline regions differs from that in the amorphous[37]. Further, on treatment with deuterium oxide, exchange of hydrogen for deuterium takes place mainly between the hydroxyl groups in the amorphous regions.

$$2ROH + D_2O \rightleftharpoons 2ROD + H_2O$$

The main effect on the spectrum is to reduce the broad band in the region $3000-3600$ cm^{-1} due to the hydroxyl groups in the amorphous regions (Fig. 129). The bands which remain are the much sharper ones characteristic of the crystalline regions but, at the same time, a broad band due to absorption by OD groups appears around 2500 cm^{-1}: this is due to the disordered regions in which deuterium exchange readily occurs.

However, the situation is made a little more complex by the fact that rehydrogenation does not give back the original curve. The OD band does

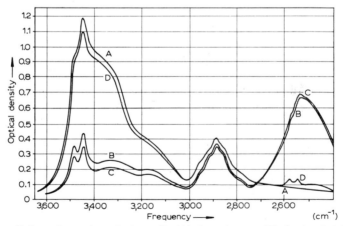

Fig. 129. Infra-red spectra of viscose[37]. (A) dry viscose, (B) deuterated in D_2O vapour for 4 h, (C) deuterated in D_2O liquid for 4 h, (D) rehydrogenated in H_2O for 4 h.

not entirely disappear and the residual OD left in the material is found in the crystalline regions[29]. The presence of deuterium in these regions has been shown to be a consequence of some molecular rearrangement; direct penetration of the crystallites does not occur. To determine the accessibility of the celluloses, the relative intensities of the OH and OD bands is adequate but, to obtain a measure of the crystallinity, Mann and Marrinan have been rather more rigid and defined crystalline regions as those which possess a three dimensional order sufficient to give a regular repeating system of hydrogen bonds. To obtain a measure of the crystallinity, the percentage of hydroxyl groups bonded in this way must be determined. In determinations of the crystallinity, the deuteration is stopped when all hydroxyl groups in the amorphous region have reacted. For this purpose, deuteration in the vapour phase is used.

Infra-red measurements on wool before and after deuteration show the amide band to disappear (*i.e.* exchange is complete) and hence amide groups are to be found in the accessible amorphous portion. Crystallinity may be found from estimating the number of peptide linkages accessible to D_2O. Crystallinities of approximately 50–60% have been found[6].

In general, the results from infra-red methods give a lower quantity of crystalline material; this may arise from the fact that some of the hydroxyl groups which lie on the surface of the crystallites may not absorb radiation at a frequency characteristic of crystalline material.

(iv) *Heat of fusion*

Heat is required to melt a crystal so that the ratio of the measured heat of a partly crystalline polymer to that of a crystalline material can be taken as the fraction of crystalline material. In practice, the situation is not no simple since the melting points are not sharp and changes in crystallinity take place over a wide range of temperatures. Instead, the heat content of the specimen is measured over a temperature range including and above its melting point. If the extrapolated curve for the liquid represents the heat content of the amorphous material, the fraction crystalline will be given by

$$\gamma = \frac{H_a - H}{\Delta H_{cr}}$$

where H is the heat content of the specimen and ΔH_{cr} the heat of fusion of crystals. For polyethylene, ΔH_{cr} can be estimated from the heats of fusion of crystalline paraffins. The method relies on the heat content of the amorphous portion being the same as that of a supercooled liquid. This is not likely to be a very exact assumption because the densities are different.

(v) *Moisture regain*

Moisture is assumed to be absorbed by the suitable groups in the amorphous regions and on the surface of the crystallites; penetration into the crystalline regions does, in general, not occur. Thus for different celluloses, it is reasonable to conclude that there will be at least an

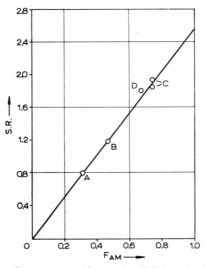

Fig. 130. The relation between sorption ratio (S.R.) and the fraction (F_{AM}) of amorphous hydroxyl groups for various types of cellulose[41].

TABLE 38

SOME RESULTS OF CRYSTALLINITY DETERMINATIONS

Polymer	% of crystalline material	Method of determination
Cellulose		
(a) Ramie	70	X-ray[40]
(b) Cotton	70	X-ray[40]
(c) Bacterial cellulose	40	X-ray[40]
	70	Infra-red[29]
(d) Viscose rayon	38–40	X-ray[40]
	26	Infra-red
(e) Viscose treated with 18% solution of sodium hydroxide	52–54	X-ray[40]
	33.5	Infra-red[29]
Polyethylene	55	Density[7]
	75	X-ray[8]
Polymethylene	95	ref. 6
Branched polyethylene	40	X-ray, density[9]
Polyethylene terephthalate	50	Density[10]
Nylon 66 (unoriented)	50–60	X-ray[11]

approximate relation between the moisture content and the percentage of hydroxyl groups in the amorphous portions. In Fig. 130, the sorption ratios (moisture regain relative to that of cotton) are plotted against the fraction of amorphous material in four cellulose samples[41]. A straight line is obtained in agreement with this suggestion. Detailed analysis of sorption isotherms is complex and will not be discussed here but it is possible to calculate the crystalline/amorphous ratio making some assumptions[41]. Some results of crystallinity determinations are given in Table 38.

4. Determination of the Orientation

From some physical techniques, information can be obtained as to disposition of the groups in the molecule and orientation of the chains. Three techniques which throw light on the disposition of molecules or groups of molecules are discussed.

(a) Birefringence

When light falls on a molecule or atom, the electron cloud suffers a displacement. In a molecule, the presence of one atom affects another and, indeed, electron displacement or polarisation of the molecule is not of the same magnitude in all directions. The interaction of an electromagnetic wave such as light will depend on the orientation of the atoms in the molecule with respect to the plane of polarisation of that light. Thus in a simple molecule such as ethane, there will be a different extent of polarisation along the C—C bond from that at right angles to it. In polyethylene whose molecule is arranged in a planar zig-zag, the polarisability in the direction of the chain will be the sum of the components in this direction from all of the bonds. This high polarisability arises from the fact that the C—C angles are greater than 90°, and hence have major components along the chain. Polarisability at right angles to the plane of the molecule is very low, since this depends on the polarisability of the C—C bonds perpendicular to the bond and on the polarisability of the C—H bonds. Both these are very low. The refractive index n increases with the polarisability σ according to the relation

$$\frac{n^2 - 1}{n^2 + 2} = K\sigma$$

where K is a constant. Hence the refractive indices along and in the two directions at right angles to the chain molecule will be different.

From this picture, it is clear that the polarisability of the polymer molecule will be modified according to the atoms involved. Thus replacement of some of the hydrogen atoms by methyl groups or chlorine atoms increases the lateral polarisability, since C—C and C—Cl bonds are more polarisable. Polyvinylidene chloride or polyisobutene chains will possess larger refractive indices at right angles to the chain than polyethylene and, indeed, in contrast to polyethylene they are negatively birefringent *i.e.* their refractive indices along the chain are less than at right angles to it. In general, the refractive indices of the chain will depend on the polarisabilities of the various groups in it and the directions in which these are oriented. The refractive indices of a fibre present a more complex picture as they depend not only on the refractive indices of the molecules themselves, but also on the degree to which they are oriented in the fibre. An isotropic filament will have the same refractive index in all directions. Stretching will orient the molecules in the filament and hence, if the refractive index is greater for light vibrating parallel to the chain, the fibre will have a higher refractive index in the direction of the fibre axis than perpendicular to it, and be positively birefringent.

In a non-crystalline fibre, the birefringence will be related to the orientation of the segments; in a crystalline one, a more complex situation exists since orientation of the fibre will be determined by orientation in both amorphous and crystalline regions. Birefringence is a measure of orientation and not crystallinity since oriented chain molecules are themselves birefringent. The birefringence of different fibres varies considerably, since it depends on the polarisability of the bonds as well as orientation. Some results[1] are given in Table 39.

TABLE 39

Material	Well oriented specimens		
	r.i. parallel to fibre axis (μ_{11})	Perpendicular to fibre axis (μ_1)	Birefringence $(\mu_{11} - \mu_1)$
Polyethylene	1.556	1.512	+0.044
Nylon 66	1.580	1.520	+0.060
Terylene	1.725	1.537	+0.188
Native ramie	1.596	1.528	+0.068
Silk	1.591	1.538	+0.053
Cellulose triacetate	1.474	1.479	—0.005

In a fibre, the precise value of the three principal indices are not known because in general single crystals are not available. However in the case of nylon, compressed or flattened fibres have been obtained in which all the crystallites are roughly parallel; such a specimen shows refractive indices of 1.475 normal to the sheet, 1.565 in the plane of the sheet at right angles to the fibre axis and 1.580 along the axis. A normal fibre does not have its crystallites ordered in the lateral sense but disposed at random so that only one refractive index exists for light vibrating perpendicularly to the fibre axis; this means that the refractive index is the mean of the two lateral ones *i.e.* for nylon quoted about equal to 1.520. The optical properties become similar to those of a uniaxial crystal.

The amorphous part of a fibre, since it has a lower density than the crystalline, has a lower refractive index; fibres vary in the extent of crystallinity so that the overall density, and hence refractive index, will be different in different specimens.

The birefringence of a fibre is related to how well the chains are oriented, and may be regarded as a parameter of the average orientation of all the molecules whether in the crystalline or amorphous regions.

The values of the birefringence B can be related to the average angle ϕ which the molecules make with the fibre axis[2]

$$\frac{B}{B_0} = 1 - \frac{3}{2}\sin^2 \phi$$

where B_0 is the value for a perfectly oriented specimen. As a method for obtaining a parameter relating to orientation, the birefringence is extremely valuable and is much used. There are difficulties in calculating ϕ in that the value of B_0 is not easy to obtain, and it is assumed that refractive indices are not modified by the presence of neighbouring chains. Further, distribution of orientation is not obtained but only an average value. The birefringence method of comparing degrees of orientation is most sensitive when the orientation is poor, but deteriorates when high extents of orientation are reached.

Birefringence is an extremely valuable measurement for following changes of orientation in fibres during manufacture. For cotton, the birefringent results are in line with the fibrils being inclined at an angle of 30° to the fibre axis. Changes in orientation accompanying chemical and mechanical treatment may be followed by birefringence. Thus the contraction of cellulosic fibres when mercerised without tension correlates with the angle of inclination of molecules as calculated from birefringence[42].

In the above discussion, textural inhomogeneities have been assumed absent. These can not be completely ignored, since placing an assembly of isotropic particles which are asymmetric in shape in a medium of different refractive index produces a system which exhibits birefringence[43]. Birefringence arising from shape factors will depend on the differences of refractive index and will be reduced to zero if the indices are the same. In semi-crystalline polymers, the crystallites are asymmetric in shape and of different refractive index from the surrounding amorphous material. Measured birefringence will therefore have a contribution arising from the shape of the crystallites. However, shape birefringence is calculated on the basis of the existence of a sharp phase boundary between the particles and the surrounding medium. In polymers, the boundary between the crystallites and the amorphous material is not considered to be sharp in the dry state but may be reasonably so when the samples are swollen in a liquid. Usually the refractive index difference between crystalline and amorphous polymers is not large so that form birefringence is very small in the dry state.

Birefringence thus gives a measure of orientation which is an average of that of the amorphous and crystalline regions. Values obtained may be modified by interaction between chains and the shape of the crystallites. Fortunately, these two effects are of a second order and measurement of birefringence gives the right order of magnitude for the orientation.

(b) X-ray Diffraction

The X-ray pattern of the crystalline regions of a polymer is characterised by discrete reflections usually in the form of short arcs. The intensity distribution along the length of these arcs may be interpreted in terms of the distribution of orientation of certain crystallographic planes. It is possible to describe the orientation in terms of average orientation of the crystallites and not each individual plane. Hermans[2] has defined the orientation factor f_x in terms of the average angle of orientation

$$f_x = 1 - \tfrac{1}{2} \sin^2 \alpha$$

Some results are given in the Table 40.

TABLE 40

Material	α	f_x
Ramie	$7°6'$	0.97
Ramie mercerised without tension	$15°0'$	0.90
Viscose rayon without stretch	$22°4'$	0.79
Viscose rayon stretched 120%	$14°3'$	0.91

(c) Infra-red Spectra

Spectra in this region are of great value for the elucidation of polymer structure since specific groups in the polymer may be detected. Furthermore, if polarised radiation is used, the absorption spectra yield information concerning the manner in which certain groups are oriented in the polymer specimen. Some instances where these studies have been useful will be discussed.

(i) Polyethylene

Polyethylene has a spectrum which shows few intense absorption bands as might be expected from its non-polar character. The bands occur in the regions of 3.5, 7 and 14 μ with a weaker one at 11–12 μ.

Studies of infra-red spectra have proved to be of value particularly with respect to branching and unsaturation. Methyl absorption bands in the region of 3.5 μ overlap the methylene bands so that detection of methyl groups in this polymer is best investigated in the 7 and 11 μ regions. The spectrum[47] is given in Fig. 131 where it is compared with the corre-

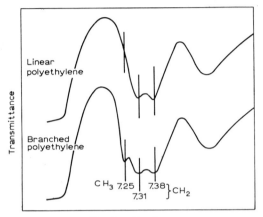

Fig. 131a. Infra-red spectrum of polyethylene near 7 μ[47].

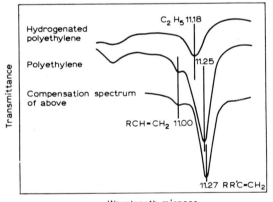

Fig. 131b. Infra-red spectrum of polyethylene near 11 μ[47].

sponding linear polyethylene. The longer wavelength band, although not suffering from interference from the absorption of the methylene groups, is complicated by a band of 11.27 μ due to the unsaturated group[47] (Fig. 131).

References p. 402

However, unsaturation may be removed by hydrogenation and, when this is done, the band at 11.18 may be used to estimate the degree of branching. Infra-red spectra show that, in high pressure commercial polyethylene, 2–4 methyl groups are present per 100 carbon atoms, whereas in the linear polyethylenes this figure is very low.

(ii) *Cellulose*

Infra-red techniques have been employed to show differences between the different crystalline forms of cellulose. Cellulose spectra have been examined with particular reference to the bands which arise from the hydrogen bonded hydroxyl groups[51]. Cellulose I gives spectra shown in Fig. 132; the spectrum labelled A is given by cellulose from bacteria

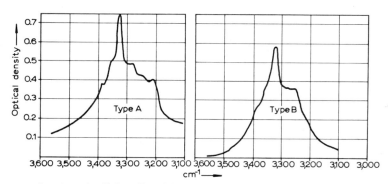

Fig. 132. Spectra of cellulose I[51]. (A) from *Valonia ventucosa*, (B) from *Tunicum*, both measured at the temperature of liquid air.

and *Valonia*; that labelled B is more common and is given by plant cellulose. The differences in these may arise from differences in packing or in degrees of perfection but, at present, the reason for these differences is not certain. Cellulose II gives only one spectrum there being no difference between regenerated or mercerised celluloses (curve A in Fig. 129).

Infra-red spectra of cellulose have been used to throw light on the structure particularly of cellulose II. Fig. 133 shows the spectra using polarised infra-red radiation. The advantage of this is that maximum absorption will occur if the direction of radiation coincides with the mode of vibration. For the hydrogen bonded hydroxyl group, maximum absorption occurs for the stretching frequency when the electric vector lies along the direction of the band (O—H...O). Thus in Fig. 133, the bands at 3484 and 3444 cm^{-1} arise from hydrogen bonds whose directions make angles smaller than 54°44′ to the chain axis whereas the other bands are from hydrogen bonds making angles greater than 54°44′. (This angle has

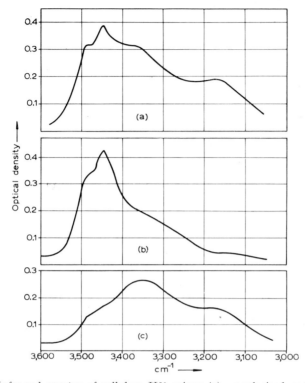

Fig. 133. Infra-red spectra of cellulose II[51] using: (a) unpolarised radiation, (b) plane polarised with the electric vector parallel to chain direction, (c) plane polarised with the electric vector perpendicular.

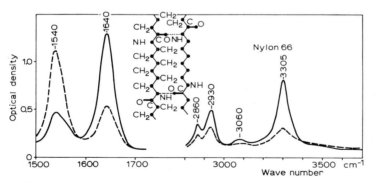

Fig. 134. Infra-red spectra of oriented nylon 66[5]. Inset crystal structure of nylon 66. Full line: electric vector perpendicular to fibre axis. Broken line: electric vector parallel to fibre axis.

References p. 402

been calculated to give a dichroic ratio of unity[52], dichroic ratio being defined as the ratio of the optical density parallel and perpendicular to the chain axis.) This investigation gives information about the disposition of the hydrogen bonds and hence enables more details of the crystal structure to be obtained. In this case, the data are in agreement with the structure for cellulose II given by Petitpas and Mering[53].

(iii) Nylon

Investigation of nylon 66[54] with polarised infra-red shows large differences (Fig. 134). In these spectra, the bands at 3305, 2930, 2860 and 1640 cm^{-1} arise from the stretching modes of the NH, CH_2, CH_2 and CO groups respectively. These are all reduced in intensity when the vector is parallel to the axis and hence result from dipole moment changes which occur perpendicular to the axis. This is in accord with the structure deduced from X-ray data.

(iv) Poly-L-alanine[5]

Interesting confirmation of the two forms of polypeptides have been obtained using infra-red radiation. In Fig. 135, the spectra of oriented

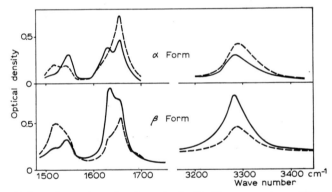

Fig. 135. Infra-red spectra of poly-L-alanine[60]. Upper spectrum: film containing dichloroacetic acid when rolled. Lower spectrum: film stretched in steam. Full line: electric vector perpendicular to direction of rolling. Broken line: electric vector parallel to direction of rolling.

poly-L-alanine films are given, where it can be seen that the dichroism is reversed in going from the α- to the β-form. This effect is to be anticipated in going from the α-helix oriented in the direction of rolling to the β-form. In the former, the NH...OC bands lie along the chain and, in the latter, normal. It must be noted that the frequencies for the bands show some differences between the α- and β-forms[55] but they are in the range which corresponds to a hydrogen bond between CO and NH. Qualitatively, the spectra of the β-form resembles that of nylon 66.

The formation of hydrogen bonds between two groups e.g. C=O and N—H will lower the frequency of both C=O and NH stretching modes. The hydrogen bond has the effect of diminishing the restoring force which operates when either the H or O atoms are displaced from their equilibrium positions and hence the frequency is changed. Deformation modes, on the other hand, show frequency increases. Studies of the spectral shifts of frequencies due to characteristic groups such as OH, CO, NH etc. enable the formation of hydrogen bonds to be detected and, in some instances, the equilibrium constant of an association such as that given below may be determined[57]

$$R_2NH + OR' \rightarrow R_2NH\ldots OR'$$

More information can be obtained by deuteration; the NH-group in amides will exchange its hydrogen on treatment with heavy water. The increased mass of the deuterium atom will lower the frequencies of the NH-group; the frequency changes in the ratio $1/1.33$ and may be used to distinguish frequencies which may overlap. In polyalanine, deuteration results in the loss of the stretching mode of the NH-group which is replaced by bands at a lower frequency (ratio ca. $1/1.33$). The interpretation of these spectra is not easy but the method is one capable of further exploitation[55].

(v) Silk

The spectrum of the water soluble film after being made insoluble gives a carbonyl peak at 1630 cm^{-1} in agreement with the β-form[56]. The frequency and dichroism of the NH deformation mode is in agreement with the β-structure. The configuration of water soluble fibroin is as yet unresolved, but it seems likely that most of its hydrogen bonds do not contribute to the interchain forces.

(vi) Keratin

Examination of keratin in the form of natural elephant hair shows[58] that the NH and CO stretching modes near 3300 and 1660 cm^{-1} exhibit parallel dichroism, hence the NH-and CO-groups tend to lie parallel to the fibre axis as would be anticipated for an oriented α-helix. The dichroism is rather low compared with that in oriented polypeptides, but the lowering of the dichroism may be caused by the amorphous regions. Replacement of NH by ND increases the dichroism[59] because the D$_2$O will interchange in the amorphous regions, confirming the idea that the low dichroism is due to a large amount of amorphous material. For the keratin in porcupine quill tip and feathers the dichroic ratios are changed from 1.5 and 1.8 to 4.5 and 4.8 respectively. Stretching horsehair and keratin causes the dichroism to change, as will be expected, to perpendicular dichroism. Again however the dichroism is low compared with that of some synthetic β-polypeptides.

REFERENCES

[1] C. W. BUNN, in *Fibres from Synthetic Polymers*, R. HILL, (Ed.), Elsevier, Amsterdam, 1953.

[2] P. H. HERMANS, *The Physics and Chemistry of Cellulose Fibres*, Elsevier, Amsterdam, 1949.

[3] H. W. STARKWEATHER, G. E. MOORE, J. E. HANSEN, T. M. RODER and R. E. BROOKS, *J. Polymer Sci.*, 21 (1956) 189.

[4] J. W. S. HEARLE and R. H. PETERS (Eds.), *Moisture in Textiles*, Butterworth, London, 1960.

[5] C. H. BAMFORD, A. ELLIOTT and W. E. HANBY, *Synthetic Polypeptides*, Academic Press, New York, 1956.

[6] R. B. RICHARDS, *J. Appl. Chem.*, 1 (1951) 370.

[7] E. HUNTER and W. G. OAKES, *Trans. Faraday Soc.*, 41 (1945) 49.

[8] J. L. MATTHEWS, H. S. PEISER and R. B. RICHARDS, *Acta Cryst.*, 2 (1949) 85. H. C. RAINE, R. B. RICHARDS and H. RYDER, *Trans. Faraday Soc.*, 41 (1945) 56.

[9] S. KRIMM and A. V. TOBOLSKY, *J. Polymer Sci.*, 7 (1951) 57.

[10] R. DE P. DAUBENY, C. W. BUNN and C. S. BROWN, in *Fibres from Synthetic Polymers*, R. HILL (Ed.), Elsevier, Amsterdam, 1953, p. 286.

[11] P. H. HERMANS and A. WEIDINGER, *J. Polymer Sci.*, 4 (1949) 135, 317, 709; *J. Appl. Phys.*, 19 (1948) 491.

[12] J. W. S. HEARLE in *Fibre Structure*, J. W. S. HEARLE and R. H. PETERS (Eds.), Butterworth, London, 1962.

[13] R. O. HERTZOG, *J. Phys. Chem.*, 30 (1926) 357. J. HENGSTENBERG and H. MARK, *Z. Krist.*, 69 (1928) 271.

[14] O. KRATKY, *Kolloid-Z.*, 120 (1951) 24.

[15] A. N. J. HEYN, *Textile Research J.*, 19 (1949) 163; *J. Am. Chem. Soc.*, 72 (1950) 5768.

[16] J. M. PRESTON (Ed.), *Fibre Science*, Textile Institute, 1953.

[17] M. HORIO, S. ONOGI, C. NAKAYAMA and K. YAMAMOTO, *J. Appl. Phys.*, 22 (1951) 966.

[18] R. MEREDITH, *J. Textile Inst.*, 37 (1946) 205T.

[19] E. OTT and H. M. SPURLIN (Eds.), *Cellulose and Cellulose Derivatives*, Vol. III, Interscience, New York, 1955, p. 1298.

[20] A. B. D. CASSIE, B. E. ATKINS and G. KING, *Nature*, 143 (1939) 163.

[21] J. B. SPEAKMAN, *Trans. Faraday Soc.*, 40 (1944) 6.

[22] J. M. PRESTON and S. DAS GUPTA, *J. Textile Inst.*, 38 (1947) 60T.

[23] P. H. HERMANS, *J. Textile Inst.*, 38 (1947) 63P.

[24] R. F. NICKERSON, *Ind. Eng. Chem.*, 33 (1941) 1022; 34 (1942) 85, 1480. R. F. NICKERSON and J. A. HABRLE, *Ind. Eng. Chem.*, 37 (1945) 1115; 38 (1946) 299; 39 (1947) 1507.

[25] G. F. DAVIDSON, *J. Textile Inst.*, 34 (1943) 87T.

[26] J. B. SPEAKMAN, *Trans. Faraday Soc.*, 26 (1930) 51. A. IWASAKI and T. MEYAMOTO, *J. Soc. Chem. Ind. Japan*, 41 (1938) 224B, 226B.

[27] A. G. ASSA, R. N. HAAS and C. B. PURVES, *J. Am. Chem. Soc.*, 66 (1944) 59.

[28] E. L. LOVELL and O. GOLDSCHMIDT, *Ind. Eng. Chem.*, 38 (1946) 811.

[29] J. MANN and H. J. MARRINAN, *Trans. Faraday Soc.*, 52 (1956) 481.

[30] R. W. BURLEY, C. H. NICHOLLS and J. B. SPEAKMAN, *J. Textile Inst.*, 46 (1955) 427T.

[31] A. SHARPLES, *J. Polymer Sci.*, 13 (1954) 393.

[32] H. J. PHILIPP, M. L. NELSON and H. M. ZIIFLE, *Textile Research J.*, 17 (1947) 585.
[33] H. W. STARKWEATHER and R. E. MOYNIHAN, *J. Polymer Sci.*, 22 (1956) 363.
[34] G. CHAMPETIER and R. VIALLARD, *Bull. soc. chim. France*, 5 (1938) 1042.
[35] V. FULLETTE, J. A. HABRLE and H. MARK, *J. Am. Chem. Soc.*, 70 (1948) 1107.
[36] W. O. BAKER, *Ind. Eng. Chem.*, 37 (1945) 246.
[37] J. MANN and H. J. MARRINAN, *J. Appl. Chem. London*, 4 (1954) 204.
[38] H. TARKOW, *Tappi*, 33 (1950) 595.
   R. F. NICKERSON, *Textile Research J.*, 21 (1951) 195.
[39] S. KRIMM and A. V. TOBOLSKY, *Textile Research J.*, 21 (1951) 805.
[40] P. H. HERMANS, *Makromol. Chem.*, 6 (1951) 25.
[41] L. VALENTINE, *Chem. and Ind. London*, 1279 (1956).
[42] J. M. PRESTON, *Modern Textile Microscopy*, London, 1933.
[43] O. WIENER, *Abhandl. sächs. Akad. Wiss. Leipzig*, 32 (1912) 581; *Kolloidchem. Beih.*, 23 (1927) 189.
[44] H. HANSDORFF, *Pittsberg Conference on Analytical Chemistry and Applied Spectroscopy*, March 1951.
[45] W. W. DANIELS and R. E. KITSON, *J. Polymer Sci.*, 33 (1958) 161.
[46] F. W. BILLMEYER, JR., *Textbook of Polymer Chemistry*, Interscience, New York, 1957.
[47] W. M. D. BRYANT and R. C. VOSTER, *J. Am. Chem. Soc.*, 75 (1953) 6113.
[48] J. B. NICHOLS, *J. Appl. Phys.*, 25 (1954) 840.
[49] R. G. J. MILLER and H. A. WILLIS, *J. Polymer Sci.*, 19 (1956) 485.
[50] H. HANSDORFF, *Pittsberg Conference on Analytical Chemistry and Applied Spectroscopy*, March, 1951.
[51] J. MANN and H. J. MARRINAN, *J. Polymer Sci.*, 21 (1956) 301.
[52] R. D. B. FRASER, *J. Chem. Phys.*, 21 (1953) 1511.
[53] T. PETITPAS and J. MERING, *Compt rend.*, 243 (1956) 47.
[54] C. W. BUNN and E. V. GARNER, *Proc. Roy. Soc. London*, 189A (1947) 39.
[55] A. ELLIOTT, *Proc. Roy. Soc. London*, 226A (1954) 408.
[56] E. J. AMBROSE, C. H. BAMFORD, A. ELLIOTT and W. E. HANBY, *Nature*, 167 (1951) 264.
[57] M. ST. C. FLETT, *J. Soc. Dyers Colourists*, 68 (1952) 59.
[58] E. J. AMBROSE and W. E. HANBY, *Nature*, 163 (1949) 483.
   E. J. AMBROSE, A. ELLIOTT and R. B. TEMPLE, *Nature*, 163 (1949) 859.
   E. J. AMBROSE and A. ELLIOTT, *Proc. Roy. Soc. London*, 206A (1951) 206.
[59] K. D. PARKER, *Thesis*, Leeds University.
   K. D. PARKER, *Biochim. et Biophys. Acta*, 17 (1955) 148.
[60] A. ELLIOTT, *Proc. Roy. Soc. London*, 226A (1954) 408.
[61] R. D. B. FRAZER, *Proc. Intern. Wool Research Conf.*, B130 (1955).

CHAPTER 15

PRODUCTION OF FIBRES

1. Introduction

The conversion of a polymer to the fibrous form necessitates solubility in suitable solvents or a melting point below the decomposition temperature to permit extrusion, but the resulting fibres will only be acceptable for textile purposes provided that other physical and chemical properties lie within certain limits. As will be discussed later, some of these properties can be controlled by treatments subsequent to extrusion, such as stretching and cross linking. The more important properties which govern the usefulness of fibres are listed in Table 41; clearly the variables are many and, before a fibre is marketed, extensive tests and trials must be made. As might be expected, no material meets all specifications exactly and a compromise is necessary.

TABLE 41

PROPERTIES OF A FIBRE IMPORTANT FOR TEXTILE USES

(a) Chemical	(b) Physical
Resistance to	Tenacity
bases	Elongation
acids	Stiffness
bleaches	Abrasion resistance
solvents	Melting-point
Heat	Glass temperature
Sunlight	Decomposition temperature
Ageing	
Dyeability	

Because of the commercial importance of the extrusion processes, accurate knowledge of compositions of the polymers and details of the extrusion conditions may not have been disclosed.

There are three ways in which a fibre may be formed *viz.* by extrusion of a solution of the polymer into a coagulation bath, extrusion into the atmosphere when the fibre is formed on evaporation of the solvent, or by extruding the molten liquid polymer when solidification occurs on cooling. Although melt spinning is preferred since solvents are not necessary, the choice of method is decided by many factors notably the heat stability, viscosity characteristics of the melt and availability of suitable solvents.

In order to make fibres of adequate strength, the filaments are stretched:

this is one of the major independent variables in the preparation and all mechanical properties are affected. Normally, stretching orients the molecules and crystallites and, in some instances, assists crystallisation. The development of crystallisation is important in obtaining good fibre properties; non-crystalline polymers do not usually make good fibres.

Branching of the chains is detrimental to fibre properties since a crystalline lattice cannot develop where branching occurs. The melting point is lowered and the polymer has less stiffness. By contrast, cross linking gives strong interchain bonding and, provided the number of links is small, may improve some of the fibre properties. Polyvinyl alcohol and protein fibres are improved considerably by cross linking.

2. Wet Spinning

(a) Cuprammonium Rayon

Cellulose was shown by Schweitzer as far back as 1857 to be soluble in a solution of copper oxide dissolved in ammonia. The first filaments from such solutions were made by Despeissis (1890) and by Fremeny and Urban (1891), but material suitable for textile uses was not produced until 1901 when Thiele invented a means of stretching the filaments as they were formed, thereby giving a product which developed an adequate strength,

In the earlier days, cuprammonium rayon was made solely from cotton linters, a product which is relatively more expensive than wood pulp. To some extent, wood pulp of a high α-cellulose content is now used. The pulp dissolves in the reagent more quickly than linters but does not give a final product of such good colour or strength. Wood pulp used for this process must be well purified and have a high α-cellulose content (90–98%). Cotton linters are purified by boiling in an autoclave or kier at 150 °C with dilute caustic soda followed by a bleaching treatment with sodium hypochlorite. The purified linters or pulp is mixed with the requisite amount of aqueous ammonia, basic copper sulphate and sodium hydroxide, and

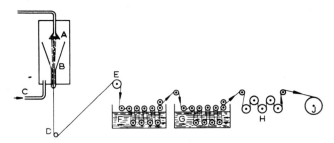

Fig. 136. Diagrammatic representation of modern continuous method of spinning cuprammonium rayon[1].

this mixture is kneaded until a clear blue solution is obtained. The solution is diluted to a cellulose content of 9–10%, deaerated and filtered. Cuprammonium solutions are relatively stable on storage, provided oxygen is excluded so that decomposition or depolymerisation of the cellulose does not take place to any great extent.

The filaments are formed when the deaerated and filtered solution is extruded through a spinneret A, Fig. 136, which may be made of nickel and which has relatively large holes (*ca.* 0.8 mm diameter). The extruded material travels through a funnel B down which is running softened water. The contact of the solution with water produces a plastic filament containing a small residue of ammonia and copper. Most of the reagents are swept away in the water. The filament from the funnel runs vertically downwards around a roller D and over a second roller E which is mounted in a trough containing acid. Treatment of the yarn with acid converts the residual copper and ammonia to sulphates and completes the coagulation of the cellulose. When the process is run "batchwise", the yarn from E is wound into hanks or into a Topham box (Fig. 137). The box is

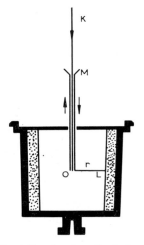

Fig. 137. Centrifugal pot method of spinning[32].

bucket-shaped and is spun so that its periphery is moving at about 50 times the rate at which the yarn is being fed in. The yarn KOL passes through the funnel and the rotation of the pot forces it to fly outwards against the inner wall of the pot. The box rotates at a speed of 7000 r.p.m. or more. The funnel M is moved up and down thereby producing a traversing action. Twist is automatically put into the yarn which builds up into a "cake". This is a cylindrical package of yarn about 8 in. in diameter and

6 in. in depth with a hollow centre. The size of the cake varies according to the size of the box. There are, however, certain limits on the use of a Topham box. If the denier of the yarn is too low, the centrifugal force may be too low; since the force also decreases as the distance from the centre, the force will be reduced as the package or cake is formed. This puts a limit on the thickness of the cake which can be formed. By such a device, the wet yarn of low tenacity may be built up into a package. During the path from the spinneret A to the funnel, the filaments undergo a considerable stretch caused by the tension developed when they are drawn off.

When the process is run continuously, the filaments (*ca.* 500–600) from the spinneret are passed directly over rollers D and E and then through two troughs or washing ranges (F and G). After lubrication, the yarn is dried on the drier H and wound on to a beam J if required for weaving.

Cuprammonium rayon is noted for the fine deniers in which it may be produced; these are on average about 1.2 but it is possible to go down to finer filaments. Under the microscope, the filaments look smooth and indeed the cross section is circular.

(b) Viscose Rayon

The viscose rayon process was founded on the work of Cross and Bevan (1891–2). The development of this material took a considerable time and owed much to the pioneer work of Courtaulds Ltd. In its early stages, there were many difficulties to be overcome such as poor wet strength, ease of creasing and so on. Since those early days, the properties of this yarn have been improved enormously and, coupled with this, the cheapness of the raw material makes viscose rayon the man-made fibre produced in the largest quantities.

The raw material for the viscose process is wood pulp of a high α-cellulose content. Most of the wood pulp is made from spruce, being pulped by the sulphite process. This process removes large quantities of lignin and other extraneous matter from the wood, leaving a pulp which is concentrated to a strength of 30% solids, bleached with hypochlorite and converted into sheets.

The sheets of pulp are soaked in 17.5% sodium hydroxide for 1–4 h when swelling takes place, and much of the hemicellulose is dissolved out in the alkaline liquor which becomes yellow-brown in colour (*ca.* 8% dissolves). The product is referred to as alkali or soda cellulose. The evenness of penetration of the alkali is very important as well as the time of contact and temperature. Sodium hydroxide concentration affects the composition and ageing of the alkali cellulose, the higher the concentration the faster the ageing. Temperature is important — the higher the temperature the less the swelling so that greater pulp reactivity arises from use of a low temperature.

Pressing of the mass removes the excess alkali, leaving a moist mass of soda cellulose. This is "shredded" and breaks down to fine crumbs. These crumbs are aged *i.e.* a certain amount of depolymerisation is allowed to take place (D.P. as determined from viscosity measurements falls from about 800 to 350) by contact with atmospheric oxygen. The ageing may take $3\frac{1}{2}$ days at room temperature (20 °C) but, with more stringent control, the ageing can be completed in $1\frac{1}{2}$ days at a higher temperature. Oxidative depolymerisation occurs in this process. The reactions, which occur when soda cellulose is exposed to air, are complex but it seems that oxidation occurs via a chain reaction; this may start with the formation of a free radical on an aldehydic end group, followed by attack on cellulose chains leading to breakage. Peroxides play a major role and hydrogen peroxide has been detected in soda cellulose[45,46].

The aged soda cellulose crumbs which contain about 30% of cellulose are treated with carbon disulphide (10% by weight) in rotating air tight churns. A deep orange mass of cellulose xanthate is formed. This colour is due to the formation of trithiocarbonate (Na_2CS_3), sulphides and polysulphides. The crumbs are normally churned at a rate of 2 r.p.m. for about 3 h. The temperature of this reaction must be accurately controlled.

These main reactions may be represented as follows:

$$CellOH + NaOH \rightarrow CellONa + H_2O$$
$$\text{soda cellulose}$$

$$CellONa + CS_2 \rightarrow SC \overset{\displaystyle SNa}{\underset{\displaystyle OCell}{\diagup\hspace{-0.3em}\diagdown}}$$
$$\text{sodium cellulose xanthate}$$

where CellOH stands for cellulose.

In practice, 70% of the theoretical quantity of carbon disulphide required to give a D.S. of 1 is found adequate.

The trixanthate of cellulose is not easy to make; it may be formed by dispersion of cellulose in tetraalkylammonium hydroxide solutions[26] followed by reaction with carbon disulphide. The degree of xanthation depends on how well the cellulose is dispersed and dixanthates may be formed under other conditions of concentration. Products containing up to two xanthate groups per glucose residue have been obtained by dissolution of the commercial cellulose xanthate followed by re-xanthation. It is possible to increase the degree of xanthation to 1 : 1 instead of the commercial $1:2$ by increasing the amount of carbon disulphide and the time of reaction[27].

The detailed mechanism of xanthation of cellulose has not been completely established. For example, conflicting evidence exists as to whether reaction occurs at the 2, 3 or 6-hydroxyl groups[27], although it has been suggested that most xanthation occurs at the 6-position with some groups in the 3-position[41]. It seems likely that the xanthate groups are distributed at random although, in the initial stages, the more accessible amorphous regions will have reacted first[95].

Other reactions may occur. Secondary reactions of the xanthate may be brought about by its instability and the reversible nature of the reaction with carbon disulphide. The following have been suggested

$$CellOCSSNa + 2NaOH \rightarrow Na_2CO_2S + NaSH + CellOH$$

$$CellOCSSNa + NaSH \rightarrow Na_2CS_3 + CellOH$$

Thiocarbonates so formed may react with sodium hydroxide forming a carbonate and hydrosulphide

$$Na_2CO_2S + NaOH \rightarrow Na_2CO_3 + NaSH$$

The reaction of carbon disulphide and sodium hydroxide may form a thiocarbonate

$$3CS_2 + 6NaOH \rightarrow 2Na_2CS_3 + Na_2CO_3 + 3H_2O$$

The reaction mechanism is not known with certainty but, in commercial preparations, secondary products consisting of carbonate, trithiocarbonate, hydrosulphide and sulphide are present.

Several factors influence the xanthation reaction $viz.$ the nature of the cellulose[27] affects the rate and degree of reaction as well as the amount of carbon disulphide required to produce good solubility; the degree of xanthation increases and solubility improves with increasing concentration of carbon disulphide, but both reach a maximum when further additions have little effect. The maximum degree of xanthation decreases with increase in temperature although, in the range 15–35 °C, solubility increases with temperature. At the end of the xanthation, excess carbon disulphide is removed by evacuation, and the material is dumped into the mixers where the xanthate is stirred with dilute sodium hydroxide solution for 4–5 h with cooling. This gives a brown viscous liquid known as viscose containing about 6.5% alkali and 7.5% cellulose. It is desirable, in order to obtain a uniform product, to blend batches from the mixers. Considerable care is taken to filter off any residual undissolved fibres and extraneous matter. The filtration is normally done through cotton wool and twice through cotton filter cloth. At this stage, if required, a delustrant (TiO₂) or a pigment may be added. The viscose solution or dope is now ripened by storage for 4–5 days at 10–19°C, during which time the viscosity of the solution falls to a minimum and then rises to almost the original value.

In the ripening process, both physical and chemical changes occur. The ripening process is exothermic. Hydrolysis is the most important reaction when the xanthate reacts with water to regenerate cellulose

$$CellOCSSNa + H_2O \rightarrow CellOH + NaOH + CS_2$$

This hydrolysis is not allowed to go to completion; the D.S. may be allowed to fall to 1 CS_2 to 3 glucose.

During the ripening process, the viscosity of the viscose solution drops gradually due to the dispersion of aggregates left from the mixing operation; this is complete when the viscosity minimum is reached. Once the minimum is achieved, the viscosity increases due to the hydrolysis reaction given above. Further, during ripening the xanthate groups may redistribute themselves. The ripening is stopped before spontaneous coagulation occurs. The changes in properties[27] are given in Fig. 138. The viscosity may be restored to the original by adding more carbon disulphide.

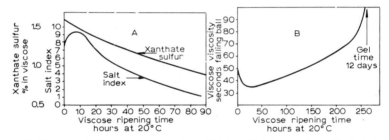

Fig. 138. Changes during viscose ripening; (A) in salt index and xanthate sulphur content, (B) in viscosity[27].

During the dissolution, the structure of the cellulose is disordered but not completely, and it is likely that the state of the viscose solution is one of molecular aggregates, micelles and micelle aggregates rather than molecules[37]. The presence of supermolecular aggregates has been detected in concentrated solutions but not in dilute solutions[38,39]. This process is fairly critical since a freshly made or "young" solution, will not extrude well, neither will it when it has "ripened" too much or is too "old". Tests for satisfactory performance are (1) dissolution in 40% acetic acid when ripe viscose dope will precipitate, (2) titration of the viscose solution (20 g in 30 ml water) with ammonium chloride (10% w/w), the end-point being coagulation to a gelatinous mass, (3) determination of the concentration of sodium chloride which is just sufficient to coagulate a small quantity of viscose, which is allowed to fall into the salt solution. This is called the Salt Index method. The condition of the viscose will be determined by the quantity of electrolyte required; the lower the figure, the riper the viscose. The first test is not now used. The ripe viscose solution is drawn off to settling tanks in which it is subjected to a vacuum to remove residual air bubbles, since these would cause discontinuities in the extruded filaments.

Spinning properties of the viscose depend among other things on the ratio of cellulose to sodium hydroxide. The optimum concentration of cellulose is of the order $6-10\%$ giving a solution whose viscosity is around $30-60$ poises and a cellulose[29] of D.P. $250-600$. The viscosity characteristics of viscose dope depend on the rate of shear. Under normal methods of measurement of viscosity (low shear), behaviour is Newtonian. Behaviour which deviates from Newtonian shows up when the shear forces are high as when the dope is passed through the spinnerets; indeed the apparent viscosity may be only $\frac{1}{10}$ to $\frac{1}{25}$th that determined under conditions of low shear (*e.g.* the falling ball test). This reduction in viscosity is fortunate, since higher pressures would be required if the liquid retained its Newtonian behaviour.

The process of manufacture normally takes about a week, although it is possible to run the shreading and ageing together, thereby reducing the time considerably[96].

The viscose dope is pumped under $2.6-5$ atm pressure to the spinneret (Fig. 139). In order to maintain constant delivery, the dope is "metered" through a gear pump. This pump is an essential in the process, since it delivers the solution to the spinneret at a constant rate determined by the speed of revolution of the pump, and not the pressure at which the liquid is delivered. The rate of delivery is one of the important factors modifying the denier of the fibre. Prior to extrusion, the viscose dope passes through a further filter usually of the candle or disc type, filtering the viscose through fabric. The spinnerets are submerged in an acid bath where coagulation occurs, and are usually arranged so that the filaments emerge at an angle to the surface of the bath. The orifices in the jet are of diameter usually ranging from 0.05 to 0.1 mm.

The spinnerets are usually made of an unreactive metal such as gold, platinum, tantalum etc. To prevent corrosion by acids, the spinning bath is made of lead sheet. The bath is kept at constant level and the overflow together with any of the run back from the godets and residue from the spinning pit is carried away in a channel. The godets are flanged pulleys, the flange of which is serrated in order to enable the filaments to grip. The filaments extruded from the spinneret, 7, are taken round the godet,

8, and thence round another, 9, and by running the second faster than the first a stretch may be imparted to the filaments. The yarn from the godet is then run through a funnel into a Topham box.

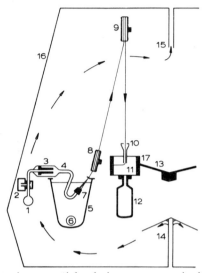

Fig. 139. Diagram showing essentials of viscose rayon spinning plant. One side of a double-sided machine is shown[1].

1. Section of main viscose feed	10. Funnel
2. Pump	11. Topham Box
3. Candle filter	12. Drive for Topham Box
4. Glass rounder end	13. Traverse
5. Coagulating bath	14. Fresh air inlet
6. Section of acid replenishing pipe	15. Fumes sucked out
7. Spinneret	16. Sliding windows
8. Bottom godet	17. Cake
9. Top godet	

The yarn as produced in the box contains impurities. The main reaction in the spinning bath is

$$2CellOCSSNa + H_2SO_4 \rightarrow 2CellOH + 2CS_2 + Na_2SO_4$$

although side reactions occur yielding products such as hydrogen sulphide, carbon dioxide and free sulphur.

To clean it up, the cake must be washed, desulphurised, bleached and rewashed. In earlier times, the yarn was wound into skeins (hanks) which were then treated but, since winding operations are relatively expensive, it is simpler and cheaper to put the cake on to a perforated cylinder or former and to pump the liquor through the cake. The cakes are washed with water followed by sodium sulphide to remove residual sulphur and

other sulphurous compounds. Bleaching if necessary is done with a slightly alkaline solution of sodium hypochlorite; the cake is then washed with
dilute hydrochloric acid and finally with water. The yarn is finally dried.

The temperature and humidity conditions of the drying operations
affects the properties of the resultant filaments, in the direction that moderate humidities and high temperatures favour the production of denser
and less absorptive fibres[26].

In the process described above, the yarn is made in batches. It is in
general more economical to organise manufacturing processes on a continuous system, provided large quantities of material are required. The
formation of cakes necessitates collection from the machine, putting into
washing and cleaning plant and then rewinding to cones or other packages.
To avoid this, continuous techniques have been worked out in which the
viscose is extruded and the yarn purified and wound in a form ready for
use in textile processing.

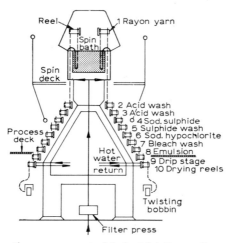

Fig. 140. Diagrammatic arrangement of Industrial Rayon Corporation Continuous
Spinning Process. N.B. The filaments are formed in the coagulating bath at the top
of the picture and work their way downwards[1].

The basic idea of continuous processing can be demonstrated by the
system developed by the Industrial Rayon Corporation of U.S.A. (Fig.
140). In this process, after passing from the spinneret, the yarn is washed
twice with acid, desulphurised and washed, bleached and rewashed. The
yarn is carried along on advancing reels and it is on these that the treatments are carried out. These advancing reels in their simplest form consist
of two rollers with slightly convergent axes (Fig. 141). The inclination of
the axes controls the rate of advance which can be a matter of millimeters

or so for each turn. This technique enables a considerable quantity of yarn to be kept moving so that the necessary reactions have time to take place. As the yarn moves along the advancing reel, various liquids (water, sodium sulphite solution etc.) may be sprayed on and the treatments achieved in a very uniform fashion.

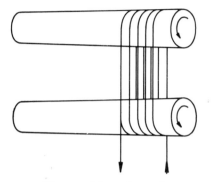

Fig. 141. Advancing reel.

In spinning viscose yarn, the condition of the coagulation bath is very important and modifications of the bath composition temperature etc. can be used to give yarns of different properties. The composition of a typical bath used at 40–55°C for normal viscose is given below:

Sulphuric acid	10 parts by weight
Sodium sulphate	18 parts by weight
Glucose	2 parts
Zinc sulphate	1 part
Water	69 parts

The function of these components is not generally known but may be roughly as follows. Sodium sulphate precipitates sodium cellulose xanthate and sulphuric acid transforms it back to cellulose. Glucose is considered to increase the viscosity of the bath and helps to retard the breakdown of the xanthate; it is considered to give a yarn of greater pliability and softness. Zinc sulphate gives additional strength to the yarn and causes the filaments to have serrated or crenullated cross sections characteristic of viscose (Fig. 2, Chapter 1).

Many agents have been examined for use in the coagulating bath. The most important are the inorganic salts. In a bath as given above, there is a combination of a salt to coagulate and dehydrate the fibre and an acid capable of regenerating the cellulose. The coagulation effect has a retarding influence on regeneration and since coagulation and regeneration do not occur at the same rate, it is possible to modify one or the other according to the bath composition, thereby modifying the characteristics of the yarn. The quality of the yarn is also dependent on the temperature, time of immersion, and stretch given to the yarn. Stretch, when applied close to the spinneret where the filament is still fluid, gave fibres with little orientation and characterised by low tenacity and high elongation.

Cross sections of a normal viscose yarn when examined under the micro-scope show two distinct parts — a skin and a core[6] (Fig. 144). Both of these contribute to the properties of the material and it is even possible to produce fibres which are all "skin" or all "core". Much then depends on the crucial spinning conditions. The formation of a skin at an early stage causes the serrated cross sections of the fibre, and allows the outside of the fibre to be sufficiently hardened so that filaments do not adhere.

Apart from the normal viscose yarn, products specially designed to show high tenacity are made under a variety of trade names.

(1) Filaments of high tenacity are required for certain end uses, notably tyre cords. High strength may be achieved by modifications of the concentrations of the components of the spinning bath, of temperature and of stretch. Thus, yarn called Tenasco has been made by extrusion into baths containing a high concentration of sodium sulphate; the yarn is then given a high stretch in a water bath at 90 °C, when a substantial increase in tenacity developed without reducing the extensibility below 16–17%.

Considerable developments have taken place as far as the control of the structure of viscose fibres is concerned. It is known that the skin structure is a more highly oriented one than the core, and this leads to greater fibre strength[88]. Changes in the proportions of skin to core is accompanied by modifications in the cross section from crenullated to smooth and almost circular. Modern fibres described commercially[89] as Tenasco 35, 70 and 105 are products in which the proportion of skin to core has been progressively increased. The changes in skin thickness have been achieved by increasing the concentration of zinc sulphate in the bath and slowing down the rate at which the cellulose is regenerated[90]. Speed of regeneration is an important factor, since the extent to which good mechanical properties develop on hot stretching of the freshly extruded filaments depends on the state of coagulation. Coagulation may be controlled by the addition of "regeneration retardants" to the dope, so that the period during which the filament is in a plastic state between being extruded and coagulated is extended. Many compounds are capable of acting as retardants e.g. aliphatic amines, quaternary ammonium compounds etc.

Filaments have also been formed by partial regeneration in a mild acid bath followed by stretching and final regeneration in a second bath. Fibres produced in this way have been made in the U.S.A. under the name "Polynosics". They have a characteristic fibrillar structure.

(2) Durafil. The viscose solution is extruded into 65% sulphuric acid giving initially filaments which are composed of the very plastic "xantho-sulphuric acid ester". This is rapidly stretched to more than twice its original length and immediately quenched in cold water, when the cellulose is rapidly regenerated. The product is usually made in very fine deniers (*ca.* 0.3) and is composed virtually of all skin. The yarn has a high tenacity but low extensibility and is rather brittle. It has never been widely used.

(3) Fortisan is made from cellulose acetate fibre which is stretched under steam to about ten times its length and saponified with alkali to regenerate the cellulose. This orientation produces a considerable increase in strength; such cellulose acetate yarn known as "Fortanese" has been marketed[91]. The cellulose acetate filaments are stretched in steam under pressure followed by saponification with caustic soda.

(4) Flat straw monofilaments can be made by modification of the shape of the spinneret orifice. Such flat filaments are used for sandals, bags, etc. Viscose fibres of different cross sections may be made by using triangular orifices[92] when the resulting filament has a cross section in the shape of a Y.

(5) Chemical modifiers may be added to the viscose solution. A kidney shaped cross section has been obtained by adding 0.3% ricinoleic acid to the dope followed by extrusion into a bath containing not less than 3% zinc sulphate[93]. Many variations in cross sections are possible by this means.

(6) Cross linked yarns. Two yarns by Courtaulds under the names Corval and Topel are made from cellulose which has been cross linked to some extent[94]. These yarns have a lower moisture adsorption and swelling but a higher wet initial modulus than normal viscose; the resistance to alkalis and the dimensional stability is improved.

(c) *Regenerated Protein Fibres*

(i) *Casein*

A British patent was granted to Hughs for making filaments from proteins as early as 1857 and filaments from casein were made by Toden-haupt in 1904 but the products suffered from being both brittle and having poor wet strength. Attempts to make a satisfactory fibre were not successful until 1935 when Ferretti produced a fibre marketed in Italy as Lanital. A corresponding fibre was made in the U.S. under the name of Aralac but is now discontinued. In this country a casein fibre — Fibrolan BX is manufactured by Courtaulds.

The raw material is obtained from skimmed milk which, on heating to

40°C with acid, coagulates. The curd is washed free of acids and salts, most of the water removed mechanically and curd dried. Prior to dissolution the casein is blended or mixed to ensure as regular a product as possible. A dispersion of casein in caustic soda solution (2.7% on weight of casein) is made and the solution clarified.

The globular proteins in spite of their high molecular weight do not display in solution the highly viscous properties met with in solutions of elongated polymers. However, on storage under appropriate alkaline conditions a gradual denaturation occurs and the viscosity of the solution increases. The suitability of the solution for spinning is achieved by control of the denaturation[10]. After filtration, the solution goes through a period of ripening and the viscosity passes through a maximum.

The preparation of the dope to be extruded is the most fundamental operation in the extrusion. If the protein is not well dispersed and if the molecules are aggregated in different degrees, they will have less chance of coming together in an orderly manner during the coagulation. Thus if the protein is originally in a dry state and not given sufficient time for preliminary swelling with water, the outer layers of the protein particles will receive a larger share of alkali than the inner. The presence of a high concentration of alkali on the outer layers tends to induce gelation on the surface of the particles, with the result that each particle becomes sheathed in gelled protein and its inner core remains untreated. Once such gelled particles have formed, they are very difficult to disperse. Protein isolated in the wet state will, on the other hand, be in a highly swollen condition and hence far easier to disperse. At the higher alkali concentrations, the dope on standing increases in viscosity and eventually gels. It has been suggested that this occurs through reformation of disulphide linkages from thiol groups. This receives confirmation from the fact that dopes which contain sodium sulphide and hence cannot form disulphide bonds, are more stable than dopes of similar alkalinity which contain no sulphide. Further, care must be taken since proteins are associated in nature with enzymes which may in the presence of oxygen cause oxidation. Such oxidation will cause changes in the viscosity and the solution will darken. The action of enzymes may be reduced by using enzyme poisons, notably cyanides or sulphides. The clarified solution is extruded into a coagulating bath containing sulphuric acid (1 part), formaldehyde (2 parts) and glucose (20 parts) dissolved in water (100 parts). There are other possible components of the spinning bath. Thus, sulphates may be useful since they increase osmosis and cause considerable shrinkage. This prevents the fibres sticking together. In fact, if the dope contains no free alkali, extrusion may be done into a bath containing neutral salts. The product is collected as masses of filaments in rope form or "tow" similar to wool slubbing. The fibre at this stage is very sensitive to water; it is therefore "hardened" by reaction with formaldehyde.

Immediately after extrusion, protein fibres are in a very vulnerable and soft condition. When the fibres are placed in water at this stage, they soon become swollen and may stick together. If they are washed and dried, they become brittle. Salt is beneficial because of its astringent effect and, if the fibres are hardened with salt and formaldehyde, the physical properties are much improved, although the fibres are still brittle. Treatment under tension improves the properties. Hardening baths invariably include salt and formaldehyde but may also contain aluminium sulphate. After hardening, casein fibres may still possess a high extension in water and may be stretched by some 60%. This stretched yarn may be dried and has a higher tenacity but on re-wetting contraction occurs. If however, the fibres are subjected under tension to a hardening bath, the contraction on re-wetting is much reduced. Patents indicate that these fibres have undergone three treatments on extrusion *viz.* hardening, stretching and hardening.

In discussing protein fibres, the term insolubilisation has been used for treatment designed to make the fibres resistant to hot liquors, especially acid ones used in dyeing. Insolubilisation may be achieved by treatment in an acid bath with formaldehyde but may also include aluminium sulphate. The fibres after these treatments must be thoroughly washed to remove salts and traces of acid.

Casein fibres are noted for their warmth and softness of handle. They are relatively weak fibres (0.8–1.10 g/denier) with an elongation at break of 15%. The main defect is the wet strength which is very low. The cross sections are almost circular. In addition to their weakness in the presence of water they are, as would be expected, sensitive to alkali which, if strong enough, will cause gelatinisation. They are, however, sufficiently strong to be stable to weak alkalis such as sodium hydrogen phosphate. They are sufficiently resistant to sulphuric acid to resist attack by 2% sulphuric acid.

(ii) *Groundnut protein*

The proteins arachin and conarachin are extracted from groundnut meal with dilute alkali. After cleaning, sulphur dioxide is passed in until the solution has a pH of 4.5. This acidification produces a copious white precipitate of protein.

The dried protein may be dissolved in aqueous alcohol containing some formaldehyde. Urea is then added to increase the viscosity to a value suitable for extrusion, and the solution extruded into a bath of acid and salts. A suitable coagulation bath contains 15% sodium sulphate and 2% sulphuric acid, and used at a temperature of 25–40 °C. The fibre so formed is treated with formaldehyde to harden it. Alternatively, the fibre may be spun from caustic soda solution and hardened with formaldehyde.

(iii) *Fibres from soya beans*

The extraction from soya beans is carried out by pressing the beans into flakes, and extracting the oil by hexane. The protein is removed by treatment with a solution of sodium sulphite (0.1%) at room temperature. After clarification of the solution, the protein is precipitated as a curd by addition of sulphuric acid (pH 4.5) until the isoelectric point is reached. After separating, washing and drying (below 60°C) the curd, a 20% solution is made by dissolution in caustic soda. A little sodium ethyl xanthate is added for stabilisation. After ageing, the solution attains the viscosity for extrusion. Extrusion is made into a bath containing salt and acid and the fibre so formed stretched and hardened by passage through formaldehyde solution. The fibre, as produced, is a light tan colour but can be bleached.

(iv) *Fibres from maize*

The protein, zein, is extracted from the corn meal by dissolution in alkali and precipitation with acid. In the Vicara process, zein which forms part of the corn protein is extracted with 70% isopropyl alcohol. The solvent can be evaporated, leaving the zein as a pale yellow powder. For the reason of uniformity, the batches of zein are blended and the solution for extrusion prepared by dissolution in dilute caustic soda making, at a 20% strength, a very viscous liquid. The solution is filtered, de-aerated and ripened by storage. In the last process, the coiled zein molecules are considered to become linear. When the viscosity has developed to a suitable degree, the solution is extruded into a coagulation bath containing formaldehyde and salts (some of which have an acid character). The components of this bath will to some extent cross link the protein molecules thereby imparting strength to the filaments. The tow so produced is conveyed to tanks where mild curing is carried out with formaldehyde. At this stage, the fibre has sufficient strength to be stretched after which the fibres are cured, this time under tension in a bath containing formaldehyde and acid saturated with sodium chloride. In this process, more cross linkages are formed thereby helping to lock the fibre in its stretched state. The fibres after this treatment are then capable of being relaxed without shrinkage.

(v) *Hardening processes*

Protein fibres are hardened by treatment with aqueous formaldehyde at *ca.* 35°C. Without this process, the fibres swell considerably in water and are brittle when dry. After hardening, the fibres may be given a

References p. 458

further treatment known as insolubilising to reduce the swelling in hot water and to withstand attack from dilute acids used in the dyeing operation. Treatment for this may be (a) formaldehyde under fairly strongly acid conditions[11], (b) acetic anhydride or ketene[12], or (c) aqueous solution of sodium nitrite[13].

(d) Synthetic Fibres

The formation of a filament by the wet spinning process is possible with some of the addition polymers. All vinyl fibres must be stretched 5–15 times during manufacture to adjust the strength and extensibility to the range desired by textile fibres.

(i) PeCe fibres

A 28% solution of the polymer — chlorinated polyvinyl chloride — is prepared in dry acetone, filtered and extruded into cold water. The spinnerets are made of tantalum and usually have 120 holes, 0.08 mm in diameter. When the polymer meets the water, coagulation occurs and the acetone dissolves; conditions are arranged so that the bath contains a concentration of approximately 4% of acetone. Before winding, the yarn is stretched; it contains 7% of acetone which must be subsequently lost by evaporation. The yarn suffers from a low softening point (100°C) and its main use may be for fire resistant cloth.

(ii) Polyvinyl alcohol

The raw material is made by deacetylation of polyvinyl acetate in methanol solution. This hydrolysis is carried out by reaction with sodium hydroxide and the polyvinyl alcohol precipitates. The product is soluble in hot water and, for extrusion, a 15% solution is formed which is spun into a coagulating bath of sodium sulphate in water. The properties of the fibre depend on the coagulation bath; for example dense strong fibres can be formed by extrusion of a 15% solution into saturated ammonium sulphate at 50°C. The fibre from the bath is made insoluble in water by treatment with formalin when intra- and some inter-molecular bridges are introduced.

Methods other than the use of formaldehyde for insolubilising the fibre have been tried *e.g.* polycarboxylic acid, benzoyl chloride, sulphuryl chloride etc.[8] but the present method seems to be the best.

This fibre called Vinylon is mainly manufactured in Japan. Its properties depend to a large degree on the orientation and stretch; it may be made with very high tensile strength. Indeed, polyvinyl alcohol fibres under stretch may be rendered water insoluble presumably due to internal hydrogen bonding. On release of stress, the orientation is to some extent destroyed and the fibre becomes soluble again in water. Claims have been made that, on stretching the fibre hot, a water insoluble material may be made[28].

The fibre is used for normal textile purposes as well as for fishing nets, filter cloths etc.

(iii) *Acrylic fibres*

There is a number of fibres on the market which are copolymers of acrylonitrile (*ca.* 90%) together with comonomers whose nature and quantity are not known with certainty. Some of them are spun "dry" and others wet. Comonomer content up to 10% makes for greater solubility, and provides dyeing sites and greater rapidity of dyeing. When the amount of the more polar comonomer reaches 30%, solubility in acetone develops and the polymer may be dry-spun.

Experiments with polyacrylonitrile have been carried out using different agents for coagulation. Extrusion of the solution into the medium with the smaller but rapidly diffusing molecules such as water, methanol, chloroform, gave filaments of circular cross section, whereas higher aliphatic alcohols, aromatic hydrocarbons etc. gave folded cross sections[42].

The acrylonitrile content of Acrilan is of the order of 85–90%, the other component is basic in character and may possibly be vinylpyridine. Although the manufacturing details are not disclosed, one method which has been described is to extrude a 20% solution of the polymer in ethylene carbonate at 120°C into a bath of 80% dipropylene glycol and 20% ethylene carbonate at 130°C. The yarn is washed, drawn 10 times at 150°C and relaxed at 140°C. Other processes have been suggested but the true method is not known. The fibre has a good strength but a low T_g.

(iv) *Vinylidene dicyanide*

The fibre marketed as Darlan is a copolymer of about equal parts of vinylidene dicyanide and vinyl acetate. It is spun from a 12% solution in dimethylformamide into water and the filaments hot stretched (about 230°C)[40].

3. Mechanism of the Formation of Filaments

When a solution of the polymer is extruded into the coagulant, a new interface of large surface area is created. The interfacial forces are very strong, so that the extruded filament tends to take on a cross section which is circular irrespective of the shape of the orifice, and it is only when the dope is coagulated very fast that the form of the filament is set by the orifice shape. Nevertheless, fibres formed by wet spinning are more often non-circular in cross section, but these deviations arise from the mechanism of coagulation.

The interfacial tension forces produce instability in a cylinder whose length is large compared with the radius. The jet of liquid, therefore, tends to break up into drops. This is counteracted by the high viscosity of the polymer solution and naturally there is a tendency to work with as high a viscosity as possible, commensurate with having a solution which can be satisfactorily filtered and extruded. Indeed, with some polymers, the highest viscosity short of the formation of gel is used[19]; with other polymer solutions, viscosity is not so critical although in general a high concentration of polymer is desirable, since less storage room is required, and the composition of the coagulation bath is altered to a lesser extent during the spinning.

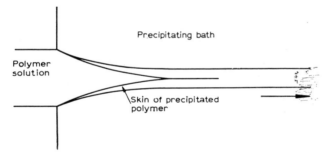

Fig. 142. Solvent spinning.

The interfacial forces also come into play in deciding whether the polymer solution on extrusion will give a filament or spread over the surface of the spinneret. The outcome depends on the balance of surface forces between the polymer solution and the spinneret and the polymer solution and the coagulating bath. Generally, spreading will occur but this is overcome when the filaments are pulled away from the face of the spinneret. The formation of the filament in its early stages is shown diagrammatically in Fig. 142.

The temperature of the operation is an important factor. Raising the temperature will reduce the viscosity so that solutions of higher concentration may be used; however, higher temperatures give rise to greater manipulative difficulties, increase the density of the fibres and make them less permeable.

During the coagulation, several processes occur simultaneously — osmosis of the solvent, diffusion of solutes which may be present in the polymer solution and coagulating bath, chemical reactions between diffusing substances and the polymer and salting out effects. In all wet spinning processes, diffusion is accompanied by osmosis. Usually osmosis acts so as to increase the polymer concentration but, occasionally, the reverse happens. Examples of the latter are the extrusion of viscose dope and cuprammonium hydroxide solutions of cellulose into water. When osmosis takes place from the coagulating bath to the filament, partly due to the dilution of the polymer solution and partly due to loss of solvent by diffusion outwards, the polymer sets to a dilute gel which can be readily attenuated or stretched. This idea of "stretch" spinning was first described many years ago in connection with the production of fibres from cellulose nitrate[44].

However, the normal direction for osmosis is to concentrate the polymer solution and, in these circumstances, the coagulation is rapid so that the filaments can not be stretched to any large extent. In the normal wet spinning of viscose, the upper limit is 2–2.5 times[20]. When a reaction occurs to cause rapid gelling, the filaments will consist of an outer gel layer surrounding a still fluid core. Subsequent osmosis brings about a greater reduction in volume in the core than the outer layer, so that the gel layer becomes folded.

In viscose production, coagulation and regeneration occur simultaneously but not necessarily at the same rate: the dominant process is determined by the concentrations of acid and salt so that fibres which have shrunk to different extents initially, and hence have different cross sections, can be obtained according to the bath and viscose compositions.

Baths with neutral salts or concentrated sulphuric acid give circular filaments with a relatively smooth outline whereas, using a bath of acid and high salt concentration, a fibre which is mainly skin can be produced.

The properties of the polymer solutions indicate the possibility of orientation of molecules during extrusion. On flowing solutions of cellulose in cuprammonium hydroxide through a narrow aperture, the shear forces caused by flowing tend to orient the molecules and the stream becomes birefringent, the effect being largest near the walls where the shear is greatest[47]. Streaming viscose solutions have also been shown to become optically anisotropic[48]. Anisotropy of the optical properties arise from orientation of the molecules under the influence of the shear forces which develop as the solution flows through the orifice and it might therefore be anticipated that the molecules during extrusion would become oriented. However, it has been shown that the thermal randomising motion of the molecules is too great for this to be so, except in a very thin outer layer where the stresses will be large and coagulation quick[49]. Orientation due to this phenomenon may in most processes be ignored.

During desolvation, considerable contraction takes place: for example, when an 8% polymer solution is converted into a swollen gel of four times that concentration, the axial contraction is about one third. Subsequent desolvation leads to a further contraction of about 25%. For viscose, the total contraction has been shown[22] to be about 50%. This contraction is counteracted by collection of the yarn at a speed at least equal to that of extrusion[23]. The actual stretch of the filaments is increased over this by collecting the yarns faster than they are extruded. The stretching which takes place will tend to increase the orientation of the polymer molecules; the degree of orientation will depend on many factors such as D.P. crystallinity, stiffness of the molecular chains etc. Unfortunately, no simple correlations exist; the phenomena are complex[24].

The resistance which the filament shows to stretching will vary considerably with the stage of coagulation. Stretching at different points in the development of the filament has been studied by moving the region of attenuation away from the spinneret[25]. The degree to which a filament may be stretched varies according to the bath conditions being 2.5 for viscose coagulated in a neutral salt bath and 4 in a concentrated acid one. Stretch applied to a filament whilst the latter is still plastic will produce more orientation the more fully coagulated is the filament.

Since viscose is a fibre of such overriding importance, some discussion on the effects of the variables on the filament properties will be given.

The action of zinc ions seems to be responsible in a large measure for the formation of the skin. Zinc ions have a high coagulating power with respect to cellulose xanthate, and cause a diminution in the degree of swelling of freshly formed filaments during the stages of coagulation[18] and regeneration[31]. The coagulating effect is even more marked in the presence of sodium ions[43]. Zinc ions also increase the amount of skin[5,50]. Other factors which increase the skin structure are a decrease in acid concentration, a decrease in temperature, changes in viscose composition and the salt figure[5].

Skin differs structurally from the core and is considered to have more desirable mechanical properties. New ways of producing thick skin or all skin filaments have been discovered notably by the addition of chemical modifiers[50,54]. As yet, no generally acceptable mechanism for the action of these materials has been suggested.

Many variables affect the properties of the filaments and the effect of one may be counterbalanced by another. Nevertheless, it seems that viscose and spinning bath compositions have a greater influence on the formation of the cellulose structure than the mechanical conditions of spinning[5,17]. Recently Cumberbirch *et al.* in a study of the influence of bath conditions on yarn structure have used standard mechanical conditions keeping the type of extrusion jet and amount of stretch applied the same throughout[4].

In this laboratory investigation[4], the amount of skin has been shown to increase with increasing concentration of zinc sulphate (Fig. 143), an

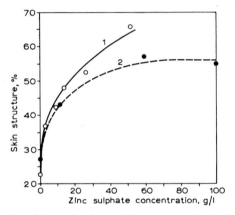

Fig. 143. Effects of variations in zinc sulphate concentration[4]. 1. Spinning bath temperature 55 °C, salt figure 4.4; 2. Spinning bath temperature 44 °C, salt figure 5.5.

effect which is less marked at the higher concentrations. Reduction in acid concentration in the presence of zinc ions also increases the amount, but this cannot be pursued too far since a limit is reached when breakdown of the freshly formed yarn occurs on passage through the spinning bath. An increase in sodium sulphate concentration gives a thicker skin but, if the ionic concentration of salts (assuming $Zn^{++} \equiv 2\,Na^+$) is kept constant, more skin is formed with the higher zinc content.

The conclusion, found from commercial experience, that a fall in spinning bath temperature increases the thickness of skin is not borne out by Cumberbirch *et al.*[4] who found the reverse, an example which emphasises the caution needed in making general statements in such a multi-variable system.

The effect of a modifier (cyclohexylamine) is quite remarkable (Fig. 144) when the crenulated cross section is changed to a circular one. The differences between skin and core arise from the fact that the molecules

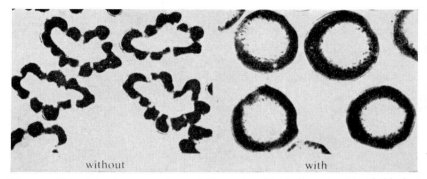

without   with

Fig. 144. Skin-stained cross sections of filaments with similar amounts of skin but spun with and without modifier[4].

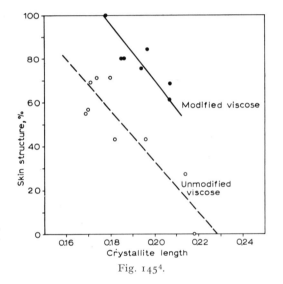

Fig. 145[4].

in the skin are tightly linked by crystallites which are both numerous and small as compared with those of the core. In Fig. 145, the crystallite length is shown to decrease as the amount of skin increases; in addition, the modifier alters the structure, a fact which is borne out by the increased crystallite length in the modified filaments and the poorer tensile properties. Crystallite length is measured by hydrolysing the amorphous regions and measuring the D.P. of the residue. Modified filaments have a greater crystalline length, lower sorption ratio and a smaller breaking extension than unmodified for a given amount of skin. The crystallite length is an important factor and some of the properties of the filaments depend on this. The moisture absorption (sorption ratio, given as the ratio of moisture absorbed by viscose at 65% r.h. relative to that of cotton) is found to vary linearly with crystallite length (Fig. 146), suggesting that the crystallite length determines the number of accessible hydroxyl groups.

Water retention (material soaked in water and centrifuged) is about nine time greater for the core as the skin, and will depend on the percentage of skin present (Fig. 147).

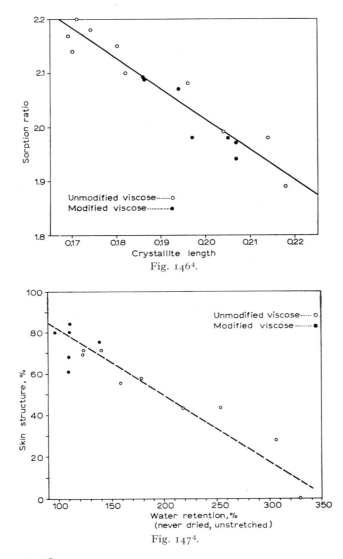

Fig. 146[4].

Fig. 147[4].

Modern super tyre yarns, have small crystallite length, high accessibility, great strength and relatively high breaking extension, and are made
with the help of modifiers[17,50,54] but there appears to be a great dissimi-
larity between the modified viscose yarns discussed above and those
commercially produced. Comparison between laboratory work and commercial products is difficult, since in the work discussed here the yarns
were made under standard conditions of stretch and not stretched to give
the properties most desirable for a commercial product.

4. Dry Spinning

(a) General

In this process, the spinning solution is extruded through a spinneret
usually downwards into fairly long, heated tubes (Fig. 148). At the same
time, air is led through the tube and solvent removed; in the process of

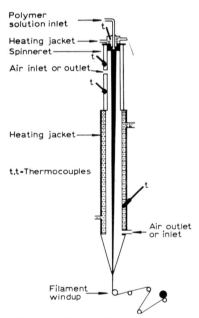

Fig. 148. Cell for dry spinning[98].

fibre formation, about 15–35% of the volume of the originally extruded
filament is removed by evaporation, so that the cross section of the fibre
contracts; this contraction causes the fibres to have a "dog bone" shaped
cross section. By contrast, wet spun fibres discussed earlier have cross

sections (Fig. 3, Chapter 1) that range from almost circular to very irregular, whereas melt spun fibres are generally circular.

Important factors governing the choice of solvent are solvent power, boiling-point, latent heat of evaporation, ease of recovery, inertness, thermal stability, toxicity and freedom from explosive hazards. As far as the viscosities of the solutions are concerned, the solvent is chosen to give the highest polymer concentration for a given viscosity. Freedom from all foreign material and incompletely dissolved polymer is essential. This is achieved by vigorous filtration.

Some data relating to dry spinning are given in Table 42.

In dry spinning, rapid solvent evaporation is necessary in order to reduce as far as possible the stress and weight on the filament as it leaves the spinneret where it is very weak. Rapid filament formation takes place in the immediate vicinity of the spinneret.

Hence, the molecules in the outside or skin of the filament which are oriented in the direction of the liquid flow in the spinneret also tend to be oriented in the direction of the extrusion, and fibre formation occurs from the skin inwards. A skin is readily formed on the outside of the filament which, coupled with the high viscosity of the polymer solution, renders diffusion of the solvent difficult. The fibres, on leaving the extrusion chamber, contain therefore a small quantity of solvent (*e.g.* cellulose acetate may have 6–15%) giving a fibre which is rather plastic.

In the spinning tube, there is a decrease in solvent concentration in the fibre from the inside to the outside as well as down the tube from spinneret to the wind up device. During spinning, it is essential to establish stationary conditions in order to avoid filament irregularities. The high viscosities of the dopes present technical difficulties; as the viscosity increases, the pressure used for pumping increases and, although this may be decreased by raising the temperature, there is a limit determined by the boiling-point of the solvent.

It is interesting to note that the only successful method of obtaining a high strength yarn is to after-stretch; this is in contrast to the wet spinning experience, where fibres with good spinning properties are produced preferably by stretching the fibre while in the precipitating bath.

When the solvent evaporates, there is a decrease in volume and the drying fibre collapses giving a crenulated cross section. Skin formation does not give rise to density changes across the fibre, in contrast to the fibres made by wet spinning technique.

(b) Secondary Cellulose Acetate

Cellulose acetate was first prepared by Schutzenberger in 1865 by heating acetic anhydride with cellulose in a sealed tube. Later (1894) Cross and

TABLE 42

SOME DRY SPINNING PROCESSES

	Solvent	Mol. wt.	Conc. (% polymer of weight)	Spinning cell		Temp. (°C)		Wind-up speed (m/min)	Refs.
				Length (m)	diam. (cm)	Spinneret	Cell		
Polyacrylonitrile	Dimethylformamide	60,000	25	2.5	–	130	400	90	52
Polyvinyl chloride	Acetone (1) Carbon bisulphide (1)	34,000	30	3.5	–	70	125	170	57,58
Copolymer vinyl chloride (90) vinyl acetate (10)	Acetone	26,800	27	–	–	50	130	–	58,59
Copolymer vinyl chloride (80) methyl acrylate (20)	Acetone (1) Methylene chloride (4)	–	20	–	–	–	80–100	80–100	–
Copolymer vinyl chloride (60) acrylonitrile (40)	Acetone	–	20	6	20	–	85–125	50–200	61,59
Cellulose acetate	Acetone	40,000–80,000	20–27	4–8	10–25	56–59	60–95	150–500	62

Bevan showed that acetylation could take place at room temperature in the presence of an acid such as sulphuric or of zinc chloride, to give the triacetate which is soluble in chloroform. It was shown by Miles (1906) that this triacetate can be partially hydrolysed to the secondary acetate whose degree of acetylation lies between 2- and 3-hydroxyl groups (*ca.* 2.3). The product so formed is no longer soluble in chloroform, but has the advantage of being soluble in the much cheaper and less toxic solvent, acetone. It was this property which led to the development of this material rather than the fully acetylated product. This secondary acetate has been made by homogeneous hydrolysis of the triacetate, so that the hydroxyl groups are distributed in a random fashion.

The acetate is made from cotton linters, although nowadays wood pulp is being used increasingly. When linters are used, scouring is necessary and is carried out by boiling with an alkaline solution (sodium hydroxide, carbonate or both) under pressure for 4–10 h, followed by rinsing, washing and bleaching with sodium hypochlorite and finally washing. The cotton is acetylated with a mixture of acetic acid, acetic anhydride and sulphuric acid. The reaction is strongly exothermic, and the reaction mixture must be cooled to reduce degradation of the cellulose. The temperature is kept below 20 °C for the first hour and allowed to rise to 25–30 °C for the next 7–8. The fibre becomes swollen and finally disintegrates to form a gelatinous viscous mass. During this, further depolymerisation occurs so that the reaction must not be too prolonged.

In the acetylation, the reaction is heterogeneous and therefore depends on the rate of diffusion of the reactants into the fibre. This depends on the physical condition of the fibre; in order to swell the fibre and hence render it more reactive, pretreatment at room temperature with acetic acid containing a small amount of water and part of the catalyst is carried out. This helps to give a more rapid, uniform and controllable reaction. The cellulose is also partly depolymerised in this step. During the acetylation reaction, samples are removed and examined; when all the fibres have dissolved and the sample is completely soluble in chloroform, acetylation is complete. For the conversion of the triacetate to the secondary, water is added to the reaction mixture to combine with the excess acetic anhydride and to give a final concentration of 95% acetic acid. The mixture is allowed to stand for 20 h at a higher temperature. The hydrolysis is monitored by taking samples and analysing for acetyl content. When the desired acetyl figure is reached, the cellulose acetate is precipitated by addition of dilute acetic acid. Acid is preferred, since it gives a fibrous precipitate and water alone may give rise to gels from which entrapped acid is difficult to remove. The D.P. of the product is in the region of 250–400. This hydrolysis process also removes sulphate groups which may have been formed in the acetylation process. This is an important function of the hydrolysis; otherwise sulphuric acid will be liberated when the rayon is subsequently stored with consequent degradation.

The secondary acetate is dissolved in about three times its weight of acetone. The viscous dope so formed is filtered and de-aerated. The preferred viscosity lies between 400–1000 poises at 40°C. The solution, after a final filtration, is extruded in a cabinet as indicated (Fig. 148). The spinneret is at the top and the solution is fed through a metering pump at a constant rate. The solution is given a final filtration prior to extrusion. The holes in the spinneret are about 0.3 mm in diameter. Through the cabinet passes a current of hot air which the extruded solution encounters on leaving the jet, acetone evaporates and the solution solidifies to form the filaments. The filaments travel downwards and are taken round a guide roller on to a cap and bobbin, when winding and some twisting takes place. The filaments are stretched in their passage downwards by their own weight and also by any tension put on them at the guide roller. The stream of hot air passes from the bottom of the cabinet and out of the top. Acetone can readily be recovered from the stream of air. The diameter of the yarn produced will depend on (i) the diameter of the jets in the spinneret, (ii) the rate of feeding of solution to the jet and (iii) the rate at which the fibre is drawn down. Some of the important factors in determining the characteristics of the fibres are the moisture content and the rate at which the air stream flows through the cabinet. The yarn collected on the bobbin has sufficient twist to be used in textiles; it is usually not after-treated, although after-stretching increases the tensile strength.

Secondary cellulose acetate rayon does not absorb much water since most of the hydroxyl groups have been esterified. Being a thermoplastic material, it softens on heating which means that, when ignited, because of simultaneous melting the spread of combustion is slow. Though the lustre of this fibre is very high, it may be delustred by incorporation of TiO_2 in the dope prior to extrusion, or by treatment of the yarn with phenol solutions. Under the microscope, the fibre appears as a smooth featureless cylinder, whereas the cross section is looped and rather similar to that of viscose. Skin formation in acetate rayon can not be demonstrated optically[32], although structural differences between skin and core have been suggested[33].

(c) Cellulose Triacetate

The first acetylated cellulose produced was triacetate and, although it was spun into filaments from chloroform solution about 1914, it never achieved large scale production because of the cost and hazards involved in using solvents such as chloroform. Recently, however, the production of filaments from triacetate has met with considerable success, because of the development of cheap solvents such as methylene dichloride which are easy to handle.

The raw material used in this process is cotton linters or high grade wood pulp; the triacetyl derivative is manufactured either by acetylation with acetic anhydride using a non-solvent such as benzene which slightly swells the triacetate but does not dissolve it, or by acetylation with acetic anhydride and acetic acid when the material dissolved.

Extrusion of this material is carried out using a 20% solution in methylene chloride (b.p. 42 °C) in the dry-spun fashion as for the secondary acetate. It is interesting to note that, provided care is taken to avoid degradation, this polymer may be melt spun[51].

The triacetate has a hydrophobic character because of the complete lack of hydroxyl groups. Fabrics made from cellulose triacetate are of particular interest because of their ability to resist creases and hold permanent ones. The melting point is higher than secondary acetate (290–300 °C); it shrinks and melts to a bead when ignited, so that combustion is slow. The fibres under the microscope show longitudinal striations and the cross section is bulbous and not very dissimilar from that of secondary acetate.

Other esters of cellulose have disadvantages when considered as textiles. The formates are too unstable and higher fatty acids are considerably more expensive than acetic. In addition, filaments from the higher esters become weaker as the molecular weight of the acyl groups increases.

Cellulose acetate yarns may be made using different shapes of orifice. Thus, coarse flat filaments with a very crisp handle called Crystal fibres are made by Tennasee Eastman and strip yarns or "Seratelle" by Courtaulds. Other possible fibres have cross sections which are in the shape of an X or Y.

(d) Synthetic Fibres

In general, synthetic fibres are after-stretched due to the fact that the dry spinning process gives rise to relatively slight stretching and consequently only slight orientation[30]. Stretching or drawing is usually carried out between rollers revolving at different speeds. The filament may be heated by passage through a hot bath of air or non-solvent, or by contact with heated rollers or plates. The temperature required must be high enough for the fibre to be thermoplastic, but not so high that the filaments stick together.

An example of the way imposed stretching modifies the mechanical properties is shown in Fig. 149 for Vinyon N yarn, where it can be seen that, as the stretch is increased, the elongation of the yarn decreases simultaneously with an increase in strength[9].

Stretching a fibre causes the molecules to orient in the direction of the fibre axis but, although being under strain, the molecules will tend to return to their original configuration when the temperature is raised to a point where this is possible. Similarly, when an untensioned fibre is heated, a point is reached at which strain is released. The value of this temperature depends on the temperature at which the filament had been previously stretched. Further increases in temperature give increased shrinkage, until a temperature is reached when all the strains are relaxed. It is then dimensionally stable at all temperatures up to this point. Some results on dry heat shrinkage of Vinyon N are given in Fig. 150.

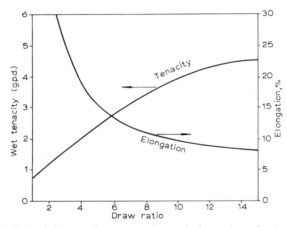

Fig. 149. Effect of draw ratio on tenacity and elongation of a typical fibre[9].

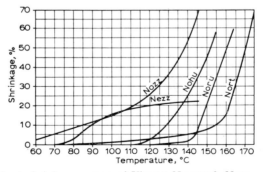

Fig. 150. Dry heat shrinkage curves of Vinyon N yarns[9]. Nezz = spun yarn unstretched. Nozz = stretched 1289%, unmodified. Nohu = stretched 1289%, heat modified at 110°C. Noru = stretched 1289%, heat modified at 135°C. Nort = stretched 1289%, heat modified at 150°C, no shrinkage allowed.

For this fibre, the greater the stretch the lower the shrinkage at a given temperature; in other instances, the shrinkage may be almost independent of the stretch applied.

However, holding the fibre under tension whilst subjecting to heat treatment or heat setting removes most of the strains, and the fibres may be subsequently heated with only minor shrinkage occurring at temperatures in excess of the expected strain release temperature. Wide variation in the properties of yarns are thus possible, depending on the degree of stretch and conditions of heat setting. This setting treatment is very important in the production of fabrics.

(i) *Polyvinyl chloride*

This fibre is spun from a mixture of carbon disulphide and acetone in the ratio $1/1$, usually followed by hot stretching[53]. Fibres from polyvinyl chloride are of considerable use because of their resistance to chemicals, weathering etc., but suffer from a very low softening temperature. At temperatures higher than $78\,^{\circ}C$, it contracts and may shrink as much as 50% at $100\,^{\circ}C$.

(ii) *Vinyon*

Vinyon is a copolymer of vinyl chloride and vinyl acetate in the ratio of $88/12$. The vinyl acetate may be regarded as a plasticiser for the hard tough polyvinyl chloride. The fibre is spun from a 23% solution of the copolymer in acetone or methyl ethyl ketone. Prior to extrusion, the solution is deaerated. The filaments are weak when first extruded, but the strength develops on stretching, usually done to an extent of nine times. This is carried out in water at $65\,^{\circ}C$.

The fibre is thermoplastic at temperatures greater than about $65\,^{\circ}C$, becomes tacky and begins to melt when the temperature reaches $150\,^{\circ}C$. It has the advantage of being chemically very resistant to acids and alkalis, and finds considerable use as filter pads and protective clothing. The filament has a dumb-bell shape.

(iii) *Dynel*

Dynel is a copolymer of vinyl chloride (60%) and acrylonitrile (40%). After extrusion, the fibre is stretched or drawn hot by as much as twelve times its original length and annealed by heat.

Polyvinyl chloride and its copolymers can be modified by prolonged heating at temperatures above about $100\,^{\circ}C$ when the polymer becomes insoluble, presumably as a result of cross linking arising from dechlorination.

References p. 458

(iv) *Fibres from acrylonitrile*

Acrylonitrile was originally polymerised alone to give Orlon. However, the original fibres made from the homopolymer suffered from poor dye uptake, and practically all the acrylic fibres now on the market (including Orlon) are copolymers of acrylonitrile with a small quantity (say about 10%) of a second vinyl compound to give dyeability and enhanced solubility in solvents. The D.P. of Orlon continuous filament is about 100,000.

Acrylonitrile was known to give polymers long before fibres were produced. The difficulties of production of fibres lay in the lack of a solvent. The interchain forces in this material are high, and it has been suggested that hydrogen bonds are formed between the nitrile groups and the hydrogen atoms attached to the carbon atoms in the backbone

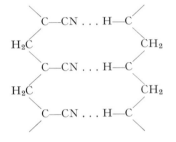

To dissolve such a material, the choice of solvent is important and only a relatively few are suitable. The most used are dimethylformamide, $HCON(CH_3)_2$, and dimethyl sulphone ($CH_3SO_2CH_3$). The true manufacturing details of acrylic fibres are not available, but might be as follows. The copolymer is dissolved in a solvent with heating and dry spun into a stream of hot nitrogen or steam. The filaments are hot stretched several times (6–15) their length. This may be carried out in special tubes at temperatures ranging from 115–170°C. For polyacrylonitrile fibres, a ten fold after-stretch gives a seven fold increase in tensile strength. There seems to be a difference in density between skin and core of Orlon fibres[32].

Orlon, when first made, did not have a good colour and was extremely difficult to dye. Nowadays two main types are sold; continuous filament type 81, and staple fibre type 42. Orlon has good resistance to mineral acids and common solvents and, although fairly stable to weak alkalis, is degraded by strong alkalis. Orlon shows characteristic behaviour to drastic heat. It progressively becomes yellow brown and black as heating is continued. Even after heating for sixty hours at 200°C, the yarn now black, retains more than half its initial strength. Heating would appear to cause a molecular rearrangement involving the loss of hydrogen. A suggested change is

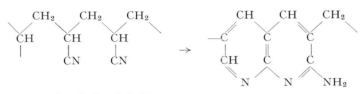

The cross section is dumb-bell.

5. Melt Spinning

Extrusion of the molten polymer has advantages over dry and wet spinning. Solvents are not required and hence neither a solvent or a spinning bath recovery process is necessary. Further, melt spinning is not complicated by the necessity for reagents to be given time to react or for the volatile solvent to be removed from the filament. Speeds of extrusion are higher than those for the dry and wet spinning.

(a) Products

Many synthetic fibres are formed by extrusion of the molten polymer. This is apparently a simple process (Fig. 151a). A supply of molten polymer

Fig. 151. (a) Diagrammatic representation of nylon spinning plant. (b) Diagrammatic representation of cold drawing[32].

A. Hopper fed with nylon chips
B. Spinning vessel
C. Electrically heated grid which melts the chips
D. Pool of molten nylon
E. Spinning jet
F. Metering pump
G. Cold air cross-flow
H. Steam chamber

J. Thread guide
K.   Feed rollers
L.   Take-up bobbin (spinning)
M, N. Thread guides
O.   Input feed rollers
P.   Deflector
Q.   Output feed roller
R.   Thread guide
S.   Take-up bobbin (drawn nylon)

References p. 458

is pumped at a constant rate and under very high pressure through small holes in the spinneret. The liquid streams emerge vertically downwards from the face of the spinneret and, on cooling, solidify. The filaments are brought together to form a thread which is wound up on bobbins. The product resembles a multifilament yarn but the molecules comprising the filaments are not oriented to give the yarn its desirable physical properties; stretching or drawing is necessary. The yarns may be used as continuous filament, or cut into desired lengths for staple fibre.

(i) *Nylon 66*

The chips are fed from a hopper A (Fig. 151a) into a vessel B and are held by an electrically heated grid C whose size of mesh is too fine to allow the chips to go through. On this grid, the chips melt and the molten nylon drops into the container, D. The pool of molten nylon is kept as small as possible, since nylon when molten is susceptible to decomposition and discolouration.

The level of the pool is kept constant automatically, and controls the feed from the hopper. To prevent attack by air, an oxygen-free nitrogen or carbon dioxide atmosphere is used[3]. The hopper may be made air tight and a pressure of gas greater than atmospheric used; this increased pressure ensures that air does not enter and helps to force the highly viscous melt into the metering pump. Steam is used as an alternative to nitrogen[55]. This is injected under atmospheric pressure at a point suitable for keeping air away from the melting zone but, in this case, a booster pump may be necessary to force molten polymer to the metering pump. The melt is metered by a pump to the spinneret E. After passing through the pump, the molten polymer is filtered through layers of graded sand. To obtain a fine yarn, a metering pump is necessary so that a constant flow of polymer reaches the spinneret; the temperatures and pressures used will be around 300 °C and 1000 lb./sq. in. The jets of the spinneret are about 0.010 in. in diameter. The molten polymer on extrusion solidifies immediately it leaves the jet, and passes through a current of cold air in a cooling chamber. The filaments emerge from the cooling chamber at a temperature of about 70 °C and enter a column H through which steam is passed. The steaming treatment wets the yarn prior to winding. The speed of extrusion is high and may be about 800 m/min.

In melting nylon, some depolymerisation may occur and to prevent this the polymer chips may be dried. However, controlling the quantity of moisture to a very low level is difficult and it is better, in order to maintain a uniform D.P. to introduce a controlled amount of moisture (*ca.* 0.16%) into the chamber containing the melt. An alternative is to maintain an atmosphere of steam above the molten polymer, when it is claimed that the depolymerisation is reduced. Whilst the polymer is molten, other changes may occur. Transamidation reactions may lead to changes in molecular weight, thermal decomposition will lead to the formation of gas bubbles which interfere with extrusion, or to branching and cross linking reactions. With nylon, decomposition gives rise to the formation of gel particles; those must be removed from the melt by a filter pack consisting of layers of graded sand between wire gauze placed just before the spinneret. These gel particles may also form on the melt grid which, in time, becomes coated with an infusible gel of low thermal conductivity. This will reduce the melting rate of the polymer, and hence the unit must be cleaned from time to time. In order to ensure reproducible filaments, the polymer must be held at a constant temperature for a constant time.

The filaments have deniers which are independent of the diameter of the spinneret holes; the fineness depends on the nature of the polymer, the rate at which polymer is pumped through the spinneret and the linear velocity at which the filaments are wound up. Filaments of non-circular cross sections can be made by using slots of different shapes provided the melt viscosity is high enough.

The filaments on being extruded have a high extensibility but a low strength. As the filaments emerge from the spinneret face and begin to cool, an air blast may be used to speed up the cooling process[56]. Solidification takes place about two feet below the spinneret. The filaments are brought together to form a twistless thread which passes vertically downwards; as spun, they are almost unoriented. Most of the stretching which occurs during the drawing down between the spinneret and wind up does so while the filament is still molten, and there is sufficient time for the molecular orientation to relax before the fibre cools and crystallises.

When the thread is first formed, the material is dry and will absorb moisture. Absorption of moisture will cause the filaments to elongate so that, if the dry fibres were wound on a bobbin, extension would occur as the bobbin equilibrated with the moisture in the atmosphere. An unstable package would result. To avoid this the filaments, when they have cooled, are run down a tube through which steam is passed[14] and then wound up. High tenacity is developed by stretching the filaments in the cold about a factor of 4 times. The drawing operation is apparently simple to perform (Fig. 151b). The yarn is pulled off the bobbin L (primary spinning package) and passed round guides M, N, between nip rollers O and then round another roller Q which has a linear speed of something like five times the feed. The random or near random orientation, of the molecules in the undrawn freshly melt spun thread is changed by drawing[15]. Drawing causes the molecules to become more or less oriented parallel to the fibre

axis, and simultaneously the denier of the filaments decreases. The degree
or order but not that of crystallinity increases[16].

When nylon is cold drawn, the filaments extend to a very large extent.
If the drawing is carried out slowly, the birefringence of all parts of the
filament increases steadily. If carried out rapidly, the filament may form
one or more necks (Fig. 152). The necking effect is more likely in heavier
denier yarn. Heavy denier filaments elongate to several times their original length, when an extremely small increase in load is exerted over that
at which flow (and hence cold drawing) starts (Fig. 153). Fine denier filaments draw only when the load is steadily increased as drawing occurs.
Necking is a phenomenon to be avoided as far as is possible in practice,
since the amount of drawing which is possible is fixed by the natural draw
ratio leaving little latitude in possible properties.

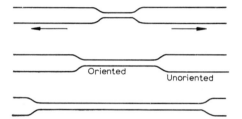

Fig. 152. Cold drawing: the shoulder effect.

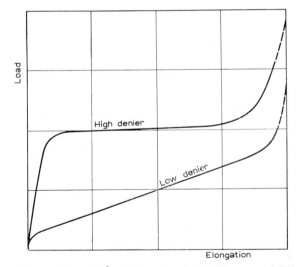

Fig. 153. Load elongation curves for undrawn nylon 66 filaments of different deniers.

Nylon 66 filaments under the microscope appear as almost featureless smooth cylinders with an almost circular cross section. Melting occurs around 263 °C under nitrogen and 250 °C in air; this melting point is sufficiently low for nylon fabrics to stick to an iron even though the temperature of the iron may only be 180 °C. Nylon fabrics like all thermoplastic materials do not burn well but melt to a glassy globule; they are very stable to chemicals but, on heating, will tend to go yellow after a long period of time. Nylon has found a wide variety of uses *e.g.* tyre cords, parachutes, stockings, socks, lingerie etc. Nylon fabrics are normally heat set, a process carried out by heat and moisture and giving a dimensional stability to the fabric or garment.

(ii) *Nylon 6*

Prior to extrusion, it is essential to remove any residual monomer which is left in the polymer; this is carried out by extraction with water. The polymer is melt spun, being extruded at a temperature of 260–270 °C. Extrusion is direct into the atmosphere; the filaments run round one roller to apply water and wetting agent and a second to apply an oil in water emulsion. The yarn is not passed through a steam chamber because the presence of monomer in the polymer would lead to sticking of the filaments in the steam chamber. The yarn is drawn to about 5 times. Perlon has a lower m.p. than nylon 66.

Like nylon 66, nylon 6 is heat set and is resistant to solvents such as chloroform, acetone etc. but will dissolve in phenols. Nylon 6 has the advantage that it will absorb acid dyes to a greater extent than nylon 66. The uses of this material are very similar to those of nylon 66.

(iii) *Polyurethan*

This polymer is made from reaction of hexamethylene diisocyanate and butanediol. The fibre is formed by melt extrusion followed by stretching to about four times. With a melting point some 80 °C below that of nylon, this material is not very suitable for wearing apparel. It is stiffer than nylon.

(iv) *Polyethylene terephthalate*

The polymer chips are dried and transferred to hoppers which act as reservoirs. The chips from the hopper are fed into the melting device and the molten polymer extruded. The polymer solidifies immediately on leaving the spinneret. The undrawn fibre is hot drawn on draw-twist machines to about 5 times. The resistance of the fibre to weak acids is good even at the boil; to strong acids, the resistance is good in the cold. The fibre is not attacked too easily by weak alkalis but may be hydrolysed

References p. 458

by strong alkalis. Solvents such as alcohol and those used in dry cleaning do not show any action, but the fibre is soluble in some phenols.

The melting point of polyethylene terephthalate is similar to nylon 66; the fibre will burn but simultaneous melting takes place. Fabrics made from this polymer can be dimensionally stabilised; indeed, fabrics from polyethylene terephthalate can be made to hold creases permanently. Heat setting is carried out by exposing the fabric, held in full width, to a temperature 30–40°C higher than that encountered in its subsequent life. It is necessary to heat set since, if this is not done, troublesome creases will be set in during washing. It has been suggested that the outstanding ability of fibres of this polymer to hold creases or be resistant to creasing lies to some extent in the stiffness of the polymer chains.

(v) Saran

Saran is prepared from a copolymer of vinylidene chloride (ca. 85%) and vinyl chloride (ca. 13%) and possibly acrylonitrile. The copolymer is extruded at about 180°C, and solidifies immediately it leaves the spinneret on coming into contact with cold air or water. The amorphous filaments are quenched rapidly and cold drawn.

The fibres are of a pale gold or straw colour and, presumably because of the high percentage of chlorine, will not burn. Chemically, this fibre is very stable but is attacked by ammonium hydroxide.

(vi) Polyethylene

The polymer may be spun at a temperature of 300°C and, after spinning, it is drawn by a factor of 6.

As a textile, the low m.p. (110–120°C) militates against its use. It is only used as a monofil. It does not have the non-flame properties of saran for example. Since polyethylene is completely non-polar, the frictional coefficient is low and fabrics have a waxy feel. Because of its stability to chemicals, it is used for protective clothing. Other uses are car upholstery, fishing nets etc.

Linear polyethylene (low pressure polymerisation with Ziegler type of catalysts) is also spun and has the advantage of a higher melting point (135°C).

(vii) Polyolefins

Considerable commercial interest has developed in the potentialities of isotactic polyolefins, because of their higher melting points as compared with the atactic polymers. Information is sparse in this field at the present time, but it seems that polypropylene is the most attractive isotactic polymer for the formation of fibres. It has the advantage of being made from a readily available and cheap raw material. Fibres may be formed by melt extrusion and drawn in the normal way. As a textile material, it has many good features (*e.g.* tensile strength) but, unfortunately, degradation on exposure to light is relatively rapid, and colouration can only easily be achieved by pigmentation of the melt. Nevertheless, it is to be anticipated that these difficulties will be overcome and that polypropylene will become an important synthetic fibre.

(viii) *Polytetrafluoroethylene*

This material is difficult to spin because of its insoluble nature and high m.p. (400 °C). The melt at this temperature is too viscous to extrude. However, polytetrafluoroethylene has been formed into filaments, a process which would seem to be carried out as follows:

The polymer is spun from an aqueous colloidal dispersion, being formed by emulsion polymerisation to give a dispersion containing about 15% of polymer. Of the particles, some 30% are ribbon-like, some being 5 μ long and 0.07 μ wide. The dispersion is extruded through an orifice of 0.5 mm diameter into an aqueous solution of hydrochloric acid (5%) at 25 °C. The filament so produced has adequate strength for further treatment. It is sintered on a metal surface *e.g.* a roller, at 385 °C for a few seconds, quenched rapidly in water and the cold filament drawn four times. In this process, the difficulties of insolubility and relative infusibility of the polymer have been overcome by polymerising under conditions where the particles are fibre shaped. When the dispersion is broken, the fibrous particles adhere sufficiently to give a filament that can be handled. On heating, the fibrous particles melt to give a continuous and strong fibre.

(b) *Mechanism of Melt-Spinning*

(i) *Extrusion*

In this process, the molten polymer is pushed through a capillary; the simplest relation between the flow M through a tube of radius r and length l is given by Poiseuille's Law

$$M = \frac{P\pi r^4 \varrho}{8l\eta}$$

where P is the applied pressure; ϱ and η the polymer density and viscosity. This equation assumes the liquid has the characteristics of Newtonian flow, so that output and pressure are linearly related. In practice, the flow rises more rapidly than anticipated from the above considerations and the relation with the fourth power of the radius breaks down. The "nonlinear" nature of the flow may arise from two causes *viz.* the viscosity may depend on the rate of shear which may be high in narrow capillaries, or

References p. 458

the melt may not be incompressible as has been assumed for Poiseuille's Law, *i.e.* it is visco-elastic[78]. In the first case the relations are essentially nonlinear, whereas in the second the flow is linearly dependent on viscosity as well as on elastic responses. The increased throughput over that for an incompressible fluid of the same viscosity arises from elastic deformation of the melt during the passage through the capillary; this effectively lowers the viscosity. Evidence has accumulated to show that the deviations from Poiseuille's Law are due to visco-elastic effects rather than non-Newtonian flow properties. For example, with the extrusion of polystyrene, extrapolation of flow data to zero shear stress gave limiting values of the viscosity which agreed well with viscosities measured in a parallel plate plastometer *i.e.* under low shear[79]. More easily observable phenomena are the development of streaming birefringence, indicating that, when a polymer flows, some uncoiling of the chains occurs and the characteristic swelling of the polymer stream develops immediately below the spinneret (Fig. 154). This swelling takes place because, on the

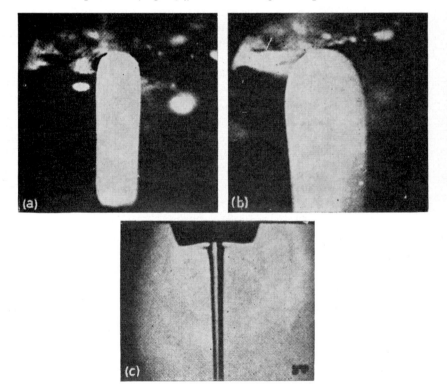

Fig. 154. Profile of extruding Terylene monofilament ($10\times$) (a) at 248°C, (b) at 220°C (threadline broken), (c) silicone oil at room temperature[80].

disappearance of the stresses, the molecules are able to coil up again and there is an elastic recovery[80]. In the extruded filament below the swelling, no birefringence is observed and the polymer has relaxed back to its isotropic form. Hence, although molecular orientation is induced during the extrusion of a polymer which has molecular flexibility, orientation is lost after extrusion and must be reintroduced by stretching or drawing.

The passage of the thread downwards from the spinneret has been studied. By photographing the filament at different distances below the spinneret using a polarising microscope, optical changes can be measured directly and the velocity and birefringence derived[81]. Tension measurements have also been made. It is found that the tension rises with distance from the spinneret even after the velocity has become constant, indicating that the drag forces due to the air as well as inertia and surface tension play a part. Further, tension is very much higher than could be supported at the spinneret by surface tension alone or created in the threadline by accelerating the mass of the polymer.

It seems then that the wind-up tension is not transmitted to the spinneret but derives from the air drag. Going down the threadline, the first tension is almost entirely surface tension which makes a smaller contribution with increasing distance from the spinneret. Beyond about 5 cm, a noticeable visco-elastic tension arises and just after this a measurable birefringence develops which is evidence of the visco-elastic affect. When the thread is about 20 cm from the orifice, the air drag becomes noticeable and at the hardening point where the velocity becomes constant, the drag is the major source of tension. Under these conditions the polymer stretches as the tension rises. The velocity is constant when the temperature reaches about 80 °C; the birefringence rises for a few more centimetres until the temperature has dropped to about 50 °C. The temperature at which the birefringence ceases to change is that expected from a knowledge of the glass transition.

In arriving at this analysis, note has to be taken of the fact that it has been necessary to calculate the tensions in parts of the thread-line where they were not directly measurable, and to assess the contribution from the various forces.

The inertia of the material and the drag of the surrounding air apparently supply sufficient tension in the form of drag on the filaments to induce some orientation of the polymer molecules in the solidification ranges. In this range, the filaments accelerate and become taut fibres. If the wind-up speed and hence the tension is increased sufficiently, high degrees of orientation may be achieved and fibres with useful properties produced. An alternative way of increasing the drag is to pass the filaments through water and again fibres with useful properties can be made. It is usual,

References p. 458

nevertheless, to make filaments of low degrees of orientation and to draw them in a separate operation.

(ii) *The drawing process*

Filaments which do not have an overall orientation of their molecules are usually not suitable for use in the textile field. Orientation of the chain molecules in the direction of the fibre axis is necessary, and is accomplished by stretching or drawing out the unoriented filaments. The problem of drawing has been investigated for melt spun polymers. Some aspects of this work will be discussed.

Drawing is carried out on a machine (Fig. 151b) which essentially consists of two rollers, one running faster than the other. The yarn is wrapped round each of these rollers a sufficient number of times to prevent slippage, and is stretched by a ratio equal to the ratio of the roller speeds. Such machines are stable only over a limited range of conditions; outside these, the filaments either break or are non-uniform[68].

Most glassy or crystalline materials have Young's Moduli in excess of 10^{11} dynes/cm², with recoverable extensibilities of about 1% beyond which they flow or break. Rubbery materials possess moduli very much lower at 10^7 to 10^8 dynes/cm² and elastic extensibilities around 500%; the elastic properties are very different from glasses or crystals. Fibrous materials fall into an intermediate range having moduli between 10^9 and 10^{11} dynes/cm² with recoverable extensibilities between 5 and 50%. Fibre structures therefore possess some molecular flexibility which distinguishes them from glasses and crystals on the one hand and, because flexibility is limited, from rubbers on the other.

Examination of load extension curves of polymers shows that they fall into two categories (Fig. 155). In the first, all points in the specimen are stretched equally, and extension increases slowly right up to the breaking point. In the second, cold drawing occurs and all points along the specimen have not necessarily undergone the same degree of extension.

The first type of load/extension curve takes on a sigmoidal shape, since at the higher extensions the long flexible molecules are reinforced in some

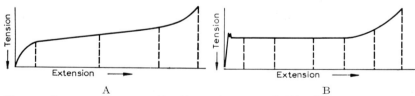

Fig. 155. Two common types of load/extension curves[68]. (A) uniform or rubber-like, (B) by necking.

way. In vulcanised rubber, this would arise from covalent cross linkages, in polyethylene terephthalate from crystallites or even by entanglement as in polymethyl methacrylate.

The behaviour referred to as "cold drawing" was first reported by Carothers and Hill[63]. The filament, on extension, necks down at one position to a smaller cross section at some point; the length of the filament increases as the shoulders of the neck move apart (Fig. 152). Although at first considered to be confined to crystalline polymers, this phenomenon turns up in a variety of materials. Thus, polymethyl methacrylate will neck when stretched[64]; filaments of sodium thymonucleate neck when stretched from a crystalline state to an amorphous one, whereas polyethylene terephthalate filaments change when stretched from an amorphous undrawn state to a crystalline drawn one. Indeed, in this material the orientation and strain markedly increases the rate of crystallisation[67,76]. Thus, because of the wide diversity of materials which, on stretching, exhibit the necking phenomenon, crystallites do not play a fundamental role. Nevertheless, the random or near random state of orientation in the undrawn melt spun filament is modified by drawing. If the undrawn filament is drawn in such a way as to avoid necking, the birefringence of all parts of the filament increases steadily and simultaneously. In general, heavy denier filaments neck more easily. Studies of the orientation in the neck have shown a progressive increase in orientation in going from the undrawn to the drawn filament across the neck[75]. An example as to the orien-

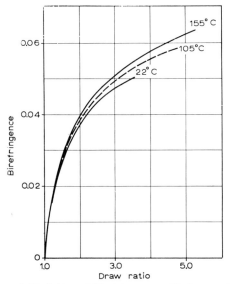

Fig. 156. Variation of birefringence with draw ratio[77].

tation changes which occur in the drawn filaments[77] is given in Fig. 156. In some materials *e.g.* nylon, crystallisation occurs when the extruded polymer cools, drawing then orients the crystallites as well as the amorphous material. There has been some discussion as to the changes which occur in the neck during drawing. Since the temperature may become quite high (*ca.* 70°C), the possibility of the crystalline material melting and reforming has been considered. However, even allowing for a possible reduction of melting point under stress, it is unlikely that a sufficiently high temperature will be reached. It is only when the yarn is thick and the speed of drawing is high that sufficient heat is developed to cause melting; a second explanation is that drawing consists of straightening and orienting the fibrillar units found in the spherulites. In general, the density and hence the degree of crystallinity, if it changes at all, suggests that a small decrease in crystallinity occurs on drawing (polyethylene and nylon[71,74]) but this does not preclude the possibility that, during the process of dragging the crystallites into line, a reduction in the size may occur since the forces of drawing may tear the crystallites apart (Fig. 157).

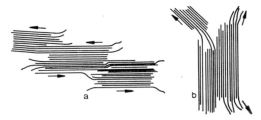

Fig. 157. (a) Crystal rupture by shearing, (b) Crystal rupture by tearing.

Tearing the crystallites is a more likely process than the breaking of the crystallite by shear; in the latter case, the maximum force operates. whereas tearing is rather akin to pulling off a piece of adhesive tape[70].

In polyethylene, crystal breaking on a larger scale may occur. If the triclinic form is present, it will be converted into the orthorhombic on drawing[35]. The subdivision takes place at the shoulder but even so there is no substantial change in the degree of crystallinity, although the size of the crystallites has decreased[36]. Unfortunately, the molecular mechanism of drawing must be regarded as unresolved.

(iii) *Necking*

When filaments of polymers such as nylon, polyethylene etc. are stretched at one or more points, shoulders or necks develop where the drawn material joins the thicker undrawn part. The thickness of the drawn position remains constant. The full extension called the natural

draw ratio and the reduction in thickness are fairly well defined. Attempts at further drawing results in a sharp increase in the stress. Although the draw ratio depends to some extent on the rate of drawing,
thickness of the specimen and temperature, it is remarkable that, for
fibres up to 1 mm in diameter drawn by hand at room temperature, the
draw ratio is very similar for the various polymers: polyethylene, polyesters and polyamides. The explanation of this remarkable constancy is not
easy. At higher temperatures, however, the shoulder becomes less marked
and the draw ratio can be varied over a wider range until, as the melting
point is approached, the features of cold drawing disappear and a gradual
thinning of the filament occurs. The natural draw ratio for nylon 66 has
been shown to decrease from 5 at room temperature to 3 at 80 °C and down
to 1 at 90–100 °C. There seems to be a temperature fairly critical for
each polymer above which necking disappears. This kind of stretching
can be carried out at room temperature only if the drawing is carried out
very slowly.

More recently workers[34,82] have treated the phenomenon of necking
macroscopically. Necking may occur under conditions which are (1) adiabatic and (2) isothermal.

Adiabatic necking. Taking an amorphous filament of polyethylene terephthalate and extending this at a constant rate, a characteristic load
extension curve is obtained. The tension rises until the extension reaches
about 2% when a neck appears. After falling slightly, the tension remains
constant until the shoulders of the neck have traversed the filament.
Continued extension thereafter is accompanied by an increase in tension.

To investigate this, a monofilament was stretched by running from one
roller to another[34]. The second roller was run at a higher speed than the
first, so that the filament was under tension determined by the ratio of
the speeds of the two rollers. As the filament passed from the feed roll, it
accelerated to the speed of the draw roll so that, if the filament stretches
by forming a neck, the behaviour of the neck may be observed. A stationary condition of the neck may be maintained, if the ratio of the roller
speeds, R, equals the natural draw ratio r. If R is greater or less than r,
the neck will move backwards or forwards between the rollers. In the
simple experiment where a filament is stretched and a load (or tension)/
extension curve obtained, it is not easy to determine with great accuracy
the natural draw ratio, since the end of the drawing process and the subsequent increase in tension is not very sharp. A better method is to follow
the velocity of the neck in the draw roll experiment. Thus, let A_1, d_1, V_1
be the cross section, density and velocity at the feed roll and A_2, d_2, V_2
these at the draw roll. The velocity of the shoulder is V_x. The rate of

change of mass between the rollers is $(V_1 d_1 A_1 - V_2 d_2 A_2)$ which will be equal to $V_x (A_1 d_1 - A_2 d_2)$

Hence

$$V_x = \frac{V_2\left(\dfrac{d_1}{d_2}\dfrac{A_1}{A_2} - \dfrac{V_2}{V_1}\right)}{\dfrac{V_2}{V_1}\left(\dfrac{d_1 A_1}{d_2 A_2} - 1\right)} = \frac{V_2\left(\dfrac{d_1}{d_2}S - R\right)}{R\left(\dfrac{d_1}{d_2}S - 1\right)}$$

where $S = A_1/A_2$.

The natural draw ratio is given by $S d_1/d_2$ so that the equation may be rewritten as

$$(V_2 - V_x)R = r(V_x R - V_2)$$

and serves as a means of calculating the draw ratio r, since V_x can be measured. Results of these experiments have shown that the draw ratio varies to some extent with draw speed (Fig. 158). Further, with poly-

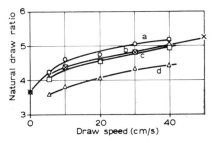

Fig. 158. Natural draw ratio of amorphous polyethylene terephthalate as a function of speed and ambient temperature. (a) 20°C, (b) 40°C, (d) 50°C, (d) 60°C[34].

ethylene terephthalate above 60°C, multiple necking occurs but, in the temperature range 70–80°C, necking may disappear. An increase in ambient temperature causes a decrease in load necessary for drawing as well as a decrease in deformation. At sufficiently high temperatures, the entire sample undergoes homogeneous strain *i.e.* an approximately adiabatic process occurring at the shoulder becomes an isothermal one over the entire sample. To obtain isothermal behaviour at lower temperatures requires drawing at low rates and with very good dispersion of heat.

The natural draw ratio at constant speed of drawing decreases as the filament diameter decreases, so that the natural draw ratio obtained is a function of experimental conditions. At the neck itself, a high temperature is reached and, if a bundle of filaments is stretched, necking occurs at the same place in each filament, presumably due to a thermal effect. If stretched separately, the necks occur at random along the filaments. The temperature reached in the neck in the drawing of polyethylene terephthalate fibres is estimated[34,66] to be some 60° above the ambient temperature of around 20°C.

The effects of temperature on the tension/extension curves have been determined in the two roller machine by passage of the filament over a hot plate. Under these conditions, it was calculated that the filament rapidly reached the temperature of the hot plate. To appreciate why necking occurs, reference must be made to the extension curves under isothermal conditions where no necking occurs. These curves are given in Fig. 159 where those which could not be obtained without necking have been given as broken lines.

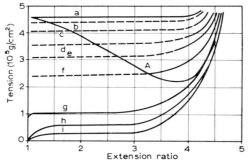

Fig. 159. Tension-extension-temperature properties of amorphous polyethylene terephthalate[34]. (a) 20°C, (b) 30°C, (c) 40°C, (d) 50°C, (e) 60°C, (f) 70°C, (g) 80°C, (h) 100°C, (i) 140°C. (A) adiabatic from 20°C.

The most important feature of these curves is that the tension decreases as the temperature is raised.

The work done in stretching must appear as an increase in elastic potential energy or heat. The quantity of energy stored as potential energy is small[65] and, in the discussion presented here[34], both this and any changes which occur in crystallinity are ignored.

On the assumption that no heat escapes, an adiabatic curve may be calculated. This curve A may be deduced from the data in Fig. 159, by calculating the temperature rises which take place by the work of successive 10% extensions and plotting the new tensions developed at these 10% intervals. Curve A shows that the tension is steadily decreased to a minimum and then rises; such a path is unstable over the range where the tension is continuously decreasing. Heat is being developed which reduces the tension. The picture may more clearly be seen from the adiabatic curve in Fig. 160, since, if a constant tension line is drawn so that it cuts the curve in R_1, R_2 and R_3, this tension can be chosen so that in going from R_1 to R_3

the work done is identical to that in going along a constant tension line. Since this demands a lower tension in the initial stages, the constant tension route is the stable one and is to be preferred. Thus in the extension from R_1 to R_2, the constant tension route uses less work but some compensation is required, whereby the work which would have been obtained

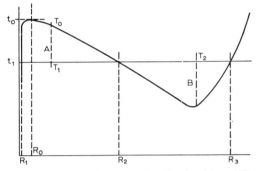

Fig. 160. Adiabatic load/extension curve for the shoulder of Fig. 159[34].

in going along the adiabatic route is compensated by the deficit in the range R_2 to R_3. This compensation is achieved by having R_1, R_2 and R_3 close together, as when the sample necks. In the neck, work produced in the stretching gives a temperature T_2 (Fig. 161), and heat is conducted to the second half of the shoulder. Thus, a heat balance is set up in the neck and this can be used in a simple model to calculate the width of the neck.

In stretching therefore, the tension reaches a value t_0 at which the system

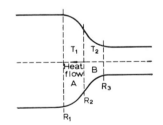

Fig. 161. Arrangement of draw ratios, temperatures and heat flow in a shoulder[34].

becomes unstable so that there is a rapid collapse from the peak tension to the stable one t_1.

Diagrammatically, the neck may be divided into two zones. Thus the heat is developed in the zone B and its conduction back to zone A reduces the temperature in B but raises the temperature in A. In practice, the adiabatic curve may be slightly different from that in Fig. 160, since the process may not occur without any heat loss although the shape remains essentially the same.

Nylon 66 has load/extension curves which are sigmoidal, dropping to lower loads at higher temperatures. Such curves are similar to the ones discussed for polyethylene terephthalate, and hence nylon will form necks at a high enough rate of extension or large enough specimen cross section. The temperature rise at the neck in nylon has been indicated as 60–70°C[69,72]. Further, with nylon 66[11] the yield load changes with moisture content so that yield stress may be related to mobility in the amorphous regions. Nylon 66 filaments exhibit crystallinity prior to cold drawing, and the crystallites change their orientation distribution from a random one to one in which the crystallites become increasingly oriented as the draw ratio increases. The many changes which occur can be followed. Birefringence, X-ray patterns and polarised infra-red spectra indicate that there is a progressive increase in orientation[73]. By contrast, the density changes only slightly so that, during the drawing process, the amount of crystalline material does not change[74].

Isothermal necking. The discussion above attributes the necking phenommenon to the development of heat in the fibre followed by subsequent instability. However, it is possible to achieve necking isothermally. The basic reason for necking lies in the non-uniformity of the filament so that some part of the specimen is subjected to higher stresses than the remainder, either because the cross sectional area is less or stress concentrations are not the same everywhere. When a stress/strain curve is rising steeply, non-uniformity does not lead to necking, since any extra stress which is applied can be supported without a great excess of strain.

Consider a Hookean body with a linear stress strain curve

$$\sigma = E\gamma \tag{1}$$

where σ is now the true stress *i.e.* load L divided by the area of cross section A and γ is the strain given by the increase in length (l_1-l_0) where l_0 and l_1 are the lengths of the filament in the unstrained and strained conditions. In terms of tension T, equation 1 is modified. If there is no change of density, then $l_1 A_1 = l_0 A_0$, where A_0 and A_1 are the cross sectional areas of the filament in the unstrained and strained conditions. Hence,

$$\sigma = \frac{L}{A_1} = \frac{L}{A_0} \frac{l_1}{l_0} = T(\gamma + 1)$$

or

$$T = E \frac{\gamma}{\gamma + 1} \tag{2}$$

Equation 2 gives a curve which is a straight line initially when γ is small and curves off for higher values, asymptotically approaching E. Examples of these equations are sketched in Fig. 162 (Curves A and C). The curve

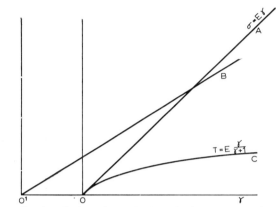

Fig. 162. Stress/strain relations for a Hookean body; curve σ refers to stress, curve T refers to tension.

has zero slope at high strain. Hence, if a stress/strain curve has a continuously concave shape it must, when translated to the conventional load vs. extension curve, show a negative slope. This situation is precisely the condition that makes the adiabatic load/extension curve unstable, and arises in this case not from the generation of heat when the material is stretched but from the elastic properties themselves. If extension proceeds at a decreasing tension and if any part of the specimen is by chance even slightly more stretched than another due to irregularities in the cross section say, this section can extend with the load decreasing whilst other sections retract or extend more slowly. A non-reinforcing visco-elastic body must extend unevenly in this way to infinite strain at one point like pitch or putty. If, however, reinforcement occurs at higher strains giving a sigmoid stress/strain curve, the corresponding load/extension curve reaches a minimum, and then increases. In these circumstances, unstable non-uniform extension can only cover a finite range and the material does not extend indefinitely at a decreasing load. This behaviour was first observed in certain ductile metals which exhibit work hardening. It is referred to as yield-point extension[83]. Metals exhibit this effect only to a small extent, in contrast to the large extensions produced in filaments. The behaviour of rubber balloons on inflation is an example of this behaviour; as the balloon is blown up, stretching at first occurs but soon two kinds of stretch develop, one high and one low coexisting at the same pressure. The criterion for the material to show instability on stretching is that the slope of the load/extension curve shall become negative. The position in the stress/strain curve at which the tension is a maximum may be determined graphically. If the specimen extrudes uniformly then

$$T = \frac{\sigma}{\gamma + 1}$$

so that if σ is plotted against $\gamma + 1$ instead of γ, straight lines from the origin will have slopes which are equal to the tension. In Fig. 163, such a case is sketched. The stress/strain curve plotted in the normal way is given by the straight line A. The straight line B has been drawn as commencing from an origin O', one unit further back from the point O. The tension corresponding to strain γ, is given by the slope of the line drawn from the origin. From the geometry, lines of differing slope drawn from the new origin O cut the line A at one point only. There exists therefore a unique tension T corresponding to every value of γ. If the stress/strain curve deviates from linearity so as to have a concavity towards the γ axis, then these lines from O' will cut the curve at two points (A and B, in Fig. 163). This means that there exist two values of γ (say γ_1 and γ_2) corresponding to one value of the tension. Further as the slope of the line is increased, the tension increases until in the limit the line becomes a tangent (C in Fig. 163). The strain at this point must therefore correspond to a maximum on the load/extension curve*. The condition therefore that

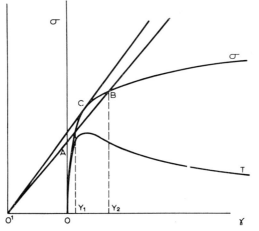

Fig. 163. Stress/strain relations for a non-Hookean body; curve σ refers to stress, curve T refers to tension.

---

* In Fig. 163 the original stress curve labelled σ has been transformed to the tension curve labelled T.

a stress/strain curve shall exhibit a maximum when transformed to a load/
extension curve is that the slope of the tangent at a point of the stress/
strain curve shall be less than the slope of the line from the transposed
origin O′ drawn to the same point, *i.e.*

$$\frac{d\sigma}{d\gamma} < \frac{\sigma}{\gamma + 1}$$

In terms of the draw ratio $(R = \gamma + 1)$ normally used, this becomes

$$\frac{d\sigma}{d\gamma} = \frac{d\sigma}{dR}\frac{dR}{d\gamma} = \frac{d\sigma}{dR} < \frac{\sigma}{R}$$

The lines of slope $\sigma/(\gamma + 1)$ are lines which give the tension for uniform
extension. However, the extension can not be uniform if there exist, at
any one tension, two possible extensions. In these circumstances, the system is unstable and necking can occur. This is an isothermal process and
does not demand the generation of heat[82,84].

In the example quoted, the curve has been taken to be concave down-

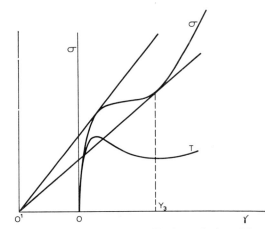

Fig. 164. Stress/strain relation for a non-Hookean body with a sigmoid curve;
curve σ refers to stress, curve T refers to tension.

wards. Specimens which have such stress/strain curves will be capable of
being extended at a reducing tension, since the slope of lines from O′ which
cut the stress/strain curves for increasing γ continuously decreases. For
many materials however, stress/strain curves are sigmoidal (Fig. 164) so
that as the σ *vs.* $\gamma + 1$ curves are constructed for points corresponding to
increasing strain, a second tangent point is reached (γ_3 in Fig. 164). This
represents a minimum for values of tension. Hence for extensions greater

than this, the curve is convex and there exists only one tension corresponding to each extension. The system is stable again and extension proceeds normally.

In practice, drawspeeds are usually high enough for heating to be important so that, even if the stress/strain curves are sigmoidal, the drawing is far from isothermal and the temperature rise will mean that the process will be at least partly adiabatic.

(iv) *Heat treatments*

After drawing, the filament passes round the draw roller at or near room temperature before tension is released. Release of tension at the draw temperature would result in a certain elastic recovery. However, when the tension is released at a lower temperature, because of the limited and temperature-sensitive molecular flexibility of fibrous polymers, the elastic recovery is smaller. Hence the bulk of the strain imposed during drawing is permanent, being locked in place by the reinforcing effect of crystallisation, a small part is recoverable when the tension is released, and a further part can be recovered as shrinkage if the filaments are heated. Secondly, it is common practice to draw a filament to an extent less than the possible maximum. This means that, if the filament is later subjected to a high tension, part of the strain will be recoverable corresponding to elastic recovery after drawing, while part will be irrecoverable corresponding to further drawing. The structure of the filament is not stable to heat or to stretching and hence is subjected to heat treatment to improve its stability.

If a drawn filament is heated under zero tension, it shrinks until the degree of flexibility at that temperature is unable to cause any greater randomisation of the structure. Hence, provided that the original shrinkage temperature is not reached, any subsequent heating will not result in further shrinkage. This process may be called preshrinkage. However, heating at constant length to a high temperature builds up a stress which will relax as far as possible due to the enhanced degree of molecular flexibility at high temperatures. The stress does not relax to zero as in a free shrinkage treatment, but it goes far enough to decrease greatly the subsequent free shrinkage of the filament. This process is known as setting[85].

The same physical process can be used to relax the stress to as low a level as possible, whilst the fibre in any constrained position is heated. If the constrained position is round a crease, the process is known as crease setting[86].

The heat setting process is a very complicated one to explain in molecular terms. A more detailed discussion is given elsewhere[87].

REFERENCES

1 R. W. Moncrieff, *Man-made Fibres*, National Trade Press, London, 1957.
2 T. Lieser, *Chemiker-Ztg.*, 60 (1936) 387; *Koll.-Z.*, 81 (1937) 234.
   T. Lieser and E. Leckzyck, *Ann.*, 522 (1936) 56.
3 *B.P.* 550,991.
4 R. J. E. Cumberbirch, J. E. Ford and R. E. Gee, *J. Textile Inst.*, 52 (1961) 330T.
5 F. P. Morehead and W. A. Sisson, *Textile Research J.*, 51 (1945) 443.
6 J. M. Preston, *J. Soc. Chem. Ind. London*, 199T (1931).
7 *U.S.P.* 2,169,250.
8 *B.P.* 542,943.
9 R. D. Glenn, J. R. Kernan and J. M. Swalin, *Chem. Eng. Progr.*, 45 (1949) 180.
10 R. H. K. Thomson and D. Trail, *J. Soc. Chem. Ind. London*, 64 (1945) 229.
   R. H. K. Thomson, *Proc. Symposium on Fibrous Proteins, Soc. Dyers Colourists, Univ. Leeds*, (1946) 173.
11 A. Ferretti, *B.P.* 483,810.
12 L. Wormell, *B.P.* 495,885.
13 *D.R.P.* 702,001.
14 *B.P.* 533,303.
15 W. H. Carothers and J. W. Hill, *J. Am. Chem. Soc.*, 54 (1932) 1579.
16 C. E. Black and M. Dole, *J. Polymer Sci.*, 3 (1948) 358.
17 D. N. Tyler and N. S. Wooding, *J. Soc. Dyers Colourists*, 74 (1958) 283.
18 H. Klare and A. Gröbe, *Faserforsch. u. Textiltech.*, 8 (1957) 348.
19 R. H. K. Thomson, *Proc. Symposium on Fibrous Proteins, Soc. Dyers Colourists, Univ. Leeds* (1946) 173.
20 H. Rauch and S. Harris, *Zellwolle u. Kunstseide*, 47 (1942) 282.
21 *U.S.P.* 2,536,014.
22 P. H. Hermans, *The Physics and Chemistry of Cellulose Fibres*, Elsevier, Amsterdam, 1949.
23 W. A. Sisson, *J. Phys. Chem.*, 40 (1936) 343.
24 P. H. Hermans, *Kolloid-Z.*, 83 (1938) 71.
25 K. Gotzer, *Chemiefasern nach dem Viskoseverfahren*, Springer-Verlag, Berlin, 1951.
26 J. M. Preston, M. V. Nimkar and S. P. Gundavda, *J. Soc. Dyers Colourists*, 67 (1951) 169; *B.P.* 611,796.
27 E. Ott, H. M. Spurlin and M. W. Grafflin, *High Polymers*, Vol. V: *Cellulose*, Part II, Interscience, New York, 1954.
   H. L. Bredee, *Kolloid-Z.*, 94 (1941) 81.
28 *U.S.P.* 2,610,359.
   U.S.P. 2,610,360.
29 H. Schwartz and H. A. Wannon, *Kolloid-Z.*, 97 (1941) 193; 99 (1942) 190.
30 R. D. Glenn, J. R. Kernan and J. M. Swalm, *Chem. Eng. Prog.*, 45 (1949) 180.
31 M. Nagano and Y. Yoshioka, *C.A.*, 46 (1952) 6827c.
   B. B. Mithel, W. R. Saxton, J. E. Morgan and J. Witkamp, *J. Polymer Sci.*, 42 (1959) 559.
32 R. Hill, *Fibres from Synthetic Polymers*, Elsevier, Amsterdam, 1953.
33 J. M. Preston and G. D. Joshi, *Kolloid-Z.*, 122 (1951) 6.
34 I. Marshall and A. B. Thompson, *Proc. Roy. Soc. London*, 221A (1954) 541.
35 P. W. Teare, in *Polythene*, (Ed.: A. Renfrew), Iliffe & Son, London, 1957, p. 113.
36 S. Krimm and A. V. Tobolsky, *J. Polymer Sci.*, 7 (1951) 57.
   H. W. Rose, *Rayon Industry of Japan*, Textile Research Inst., U.S.A., 1946, p. 49.
37 B. G. Rånby, H. W. Giertz and E. Treiber, *Svensk Papperstiddn.*, 59 (1956) 117, 205.
38 S. Claesson and H. H. Brunn, *Svensk. Papperstiddn.*, 60 (1957) 336.
   H. H. Brunn, *Svensk. Papperstiddn.*, 60 (1957) 657.
   E. Treiber, *Svensk. Papperstiddn.*, 61 (1958) 794.
39 L. Oldsberg and O. Samuelson, *Svensk. Papperstiddn.*, 60 (1957) 745.
40 *Fibres, London*, 18, No. 1 (1957) 1.

[41] E. G. Adamek and C. B. Purves, *Can. J. Chem.*, 35 (1957) 960.
  A. K. Sanyal, E. L. Falconer, D. L. Vincent and C. B. Purves, *Can. J. Chem.*, 35 (1957) 1164.
  E. P. Swan and C. B. Purves, *Can. J. Chem.*, 35 (1957) 1522.
[42] V. Grobe and K. Meyer, *Faserforsch. u. Textiltech.*, 10 (1959) 214.
[43] M. Horio, *Textile Research J.*, 20 (1950) 373.
[44] F. Lehner, *G.P.* 58,508 (1890).
[45] P. Entwistle, E. H. Cole and N. S. Wooding, *Textile Research J.*, 19 (1949) 527, 609.
[46] T. Kleinert, *Pulp Paper Mag. Can.*, 56 (1955) 210.
[47] J. M. Preston, *Nature*, 128 (1931) 796.
[48] V. E. Gonsalves, *Proc. Intern. Rheol. Congr.* II, 239; III, 66 (1948).
[49] J. M. Preston and G. D. Joshi, *Kolloid-Z.*, 122 (1951) 6.
[50] D. K. Smith, *Textile Research J.*, 29 (1959) 32.
[51] M. W. Alford, *J. Textile Inst.*, 52 (1961) 246P.
[52] *U.S.P.* 2,404,714.
[53] *F.P.* 913,164.
[54] N. A. Sisson, *Textile Research J.*, 30 (1960) 153.
[55] *B.P.* 653,757.
[56] *B.P.* 533,304.
  B.P. 541,238.
[57] *F.P.* 913,927.
[58] *F.P.* 913,919.
[59] *U.S.P.* 2,418,507.
[60] Fr. Kainer, *Melliand Textilber.*, 31 (1950) 266.
[61] *U.S.P.* 2,420,565.
[62] F. Ullmann, *Enzyklopädie der Technischen Chemie*, 3rd Ed.
[63] W. H. Carothers and J. W. Hill, *J. Am. Chem. Soc.*, 54 (1932) 1579.
[64] E. A. W. Hoff, *J. Appl. Chem.*, 2 (1952) 441.
[65] L. R. G. Treloar, *The Physics of Rubber Elasticity*, Clarendon Press, Oxford, 1949.
[66] S. Newman, *J. Polymer Sci.*, 27 (1958) 563.
[67] W. J. Dulmage and A. L. Geddes, *J. Polymer Sci.*, 30 (1958) 499.
[68] I. Marshall and A. B. Thompson, *J. Appl. Chem.*, 4 (1954) 145.
[69] P. Brauer and F. H. Muller, *Kolloid-Z.*, 135 (1954) 65.
[70] C. W. Bunn and T. C. Alcock, *Trans. Faraday Soc.*, 41 (1945) 323.
[71] G. Cartola, *Conf. intern. tecnica. textil Barcelona*, Section 3, No. 48, (1954) 7.
  S. Krimm and A. V. Tobolsky, *J. Polymer Sci.*, 7 (1957) 57.
[72] D. C. Hookway, *J. Textile Inst.*, 49 (1958) 292P.
[73] G. Caroti and J. H. Dusenbury, *J. Polymer Sci.*, 22 (1956) 399.
[74] N. J. Abbott and A. C. Goodings, *J. Textile Inst.*, 40 (1949) 232T.
  C. E. Black and M. Dole, *J. Polymer Sci.*, 3 (1948) 358.
[75] I. Fankuchen and H. Mark, *J. Appl. Phys.*, 15 (1944) 364.
[76] A. B. Thompson, *J. Polymer Sci.*, 34 (1959) 741.
[77] C. G. Cannon and F. P. Chappel, *Brit. J. Appl. Phys.*, 10 (1959) 68.
[78] F. D. Dexter and G. J. Dienes, *J. Colloid Sci.*, 5 (1950) 228.
[79] R. S. Spencer and R. E. Dillon, *J. Colloid Sci.*, 3 (1948) 163.
  G. J. Dienes and F. D. Dexter, *Ind. Eng. Chem.*, 40 (1948) 2319.
[80] A. S. Lodge, *Rheology of Elastomers*, Pergamon Press, London, 1958, p. 70.
[81] A. B. Thompson, in *Fibre Structure*, Butterworth, London, 1962.
[82] P. I. Vincent, *Polymer*, 1 (1960) 7.
[83] A. Nadai, *Theory of Fracture of Solids*, McGraw Hill, New York, 1950.
[84] J. S. Lazurkin, *J. Polymer Sci.*, 30 (1958) 595.
[85] G. K. Mecklenburgh, *J. Textile Inst.*, 41 (1950) 161P.
  D. N. Marvin, *J. Soc. Dyers Colourists*, 70 (1954) 16.
[86] N. M. Mimms and E. D. Rossiter, *J. Textile Inst.*, 47 (1956) 704T.
[87] J. W. S. Hearle and R. H. Peters, (Eds.), *Fibre Structure*, Butterworth, London, 1962.

[88] J. W. S. HEARLE, *Skinner's Silk & Rayon Record*, 1958.
[89] CARROL-PORCZYNSKI, *Natural Polymer Man-Made Fibres*, Natl. Trade Press, London, 1961.
[90] D. ENTWISTLE, *Ind. Textile*, 4 (1959) 24.
[91] *B.P.* 438,584/5, 438,655/6, 433,707.
[92] *U.S.P.* 2,829,027.
[93] *B.P.* 792,548.
[94] CORVAL and TOPEL, *Ann. Text. World* (1959).
[95] T. TIMIELL, *Studies on Cellulose Reactions*, Stockholm, 1950, p. 196.
[96] B. R. DESAI, *Ind. Textile J.*, 62 (1952) 722.
[97] P. MASON and N. WOOKEY, (Eds.), *The Rheology of Elastomers*, Pergamon Press, London, 1958.
[98] F. W. BILLMEYER, *Textbook of Polymer Chemistry*, Interscience, New York, 1957.

SUBJECT INDEX